Brendan Kelly
Professor of Mathematics
Faculty of Education
University of Toronto
Ontario

Bob Alexander
Assistant Co-ordinator of Mathematics
Toronto Board of Education
Toronto, Ontario

Paul Atkinson
Superintendent of Schools
Waterloo County Board of Education
Kitchener, Ontario

ADDISON-WESLEY MATHEMATICS 11

Addison-Wesley Publishers Limited

Don Mills, Ontario
Reading, Massachusetts
Menlo Park, California
Wokingham, Berkshire
Amsterdam • Sydney
Singapore • Tokyo
Madrid • Bogotá
Santiago • San Juan

Design: John Zehethofer

Art: Frank Zsigo

Photo Credits

Addison-Wesley Photo Library, 38, 39, 269 (top left), 354; Bob Alexander, 170, AP/Wide World Photos, 384; Paul Atkinson, 35, 217, 287; Bank of Canada, 397; B.C. Lions Football Club, 235; The Bettmann Archive/BBC Hulton, 359; Canadian Amateur Hockey Association, 316; Canadian Imperial Bank of Commerce, 392; Canadian National Exhibition, 262 (bottom); Allsport Photographic/Masterfile, 349; CP Rail, 195; Lynne Dalkner, 269 (centre), 350 (right, 391, 435; Deerhurst Inn, Ian Tudhope, 262 (top right); Don Mills Collegiate, 168 (bottom); Agustin Estrada, 218; Fraser Day Photography, 1; Government of Quebec, Tourist Branch, 373 (right); Gulf Canada Limited, 178; Erich Hoyt, 33; Jandec Inc., 101; Brendan Kelly, 161; John P. Kelly, 138; Armour Landry, 211 (bottom); Manitoba Government Travel, 34 (bottom); Mary Martin, 265; McCullagh Studio, 439; Metropolitan Toronto Police Academy, 269 (top right); 321; Mexican Government Tourism Office, 102, 122; Miller Services Ltd., 177; Ministry of Agriculture & Food, 361; Montreal Concordes, 350 (left); NASA, 63, 201; NFB Photothèque, 211 (top); Ontario Grape Growers' Marketing Board, 238 (left & right); Ontario Tennis Association, 56; Tim O'Shea, 221; Parker Brothers, 222; Pioneer Racing, 145; Ricoh Canada Ltd., 366; Royal Canadian Mint, 166, 168 (top); Toronto General Hospital, 34 (top), 146, 275; The Toronto Star, 53, 250, 422; Travel Alberta, 169; Mel DiGiacomo/ The Image Bank Canada, 261; Four By Five Inc./L. Chiger, 7, T. Rosenthal, 262, 373

Written, printed, and bound in Canada

H – BP – 95 ISBN 0-201-18604-7

Features of Mathematics 11

CONCEPT DEVELOPMENT

Mathematics 11 is carefully sequenced to develop concepts in mathematics. Concepts are explained with several examples, each of which has a detailed solution.

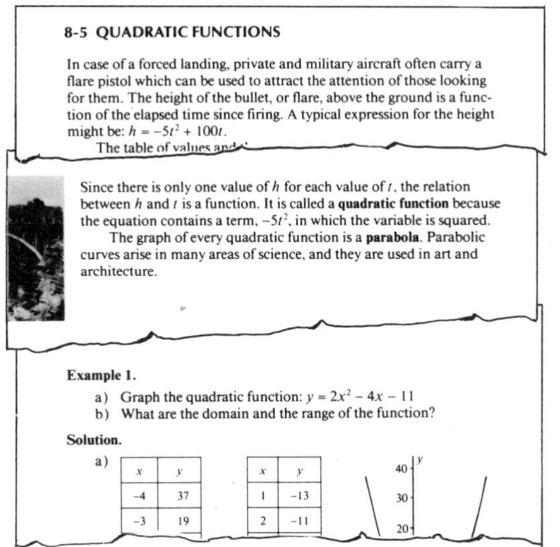

8-5 QUADRATIC FUNCTIONS

In case of a forced landing, private and military aircraft often carry a flare pistol which can be used to attract the attention of those looking for them. The height of the bullet, or flare, above the ground is a function of the elapsed time since firing. A typical expression for the height might be: $h = -5t^2 + 100t$.

The table of values and ...

Since there is only one value of h for each value of t, the relation between h and t is a function. It is called a **quadratic function** because the equation contains a term, $-5t^2$, in which the variable is squared.

The graph of every quadratic function is a **parabola**. Parabolic curves arise in many areas of science, and they are used in art and architecture.

Example 1.

a) Graph the quadratic function: $y = 2x^2 - 4x - 11$
b) What are the domain and the range of the function?

Solution.

a)

x	y
−4	37
−3	19

x	y
1	−13
2	−11

REINFORCEMENT

An abundance of exercises is provided to reinforce skills and concepts. These exercises are graded by difficulty with an appropriate balance of A, B, and C exercises. The A exercises may sometimes be completed mentally and the answers given orally or the questions may be used as additional examples when teaching the lesson. The B exercises are intended for the students to consolidate their learning of the concepts that were taught. The C exercises present a challenge and usually involve extensions of the concepts taught in that section.

Review Exercises and *Cumulative Reviews* provide additional practice. Answers to all questions are included in the text.

TECHNOLOGY

A contemporary mathematics program must reflect the impact of calculators and computers on society.

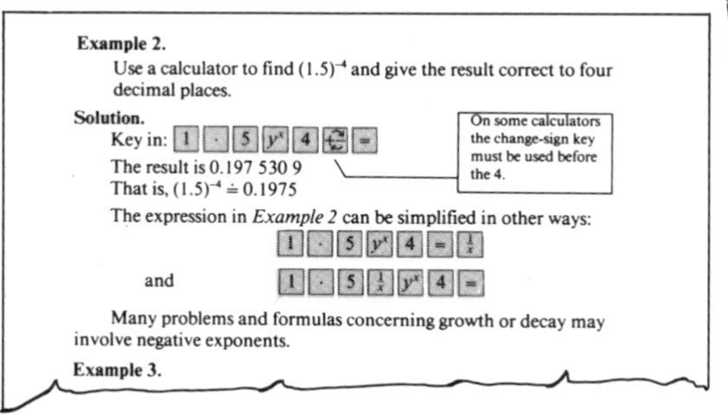

Example 2.

Use a calculator to find $(1.5)^{-4}$ and give the result correct to four decimal places.

Solution.

Key in: 1 . 5 y^x 4 +/− =

On some calculators the change-sign key must be used before the 4.

The result is 0.197 530 9

That is, $(1.5)^{-4} \doteq 0.1975$

The expression in *Example 2* can be simplified in other ways:

1 . 5 y^x 4 = $\frac{1}{x}$

and

1 . 5 $\frac{1}{x}$ y^x 4 =

Many problems and formulas concerning growth or decay may involve negative exponents.

Example 3.

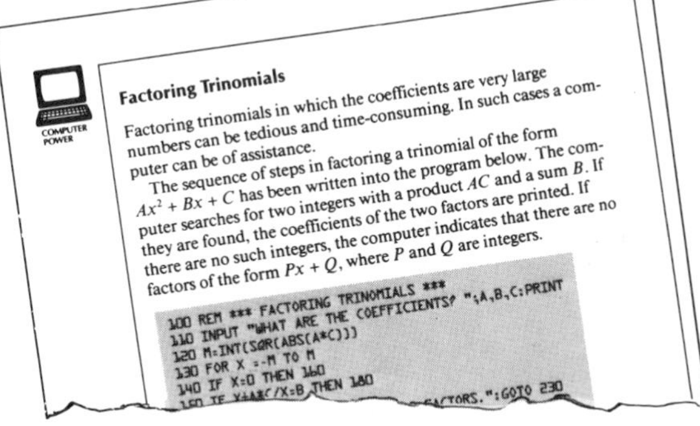

Factoring Trinomials

Factoring trinomials in which the coefficients are very large numbers can be tedious and time-consuming. In such cases a computer can be of assistance.

The sequence of steps in factoring a trinomial of the form $Ax^2 + Bx + C$ has been written into the program below. The computer searches for two integers with a product AC and a sum B. If they are found, the coefficients of the two factors are printed. If there are no such integers, the computer indicates that there are no factors of the form $Px + Q$, where P and Q are integers.

```
100 REM *** FACTORING TRINOMIALS ***
110 INPUT "WHAT ARE THE COEFFICIENTS? ";A,B,C:PRINT
120 M=INT(SQR(ABS(A*C)))
130 FOR X =-M TO M
140 IF X=0 THEN 160
150 IF X+A*C/X=B THEN 180
...FACTORS.":GOTO 230
```

Mathematics 11 assumes that students will use calculators, as needed.

Keying sequences are given for scientific calculators and 4-function calculators, where appropriate.

COMPUTER POWER features provide opportunities for students to explore mathematical problems using a computer. It is assumed that students know how to enter a program in BASIC, but it is not necessary for them to understand the program.

APPLICATIONS OF MATHEMATICS

Students can better understand mathematical principles when they are related to their applications. For this reason, applications are integrated throughout *Mathematics 11*.

Every chapter begins with an applied problem that is solved as an example in the chapter.

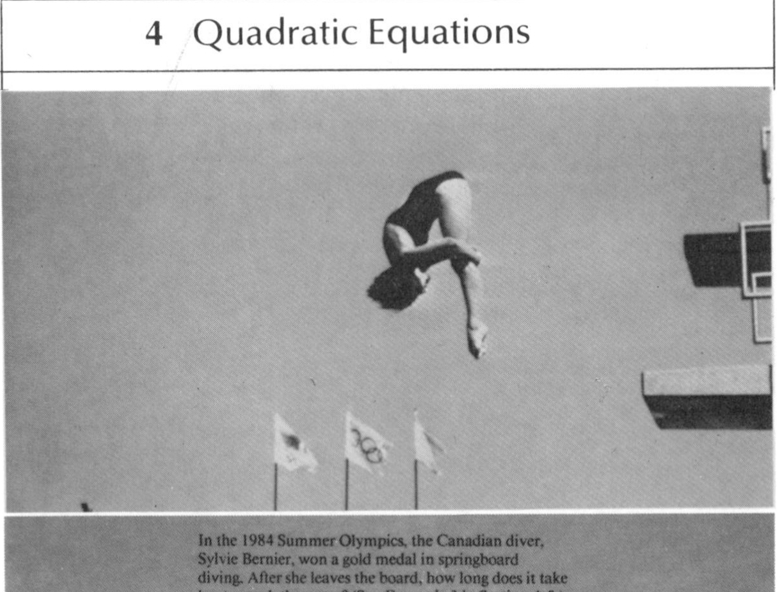

4 Quadratic Equations

In the 1984 Summer Olympics, the Canadian diver, Sylvie Bernier, won a gold medal in springboard diving. After she leaves the board, how long does it take her to reach the water? (See *Example 3* in Section 4-5.)

Many sections begin with an application which illustrates the necessity for the mathematics that follows.

7-1 SOLVING SYSTEMS OF LINEAR EQUATIONS BY GRAPHING

Every so often, a new board game captures the public's imagination and it is in great demand. The sales of one such game, at the height of its popularity, topped 10 000 per week.

Suppose that it costs \$40 000 to develop a board game and \$5.00 to manufacture each one. If the games are sold at \$20.00 each, how many games must be sold to break even? This problem can be answered using graphs.

Applications are also included throughout the exercises.

17. The population of a colony of birds triples every 10 years. At the present time there are about 250 birds in the colony.
    a) Which of the following represents the number of birds in the colony after n years:
       i) 250×3^{10n} ii) $250 \times n^{30}$
       iii) $250 \times 3^{\frac{n}{10}}$ iv) $250 \times 3^{\frac{10}{n}}$
    b) About how many birds will be in the colony:
       i) 1 year from now ? ii) 3 years from now ?
       iii) 5 years from now?
    c) About how many birds were in the colony:
       i) 1 year ago ? ii) 3 years ago ? iii) 5 years ago ?

PROBLEM SOLVING

Problem solving is integrated throughout the program in the text sections and special features.

Many of the exercises provide challenging problems for the students to solve.

11. When a projectile is fired, the vertical component of its initial velocity is such that its height h, in metres, t seconds after firing is given by $h = 250t - 4.9t^2$. Is it possible for the projectile to reach a height of 2.75 km? 4.0 km?
12. A small change in the value of the constant term of some quadratic equations has a significant effect on the roots.
    a) Illustrate the truth of this statement by solving:
    $x^2 + 50x + 624 = 0$, $x^2 + 50x + 625 = 0$, $x^2 + 50x + 626 = 0$.
    b) Explain why in terms of the graphs of the equations.
13. Show that, if k is any real number, each of the following equations always has real roots:
    a) $kx^2 + (3k + 2)x + (2k + 3) = 0$
    b) $(k + 1)x^2 + 2kx + (k - 1) = 0$
14. Show that there are no real numbers x and y such that:
    $$\frac{1}{x+y} = \frac{1}{x} + \frac{1}{y}, \quad (x, y \neq 0).$$

Frequent brief *INVESTIGATE* features are starting points for mathematical investigations to help the students develop analytic skills. These features always relate to the concepts that are developed in the sections in which they occur.

INVESTIGATE

Graph the parabola and the line on the same axes:

$y = x^2 - 4x + 3$

$y = -4x + 3$

Compare the graphs. Is there any geometric relation between the parabola and the line?

Determine if the relation holds for other parabolas.

Write a report of your findings.

MATHEMATICS PROJECT features are longer investigations which challenge students and extend mathematical concepts.

Patterns in Products

The product of two binomials such as $(x + 1)(x - 1)$ is significant because two terms of the product *add to zero*.

These products. . .these terms. . .add to zero.

$$(x + 1)(x - 1) = x^2 - x + x - 1$$
$$= x^2 - 1$$

Are there other products in which some of the terms add to zero? To answer this question, we could start with $(x + 1)(x - 1)$ and change one or both factors in a systematic way. For example, use higher powers of x and different combinations of signs. Here are a few of the many possibilities that could be considered.

The *MATHEMATICS AROUND US* features outline applications of mathematics in the sciences, the arts, business, and industry.

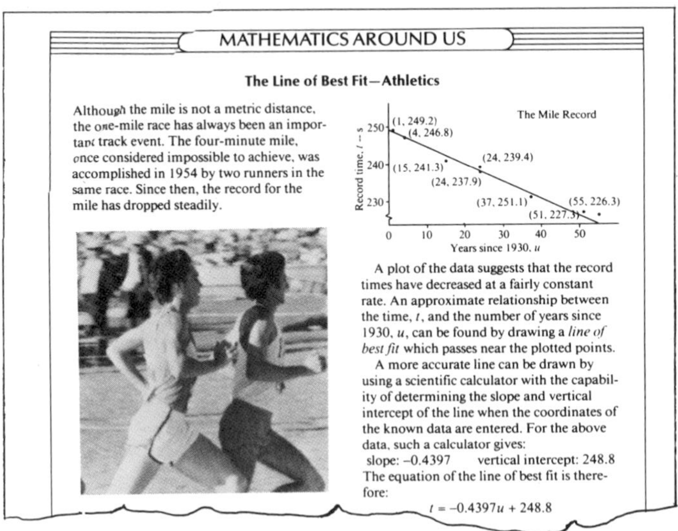

MATHEMATICS AROUND US

The Line of Best Fit—Athletics

Although the mile is not a metric distance, the one-mile race has always been an important track event. The four-minute mile, once considered impossible to achieve, was accomplished in 1954 by two runners in the same race. Since then, the record for the mile has dropped steadily.

A plot of the data suggests that the record times have decreased at a fairly constant rate. An approximate relationship between the time, t, and the number of years since 1930, u, can be found by drawing a *line of best fit* which passes near the plotted points.

A more accurate line can be drawn by using a scientific calculator with the capability of determining the slope and vertical intercept of the line when the coordinates of the known data are entered. For the above data, such a calculator gives:

slope: −0.4397 vertical intercept: 248.8

The equation of the line of best fit is therefore:

$$t = -0.4397u + 248.8$$

THE MATHEMATICAL MIND features offer insights into the work of mathematicians and the historical development of mathematics. Anecdotes of human interest that are part of its history are included. In this feature, problems related to the topic are presented for the students to solve.

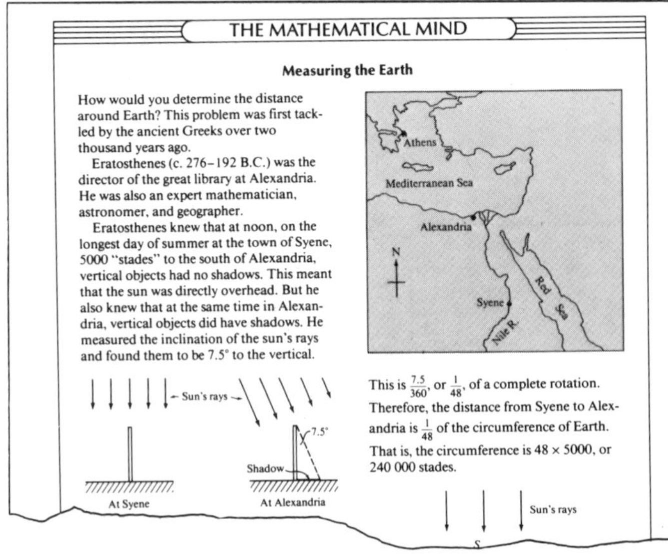

THE MATHEMATICAL MIND

Measuring the Earth

How would you determine the distance around Earth? This problem was first tackled by the ancient Greeks over two thousand years ago.

Eratosthenes (c. 276–192 B.C.) was the director of the great library at Alexandria. He was also an expert mathematician, astronomer, and geographer.

Eratosthenes knew that at noon, on the longest day of summer at the town of Syene, 5000 "stades" to the south of Alexandria, vertical objects had no shadows. This meant that the sun was directly overhead. But he also knew that at the same time in Alexandria, vertical objects did have shadows. He measured the inclination of the sun's rays and found them to be 7.5° to the vertical.

This is $\frac{7.5}{360}$, or $\frac{1}{48}$, of a complete rotation. Therefore, the distance from Syene to Alexandria is $\frac{1}{48}$ of the circumference of Earth. That is, the circumference is 48×5000, or 240 000 stades.

Contents

3 Polynomials and Rational Expressions

4 Quadratic Equations

5 Ratio and Proportion

6 Analytic Geometry: Lines and Circles

7 Analytic Geometry: Systems of Equations

8 Functions: Linear and Quadratic

1 The Real Numbers

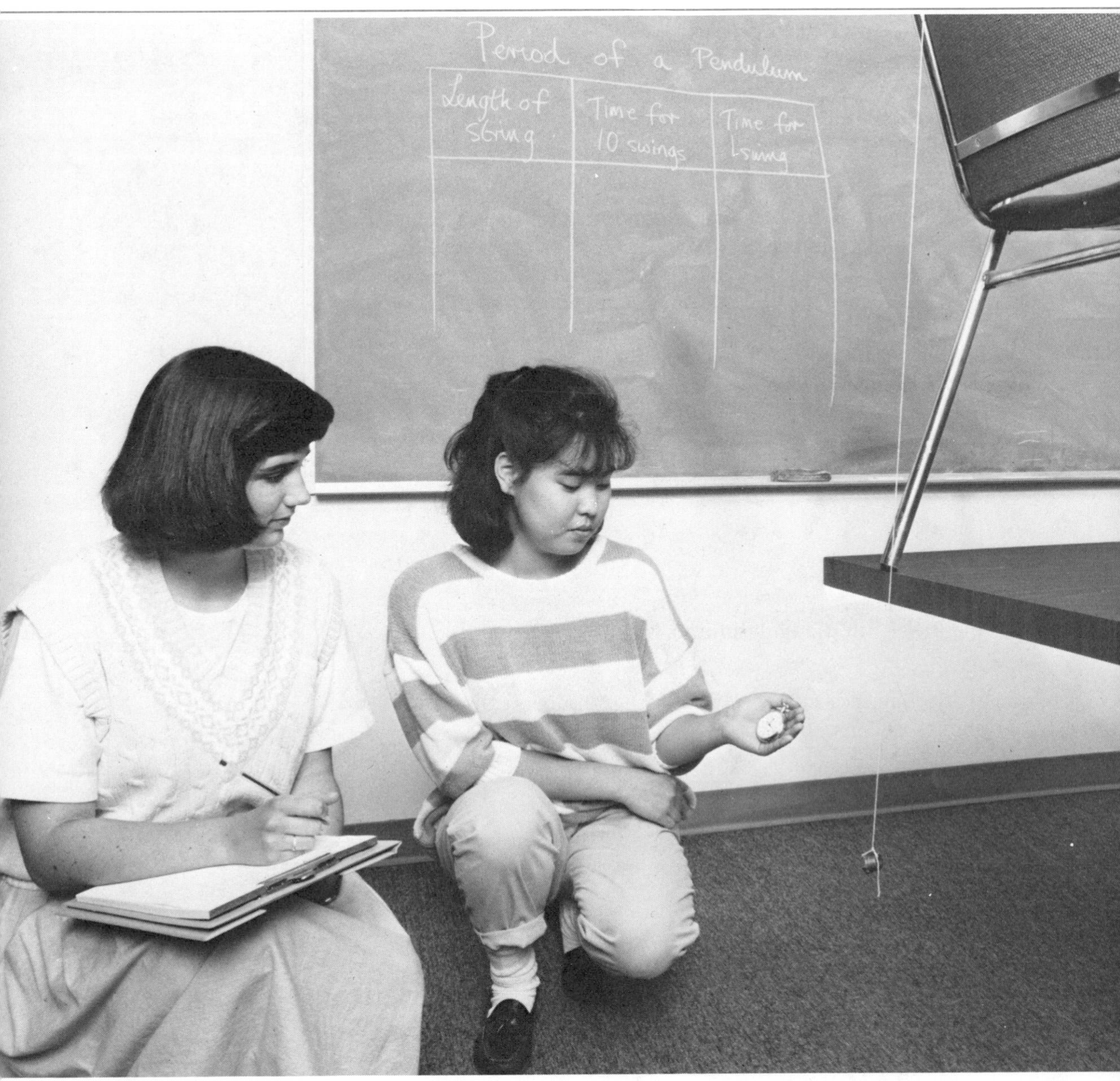

Jennifer and Lisa are conducting an experiment to measure the period of a pendulum. What effect on the period does tripling the length of the pendulum have? (See *Example 4* in Section 1-5).

1-1 THE NATURAL NUMBERS

Over 5000 years ago the Egyptians used symbols to describe quantities up to and beyond one million. Today we use the Hindu-Arabic numerals and place value to represent such numbers:

$$1, 2, 3, \ldots 98, 99, 100, \ldots 998, 999, 1000, \ldots$$

Mathematicians refer to these counting numbers as the set of **positive integers**, or **natural numbers**.

From about 550 B.C. to 250 B.C. mathematics flourished in ancient Greece. Since the Greeks were mainly interested in geometry, they classified numbers according to the shapes they could represent. For example, numbers which correspond to a triangular array of dots are called **triangular numbers**.

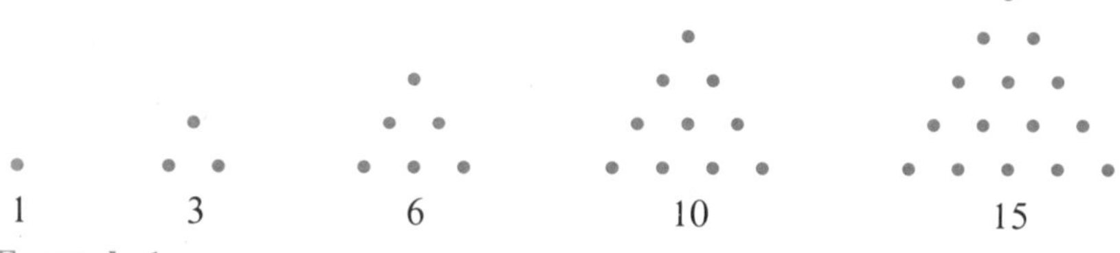

Example 1.

Find the eighth triangular number.

Solution.

A pattern in the sequence of triangular numbers can be found by subtracting consecutive terms:

According to the pattern, the next three differences in the sequence are 6, 7, 8. The eighth triangular number is 15 + 6 + 7 + 8, or 36.

Since a **composite number** is a product of at least two factors (greater then 1), any composite number can be represented by a rectangular array of dots. A **prime number**, having no factor greater than 1 (except itself), cannot be represented in this way.

Every composite number can be written as a product of prime factors in only one way (except for the order of the factors). Our method of finding this product, or **prime factorization**, is the same as that used by the Greeks over 2000 years ago, except that we have the assistance of calculators.

Example 2.

Express as a product of prime factors: a) 1683 b) 659

Solution.

a) By calculator, $\sqrt{1683} \doteq 41$. If 1683 has prime factors, at least one of them must be less than 41 otherwise their product would be greater than 1683. The prime numbers less than 41 are:
2, 3, 5, 7, 11, 13, 17, 19, 23, 29, 31, 37
2 is *not* a factor of 1683.
3 *is* a factor of 1683: $1683 \div 3 = 561$
3 *is* a factor of 561: $561 \div 3 = 187$
3, 5, and 7 are *not* factors of 187.
11 *is* a factor of 187: $187 \div 11 = 17$
Since 17 is also prime, the prime factorization of 1683 is:
$$3 \times 3 \times 11 \times 17$$
or, $1683 = 3^2 \times 11 \times 17$

b) By calculator, $\sqrt{659} \doteq 26$. The possible prime factors of 659 are: 2, 3, 5, 7, 11, 13, 17, 19, 23. Using a calculator, it is quickly found that none of these primes is a factor of 659. Therefore, 659 is a prime number.

Example 3.

Some archaeologists found a bag of coins. They discovered that whether the coins were divided into sets of 2, 3, 5, or 7, there was always exactly one coin left over. What was the smallest possible number of coins in the bag?

Solution.

Let n represent the number of coins in the bag.
Then, $n - 1$ is divisible by 2, 3, 5, and 7.
The smallest number divisible by 2, 3, 5, and 7 is:

$2 \times 3 \times 5 \times 7$, or 210.

That is, $n - 1 = 210$
$n = 211$

The smallest possible number of coins in the bag was 211.

EXERCISES 1-1

(A)

1. Which of the following are prime numbers?

a) 51	b) 37	c) 67	d) 91	e) 127
f) 143	g) 159	h) 173	i) 193	j) 231

2. Express as a product of prime factors:

a) 27	b) 42	c) 68	d) 95	e) 102
f) 145	g) 180	h) 225	i) 228	j) 387

3. a) Continue this pattern for three more square numbers:

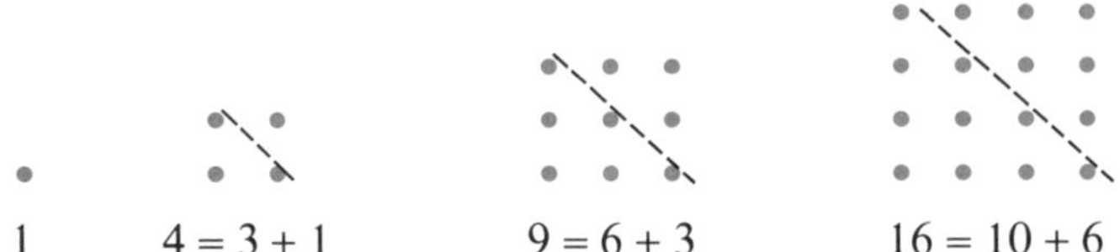

b) What does the pattern in (a) suggest about the sum of any two consecutive triangular numbers?

4. Describe the pattern and find the next three numbers:
a) 1, 4, 7, 10,...
b) 2, 6, 18, 54,...
c) 1, 4, 9, 16,...
d) 1, 3, 7, 13, 21,...
e) 1, 5, 14, 30, 55,...
f) 1, 4, 10, 20, 35,...

5. a) Continue this pattern for three more lines:

$$1 = 1^2$$
$$1 + 2 + 1 = 2^2$$
$$1 + 2 + 3 + 2 + 1 = 3^2$$

b) Draw a series of diagrams to illustrate the patterns in (a).

6. A box of chocolates could be divided equally among 2, 3, 4, 5, or 6 people if it contained one chocolate more. What is the least number of chocolates in the box?

(B)

7. How many 3-digit perfect squares can be formed using the digits 1, 6, and 9? What are they?

8. Give all the 2-digit primes that form primes when their digits are reversed. Example: 17 and 71 are both prime.

9. The following number patterns begin with primes. Continue the patterns for several more numbers. Are all the numbers in each pattern prime?
a) 41, 47, 53, 59,...
b) 5, 17, 29, 41,...
c) 11, 13, 17, 23,...

10. The sum and difference of two squares may both be prime. Example: $4 + 9 = 13$, and $9 - 4 = 5$. Find other examples in which the sum and difference of two squares are:
a) both prime;
b) both composite;
c) one prime and one composite.

11. $259 \times 429 = 111\ 111$ and $1221 \times 91 = 111\ 111$. Use a calculator to find other pairs of numbers with the same product, 111 111.

12. Show that:
a) the sum of any two primes greater than 2 is even;
b) the product of any two primes greater than 2 is odd.

13. In 1640, Pierre de Fermat proved that every prime number of the form $4n + 1$ can be expressed as the sum of two squares in exactly

INVESTIGATE

4 and 9 are two squares with sum and difference both prime:

$$9 + 4 = 13$$
$$9 - 4 = 5$$

Find other pairs of squares with sum and difference both prime.

Write a report of your findings.

one way. Example: $41 = 4(10) + 1$ is the sum of 25 and 16.

a) Which primes less than 50 are of the form $4n + 1$?

b) Express the primes in (a) as the sum of two squares.

14. Fermat also stated that no prime of the form $4n + 3$ can be expressed as the sum of two squares. Example: $23 = 4(5) + 3$. No two squares have a sum of 23.

a) Which primes less than 50 are of the form $4n + 3$?

b) Check that none of the primes in (a) can be expressed as the sum of two squares.

15. Carl Friedrich Gauss was the first to discover that every natural number is either triangular or the sum of two or three triangular numbers. Examples: $13 = 3 + 10$, $23 = 1 + 1 + 21$. Write as the sum of two or three triangular numbers:

a) 11 b) 19 c) 29 d) 30 e) 33 f) 50

16. This question about primes has never been answered: If n is any natural number, is there always at least one prime between n^2 and $(n + 1)^2$? Answer the question for values of n up to 10.

Ⓒ

17. Show that if any two consecutive primes (greater than 2) are added, the sum can be expressed as a product of three or more prime numbers greater than 1. Example: $23 + 29 = 52$, and $52 = 2 \times 2 \times 13$.

18. Show that, except for 2 and 3, every prime number can be written in the form $6n + 1$ or $6n - 1$, where n is a natural number.

19. a) In the triangle of numbers shown, what numbers are in:

i) the 10th row?

ii) the nth row?

b) Describe a method that could be used to determine:

i) in which row any given number, x, appears;

ii) the color of the triangle in which any given number, x, appears.

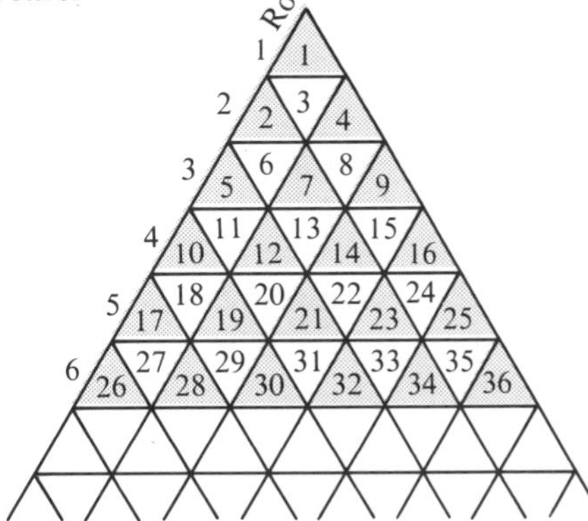

20. a) Show that 1225 is both a triangular and a square number.

b) Find a 2-digit number which is both triangular and square.

THE MATHEMATICAL MIND

The Search for Larger Primes

More than two thousand years ago, Euclid proved that there are infinitely many prime numbers. Since then, mathematicians have tried to find larger and larger primes. In 1644, the Frenchman, Marin Mersenne, conjectured that the numbers $2^n - 1$ were prime for the following values of n: 2, 3, 5, 7, 13, 17, 19, 31, 67, 127, 257. Although it has since been proved that $2^{67} - 1$ and $2^{257} - 1$ are composite, primes of the form $2^n - 1$ are called **Mersenne primes**. The following gives an idea of how the search has progressed since then.

In 1772, the great Swiss mathematician, Leonhard Euler, proved that $2^{31} - 1$ is prime.

In 1978, two high school students, Laura Nickel and Curt Knoll, used a computer at California State University to find a prime larger than any previously known. It took several hundred hours of computer time to discover and verify that their number, $2^{21701} - 1$, is a prime. This number has 6533 digits, and is so large that the computer print-out was 51 lines long.

In 1984, David Slowinski of Cray Research Incorporated, the manufacturer of one of the world's fastest computers, found an even larger prime—$2^{123049} - 1$, a number with 39 751 digits. Although each of the two processors of the computer is capable of 200 000 000 computations per second, it took one of them 65 min to find the new prime.

The following computer program in BASIC can be used to test the primality of any number which your microcomputer does not round off. (This usually means any number of eight or fewer digits.)

```
100 REM *** PRIME TESTER ***
110 INPUT "WHAT NUMBER DO YOU WANT TO
    TEST? " ;N
120 IF N=1 THEN 200
130 IF N=2 THEN 180
140 FOR I=2 TO SQR(N)
150 IF ABS(N/I-INT(N/I))>0.0000001
    THEN 170
160 PRINT:PRINT I,N/I:GOTO 190
170 NEXT I
180 PRINT:PRINT N;" IS A PRIME
    NUMBER":GOTO 210
190 PRINT:PRINT "NUMBERS ABOVE ARE TWO
    FACTORS OF ";N:GOTO 210
200 PRINT:PRINT "1 IS NEITHER PRIME NOR
    COMPOSITE"
210 PRINT:INPUT "PRESS S TO STOP,
    RETURN TO REPEAT ";Y$
220 PRINT:IF Y$<>"S" THEN 110:END
```

1. Use the above program to determine which of these numbers are prime:
   a) 4009 b) 7207
   c) 8611 d) 65537
2. Use the program to find the prime factorization of:
   a) 3604; b) 404629;
   c) 1018161; d) 6563647.
3. There is only one composite number in this list. Use the program to find the number:
   31
   331
   3331
   33331
   333331
   3333331
   33333331
   333333331
4. Use the program to test as many Mersenne numbers for primality as you can.

MATHEMATICS AROUND US

Prime Numbers vs Computer Crime

Unless a subject under study is seen to have an application, there is little interest in it. This has been true in the past of mathematical topics which have later proved to be useful tools of engineering and social science. More recently, it has been true of the search for large prime numbers. There was little interest in the search until the emergence of a new field of mathematics called **coding theory**. Coding theory can provide us with almost unbreakable codes for protection against computer crime.

Vast quantities of personal data are kept on computer files and it is obviously necessary to restrict access to this data to authorized persons. The now-favored method of doing this, discovered in 1977, is based on the fact that it is much easier to multiply two large primes than it is to factor the product.

Data is encoded using a very large number (say 200 digits) that is known to be the product of two large primes, each with about 100 digits. Only someone who knows the two 100-digit prime factors can decode the data. An unauthorized person would need to factor the 200-digit number, a task so difficult that it would take the most powerful computer about a billion years.

The question below will give you an understanding of the difficulty of factoring a very large composite number that is known to be the product of two primes.

QUESTION

The number given is the product of two primes less than 500. Find the primes using the table and a calculator.

a) 245 009 b) 158 177

c) 76 633 d) 102 821

Primes Less Than 500

2	3	5	7	11	13
17	19	23	29	31	37
41	43	47	53	59	61
67	71	73	79	83	89
97	101	103	107	109	113
127	131	137	139	149	151
157	163	167	173	179	181
191	193	197	199	211	223
227	229	233	239	241	251
257	263	269	271	277	281
283	293	307	311	313	317
331	337	347	349	353	359
367	373	379	383	389	397
401	409	419	421	431	433
439	443	449	457	461	463
467	479	487	491	499	

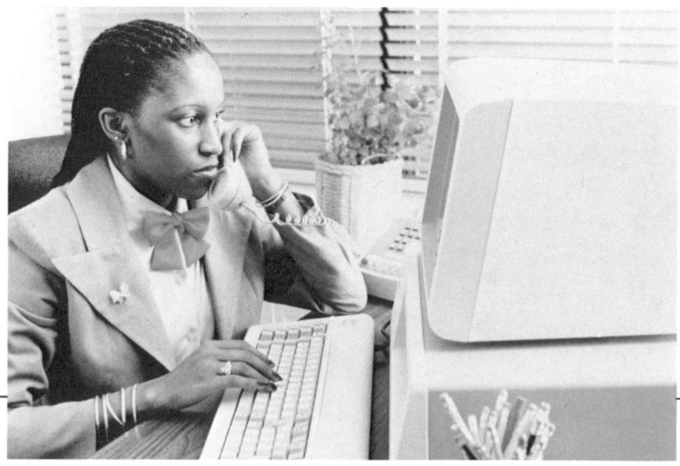

1-2 QUOTIENTS OF NATURAL NUMBERS

When two natural numbers are added or multiplied, the result is a natural number. However, in ancient times when mathematicians attempted to divide a natural number into equal parts, they found that the quotient was not always a natural number. This led to the development of fractions.

About 1650 B.C., the Egyptians had a cumbersome system of writing fractions. They would write a fraction, such as $\frac{7}{8}$, as the sum of unit fractions: $\frac{1}{2} + \frac{1}{4} + \frac{1}{8}$. Since they did not use Hindu-Arabic numerals and had not developed symbols for addition or equality, the expressions they wrote were quite different in appearance from the one above.

A thousand years earlier still, the Babylonians expressed fractions quite differently. Instead of using a fixed numerator, they used denominators that were powers of 60. For the fraction $\frac{7}{8}$ they wrote: $\frac{49}{60} + \frac{210}{3600}$. This seems awkward to us, but our units of time are derived from it. (1 min $= \frac{1}{60}$ h, and 1 s $= \frac{1}{3600}$ h)

Our system of writing fractions as decimals was developed within the last 300 years. It is similar to the Babylonian system, but we use denominators that are powers of 10. To express $\frac{7}{8}$ as a decimal, we divide 7 by 8 and write:

$$\frac{7}{8} = 0.875, \text{ which means: } \frac{8}{10} + \frac{7}{100} + \frac{5}{1000}$$

Example 1.

Express $\frac{5}{27}$ as a decimal.

Solution.

By calculator: $5 \div 27 = 0.1851851$

By calculation:

$$\begin{array}{r} 0.185 \\ 27\overline{)5.000} \\ \underline{2\,7} \\ 2\,30 \\ \underline{2\,16} \\ 140 \\ \underline{135} \\ 5 \end{array}$$

Since 5 is the original numerator, the process repeats. $\frac{5}{27} = 0.\overline{185}$, the bar shows the part of the decimal that repeats.

The decimal expansion in *Example 1* must begin to repeat when a remainder recurs. Since division by 27 can yield only 26 different non-zero remainders (1, 2, 3,..., 26), the decimal expansion must repeat after no more than 26 digits. In this case, it repeated after 3 digits.

> Any fraction in the form $\frac{m}{n}$, where m and n are natural numbers, may be expressed as a terminating decimal or a repeating decimal. In the latter case, the repeating part has no more than $n - 1$ digits.

The next example shows how to find the fraction which corresponds to a given repeating decimal.

Example 2.

Express $3.1\overline{72}$ in the form $\frac{m}{n}$, where $n \neq 0$.

Solution.

Let $x = 3.17272\ldots$ ①

Multiply ① by 10 to isolate the repeating digits: $10x = 31.7272\ldots$ ②

Multiply ② by 100 since the number of repeating digits is 2: $1000x = 3172.7272\ldots$ ③

Subtract ② from ③: $990x = 3141$

$$x = \frac{3141}{990}$$

Therefore, $3.1\overline{72} = \dfrac{3141}{990}$

EXERCISES 1-2

Ⓐ

1. Express in decimal form:

a) $\frac{9}{4}$ b) $\frac{7}{16}$ c) $\frac{5}{12}$ d) $\frac{11}{27}$

e) $\frac{2}{9}$ f) $\frac{11}{7}$ g) $\frac{20}{11}$ h) $\frac{25}{99}$

2. Express in the form $\frac{m}{n}$:

a) $2.\overline{54}$ b) $0.\overline{415}$ c) $1.6\overline{35}$ d) $4.29\overline{3}$

e) $3.\overline{125}$ f) $6.2\overline{8}$ g) $0.4\overline{75}$ h) $5.\overline{082}$

3. Use a calculator to verify:

   a) $\frac{9}{10} = \frac{1}{2} + \frac{1}{4} + \frac{1}{10} + \frac{1}{20}$
   b) $\frac{4}{9} = \frac{26}{60} + \frac{40}{3600}$

   c) $\frac{13}{15} = \frac{1}{3} + \frac{1}{4} + \frac{1}{5} + \frac{1}{12}$
   d) $\frac{5}{6} = \frac{47}{60} + \frac{180}{3600}$

   e) $\frac{29}{20} = \frac{1}{2} + \frac{1}{3} + \frac{1}{4} + \frac{1}{5} + \frac{1}{6}$
   f) $\frac{5}{9} = \frac{33}{60} + \frac{20}{3600}$

4. The Rhind papyrus, an Egyptian scroll dating from about 1650 B.C., is a collection of 85 problems in arithmetic and geometry. Problem 6 shows that to divide 9 loaves among 10 men each man should be given $\frac{2}{3}$, then $\frac{1}{5}$, and then $\frac{1}{30}$ of a loaf. Verify that this is correct.

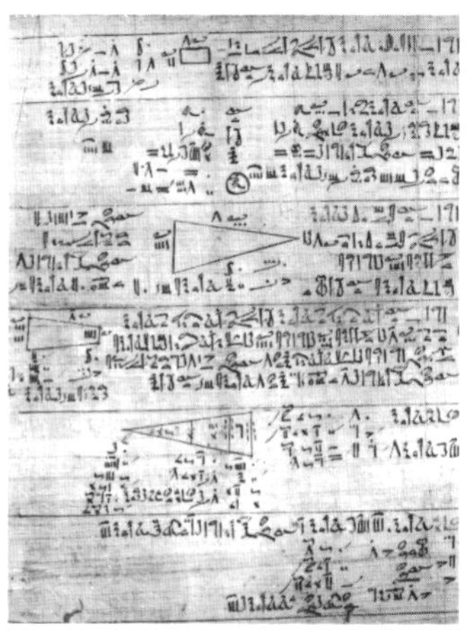

Reproduced by courtesy of the Trustees of the British Museum

5. In the Rhind papyrus, the expression for:

   a) $\frac{2}{7}$ was $\frac{1}{4} + \frac{1}{28}$;
   b) $\frac{2}{99}$ was $\frac{1}{66} + \frac{1}{198}$;

   c) $\frac{2}{61}$ was $\frac{1}{40} + \frac{1}{244} + \frac{1}{488} + \frac{1}{610}$.

   Use a calculator to verify that the expressions are correct.

6. Express as a common fraction:

   a) $1.\overline{465}$
   b) $3.0\overline{27}$
   c) $5.\overline{41}$

   d) $0.73\overline{6}$
   e) $1.\overline{4142}$
   f) $0.7\overline{259}$

7. a) Express $0.\overline{9}$ as the quotient of two integers.

   b) Verify the result of (a) by multiplying both sides of the equation $\frac{1}{3} = 0.3333\ldots$ by 3.

8. Express as a repeating decimal:

   a) $0.\overline{7} - 0.\overline{3}$
   b) $0.\overline{26} + 0.\overline{31}$
   c) $0.\overline{42} - 0.\overline{1}$

   d) $0.\overline{6} \times 0.5$
   e) $0.\overline{3} \times 0.\overline{2}$
   f) $0.\overline{36} \times 0.41\overline{6}$

9. a) Continue the pattern:

   $$\frac{1}{2} + \frac{1}{2 \times 1} = 1$$
   $$\frac{1}{3} + \frac{1}{3 \times 2} = \frac{1}{2}$$
   $$\frac{1}{4} + \frac{1}{4 \times 3} = \frac{1}{3}$$

   b) Assuming that the pattern in (a) continues, write these fractions as the sum of unit fractions:

   i) $\frac{1}{9}$
   ii) $\frac{1}{12}$
   iii) $\frac{1}{20}$

10. a) Continue the pattern:

i)
$$\frac{1}{2\times1}=\frac{1}{2}$$
$$\frac{1}{2\times1}+\frac{1}{3\times2}=\frac{2}{3}$$
$$\frac{1}{2\times1}+\frac{1}{3\times2}+\frac{1}{4\times3}=\frac{3}{4}$$

ii)
$$\frac{1}{3\times1}=\frac{1}{3}$$
$$\frac{1}{3\times1}+\frac{1}{5\times3}=\frac{2}{5}$$
$$\frac{1}{3\times1}+\frac{1}{5\times3}+\frac{1}{7\times5}=\frac{3}{7}$$

b) Use the patterns in (a) to write as a sum of unit fractions:

i) $\frac{8}{9}$ ii) $\frac{8}{17}$

Ⓒ

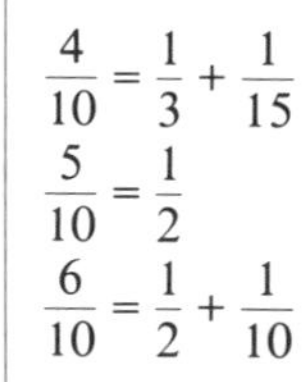

$$\frac{4}{10}=\frac{1}{3}+\frac{1}{15}$$
$$\frac{5}{10}=\frac{1}{2}$$
$$\frac{6}{10}=\frac{1}{2}+\frac{1}{10}$$

11. Use the table to express the following as a sum of unit fractions:
a) 0.45 b) 0.55 c) 0.65

12. A vessel holds a quantity of water; another vessel holds an equal quantity of wine. A glass of water is taken from the first vessel, poured into the wine, and the contents stirred. A glass of the mix is then taken and poured into the water. Is there more water in the wine or more wine in the water?

MATHEMATICS PROJECT

Interesting Numbers

The number, 252, is interesting.
The sum of the first two digits: $2 + 5 = 7$
The sum of the last two digits: $5 + 2 = 7$
The number, 252, is divisible by 7: $252 \div 7 = 36$

The number, 343, has the same characteristics.

$$3 + 4 = 7 \qquad 4 + 3 = 7 \qquad 343 \div 7 = 49$$

1. Find other three-digit numbers with the same characteristics.
2. Numbers like 252 are of the form:
$$100a + 10b + a$$
Show that numbers of this form, where $a + b = 7$, are divisible by 7.
3. Consider the number, 494.
$$4 + 9 = 13 \qquad 9 + 4 = 13 \qquad 494 \div 13 = 38$$
Find other three-digit numbers with these characteristics.
4. Show that a number of the form, $100a + 10b + a$, where $a + b = 13$ are divisible by 13.
5. Investigate other three-digit numbers, having similar characteristics, with other divisors. Try four-digit and five-digit numbers. Summarize your investigations.

COMPUTER POWER

An Unsolved Arithmetic Problem

Start with any positive integer.
If it is even, divide it by 2; if it is odd, multiply it by 3 and add 1.
Repeat this procedure until the number 1 occurs.

For example, starting with 35, the result is:

35 106 53 160 80 40 20 10 5 16 8 4 2 1

There are 14 numbers in this row, and the greatest is 160.

If other starting numbers are used, is the final number always 1?

No one knows the answer to this question, but it has been checked on a computer by Nabuo Yoneda of the University of Tokyo for every starting number up to 2^{40}, or 1 099 511 627 776. In every case the number 1 eventually occurred.

The following BASIC program can be used to generate the string of numbers for any starting number. The computer also gives the number of terms and the greatest term.

```
100 REM *** AN UNSOLVED ARITHMETIC
    PROBLEM ***
110 INPUT "WHAT IS THE STARTING
    NUMBER? ";A
120 N=1:MAX=A
130 IF A=INT(A/2)*2 THEN 150
140 A=3*A+1:GOTO 160
150 A=A/2
160 PRINT A:N=N+1
170 IF A <=MAX THEN 190
180 MAX=A
190 IF A>1 THEN 130
200 PRINT "NUMBER OF TERMS: ";N
210 PRINT "GREATEST TERM: ";MAX
220 PRINT:INPUT "PRESS S TO STOP,
    RETURN TO REPEAT ";Y$
230 PRINT:IF Y$<>"S" THEN 110:END
```

1. Use the program to obtain the strings of numbers for different starting numbers, including 27 and 255.
2. Can you explain why the greatest term is always even?
3. Find some results in which the starting number itself is the greatest term.
4. a) Find a starting number less than 25 which gives a string of 11 numbers.
   b) Find two consecutive starting numbers less than 25 which give strings of 10 numbers.
5. Can a result always be found having a given number of terms?

To investigate further, change the program as follows. Type LIST, and then enter the following lines. With this modified program, strings of numbers can be investigated for 20 consecutive starting numbers. The computer will print the number of terms and the greatest term for each string.

```
115 K=0:S=A
120 K=K+1:N=1:MAX=A
160 N=N+1
200 PRINT S,N,MAX
210 S=S+1:A=S
215 IF K<20 THEN 120
```

6. Use the modified program to investigate 20 strings at a time, beginning with different starting numbers, including 120 and 380. What observations can you make?
7. Investigate other rules for generating strings of numbers like these.

1-3 THE INTEGERS AND RATIONAL NUMBERS

The natural numbers and fractions have been in use for thousands of years. The negative numbers and zero first appeared in the seventh century A.D. Even then the negative numbers were not generally accepted for another thousand years, for the great mathematicians thought it absurd to have numbers less than zero. Integers and their quotients, called rational numbers, have been a part of mathematics for only the last 200 years.

These numbers are called **integers:**

$$\ldots, -3, -2, -1, 0, 1, 2, 3, \ldots$$

Any number that can be written in the form $\frac{m}{n}$, where m and n are integers and $n \neq 0$, is called a **rational number.**

Example 1.

Simplify:

a) $7[(+6)(-3) - (-8)(-4)]$

b) $\frac{+3}{(+2)(-4)} - \frac{(-5)}{(+2)}$

Solution.

a) $7[(+6)(-3) - (-8)(-4)] = 7[(-18) - (+32)]$
$= 7[-50]$
$= -350$

b) $\frac{+3}{(+2)(-4)} - \frac{(-5)}{(+2)} = \frac{3}{-8} + \frac{5}{2}$
$= -\frac{3}{8} + \frac{20}{8}$
$= \frac{17}{8}$, or 2.125

Example 2.

Find the value of the expression $x^2 - \frac{3x}{y}$ if:

a) $x = -3, y = 4$;

b) $x = -\frac{1}{2}, y = -\frac{5}{4}$.

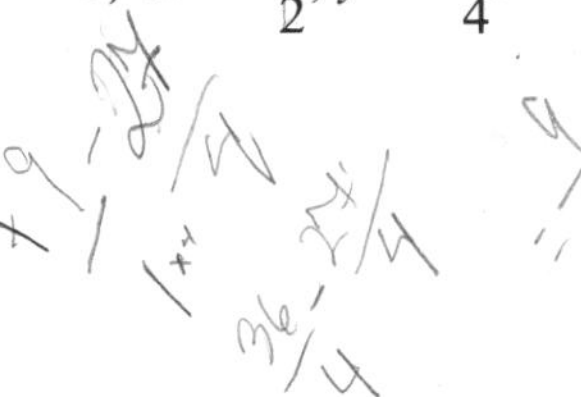

Solution.

a) $$x^2 - \frac{3x}{y} = (-3)^2 - \frac{3(-3)}{4}$$
$$= 9 + \frac{9}{4}$$
$$= \frac{45}{4}, \text{ or } 11.25$$

b) $$x^2 - \frac{3x}{y} = \left(-\tfrac{1}{2}\right)^2 - \frac{3\left(-\tfrac{1}{2}\right)}{-\tfrac{5}{4}}$$
$$= \tfrac{1}{4} - 3\left(-\tfrac{1}{2}\right)\left(-\tfrac{4}{5}\right)$$
$$= \frac{1}{4} - \frac{6}{5}$$
$$= \frac{5 - 24}{20}$$
$$= -\frac{19}{20}, \text{ or } -0.95$$

The impetus for the extension of the concept of number to include integers and rational numbers grew out of attempts to interpret roots of equations. Originally, equations with negative roots, such as those in the following example, were rejected as not solvable.

Example 3.

Solve: a) $3 - 2(5 + x) = 2x - (1 - x)$

b) $\dfrac{1 - 2x}{2} - 1 = \dfrac{2x + 1}{3}$

Solution.

a) $$3 - 2(5 + x) = 2x - (1 - x)$$
$$3 - 10 - 2x = 2x - 1 + x$$
$$-7 - 2x = 3x - 1$$
$$-2x - 3x = -1 + 7$$
$$-5x = 6$$
$$x = -\frac{6}{5}$$

b) $$\frac{1 - 2x}{2} - 1 = \frac{2x + 1}{3}$$

Multiply both sides by 6:

$$3(1 - 2x) - 6 = 2(2x + 1)$$
$$3 - 6x - 6 = 4x + 2$$
$$-5 = 10x$$
$$x = -\frac{1}{2}$$

EXERCISES 1-3

(A)

1. Simplify:
   a) $(-27) - 11 - (-9)$
   b) $36 \div (-3) \div 4$
   c) $(-3)(-4)(-2)(-5)$
   d) $(-8)(3) + (-12) - 14$
2. Simplify:
   a) $12 \div (-4) + (5)(-3)$
   b) $52 - 7(-3) + (-20)$
   c) $3[6 + 14 \div (-5) - 5 \times 2]$
   d) $[8 - (6 \div 3 \times 10)][3 - 8]$
   e) $[-7 - 10 \times 2] - 6(-4)$
   f) $6[4 + 8 - 3(9 - 7) - 13]$
3. If $x = -3$, $y = 2$, and $z = -1$, evaluate:
   a) $2x^2yz$
   b) $5x - 3y + 4z$
   c) $xy^2 - xz^2 - xyz$
   d) $2y^2z - 3x^2y + xz$
   e) $\dfrac{3x + 2y}{xz} + \dfrac{xy}{z}$
4. Simplify:
   a) $\dfrac{13}{6} \times (-9)$
   b) $-\dfrac{21}{8} \times \left(-\dfrac{11}{3}\right)$
   c) $\dfrac{3}{4} \times \dfrac{-3}{-10}$
   d) $\dfrac{3}{-8} \times \dfrac{-2}{15}$
   e) $\dfrac{3}{8} \div \left(-\dfrac{9}{16}\right)$
   f) $-\dfrac{11}{3} \div \dfrac{5}{-3}$
5. Simplify:
   a) $\dfrac{-3}{8} - \dfrac{-3}{4}$
   b) $\dfrac{-5}{9} + \dfrac{11}{24}$
   c) $\dfrac{-4}{-3} - \dfrac{3}{-2}$
   d) $\dfrac{13}{4} + \left(-\dfrac{13}{3}\right)$
   e) $-\dfrac{13}{4} - \dfrac{13}{3}$
   f) $\dfrac{17}{15} - \dfrac{19}{6}$
6. Simplify:
   a) $-\dfrac{3}{5} + \dfrac{8}{-2} \times \left(\dfrac{-6}{5}\right)$
   b) $\left(\dfrac{-3}{4} - \dfrac{3}{-4}\right) \div 3$
   c) $-8\left(\dfrac{3}{5} - \dfrac{1}{2}\right)$
   d) $\dfrac{2}{5}\left(-\dfrac{1}{3}\right)\left(-\dfrac{6}{2}\right) + \dfrac{3}{5}$
   e) $\dfrac{9}{8} \times \dfrac{1}{3} - \dfrac{1}{4}\left(\dfrac{-5}{6}\right) + \dfrac{2}{3}\left(-\dfrac{1}{4}\right)$
   f) $\left[\left(-\dfrac{4}{5}\right) \div \dfrac{5}{2}\right] - \left[\dfrac{3}{-4} \times \left(-\dfrac{7}{5}\right)\right]$
7. If $x = -\dfrac{1}{4}$ and $y = -\dfrac{2}{3}$, evaluate:
   a) $xy - 3y^2$
   b) $3x^2y + y^2$
   c) $2x^2y - \dfrac{3}{2}xy$
8. Solve:
   a) $9x - 4 = 23$
   b) $5y + 3 = -32$
   c) $3x - (5x - 11) = -13$
   d) $x + 5 = 4(5 + x)$
   e) $\dfrac{3x - 2}{6} = \dfrac{5}{3}$
   f) $\dfrac{x}{3} + \dfrac{x}{5} = \dfrac{1}{3} - \dfrac{2x}{5}$

(B)

9. If $a = \frac{3}{-4}$ and $b = \frac{-1}{3}$, evaluate:
   a) $\frac{2a^2 + 4b}{14b^2}$ b) $\frac{12ab + 4b}{5b}$ c) $\frac{2a + 7b - ab}{7a^2}$

10. The cost, C, in dollars per hour, of operating a certain type of aircraft is given by the formula: $C = 1150 + \frac{m}{250} + \frac{20\,000\,000}{m}$, where m is the cruising altitude in metres. Find the hourly cost of operating the aircraft at 7500 m; at 10 000 m.

11. Solve:
   a) $3(5x - 11) + 9 = 3(x - 7) - 15$
   b) $4(3x - 1) + 7 = 17x - 9(1 + x)$
   c) $2(3x + 17) + 2x = 4(x - 9) + 52$
   d) $\frac{6(x - 2)}{5} = \frac{5(x - 2)}{4}$
   e) $4(2x - 7) + 34 = 4(3x + 1) - 6(x - 3)$
   f) $\frac{x - 7}{2x + 1} = 3$

12. The coin box of a vending machine contains twice as many dimes as quarters. If the total value of the coins is $22.50, how many quarters are there?

(C)

13. If $x = 5$ is the solution of each equation, find the value of k.
   a) $2x - k = 3 - x$ b) $2 + 3x = 8 - (x - k)$
   c) $2x + k = kx - 6$
   d) $k - x - 1 = 2(x - 3) + k(1 + 2x)$

14. Solve, if possible:
   a) $5(n + 2) = 6(n - 3) + n$ b) $y + (1 + y) = 2(y + 1)$
   c) $80 - 4x = 3(20 - x)$ d) $3(q + 3) = 4(q - 1) - q$

1-4 FROM RATIONALS TO IRRATIONALS

The followers of the Greek mathematician, Pythagoras, made a considerable study of numbers. These Pythagoreans were a secret society who combined mathematical investigation with numerology and mysticism. To them is attributed the discovery of many geometrical theorems, as well as the analysis of triangular, square, and other numbers discussed earlier.

The Pythagoreans found points on the number line which do not correspond to any rational number. New numbers had to be defined to represent such points. Since they are not rational numbers, they are called **irrational numbers**.

An **irrational number** is one that cannot be represented in the form $\frac{m}{n}$, where m and n are integers and $n \neq 0$. The decimal expansion of an irrational number neither terminates nor repeats.

The Greeks found several examples of irrational numbers, and it was eventually proved that any number of the form $\sqrt{n}$, where n is not a perfect square, is irrational. An irrational number in this form is called a **radical**.

Example 1.

Which of these numbers are irrational?

a) $\sqrt{7}$
b) $\sqrt{144}$
c) $\sqrt{p}$, where p is prime
d) $\sqrt{11} - 1$

Solution.

a) Since 7 is not a perfect square, $\sqrt{7}$ is irrational.
b) Since $144 = 12^2$, $\sqrt{144} = 12$, which is rational.
c) Primes are not perfect squares, therefore $\sqrt{p}$ is irrational.
d) Since 11 is not a perfect square, $\sqrt{11}$ is irrational. Subtracting 1 does not affect the decimal portion of the expansion of $\sqrt{11}$, therefore $\sqrt{11} - 1$ is irrational.

Example 1 suggests that the result of adding or subtracting a rational number from an irrational number is an irrational number.

Example 2.

Show that $\sqrt{2} \times \sqrt{5} = \sqrt{2 \times 5}$

Solution.

$$(\sqrt{2} \times \sqrt{5})^2 = \sqrt{2} \times \sqrt{5} \times \sqrt{2} \times \sqrt{5}$$
$$= (\sqrt{2})^2 \times (\sqrt{5})^2$$
$$= 2 \times 5$$

Taking the square root of each side:

$$\sqrt{2} \times \sqrt{5} = \sqrt{2 \times 5}$$

The above result suggests the following property for radicals:

$$\sqrt{a} \times \sqrt{b} = \sqrt{a \times b}, \quad a, b \geqslant 0$$

The next example applies this property, and shows that the product of two or more irrational numbers is not necessarily irrational.

INVESTIGATE

Use a calculator to compare: $\sqrt{2} \times \sqrt{5}$ and $\sqrt{2 \times 5}$, $\sqrt{44}$ and $2\sqrt{11}$.
On some calculators, the results in each case may not be exactly the same. Why?
Compare the results using different calculators.

Example 3.

Simplify: a) $3\sqrt{2} \times 2\sqrt{7}$ b) $5\sqrt{6} \times \sqrt{10} \times 2\sqrt{15}$

Solution

a) $3\sqrt{2} \times 2\sqrt{7} = 3 \times 2 \times \sqrt{2 \times 7}$
$= 6\sqrt{14}$

b) $5\sqrt{6} \times \sqrt{10} \times 2\sqrt{15} = 2 \times 5 \times \sqrt{6 \times 10 \times 15}$
$= 10\sqrt{900}$
$= 10 \times 30$, or 300

The same property can be used to express radicals in simplest form.

Example 4.

Simplify: a) $\sqrt{44}$ b) $\sqrt{72}$

Solution.

a) $\sqrt{44} = \sqrt{4 \times 11}$
$= \sqrt{4} \times \sqrt{11}$
$= 2\sqrt{11}$

b) $\sqrt{72} = \sqrt{36} \times \sqrt{2}$
$= 6\sqrt{2}$

Many irrational numbers are not radicals. The best known of the non-radical irrational numbers is the number we denote by π. In 1761, the German mathematician, Lambert, proved that π was irrational. Today, computers have generated a sixteen-million-digit decimal expansion of π and, as expected, it never repeats.

EXERCISES 1-4

Ⓐ

1. Which of these numbers are irrational?
   a) $\sqrt{17}$ b) $\sqrt{196}$ c) $\sqrt{21} + 1$
   d) $\sqrt{31}$ e) $\sqrt{7} + \sqrt{9}$ f) $\sqrt{51} \times \sqrt{51}$
   g) $11 - \sqrt{73}$ h) $\sqrt{36 - 25}$ i) $(\sqrt{101})^2$
2. Simplify:
   a) $\sqrt{36 + 64}$ b) $\sqrt{2.56}$ c) $\sqrt{0.09}$
   d) $\sqrt{\frac{49}{81}}$ e) $\sqrt{\frac{121}{36}}$ f) $3\sqrt{1.69}$
3. Simplify:
   a) $\sqrt{6} \times \sqrt{5}$ b) $\sqrt{7} \times \sqrt{3}$ c) $(8\sqrt{3})(7\sqrt{2})$
   d) $(-5\sqrt{6})(-3\sqrt{7})$ e) $(12\sqrt{7})(-8\sqrt{11})$ f) $(-15\sqrt{7})(-5\sqrt{10})$
4. Simplify
   a) $\sqrt{18}$ b) $\sqrt{12}$ c) $\sqrt{50}$ d) $\sqrt{80}$
   e) $\sqrt{75}$ f) $\sqrt{48}$ g) $\sqrt{112}$ h) $\sqrt{132}$
5. Simplify:
   a) $2\sqrt{6} \times 5\sqrt{3}$ b) $4\sqrt{5} \times 7\sqrt{10}$ c) $8\sqrt{10} \times 3\sqrt{6}$
   d) $(9\sqrt{15})(-4\sqrt{6})$ e) $(-6\sqrt{6})(5\sqrt{12})$ f) $(-5\sqrt{10})(-7\sqrt{8})$

Ⓑ

6. Simplify
   a) $2\sqrt{3} \times 5\sqrt{6} \times 3\sqrt{2}$ b) $4\sqrt{10} \times 6\sqrt{6} \times 3\sqrt{5}$
   c) $3\sqrt{6} \times 2\sqrt{18} \times \sqrt{15}$ d) $(5\sqrt{8})(-3\sqrt{6})(2\sqrt{15})$
   e) $(-9\sqrt{10})(-4\sqrt{15})(-7\sqrt{3})$ f) $(3\sqrt{14})(2\sqrt{35})(-8\sqrt{15})$
7. Estimate:
   a) $\sqrt{30}$ b) $\sqrt{200}$ c) $\sqrt{125}$
   d) $\sqrt{0.9}$ e) $\sqrt{150}$ f) $\sqrt{2.52}$
8. Use a calculator to arrange in order from least to greatest:
   a) $5\sqrt{2}, 4\sqrt{3}, 3\sqrt{6}, 2\sqrt{14}, 2\sqrt{10}$
   b) $-6\sqrt{2}, -4\sqrt{5}, -2\sqrt{17}, -5\sqrt{3}, -4\sqrt{6}$
   c) $4\sqrt{7}, 5\sqrt{5}, 6\sqrt{3}, 8\sqrt{2}, 3\sqrt{14}$
9. Use the diagram to show that $\sqrt{20} = 2\sqrt{5}$ and $\sqrt{45} = 3\sqrt{5}$.

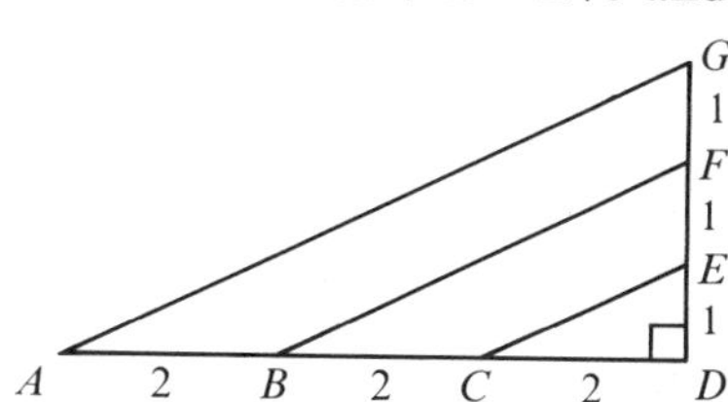

10. In the diagram, P, Q, R, S are the midpoints of the sides of the square $ABCD$. If $AB = 4\sqrt{2}$ cm, find the area of $PQRS$.

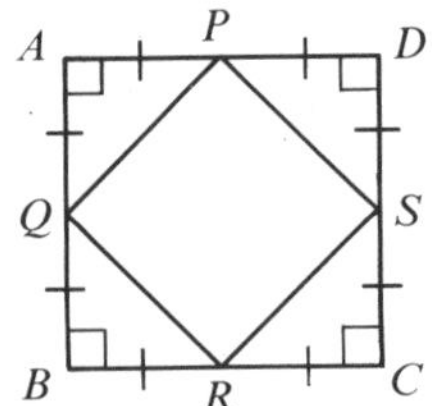

Ⓒ

11. Which number of each pair is the greater? (Do not use a calculator.)
    a) $5\sqrt{3}, 6\sqrt{2}$ b) $7\sqrt{2}, 4\sqrt{6}$ c) $3\sqrt{5}, 4\sqrt{3}$
    d) $-8\sqrt{3}, -10\sqrt{2}$ e) $2\sqrt[3]{7}, 3\sqrt[3]{2}$ f) $\frac{3}{4}\sqrt{12}, \frac{2}{3}\sqrt{14}$

12. a) By substituting convenient values for a and b, show that, in general, $\sqrt{a} + \sqrt{b} \neq \sqrt{a + b}$.
    b) Are there any values of a and b such that $\sqrt{a} + \sqrt{b} = \sqrt{a + b}$?

If n is a perfect square, what is the next perfect square?

SIDE TRIP Counting Methods I

For a trip, Norma plans on packing four blouses—white, red, yellow, and blue—and three skirts—beige, denim and pink. She wonders if this gives her enough choice. By drawing this diagram, she sees that she has twelve outfits.

White Red Yellow Blue

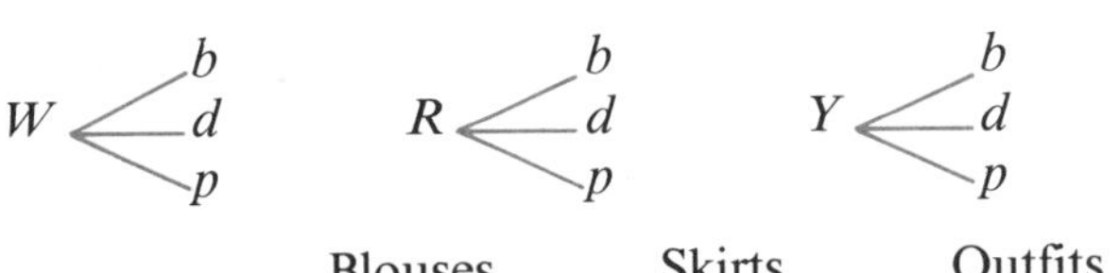

Blouses		Skirts		Outfits
4	×	3	=	12

> If there are m ways of doing one thing, and after that, n ways of doing something else, then there are $m \times n$ ways of doing them together.

1. For her trip, Mary plans to take two skirts and five blouses. How many outfits will she have?
2. In a shopping mall on two levels, there are 5 "up" escalators and 4 "down" escalators. In how many ways can a shopper go up, and then down?
3. A picnic menu is shown. In how many ways can a person have one of each item?

Meat	Dessert	Drink
Hot dog	Cake	Milk
Hamburger	Pie	Iced Tea
	Ice Cream	Cola

4. a) In Question 3, the rule was extended to three items. Do you think it can be extended to any number of items?
   b) How many arrangements of four different letters each can be made using the letters in FACT?

1. 10 2. 20 3. 18 4. a) Yes b) 24

THE MATHEMATICAL MIND

The Dilemma of the Pythagoreans

The Pythagoreans knew how to represent points on a number line by rational numbers. They believed intuitively that since a rational number can be written as a ratio of any two natural numbers, all points on the line can be represented in this way.

However, by the end of the fifth century B.C. the Pythagoreans found a point on the number line that does not correspond to a rational number. They proved that the length of the diagonal of a unit square cannot be written in the form $\frac{m}{n}$. This meant there is no rational number for the point P on the number line shown.

The Pythagoreans proved that $\sqrt{2}$ is not a rational number by the technique known as "indirect proof" or "proof by contradiction".

If $\sqrt{2}$ is a rational number, then there are natural numbers, m and n, such that

$$\sqrt{2} = \frac{m}{n}$$

Square both sides: $(\sqrt{2})^2 = \left(\frac{m}{n}\right)^2$

$$2 = \frac{m^2}{n^2}$$

$$2n^2 = m^2$$

Since a perfect square has an even number of prime factors, then m^2 has an even number of prime factors and $2n^2$ has an odd number. This is impossible. Therefore, $\sqrt{2}$ cannot be a rational number.

This, then, was the dilemma of the Pythagoreans. The number, $\sqrt{2}$, existed because it was the length of the diagonal of a unit square. Yet, they did not see how it could exist since it was not a rational number.

To the Greeks, numbers meant whole numbers or their ratios. They were surprised by the discovery that some numbers appeared to be irrational and refused to accept them as numbers. This was a major limitation of Greek mathematics, and the problem of whether irrational numbers were really numbers troubled mathematicians for the next two thousand years.

1. Prove that $\sqrt{3}$ is irrational by indirect proof.
2. Use the fact that $\sqrt{2}$ is irrational to prove that $\sqrt{2} + 5$ is irrational.
3. Can the length, width, and diagonal of a rectangle all be rational numbers? Explain.

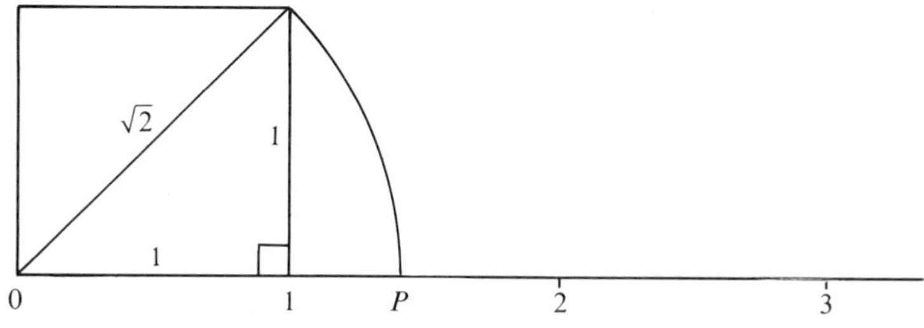

1-5 RADICAL ARITHMETIC

Although the ancient Greeks discovered irrational numbers, they never developed the symbols needed to use radicals. It wasn't until 1525 that the square root symbol appeared, possibly derived from the written letter "r" (for *root*).

To add or subtract radicals, first simplify each radical by extracting all perfect-square factors. Then combine like radicals.

Example 1.

Simplify: a) $\sqrt{12} + \sqrt{27}$

b) $3\sqrt{8} + 2\sqrt{3} - 2\sqrt{75} + 4\sqrt{50}$

Solution.

a) $\sqrt{12} + \sqrt{27} = \sqrt{4 \times 3} + \sqrt{9 \times 3}$
$= 2\sqrt{3} + 3\sqrt{3}$, or $5\sqrt{3}$

b) $3\sqrt{8} + 2\sqrt{3} - 2\sqrt{75} + 4\sqrt{50}$
$= 3 \times 2\sqrt{2} + 2\sqrt{3} - 2 \times 5\sqrt{3} + 4 \times 5\sqrt{2}$
$= 6\sqrt{2} + 20\sqrt{2} + 2\sqrt{3} - 10\sqrt{3}$
$= 26\sqrt{2} - 8\sqrt{3}$

Use a calculator to compare: $\sqrt{12} + \sqrt{27}$ and $5\sqrt{3}$.
Compare the results using different calculators.

Products involving radicals can be expanded using the distributive law.

Example 2.

Expand and simplify:

a) $5\sqrt{2}(2\sqrt{3} - \sqrt{8})$

b) $2\sqrt{3}(\sqrt{3} - 1) + \sqrt{3}(\sqrt{18} - \sqrt{2})$

c) $(5\sqrt{7} - 2\sqrt{3})(\sqrt{7} + 4\sqrt{3})$

d) $(3 - 2\sqrt{5})(3 + 2\sqrt{5})$

Solution.

a) $5\sqrt{2}(2\sqrt{3} - \sqrt{8}) = 10\sqrt{6} - 5\sqrt{16}$
$= 10\sqrt{6} - 20$

b) $2\sqrt{3}(\sqrt{3} - 1) + \sqrt{3}(\sqrt{18} - \sqrt{2})$
$= 2(\sqrt{3})^2 - 2\sqrt{3} + \sqrt{3}(3\sqrt{2} - \sqrt{2})$
$= 6 - 2\sqrt{3} + \sqrt{3}(2\sqrt{2})$
$= 6 - 2\sqrt{3} + 2\sqrt{6}$

c) $(5\sqrt{7} - 2\sqrt{3})(\sqrt{7} + 4\sqrt{3})$
$= 5(\sqrt{7})^2 + 20\sqrt{21} - 2\sqrt{21} - 8(\sqrt{3})^2$
$= 35 - 24 + 20\sqrt{21} - 2\sqrt{21}$
$= 11 + 18\sqrt{21}$

$20\sqrt{21}$
35
$(5\sqrt{7} - 2\sqrt{3})(\sqrt{7} + 4\sqrt{3})$
$-2\sqrt{21}$
-24

d) $(3 - 2\sqrt{5})(3 + 2\sqrt{5}) = 3^2 - (2\sqrt{5})^2$
$= 9 - 20$
$= -11$

Example 2d shows that the product of expressions involving radicals can be a rational number.

Division is the inverse of multiplication.

$54 \div 6 = 9$ since $9 \times 6 = 54$

Likewise, $\sqrt{21} \div \sqrt{3} = \sqrt{7}$ since $\sqrt{7} \times \sqrt{3} = \sqrt{21}$

Example 3.

Using $\sqrt{2} = 1.4142$, simplify the following by paper-and-pencil arithmetic:

$\frac{3}{\sqrt{2}}$ and $\frac{3\sqrt{2}}{2}$

Which is easier to calculate? Why?

Simplify: a) $\frac{\sqrt{76}}{\sqrt{2}}$ b) $\frac{12\sqrt{42}}{4\sqrt{6}}$ c) $\frac{4\sqrt{90}}{3\sqrt{72}}$

Solution.

a) $\frac{\sqrt{76}}{\sqrt{2}} = \sqrt{38}$

b) $\frac{12\sqrt{42}}{4\sqrt{6}} = \frac{12}{4} \times \sqrt{\frac{42}{6}}$, or $3\sqrt{7}$

c) It is often best to express radicals in simplest form before dividing.

$\frac{4\sqrt{90}}{3\sqrt{72}} = \frac{4 \times 3\sqrt{10}}{3 \times 6\sqrt{2}}$
$= \frac{2\sqrt{10}}{3\sqrt{2}}$, or $\frac{2\sqrt{5}}{3}$

Example 4.

The time it takes for a pendulum to swing back and forth once depends only on the length of the pendulum. This period, T, in seconds, is given by the formula:

$T = 2\pi\sqrt{\frac{l}{9.8}}$, where l is the length of the pendulum in metres. By what factor is the period increased when the pendulum length is tripled?

Solution.

For pendulum length l: $T_1 = 2\pi\sqrt{\frac{l}{9.8}}$, or about $2\sqrt{l}$

For pendulum length $3l$: $T_2 = 2\pi\sqrt{\frac{3l}{9.8}}$, or about $2\sqrt{3l}$

$$\frac{T_2}{T_1} = \frac{2\sqrt{3l}}{2\sqrt{l}}, \text{ or } \sqrt{3}$$

The period is increased by a factor of $\sqrt{3}$ when the length of the pendulum is tripled.

EXERCISES 1-5

Ⓐ

1. Simplify:
   a) $\sqrt{20} + \sqrt{5}$ b) $\sqrt{12} + \sqrt{3}$ c) $2\sqrt{18} - \sqrt{2}$
   d) $3\sqrt{7} + 5\sqrt{28}$ e) $3\sqrt{40} + 2\sqrt{10}$ f) $5\sqrt{48} - 11\sqrt{3}$
2. Simplify:
   a) $\sqrt{50} - \sqrt{18}$ b) $\sqrt{12} + \sqrt{75}$ c) $\sqrt{24} + \sqrt{54}$
   d) $\sqrt{8} - \sqrt{32}$ e) $\sqrt{175} + \sqrt{63}$ f) $\sqrt{80} - \sqrt{45}$
3. Simplify:
   a) $5\sqrt{12} - 2\sqrt{48}$ b) $7\sqrt{24} + 3\sqrt{96}$ c) $8\sqrt{63} - 3\sqrt{175}$
   d) $9\sqrt{32} - 12\sqrt{18}$ e) $11\sqrt{54} + 6\sqrt{150}$ f) $7\sqrt{20} - 6\sqrt{45}$
4. Simplify:
   a) $\sqrt{3}(\sqrt{5} + \sqrt{7})$ b) $4\sqrt{3}(7\sqrt{2} - 3\sqrt{5})$ c) $5\sqrt{6}(2\sqrt{3} + 4\sqrt{5})$
   d) $9\sqrt{5}(2\sqrt{15} - 7\sqrt{3})$ e) $2\sqrt{6}(4\sqrt{2} - 3\sqrt{6})$ f) $7\sqrt{2}(3\sqrt{18} + 2\sqrt{2})$
5. Simplify:
   a) $(\sqrt{3} + \sqrt{5})(2\sqrt{3} - \sqrt{5})$ b) $(2\sqrt{5} - 3\sqrt{7})(\sqrt{5} + 2\sqrt{7})$
   c) $(3\sqrt{2} - 2\sqrt{6})(5\sqrt{2} + 3\sqrt{6})$ d) $(2\sqrt{3} - 3\sqrt{2})(4\sqrt{3} - \sqrt{2})$
   e) $(4\sqrt{6} + 2\sqrt{3})(7\sqrt{6} + 4\sqrt{3})$ f) $(8\sqrt{5} - 3\sqrt{7})(2\sqrt{5} - 5\sqrt{7})$
6. Simplify:
   a) $\frac{24\sqrt{14}}{8\sqrt{2}}$ b) $\frac{-15\sqrt{30}}{45\sqrt{6}}$ c) $\frac{18\sqrt{39}}{-6\sqrt{3}}$ d) $\frac{54\sqrt{70}}{9\sqrt{5}}$
   e) $\frac{-36\sqrt{22}}{-90\sqrt{2}}$ f) $\frac{60\sqrt{51}}{-4\sqrt{3}}$ g) $\frac{32\sqrt{35}}{4\sqrt{7}}$ h) $\frac{28\sqrt{55}}{42\sqrt{11}}$

Ⓑ

7. Simplify
   a) $4\sqrt{45} + 3\sqrt{80} - 11\sqrt{20}$ b) $3\sqrt{50} + 6\sqrt{32} - 4\sqrt{18}$
   c) $2\sqrt{150} - 5\sqrt{54} - 3\sqrt{24}$ d) $5\sqrt{18} + 6\sqrt{8} - 2\sqrt{32}$
   e) $3\sqrt{40} - 5\sqrt{90} - 2\sqrt{160}$ f) $9\sqrt{45} + 5\sqrt{125} - 6\sqrt{245}$

8. Simplify:
   a) $3\sqrt{2}(4\sqrt{7} - 5\sqrt{2})$ b) $6\sqrt{3}(3\sqrt{12} - 2\sqrt{75})$
   c) $-5\sqrt{6}(2\sqrt{3} - 3\sqrt{2})$ d) $4\sqrt{3}(3\sqrt{6} + 2\sqrt{7} - 5\sqrt{3})$
   e) $5\sqrt{2}(\sqrt{18} + 7\sqrt{2} - 5\sqrt{8})$ f) $8\sqrt{6}(4\sqrt{2} - 2\sqrt{3} - 3\sqrt{6})$
9. Simplify:
   a) $(\sqrt{5} + \sqrt{2})(\sqrt{5} - \sqrt{2})$ b) $(3\sqrt{5} - 2\sqrt{3})(3\sqrt{5} + 2\sqrt{3})$
   c) $(4\sqrt{6} + 8\sqrt{2})(4\sqrt{6} - 8\sqrt{2})$ d) $(5\sqrt{2} - 3\sqrt{6})^2$
   e) $(7\sqrt{3} + 4\sqrt{5})^2$ f) $2\sqrt{2}(3\sqrt{3} + 5\sqrt{7})^2$
10. Simplify:
   a) $\dfrac{12\sqrt{20}}{3\sqrt{5}}$ b) $\dfrac{18\sqrt{24}}{-3\sqrt{8}}$ c) $\dfrac{-24\sqrt{45}}{72\sqrt{20}}$ d) $\dfrac{-30\sqrt{40}}{-5\sqrt{18}}$
   e) $\dfrac{45\sqrt{54}}{18\sqrt{12}}$ f) $\dfrac{-60\sqrt{96}}{12\sqrt{27}}$ g) $\dfrac{12\sqrt{40}}{8\sqrt{45}}$ h) $\dfrac{15\sqrt{84}}{10\sqrt{63}}$
11. From a height of h m, the distance, d, in kilometres, to the horizon is given by the formula: $d \doteq 3.6\sqrt{h}$.
   a) By what factor is the distance to the horizon increased when
      i) the height is doubled?
      ii) the height is tripled?
   b) By what factor must the height be increased so that the distance to the horizon is doubled?
12. The period of a pendulum, T, in seconds, is given by the formula:
   $T = 2\pi\sqrt{\dfrac{l}{9.8}}$, where l is the length of the pendulum in metres.
   a) By what factor is the period increased when the length is:
      i) quadrupled? ii) increased fivefold?
   b) By what factor must the length be increased for the period:
      i) to triple?
      ii) to increase by a factor of $2\sqrt{2}$?

Ⓒ

1 μs is one millionth of a second.

13. When at rest, a meson decays radioactively in t_0 μs (microsecond). At a speed v, the time for decay is increased to t μs, where
   $t = \dfrac{t_0}{\sqrt{1 - \left(\dfrac{v}{c}\right)^2}}$, c being the speed of light. By what factor is the decay time increased when the meson is travelling at half the speed of light?

1-6 RATIONALIZING THE DENOMINATOR

When radicals first began to be used, mathematicians quickly discovered that not all expressions with radicals in the denominator, such as $\frac{5}{\sqrt{2}}$, could be simplified by division. The division operation was impossible to perform because the divisor was an infinite non-repeating decimal. They therefore rewrote the expression, multiplying numerator and denominator by the radical in the denominator. This makes the denominator a rational number.

$$\frac{5}{\sqrt{2}} = \frac{5}{\sqrt{2}} \times \frac{\sqrt{2}}{\sqrt{2}} \quad \text{Equivalent to multiplying by 1.}$$
$$= \frac{5\sqrt{2}}{2}$$

This procedure is called **rationalizing the denominator.**

Example 1.

Rationalize the denominator:

a) $\frac{3}{\sqrt{6}}$ b) $\frac{2}{\sqrt{18}}$ c) $\frac{3\sqrt{2}-5}{\sqrt{2}}$

Solution.

a) $\frac{3}{\sqrt{6}} = \frac{3}{\sqrt{6}} \times \frac{\sqrt{6}}{\sqrt{6}}$
$= 3\frac{\sqrt{6}}{6}$,
$= \frac{\sqrt{6}}{2}$

b) $\frac{2}{\sqrt{18}} = \frac{2}{3\sqrt{2}}$
$= \frac{2}{3\sqrt{2}} \times \frac{\sqrt{2}}{\sqrt{2}}$
$= \frac{2\sqrt{2}}{6}$, or $\frac{\sqrt{2}}{3}$

c) $\frac{3\sqrt{2}-5}{\sqrt{2}} = \frac{3\sqrt{2}-5}{\sqrt{2}} \times \frac{\sqrt{2}}{\sqrt{2}}$
$= \frac{6-5\sqrt{2}}{2}$, or $3 - \frac{5}{2}\sqrt{2}$

In *Example 2d* of the previous section, we found that the result of simplifying $(3 - 2\sqrt{5})(3 + 2\sqrt{5})$ was -11, a rational number. $(3 - 2\sqrt{5})$ and $(3 + 2\sqrt{5})$ are called **conjugates**, and the fact that the product of conjugates is a rational number can be used to simplify expressions having binomial denominators with radical terms.

Example 2.

Simplify: a) $\frac{14}{3+\sqrt{2}}$ b) $\frac{3\sqrt{2}-2\sqrt{5}}{2\sqrt{2}-\sqrt{5}}$

Solution.

The conjugate of $3 + \sqrt{2}$ is $3 - \sqrt{2}$. Multiply numerator and denominator by $3 - \sqrt{2}$.

a) $$\frac{14}{3 + \sqrt{2}} = \frac{14}{3 + \sqrt{2}} \times \frac{3 - \sqrt{2}}{3 - \sqrt{2}}$$
$$= \frac{14(3 - \sqrt{2})}{9 - 2}$$
$$= 2(3 - \sqrt{2}), \text{ or } 6 - 2\sqrt{2}$$

Multiply numerator and denominator by $2\sqrt{2} + \sqrt{5}$.

b) $$\frac{3\sqrt{2} - 2\sqrt{5}}{2\sqrt{2} - \sqrt{5}} = \frac{3\sqrt{2} - 2\sqrt{5}}{2\sqrt{2} - \sqrt{5}} \times \frac{2\sqrt{2} + \sqrt{5}}{2\sqrt{2} + \sqrt{5}}$$
$$= \frac{12 + 3\sqrt{10} - 4\sqrt{10} - 10}{8 - 5}$$
$$= \frac{2 - \sqrt{10}}{3}$$

EXERCISES 1-6

(A)

1. Rationalize the denominator:

a) $\frac{2}{\sqrt{5}}$ b) $\frac{7}{\sqrt{11}}$ c) $\frac{-4}{\sqrt{3}}$ d) $\frac{5\sqrt{2}}{\sqrt{7}}$

e) $\frac{6\sqrt{10}}{-\sqrt{3}}$ f) $\frac{12\sqrt{7}}{7\sqrt{5}}$ g) $\frac{18\sqrt{5}}{3\sqrt{2}}$ h) $\frac{20\sqrt{7}}{-4\sqrt{3}}$

2. Express in simplest form:

a) $\frac{3\sqrt{6}}{\sqrt{20}}$ b) $\frac{4\sqrt{5}}{\sqrt{8}}$ c) $\frac{-9\sqrt{12}}{\sqrt{18}}$ d) $\frac{15\sqrt{3}}{3\sqrt{8}}$

e) $\frac{-24\sqrt{7}}{-3\sqrt{12}}$ f) $\frac{14\sqrt{3}}{2\sqrt{28}}$ g) $\frac{20\sqrt{24}}{3\sqrt{20}}$ h) $\frac{36\sqrt{18}}{8\sqrt{8}}$

3. Simplify:

a) $\frac{2\sqrt{3} + 4}{\sqrt{3}}$ b) $\frac{5\sqrt{7} - 3}{\sqrt{7}}$ c) $\frac{4\sqrt{5} - 2}{\sqrt{5}}$ d) $\frac{6\sqrt{2} - \sqrt{3}}{\sqrt{3}}$

e) $\frac{8\sqrt{6} + \sqrt{5}}{\sqrt{5}}$ f) $\frac{3\sqrt{10} - \sqrt{2}}{\sqrt{2}}$ g) $\frac{5\sqrt{8} + 2\sqrt{3}}{\sqrt{6}}$ h) $\frac{3\sqrt{12} - 4\sqrt{3}}{2\sqrt{2}}$

4. Rationalize the denominator:

a) $\frac{\sqrt{3}}{\sqrt{5} - \sqrt{2}}$ b) $\frac{\sqrt{5}}{\sqrt{7} + \sqrt{3}}$ c) $\frac{\sqrt{11}}{8 - \sqrt{5}}$ d) $\frac{2\sqrt{5}}{\sqrt{6} + \sqrt{3}}$

e) $\frac{5\sqrt{6}}{\sqrt{12} - 5}$ f) $\frac{4\sqrt{7}}{\sqrt{15} - \sqrt{10}}$ g) $\frac{6\sqrt{3}}{5 + \sqrt{2}}$ h) $\frac{9\sqrt{5}}{\sqrt{11} - \sqrt{5}}$

5. Simplify:

a) $\dfrac{3\sqrt{2}+\sqrt{3}}{2\sqrt{3}+\sqrt{2}}$ b) $\dfrac{5\sqrt{3}+\sqrt{2}}{2\sqrt{3}-\sqrt{2}}$ c) $\dfrac{5\sqrt{3}-3\sqrt{5}}{\sqrt{5}-\sqrt{3}}$

d) $\dfrac{3+2\sqrt{5}}{3\sqrt{5}-4}$ e) $\dfrac{2\sqrt{7}-4\sqrt{3}}{3\sqrt{7}+\sqrt{3}}$ f) $\dfrac{\sqrt{7}+3\sqrt{2}}{9+2\sqrt{14}}$

6. Which of these pairs are conjugates?

a) $3+\sqrt{2},\ \ 3-\sqrt{2}$ b) $10-\sqrt{6},\ \ \sqrt{6}+10$

c) $\sqrt{2}+5,\ \ \sqrt{2}-5$ d) $2+\sqrt{6},\ \ -2-\sqrt{6}$

e) $7-\sqrt{3},\ \ 3+\sqrt{7}$ f) $1+3\sqrt{8},\ \ 1-6\sqrt{2}$

(B)

7. Rationalize the denominator of the reciprocal:

a) $\sqrt{2}$ b) $\sqrt{12}$ c) $\sqrt{50}$

d) $\sqrt{2}-1$ e) $\sqrt{3}+\sqrt{2}$ f) $2\sqrt{5}-3\sqrt{2}$

8. Simplify:

a) $\dfrac{1}{2+\sqrt{3}}+\dfrac{1}{2-\sqrt{3}}$ b) $\dfrac{3}{\sqrt{5}-\sqrt{2}}-\dfrac{1}{\sqrt{5}+\sqrt{2}}$

c) $\dfrac{6}{\sqrt{2}}+\dfrac{2}{\sqrt{2}+1}$ d) $\dfrac{3}{2+\sqrt{5}}+\dfrac{2}{\sqrt{5}}$

e) $\dfrac{4}{1-\sqrt{3}}-\dfrac{1}{\sqrt{3}}$ f) $\dfrac{1}{\sqrt{2}+1}+\dfrac{1}{\sqrt{3}+1}$

Number Triplets

Sets of numbers such as (2, 6, 7) and (3, 4, 8) are often called triples. These two triples are related in an interesting way:

$2+6+7=3+4+8$ Their sums are equal.

$2^2+6^2+7^2=3^2+4^2+8^2$ The sums of their squares are equal.

Because of the way these triples are related, we might call them *triplets*.

1. Find the missing members of these triplets:
   a) (3, –, 8) and (4, –, 9) b) (–, 5, 6) and (2, –, 7)
   c) (4, 8, 9) and (–, 6, –)
2. Show that for any integer, k, the following are triplets:

   $(k, k+4, k+5)$ and $(k+1, k+2, k+6)$
3. Generate a number of triplets. Compare yours with those of a classmate. Write a report of any patterns that appear.

1-7 THE REAL NUMBERS

In the fifth century B.C., the Pythagoreans found points on the number line that did not correspond to rational numbers. In the nineteenth century A.D., mathematicians wondered if there were points on the number line with no corresponding decimal. It wasn't until 1876 that the German mathematician, Richard Dedekind, proved that every point on the number line has a corresponding decimal, and conversely, every decimal corresponds to a point on the number line.

> All numbers that can be represented by decimals are real numbers. These numbers correspond to every point on the number line.

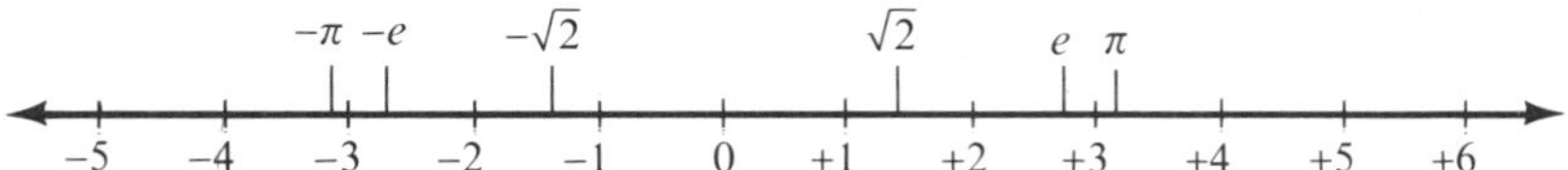

The diagram below shows how the various types of numbers are related.

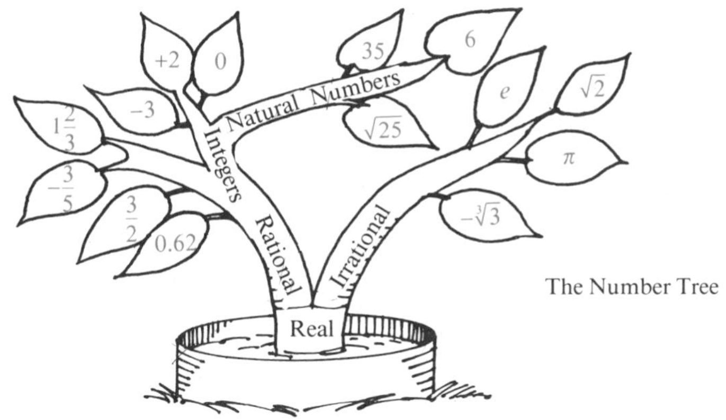

The Number Tree

Example.

Classify as rational or irrational:

a) $7.3\overline{756}$ b) 0.010 010 001 000 010... c) $\dfrac{\sqrt{3}}{\sqrt{48}}$ d) 7π

Solution.

a) $7.3\overline{756}$ is a repeating decimal and therefore a rational number.
b) The digits follow a pattern, but a non-repeating pattern. 0.010 010 001 000 010... is irrational.
c) $\dfrac{\sqrt{3}}{\sqrt{48}} = \sqrt{\dfrac{1}{16}}$, or $\dfrac{1}{4}$, which is rational.

d) If 7π were rational, we could write: $7\pi = \frac{a}{b}$, where a and b are natural numbers.

It would follow that $\pi = \frac{a}{7b}$, which is rational. But π is irrational. Therefore, 7π cannot be rational. It is irrational.

EXERCISES 1-7

Ⓐ

1. Which numbers appear to be irrational?
   - a) 2.363 663 666 3...
   - b) −0.123 456 78...
   - c) 1.407 240 724...
   - d) 5.312 312 231...
   - e) −17.717 177 17...
   - f) 4.925 529 92...
   - g) 8.069 066 906...
   - h) −24.734 659 28...
2. Which of the following are irrational?
   - a) $\sqrt{34}$
   - b) $\sqrt{256}$
   - c) $\sqrt{36 + 49}$
   - d) $2\sqrt{18} - \sqrt{3}$
   - e) $\sqrt{25 + 56}$
   - f) $\sqrt{6.25}$
   - g) $\sqrt{16} - \sqrt{12}$
   - h) $\sqrt{\frac{65}{9}}$
   - i) $7 - \sqrt{169}$
3. Which are rational and which are irrational?
   - a) 0.010 120 230 123 4...
   - b) 3.131 313 131 313...
   - c) −1.357 957 957 957...
   - d) 0.707 007 000 700...
   - e) 2.179 652 389 57...
   - f) −5.246 810 121 4...

Ⓑ

4. To which of the sets of numbers listed does each of the following belong?
   - a) $\sqrt{37}$
   - b) $-5.1\overline{62}$
   - c) $\sqrt{169}$
   - d) −2.357 911 13...
   - e) $-\frac{29}{5}$
   - f) $\sqrt{2}$
   - g) $\sqrt{49 + 16}$
   - h) $\sqrt{48} - \sqrt{18}$
   - i) $17 - 25$

Natural numbers, N
Integers, I
Rational numbers, Q
Irrational numbers, Q'
Real numbers, R

5. Using the [√] key on a calculator, $\sqrt{5} = 2.236\ 067\ 9$. This is a rational number, but $\sqrt{5}$ is irrational. Can a number be both rational and irrational? Explain.
6. Find a rational number and an irrational number between:
   - a) $2.\overline{5791}$ and $2.\overline{5792}$;
   - b) $-6.\overline{327}$ and −6.327 332 733 2...;
   - c) 4.190 119 011 190...and 4.190 219 021 190...

Ⓒ

7. Using the $\boxed{\sqrt{\ }}$ key on a calculator, $\sqrt{0.444\,444\,4} = 0.666\,666\,6$.
   a) Write fractions in the form $\frac{m}{n}$ for 0.444 444 4 and 0.666 666 6, and use them to explain the calculator result.
   b) Find another number which gives a similar result.
8. The solution of $3x + 12 = 3$ is real, rational, and an integer. Describe the solution(s) of each of the following:
   a) $3x + 5 = 17$ b) $19 + 6x = 7$
   c) $5 + 4x = 11$ d) $x^2 + 3 = 12$
   e) $x^2 + 1 = 4$ f) $x^2 + 4 = 1$

Review Exercises

1. Express as a product of prime factors:
   a) 1470 b) 1365 c) 5236
2. Express as a common fraction:
   a) $1.7\overline{36}$ b) $1.5\overline{85}$ c) $2.\overline{123}$
   d) $3.\overline{14}$ e) $0.\overline{831}$ f) $5.01\overline{5}$
3. Express as a repeating decimal:
   a) $0.\overline{4} - 0.\overline{1}$ b) $0.\overline{83} + 0.\overline{07}$ c) $4.\overline{14} - 3.\overline{9}$
   d) $0.\overline{7} \times 0.\overline{6}$ e) $0.\overline{8} \times 0.\overline{3}$ f) $1.\overline{25} \times 0.7\overline{5}$
4. If $x = -\frac{2}{3}$ and $w = \frac{1}{-4}$, evaluate:
   a) $\frac{3x^2 - 2w}{3w^2}$ b) $\frac{7xw + 3w}{5w}$ c) $\frac{3x + 2w - 2xw}{4x^2}$
5. Solve:
   a) $2(3x - 7) + 7 = 5(x - 9) - 17$
   b) $19(2x - 1) + 11 = 15x - 5(2 - 3x)$
   c) $\frac{7(x - 3)}{8} = \frac{8(x + 2)}{3}$
   d) $6(3x - 5) + 27 = 5(2x + 3) - 7(x + 3)$
6. For every two quarters in a coin bank there are three dimes. If the two kinds of coin total \$12.80, how many quarters and dimes are there?
7. Simplify:
   a) $2\sqrt{5} \times 3\sqrt{2} \times \sqrt{10}$ b) $5\sqrt{3} \times 2\sqrt{2} \times 2\sqrt{6}$
   c) $5\sqrt{5} \times 8\sqrt{3} \times 2\sqrt{15}$ d) $(-4\sqrt{3})(-3\sqrt{2})(-5\sqrt{7})$
   e) $7\sqrt{12} \times 3\sqrt{15} \times 6\sqrt{5}$ f) $(11\sqrt{14})(-7\sqrt{3})(-5\sqrt{2})$

8. Arrange in order from least to greatest:
   a) $7\sqrt{6},\ 8\sqrt{5},\ 9\sqrt{3},\ 6\sqrt{7},\ 10\sqrt{2}$
   b) $-4\sqrt{3},\ -5\sqrt{2},\ -3\sqrt{5},\ -2\sqrt{7},\ -\sqrt{19}$
   c) $5\sqrt{5},\ \sqrt{111},\ 6\sqrt{2},\ 3\sqrt{6},\ 2\sqrt{26}$
9. Simplify:
   a) $3\sqrt{30} + 2\sqrt{64} - 5\sqrt{12}$
   b) $4\sqrt{40} + 8\sqrt{24} - 3\sqrt{48}$
   c) $7\sqrt{120} - 3\sqrt{52} - 2\sqrt{28}$
   d) $8\sqrt{24} + 3\sqrt{6} - 4\sqrt{54}$
   e) $4\sqrt{60} - 3\sqrt{70} - 2\sqrt{80}$
   f) $7\sqrt{45} + 4\sqrt{196} - 6\sqrt{175}$
10. Simplify:
   a) $2\sqrt{3}(3\sqrt{8} - 4\sqrt{2})$
   b) $7\sqrt{3}(4\sqrt{24} - 3\sqrt{50})$
   c) $(5\sqrt{5} + 2\sqrt{3})(5\sqrt{5} - 2\sqrt{3})$
   d) $(6\sqrt{3} - 2\sqrt{6})^2$
   e) $(4\sqrt{3} + 3\sqrt{5})^2$
   f) $3\sqrt{3}(2\sqrt{2} + 5\sqrt{6})$
11. Simplify:
   a) $\dfrac{12\sqrt{12}}{4\sqrt{2}}$
   b) $\dfrac{16\sqrt{50}}{-5\sqrt{10}}$
   c) $\dfrac{-40\sqrt{50}}{-8\sqrt{125}}$
   d) $\dfrac{3\sqrt{5} + 5}{\sqrt{5}}$
   e) $\dfrac{6\sqrt{7} - 4}{\sqrt{7} - \sqrt{2}}$
   f) $\dfrac{4\sqrt{18} - 3\sqrt{2}}{\sqrt{5} + \sqrt{3}}$
12. Which of the following are irrational?
   a) $\sqrt{35}$
   b) $\sqrt{169}$
   c) $\sqrt{25 + 36}$
   d) $\sqrt{\dfrac{49}{6}}$
   e) $\sqrt{144 - 23}$
   f) $3\sqrt{12} - \sqrt{3}$
   g) $-2.083\,091\,309\,130\ldots$
   h) $4.008\,009\,987\ldots$

2 Powers

Canada's most massive tree is a Douglas fir on Vancouver Island. How can its height be estimated from the diameter of its base? (See *Example 5* in Section 2-4.)

2-1 POWERS AND EXPONENTS

A flu virus is about 10^{-5}mm in diameter.

10^{63} grains of sand would fill the observable universe.

Exponential notation was introduced into mathematics in 1637 by the French mathematician, René Descartes. This notation allows scientists such as biologists, astronomers, and statisticians to express both very large and very small numbers more compactly. Not only is it a convenient symbolism for representing powers, it has also been possible to develop techniques for operating with them.

Example 1.

a) Write as a power:
   i) $7 \times 7 \times 7$ ii) $w \cdot w \cdot w \cdot w \cdot w$

b) Simplify: $2(-2)^3 + 4(3)^2$

Solution.

a) i) $7 \times 7 \times 7 = 7^3$ ii) $w \cdot w \cdot w \cdot w \cdot w = w^5$

b) $2(-2)^3 + 4(3)^2 = 2(-8) + 4(9)$
$= -16 + 36$, or 20

Example 2.

Use a calculator to find 2^{26}.

Solution.

On most calculators with a $\boxed{y^x}$ key, we can find 2^{26} by pressing:

$$\boxed{2}\ \boxed{y^x}\ \boxed{2}\ \boxed{6}\ \boxed{=}$$

The display will be 67 108 864.

Example 3.

The number of insects in a colony doubles every month. There are currently about 1000 insects in the colony.

a) How many insects will there be after one year?

b) Write an expression to represent the number of insects after n months.

Solution.

a) Number of insects after 12 months:

$$1000 \times 2^{12} = 1000 \times 4096, \text{ or } 4\ 096\ 000$$

There would be about four million insects.

b) After n months, the number of insects would be:

$$1000 \times 2^n.$$

Exponents have many applications in financial problems.

Example 4.

A bank pays interest at the rate of 12% per annum. What is the balance after 3 years on a deposit of \$1000 if interest is compounded annually?

Solution.

After 3 years at 12% per annum, the balance is:

$$\$1000(1.12)^3 = \$1404.93$$

EXERCISES 2-1

(A)

1. Write as a power:
   a) $2 \times 2 \times 2 \times 2 \times 2 \times 2 \times 2$ b) $a \cdot a \cdot a \cdot a \cdot a \cdot a \cdot a$
   c) $\left(-\frac{3}{4}\right)\left(-\frac{3}{4}\right)\left(-\frac{3}{4}\right)\left(-\frac{3}{4}\right)\left(-\frac{3}{4}\right)$ d) $(3x)(3x)(3x)(3x)$
2. Simplify:
   a) $6^2 + 8^2$ b) $(6 + 8)^2$ c) $(-3)^3 - 5^2$
   d) $(-1)^5 + (-2)^3$ e) $2(-1)^4 + 5(-3)^2$ f) $3(2)^3 - 2(3)^2$
3. Find, using a calculator:
   a) 3^7 b) 5^6 c) $(1.2)^4$
   d) π^3 e) 7^{12} f) 2^{30}
4. Evaluate for: i) $n = 3$; ii) $n = 6$.
   a) 100×2^n b) 100×3^n c) $100 \times (0.5)^n$
   d) $5000 \times (0.8)^n$ e) $25 \times (0.75)^n$ f) $1.8 \times (1.15)^n$
5. A hive contains 100 bees. If the population doubles every month:
   a) which expression represents the number of bees after 5 months?
      i) 100×5^2 ii) 100×2^5 iii) $(100 \times 2)^5$ iv) $(100 \times 5)^2$
   b) how many bees are there after: i) 3 months? ii) 7 months?

6. A tractor costs \$65 000. If its value each year is 85% of its value the previous year, find its value:
   a) after 7 years, to the nearest \$100;
   b) after n years.
7. A bank pays interest at the rate of 10% per annum. What is the balance after 4 years on a deposit of \$5000 if interest is compounded annually?

(B)

8. Express the first number as a power of the second:
   a) 27, 3 b) 125, 5 c) −32, −2
   d) 729, 9 e) 81, −3 f) 2.0736, 1.2
9. Which is the greater:
   a) 2^7 or 5^3? b) 3^4 or 4^3?
   c) 3^6 or 9^3? d) 2^{10} or 10^3?

10. Arrange from greatest to least:
a) 3^3, 2^3, 4^2, 7^2, 3^2 b) $(-3)^4$, 2^7, $(-5)^3$, $(-2)^8$, $(-2)^9$
c) $(1.2)^3$, $(1.1)^5$, 1.4, $(1.3)^2$

11. If a cottage, originally bought for $30 000, appreciates at the rate of 7% per year, what is it worth after:
a) 5 years? b) 12 years? c) n years?

12. If the rate of inflation is 8% per year, how much would you expect to pay for a loaf of bread now priced at 89¢ in:
a) 3 years? b) 5 years? c) 10 years?

13. The table shows the 1985 population of some of the world's largest cities and their approximate annual growth rate. Assuming that these growth rates are maintained, estimate the population of each city in the year a) 2000 b) 2025.

City	Population in millions (1985)	Annual growth rate
Mexico City	16	4.0%
Lagos, Nigeria	5	4.1%
New York	15	0.5%
Tokyo	17	0.1%
Delhi	7	3.2%
Calcutta	11	3.0%

14. Radium-226 is a radioactive substance with a half-life of 1600 years. This means that over this period half the atoms in a sample will have decayed to form other substances.
a) What percent of radium-226 remains after:
i) 3200 years? ii) 6400 years?
b) Write an expression to represent the percent of radium-226 remaining after n years.

15. A pump removes 10% of the air in a tank each minute.
a) What percent of the air is left after
i) 1 min? ii) 2 min? iii) 5 min? iv) 20 min?
b) How long would it take to reduce the air in the tank to:
i) 50%? ii) 10%?
c) Write an expression to represent the percent of air remaining after n minutes.

16. If a ball is dropped from a height of 2.5 m and allowed to bounce freely, the height, h, in metres, to which it bounces is given by the formula: $h = 2.5(0.8)^n$, where n is the number of bounces.
a) What height does the ball reach after:
i) the third bounce? ii) the tenth bounce?
b) After what bounce does the ball reach a height of approximately 0.5 m?

17. Each year, the value of a car depreciates to 70% of its value the previous year. If a car was bought new for $10 000:
    a) find its value after 5 years to the nearest $100;
    b) write an expression to represent its value after n years.

The only example that has ever been found of two powers differing by 1 is 2^3 and 3^2.
Find examples of powers that differ by 2, by 3, by 4, by 5,...
Write a report of your findings.

18. a) Use a calculator to verify that the final digit of
    i) 3^5 is 3; ii) 12^5 is 2; iii) 27^5 is 7.
    b) Investigate the final digit of other fifth powers. What do you notice?
    c) Use the result in (b) to predict the final digit of the following powers and check with a calculator:
    i) 13^6 ii) 8^{10} iii) 7^{11}

(C)

19. Show that the property in Exercise 18 is true for the fifth power of any natural number.

MATHEMATICS PROJECT

The Accuracy of Calculators and Computers

To find how accurately a calculator or computer performs successive calculations:

1. Enter the number 1.000 000 1 in a calculator and press the x^2 key 27 times. Compare your results with those of students using different calculators.
2. Use a computer to square 1.000 000 1 twenty-seven times and compare the result with those above.
3. The correct result, accurate to 8 significant digits, is 674 530.47. Which calculator or computer gave:
   i) the most accurate result? ii) the least accurate result?
4. The procedure of squaring 1.000 000 1 twenty-seven times is equivalent to evaluating $(1.000\ 000\ 1)^n$ for a certain value of n. What is the value of n?

MATHEMATICS AROUND US

The Energy Crisis

The fossil fuels—oil, coal, and natural gas—are non-renewable resources; once they have been exhausted they can never be replaced.

The graph below compares the production of crude oil up to 1980 with the estimated total world resources represented by the large rectangle. As can be seen from the graph, production has been doubling about every 10 years.

Oil Production and Estimated World's Resources

Before 1950
1950–1960
1960–1970
1970–1980

QUESTIONS

1. Assuming that production continues to double about every 10 years, estimate how long the world's supply of crude oil will last.
2. Up to 1950, about 5×10^{10} barrels of crude oil had been produced.
   a) Estimate the world's total supply of crude oil.
   b) How much more oil would have to be discovered to allow oil production to continue to grow at the same rate for an additional 10 years?
3. World coal reserves are estimated to be about eight times as great as the oil reserves. If oil were replaced by coal as a source of energy, about how many years would the coal last if production grew at the same rate?
4. Give reasons why the rate of consumption of oil may not continue to double every 10 years.

2-2 EXPONENT LAWS FOR POSITIVE INTEGRAL EXPONENTS

The Milky Way Galaxy

Is there life anywhere else in the universe, or are we alone? That life does exist elsewhere in our galaxy is not beyond the bounds of possibility. Frank Drake of Cornell University has even developed an equation to estimate the number of extraterrestrial technological civilizations (ETC's) that exist at any moment. His equation is:

$$\text{Number of ETC's at any moment} = \text{Number of ETC's that ever existed} \times \frac{\text{Average lifetime of such a civilization}}{\text{Age of the galaxy}}$$

For our galaxy, we have the following:

$$\text{Number of ETC's at any moment} = 10^7 \times \frac{10^6}{10^{10}}$$
$$= 10^3, \text{ or } 1000$$

There is a possibility of 1000 planets possessing intelligent life. We are presently trying to communicate with them.

This illustration involves two of the laws for operating with exponents. In this section, more of these laws will be reviewed and applied.

Example 1.

Simplify:

a) $x^5 \cdot x^2$ b) $m^7 \div m^3$

c) $(a^2)^3$ d) $(ab)^4$ e) $\left(\frac{x}{y}\right)^2$

Solution.

In each case, the definition of an exponent, as indicating repeating factors, is used.

a) $x^5 \cdot x^2 = (x \cdot x \cdot x \cdot x \cdot x)(x \cdot x)$
$= x^7$

b) $m^7 \div m^3 = \dfrac{m \cdot m \cdot m \cdot m \cdot m \cdot m \cdot m}{m \cdot m \cdot m}$
$= m^4$

c) $(a^2)^3 = a^2 \cdot a^2 \cdot a^2$
$= (a \cdot a)(a \cdot a)(a \cdot a)$
$= a^6$

d) $(ab)^4 = ab \cdot ab \cdot ab \cdot ab$
$= (a \cdot a \cdot a \cdot a)(b \cdot b \cdot b \cdot b)$
$= a^4b^4$

e) $\left(\frac{x}{y}\right)^2 = \left(\frac{x}{y}\right)\left(\frac{x}{y}\right)$
$= \dfrac{x^2}{y^2}$

The results of *Example 1* illustrate the following exponent laws, where m and n are positive integers.

1. $x^m \cdot x^n = x^{m+n}$
2. $x^m \div x^n = x^{m-n}$ $(m > n, x \neq 0)$
3. $(x^m)^n = x^{mn}$
4. $(xy)^n = x^n y^n$
5. $\left(\frac{x}{y}\right)^n = \frac{x^n}{y^n}$ $(y \neq 0)$

The restrictions that m and n are positive integers and $m > n$ in the second law will be dropped in the next two sections.

The exponent laws may be used to simplify products and quotients involving powers.

Example 2.

Simplify: a) $\frac{(x^2)^3}{(2x)^2}$ b) $(a^m b^3)^n (ab^n)^2$

Solution.

a) $\frac{(x^2)^3}{(2x)^2} = \frac{x^6}{4x^2}$

$= \frac{x^{6-2}}{4}$

$= \frac{1}{4}x^4$

b) $(a^m b^3)^n (ab^n)^2 = a^{mn}b^{3n} \cdot a^2 b^{2n}$

$= a^{mn+2}b^{3n+2n}$

$= a^{mn+2}b^{5n}$

Example 3.

If $x = m^3$ and $y = 2n^2$, write these expressions in terms of m and n:

a) $2x^2y^4$ b) $\left(\frac{3x^3y^2}{2xy}\right)^3$

Solution.

a) $2x^2y^4 = 2(m^3)^2(2n^2)^4$

$= 2m^6 \times 16n^8$

$= 32m^6n^8$

b) Simplify the expression before substituting.

$\left(\frac{3x^3y^2}{2xy}\right)^3 = \left(\frac{3}{2}x^2y\right)^3$

$= \frac{27}{8}x^6y^3$

$\frac{27}{8}x^6y^3 = \frac{27}{8}(m^3)^6(2n^2)^3$

$= \frac{27}{8}m^{18} \times 8n^6$

$= 27m^{18}n^6$

EXERCISES 2-2

(A)

1. Simplify:
   a) $x^9 \times x^{23}$ b) $m^{17} \div m^7$ c) $y^4 \times y^{11}$
   d) $a^{12} \div a^3$ e) $c^8 \times c^{15} \times c^4$ f) $x^{32} \div x^8 \div x^4$
2. Simplify:
   a) $9x^5 \times 7x^{12}$ b) $75m^{18} \div 15m^6$ c) $(-2n^3)^2$
   d) $-24a^{20} \div 6a^{10}$ e) $12y^9 \times 8y^{12}$ f) $(-3c^4)^5$
3. Simplify:
   a) $a^7b^4 \times a^9b^3$ b) $m^{11}n^8 \div m^5n^4$
   c) $-7c^{12}d^5 \times 6c^8d^6$ d) $(xy^2)^3$
   e) $36a^{15}b^{12} \div 9a^5b^4$ f) $(x^2y^3)^2(x^2y)^4$

(B)

4. Simplify:
   a) $(x^3)^2(3x)^2$ b) $(2a^3)^4(5a^2)^3$
   c) $(4m^3n^5)^3(-3m^2n^6)^3$ d) $\left(\frac{12x^3y^2}{9xy}\right)\left(\frac{18x^5y^3}{4x^2y^2}\right)$
   e) $\frac{(a^2b^3)^4}{(ab^2)^3}$ f) $\left(\frac{24c^8d^5}{-8c^2d}\right)\left(\frac{15c^3d^9}{18cd^5}\right)$
5. Evaluate for $x = 2$ and $y = -1$:
   a) $(x^3y^2)(x^2y^4)$ b) $x^8y^{12} \div x^4y^4$ c) $(3x^4y)(5x^2y^6)$
   d) $\frac{(-6x^5y^2)(8x^3y)}{(4x^2)^2}$ e) $\frac{9x^3y^5 \times 8x^4y^3}{18x^5y^7}$ f) $\frac{(4x^3y^2)^2(3x^5y^9)^3}{(6x^7y^2)^2}$
6. Simplify:
   a) $(x^a)^3(x^{a+1})^2$ b) $(3^m)^2(3^{m+4})$ c) $(c^{2a})^3(c^{a+2})^4$
   d) $\frac{(2a^{3x})(3a^{2x-1})^4}{(6a^x)^2}$ e) $\frac{(r^{5x})^{2y}}{(r^{xy})^4}$ f) $\frac{(x^{2m}y^{n+1})^3}{x^{3m+1}y^n}$
7. Express as a power of 2:
   a) $2^n \times 4^n$ b) $16^n \div 2^n$
   c) $(2^n)(4^{n+1})(8^{n+2})$ d) $8^{3n} \div 4^{2n}$
   e) $\frac{(4^n)(2^{n+3})}{8^{n+1}}$ f) $(4^{3n+1})(2^{n+5}) \div 16^{n+1}$
8. a) Find, using a calculator: i) 2^{10} ii) 5^{10} iii) 6^9
   b) Use the results of (a) to estimate:
      i) 2^{13} ii) 2^{50} iii) 5^{20}
      iv) 5^{12} v) 6^{27} vi) 6^{11}
9. If $x = 3m^2$ and $y = m^3$, express the following in terms of m:
   a) $2x^2y$ b) $(x^3y^2)^2$
   c) $5x^3y^4 \div (3xy)^2$ d) $\left(\frac{5x^3y^2}{2xy}\right)^2$

10. If $x = a^2$ and $y = 2b^3$, express in terms of a and b:
    a) $3x^3y^2$
    b) $(2x^2y^3)^2$
    c) $\dfrac{5x^4y^3}{2x^2y}$
    d) $\left(\dfrac{3x^7y^4}{6x^4y^2}\right)^2$

11. If $m = x^a$, express in terms of x and a:
    a) m^2
    b) m^a
    c) $(mx)^2\left(\dfrac{m}{x}\right)^3$

12. Some bacteria reproduce by splitting into two new cells about every half hour.
    a) If a single bacterium began reproducing at noon, about how many bacteria would be present at:
       i) 3 p.m.? ii) 6 p.m.? iii) midnight?
       iv) noon the next day?
    b) Write an expression which represents the number of bacteria present after n hours.
    c) Give reasons why the growth of bacteria must ultimately slow down.

Ⓒ

13. Given: $b = a^3$ and $c = a^5$.
    a) Express as a power of a: i) b^2c ii) b^3c
    b) Express as a product of powers of b and c: i) a^{13} ii) a^{16}
    c) Show that if x is any integer greater than 7, a^x can be expressed in one of the forms: b^m, c^n, or b^mc^n, where m and n are natural numbers.

14. Simplify, without using a calculator:
    a) $\dfrac{5 \times 2^{12} - 2^{10}}{2^6}$
    b) $\dfrac{2^{12} + 2^{15}}{2^{12} + 2^{14}}$

15. Show that:
    a) $2^x + 2^{x+1} = 3 \times 2^x$
    b) $2^x + 2^{x+1} + 2^{x+2} = 7 \times 2^x$

16. Find the exact value of:
    a) 2^{30};
    b) 5^{12};
    c) 3^{20}.

2-3 EXTENDING THE EXPONENT LAWS: INTEGRAL EXPONENTS

Powers such as 5^0 and 2^{-3} cannot be defined in terms of repeated factors because the exponents are not positive integers. If the exponent law: $x^m \div x^n$ $(m > n)$, is extended to the cases where $m = n$ and $m < n$, we can give meaning to expressions such as 5^0 and 2^{-3}.

By extending the law:

$$\frac{5^2}{5^2} = 5^{2-2}, \text{ or } 5^0 \qquad \frac{2^4}{2^7} = 2^{4-7}, \text{ or } 2^{-3}$$

Since $\frac{5^2}{5^2} = 1$, then $5^0 = 1$

Since $\frac{2^4}{2^7} = \frac{\not{2} \times \not{2} \times \not{2} \times \not{2}}{\not{2} \times \not{2} \times \not{2} \times \not{2} \times 2 \times 2 \times 2}$, or $\frac{1}{2^3}$, then $2^{-3} = \frac{1}{2^3}$

These examples suggest that x^0 should be defined to equal 1, and that x^{-n} should be defined as the reciprocal of x^n.

$$x^0 = 1 \quad (x \neq 0) \qquad x^{-n} = \frac{1}{x^n} \quad (n \in I, x \neq 0)$$

$\in$ means: "is a member of".

Example 1.

Find:

a) 3^{-4} b) $(0.1)^{-3}$ c) $\left(\frac{2}{3}\right)^{-2}$ d) $x^{-1} + y^{-1}$

Solution.

a) $$3^{-4} = \frac{1}{3^4} = \frac{1}{81}$$

b) $$(0.1)^{-3} = \left(\frac{1}{10}\right)^{-3} = \frac{1}{\left(\frac{1}{10}\right)^3} = \frac{1}{\frac{1}{1000}}, \text{ or } 1000$$

c) $$\left(\frac{2}{3}\right)^{-2} = \frac{1}{\left(\frac{2}{3}\right)^2} = \frac{1}{\frac{4}{9}} = \frac{9}{4}$$

d) $$x^{-1} + y^{-1} = \frac{1}{x} + \frac{1}{y} = \frac{x + y}{xy}$$

Example 2.

Use a calculator to find $(1.5)^{-4}$ and give the result correct to four decimal places.

Solution.

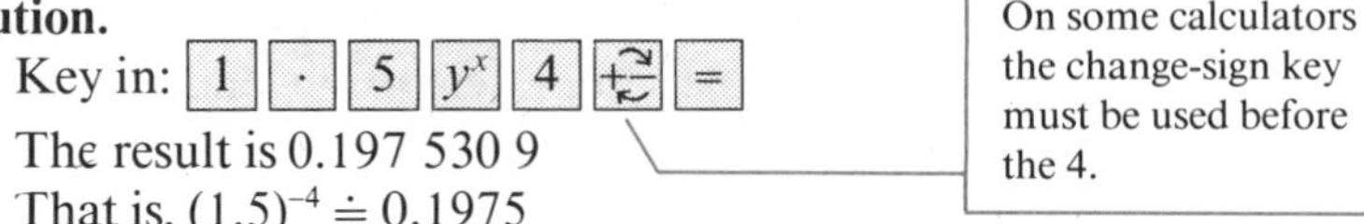

Key in: 1 · 5 y^x 4 +/- =
On some calculators the change-sign key must be used before the 4.

The result is 0.197 530 9

That is, $(1.5)^{-4} \doteq 0.1975$

The expression in *Example 2* can be simplified in other ways:

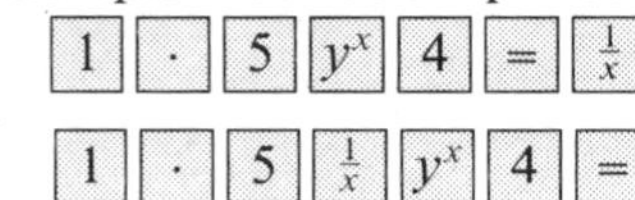

Many problems and formulas concerning growth or decay may involve negative exponents.

Example 3.

The number of insects in a colony doubles every month. If there are now 1000 insects in the colony, about how many were in the colony three months ago?

Solution.

Let x be the number of insects 3 months ago. Then, after 3 successive doublings the colony grows to 1000 insects.

$$x \times 2^3 = 1000$$

$$x = \frac{1000}{2^3}, \text{ or } 125$$

or

From *Example 3* in Section 2-1, the number of insects after n months is 1000×2^n. Substitute -3 for n to obtain:

$$1000 \times 2^{-3} = 1000 \times \frac{1}{2^3}$$

$$= \frac{1000}{8}, \text{ or } 125$$

There were about 125 insects in the colony 3 months ago.

EXERCISES 2-3

Ⓐ

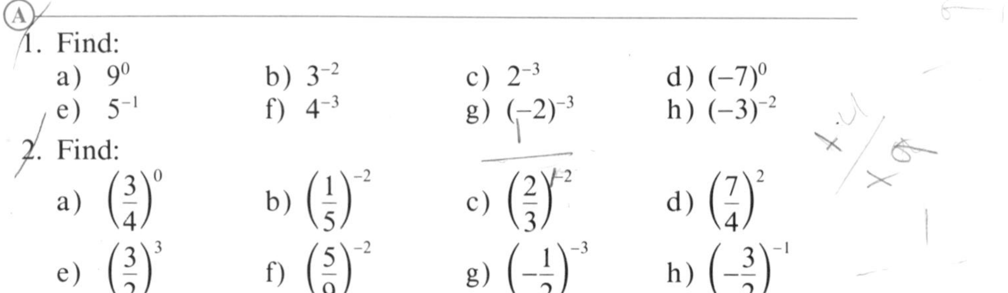

1. Find:

a) 9^0 b) 3^{-2} c) 2^{-3} d) $(-7)^0$

e) 5^{-1} f) 4^{-3} g) $(-2)^{-3}$ h) $(-3)^{-2}$

2. Find:

a) $\left(\frac{3}{4}\right)^0$ b) $\left(\frac{1}{5}\right)^{-2}$ c) $\left(\frac{2}{3}\right)^{-2}$ d) $\left(\frac{7}{4}\right)^2$

e) $\left(\frac{3}{2}\right)^3$ f) $\left(\frac{5}{9}\right)^{-2}$ g) $\left(-\frac{1}{2}\right)^{-3}$ h) $\left(-\frac{3}{2}\right)^{-1}$

3. Find, using a calculator. Give the result correct to four decimal places.
   a) 2^{-3} b) 10^{-4} c) 5^{-5} d) $(1.7)^{-4}$
   e) $(2.3)^{-3}$ f) $(1.01)^{-12}$ g) $(0.4)^{-5}$ h) $(1.25)^{-7}$

4. Simplify, using a calculator:
   a) $100(1.05)^8$ b) $100(1.02)^{-10}$ c) $450(1.15)^7$
   d) $750(1.09)^{-5}$ e) $3000(1.12)^{-6}$ f) $825(1.08)^{-12}$

5. Evaluate, correct to 3 decimal places, for: i) $n = -2$, ii) $n = -5$:
   a) 3^n b) 10^n c) $(1.5)^n$
   d) $(1.06)^n$ e) $(1.18)^n$ f) $(0.92)^n$

6. A colony of 10 000 bees doubles in number every month.
   a) Which expression represents the number of bees 3 months ago?
      i) $10\,000 \times 2^3$ ii) $10\,000 \times 3^{-2}$ iii) $10\,000 \times 2^{-3}$
   b) How many bees were there:
      i) 2 months ago? ii) 5 months ago?

B

7. Simplify:
   a) $3^2 - 3^{-2}$ b) $2^{-1} - 2^{-2}$ c) $(-2)^{-3} + 3^{-2}$
   d) $\dfrac{2^{-1}}{2^{-2} - 2^{-3}}$ e) $\dfrac{3^{-1} - 3^{-2}}{(3^{-1})(3^{-2})}$ f) $\dfrac{7^0}{(4^{-2} - 2^{-3})^{-1}}$

8. Evaluate for $x = 2$ and $y = -3$:
   a) x^{-3} b) y^{-2} c) $(xy)^{-2}$ d) 5^x
   e) 2^{-y} f) 7^{-x} g) y^y h) $(x^y)(y^x)$

9. Evaluate for $x = -2$ and $y = 5$:
   a) $2^x + y^{-1}$ b) $3^{-x} - y$ c) $4x^3 + y^2$
   d) $2x^{-1} + 5y^{-1}$ e) $(3x^{-1} - y^{-1})^{-2}$ f) $y^{-x} + x^{-y}$

10. Which number of each pair is the greater?
    a) 7^{-1}, 7^{-2} b) 2^{-3}, 3^{-2} c) $\left(\frac{5}{3}\right)^{-2}$, $\left(\frac{3}{5}\right)^{-2}$
    d) $\left(-\frac{1}{3}\right)^{-5}$, $\left(-\frac{1}{5}\right)^{-3}$ e) 10^{-1}, $(0.1)^2$ f) $(-3)^{-5}$, $(-9)^{-3}$

11. In how many different ways can you simplify 2×5^{-3} using a calculator?

12. Simplify:
    a) $x^7 \times x^{-12}$ b) $m^4 \div m^6$
    c) $5a^{-3} \times 8a^{-9}$ d) $-24c^5d^3 \div 4c^8d^{-3}$
    e) $8x^{-4}y^7 \times 3x^8y^{-3}$ f) $\dfrac{12m^5n^{-2} \times 5m^{-11}n^6}{15m^3n^{-4}}$

13. Simplify, and check with a calculator:
    a) $3^5 \times 3^{-7}$ b) $2^7 \times 2^6 \times 2^{-10}$ c) $5^{-8} \div 5^{-10}$
    d) $12^{-11} \times 12^9 \div 12^{-4}$ e) $(7^8)^{-2} \div 7^4 \times 7^{11}$ f) $2^5 \times 3^4 \times 3^{-5} \times 2^{-4}$

14. Evaluate for $a = 4$ and $b = -3$:
a) $a^3 \times a^{-2}$ b) $a^7b^2 \div a^5b^4$ c) $2a^{-3}b^2 \times 7a^2b^{-1}$
d) $45a^{-2}b^5 \div 9a^{-4}b^3$ e) a^{b+1} f) $(3b^a)^0 - \left(\frac{a}{b}\right)^{-1}$

15. A radioactive element has a half-life of one week. How much of a 1000 g sample of the element:
a) will there be in: i) 3 weeks? ii) 7 weeks?
b) was there: i) 4 weeks ago? ii) 9 weeks ago?

16. What amount of money invested at 12% compounded annually will grow to $2500 in 4 years?

(C)

17. Given: $b = a^3$ and $c = a^7$
a) Express as a power of a: i) b^3c^{-1} ii) $b^{-2}c$
b) Express in the form b^mc^n, where m and n are integers:
i) a^{11} b) a^0 c) a^{-1}
c) Show that if x is any integer, a^x can always be expressed in the form b^mc^n, where m and n are integers.

18. Find the exact value of:
a) 2^{-8}; b) 2^{-10}; c) 25^{-4}.

LEADERS IN MATHEMATICS

Al-Khwarizmi

You have probably encountered the word *algorithm* in your mathematics studies. It is derived from the name of the ninth century Arab mathematician, Al-Khwarizmi. He was one of the many scholars gathered together by the Caliph of Baghdad, a city on the Tigris river and the capital of present-day Iraq.

Little is known of his personal life. It is thought that he lived from about A.D. 780 to A.D. 850. His scientific work, however, is widely known and well documented.

His early work involved the astrolabe and sundial and the measurement of one degree of Earth's circumference. He also produced a popular work on solving equations, *Al-Kitab Al-jabr wa'l muqabalah*. Loosely translated, this means "The Book of Completion and Cancellation". The ideas in his book came to be called *algebra*.

Al-Khwarizmi seemed to write with a deep concern for his readers' difficulties. He often explained several ways to consider a problem. Both his *Al-jabr* and an arithmetic book, written well over 1000 years ago, are still influencing writers of mathematics today.

2-4 EXTENDING THE EXPONENT LAWS: RATIONAL EXPONENTS

The exponent laws were first established for positive integral exponents. They were later extended to all integral exponents using the following definition of a negative exponent:

$$x^{-n} = \frac{1}{x^n}$$

Finally, in 1655, John Wallis completed the extension of the exponent laws to all fractional and therefore all rational exponents.

To give meanings to such expressions as $3^{\frac{1}{2}}$ and $5^{-\frac{1}{3}}$, the exponent law $x^m \cdot x^n = x^{m+n}$ is extended to cases where m and n are rational numbers.

By extending the law:

$$3^{\frac{1}{2}} \times 3^{\frac{1}{2}} = 3^{\frac{1}{2}+\frac{1}{2}} = 3$$

Since $\sqrt{3} \times \sqrt{3} = 3$

then $3^{\frac{1}{2}} = \sqrt{3}$

$$5^{-\frac{1}{3}} \times 5^{-\frac{1}{3}} \times 5^{-\frac{1}{3}} = 5^{-\frac{1}{3}-\frac{1}{3}-\frac{1}{3}} = 5^{-1}, \text{ or } \frac{1}{5}$$

Since $\sqrt[3]{\frac{1}{5}} \times \sqrt[3]{\frac{1}{5}} \times \sqrt[3]{\frac{1}{5}} = \frac{1}{5}$

then $5^{-\frac{1}{3}} = \sqrt[3]{\frac{1}{5}}$, or $\frac{1}{\sqrt[3]{5}}$

These examples suggest that $x^{\frac{1}{n}}$ should be defined as the nth root of x, and $x^{\frac{-1}{n}}$ as its reciprocal.

$x^{\frac{1}{n}} = \sqrt[n]{x}$ and $x^{-\frac{1}{n}} = \frac{1}{\sqrt[n]{x}}$

$n \in N$
$x \geqslant 0$ if n is even.

$n \in N, x \neq 0$
$x > 0$ if n is even.

Example 1.

Find: a) $49^{\frac{1}{2}}$ b) $(-8)^{\frac{1}{3}}$ c) $16^{-\frac{1}{4}}$ d) $(-64)^{-\frac{1}{3}}$

Solution.

a) $49^{\frac{1}{2}} = \sqrt{49}$, or 7

b) $(-8)^{\frac{1}{3}} = \sqrt[3]{-8}$, or -2

c) $16^{-\frac{1}{4}} = \frac{1}{16^{\frac{1}{4}}} = \frac{1}{\sqrt[4]{16}} = \frac{1}{2}$

d) $(-64)^{-\frac{1}{3}} = \frac{1}{(-64)^{\frac{1}{3}}} = \frac{1}{\sqrt[3]{-64}} = -\frac{1}{4}$

Example 2.

Find $\sqrt[3]{7.6}$, giving the result correct to four decimal places.

Solution.

On a scientific calculator, key in: [7] [·] [6] [y^x] [3] [$\frac{1}{x}$] [=],

The result is 1.966 095 1. That is, $\sqrt[3]{7.6} \doteq 1.9661$

In *Example 2*, another way of finding $\sqrt[3]{7.6}$ is by keying in:

[7] [·] [6] [Inv] [y^x] [3] [=]

or, since $\sqrt[3]{7.6} = (7.6)^{\frac{1}{3}}$:

[7] [·] [6] [y^x] [(] [1] [÷] [3] [)] [=]

The result is 1.966 095 1 as before.

Example 3.

Express as a power:

a) $\sqrt{2}$ b) $\sqrt[3]{36}$ c) $\dfrac{1}{\sqrt[3]{5}}$ d) $\dfrac{1}{\sqrt[4]{11}}$

Solution.

a) $\sqrt{2} = 2^{\frac{1}{2}}$ b) $\sqrt[3]{36} = 36^{\frac{1}{3}}$

c) $\dfrac{1}{\sqrt[3]{5}} = 5^{-\frac{1}{3}}$ d) $\dfrac{1}{\sqrt[4]{11}} = 11^{-\frac{1}{4}}$

Since $36 = 6^2$, the expression in *Example 3b* may be written in other ways.

$$\sqrt[3]{36} = \sqrt[3]{6^2} = (6^2)^{\frac{1}{3}} \quad \text{or} \quad \sqrt[3]{36} = \sqrt[3]{6} \times \sqrt[3]{6} = 6^{\frac{1}{3}} \times 6^{\frac{1}{3}}, \text{ or } (6^{\frac{1}{3}})^2$$

Since we have extended the exponent laws to hold for rational numbers, we may write each of the above results as $6^{\frac{2}{3}}$. This suggests the following definition for $x^{\frac{m}{n}}$, where n is a positive integer:

$$x^{\frac{m}{n}} = \sqrt[n]{x^m} = (\sqrt[n]{x})^m \qquad x \geqslant 0 \text{ if } n \text{ is even.}$$

Example 4.

Find: a) $25^{\frac{3}{2}}$ b) $(-8)^{\frac{2}{3}}$ c) $81^{0.75}$ d) $\left(-\frac{1}{8}\right)^{-\frac{2}{3}}$

Solution.

a) $25^{\frac{3}{2}} = (\sqrt{25})^3 = 5^3$, or 125

b) $(-8)^{\frac{2}{3}} = (\sqrt[3]{-8})^2 = (-2)^2$, or 4

c) $81^{0.75} = 81^{\frac{3}{4}} = (\sqrt[4]{81})^3 = 3^3 = 27$

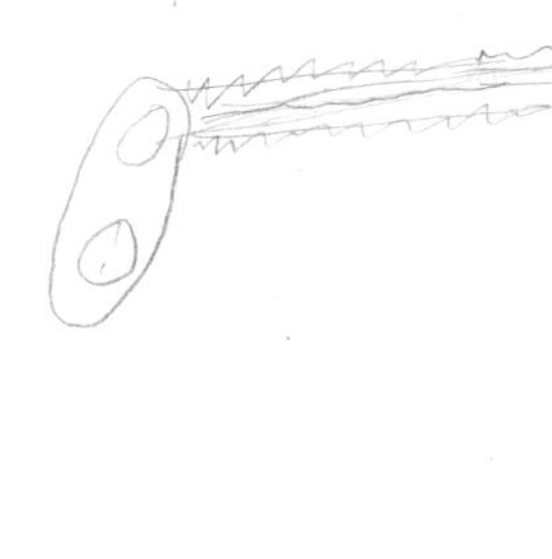

d) $\left(-\frac{1}{8}\right)^{-\frac{2}{3}} = \dfrac{1}{\left(-\frac{1}{8}\right)^{\frac{2}{3}}}$

$= \dfrac{1}{\left(\sqrt[3]{-\frac{1}{8}}\right)^2}$

$= \dfrac{1}{\frac{1}{4}}$, or 4

Problems and formulas may involve fractional exponents.

Example 5.

The height, h, in metres, of a Douglas fir tree can be estimated from the formula: $h = 34.1 \times d^{0.67}$, where d is the diameter, in metres, at its base. Estimate the height of Canada's largest tree, which has a base diameter of 4.35 m.

Solution.

Substitute 4.35 for d in the formula:

$$h = 34.1 \times (4.35)^{0.67}$$
$$\doteq 34.1 \times 2.677\,86$$
$$\doteq 91.3$$

Using the y^x key on a scientific calculator

Canada's largest tree has a height of about 91 m.

EXERCISES 2-4

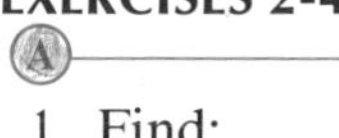

1. Find:
   a) $64^{\frac{1}{2}}$ b) $36^{\frac{1}{2}}$ c) $8^{\frac{1}{3}}$ d) $32^{\frac{1}{5}}$
   e) $400^{0.5}$ f) $-125^{\frac{1}{3}}$ g) $(0.09)^{0.5}$ h) $81^{0.25}$
2. Express as a power:
   a) $\sqrt{7}$ b) $\sqrt{135}$ c) $\sqrt[3]{12}$ d) $\sqrt[4]{21}$
   e) $\sqrt{29}$ f) $\sqrt[5]{19}$ g) $\sqrt[3]{-91}$ h) $\sqrt[4]{0.7}$
3. Find:
   a) $8^{\frac{2}{3}}$ b) $16^{\frac{3}{2}}$ c) $36^{\frac{3}{2}}$ d) $27^{\frac{2}{3}}$
   e) $100^{0.5}$ f) $16^{0.75}$ g) $(0.49)^{1.5}$ h) $(0.0256)^{\frac{3}{4}}$
4. Find:
   a) $4^{2.5}$ b) $(-8)^{\frac{5}{3}}$ c) $81^{1.5}$ d) $(32)^{0.6}$
   e) $(0.16)^{1.5}$ f) $(-27)^{\frac{4}{3}}$ g) $(1.21)^{1.5}$ h) $16^{1.75}$
5. Find:
   a) $9^{-\frac{1}{2}}$ b) $8^{-\frac{1}{3}}$ c) $25^{-\frac{1}{2}}$ d) $16^{-\frac{1}{4}}$
   e) $81^{-0.5}$ f) $81^{-0.25}$ g) $64^{-\frac{1}{6}}$ h) 243^{0}

6. Find:

a) $27^{-\frac{2}{3}}$ b) $16^{-1.5}$ c) $81^{\frac{3}{4}}$ d) $32^{-0.4}$
e) $8^{\frac{4}{3}}$ f) $16^{-\frac{3}{4}}$ g) $625^{0.75}$ h) $4^{-\frac{5}{2}}$

7. Find:

a) $\left(\frac{9}{16}\right)^{\frac{1}{2}}$ b) $\left(\frac{1}{9}\right)^{-\frac{3}{2}}$ c) $\left(-\frac{1}{32}\right)^{0.8}$ d) $\left(\frac{16}{54}\right)^{-\frac{2}{3}}$
e) $\left(\frac{81}{16}\right)^{-0.75}$ f) $\left(\frac{49}{25}\right)^{\frac{3}{2}}$ g) $\left(-\frac{27}{125}\right)^{-\frac{4}{3}}$ h) $\left(\frac{625}{343}\right)^{0}$

8. Find with a calculator, giving the result correct to four decimal places:

a) $10^{\frac{1}{4}}$ b) $30^{0.7}$ c) $7^{\frac{2}{3}}$
d) $15^{1.4}$ e) $\sqrt[8]{2.17}$ f) $\sqrt[1.5]{6.4}$

9. The number of trout in a stocked lake is given by the expression $1800(1.12)^n$, where n is the number of months since the start of the trout season.

a) How many trout will there be in:
   i) 1.25 months ? ii) 3.4 months ?
b) How many trout were there:
   i) 0.5 month before the season opened?
   ii) 2.8 months before the season opened?

(B)

10. Express as a power:

a) $(\sqrt[3]{10})^2$ b) $(\sqrt[4]{12})^5$ c) $(\sqrt[7]{36})^3$
d) $(\sqrt[5]{94})^{17}$ e) $\frac{1}{(\sqrt[3]{25})^4}$ f) $\frac{1}{(\sqrt{52})^7}$

11. Express the first number as a power of the second:

a) $(\sqrt[3]{2})^7$, 2 b) $\sqrt[4]{6^3}$, 6 c) $\sqrt{8^3}$, 2
d) $(\sqrt[5]{25})^4$, 5 e) $\sqrt[3]{49^5}$, 7 f) $(\sqrt[7]{81})^4$, 3

12. A cube has a volume of V cm^3. Write as a power of V:

a) the length of an edge; b) the area of a face.

13. Simplify:

a) $8^{\frac{1}{3}} \times 9^{\frac{1}{2}}$ b) $25^{\frac{3}{2}} \times 8^{\frac{2}{3}}$ c) $81^{\frac{1}{4}} \times 27^{\frac{2}{3}}$
d) $32^{\frac{2}{5}} \times 243^{\frac{2}{5}}$ e) $64^{\frac{2}{3}} \times 125^{\frac{1}{3}}$ f) $4^{\frac{5}{2}} \times 81^{\frac{3}{4}}$

14. Simplify:

a) $(\sqrt[4]{9})^2$ b) $25^{\frac{1}{2}} - 8^{\frac{4}{3}}$ c) $\sqrt[3]{2^{-6}}$ d) $9^{\frac{1}{2}} - \left(\frac{1}{8}\right)^{-\frac{2}{3}}$
e) $(8^{\frac{1}{3}} + 27^{\frac{1}{3}} + 64^{\frac{1}{3}})^{\frac{1}{2}}$ f) $(\sqrt[3]{125^{\frac{1}{3}} + 32^{\frac{4}{5}} + 36^{\frac{1}{2}}})^2$

15. If $10^{0.3} \doteq 1.995$, find the following without using a calculator:

a) $10^{1.3}$ b) $10^{2.3}$ c) $10^{-0.7}$ d) $10^{-1.7}$

16. Evaluate for $x = 64$:
    a) $(x^{\frac{1}{2}})(x^{\frac{1}{3}})$ b) $x^{\frac{1}{2}} \div x^{\frac{1}{3}}$ c) $(x^{-\frac{2}{3}})(x^{\frac{3}{2}})$
    d) $(x^{\frac{-1}{2}})^3$ e) $(x^{-\frac{4}{3}})^{-\frac{1}{2}}$ f) $(x^{-\frac{1}{3}})^{-3}$

17. The population of a colony of birds triples every 10 years. At the present time there are about 250 birds in the colony.
    a) Which of the following represents the number of birds in the colony after n years:
       i) 250×3^{10n} ii) $250 \times n^{30}$
       iii) $250 \times 3^{\frac{n}{10}}$ iv) $250 \times 3^{\frac{10}{n}}$
    b) About how many birds will be in the colony:
       i) 1 year from now ? ii) 3 years from now ?
       iii) 5 years from now?
    c) About how many birds were in the colony:
       i) 1 year ago ? ii) 3 years ago ? iii) 5 years ago ?

18. There are approximately 500 wolves in Algonquin Provincial Park. Under ideal conditions this population would double every 35 years.
    a) What is the possible wolf population of the Park in:
       i) 10 years ? ii) 25 years ? iii) 50 years ?
    b) How many wolves were in the Park:
       i) 10 years ago ? ii) 20 years ago ?
    c) Do you think that the wolves in Algonquin Park live under "ideal" conditions ?

19. The skin area, A, in square metres, of a person's body can be estimated from the formula: $A = 0.025\ h^{0.42}w^{0.5}$, where h is the person's height in centimetres and w the mass in kilograms.
    a) Estimate the skin area of a person 170 cm tall who has a mass of 80 kg.
    b) Estimate the area of your skin.

Ⓒ

20. When a satellite is h kilometres above Earth, the period, T, or time for one complete revolution, is given in minutes by the formula: $T = 1.66 \times 10^{-4}(6370 + h)^{1.5}$.
    a) Calculate the period of a satellite at an altitude of:
       i) 200 km; ii) 600 km.
    b) If the satellite has the same angular velocity as Earth, it appears to be stationary.
       i) What is the period, in minutes, of such a satellite?
       ii) What is the altitude of a "stationary" satellite?

21. A filter 1 cm thick transmits 90% of the light falling on it.
    a) What percent of the light will be transmitted by a filter of the same material of thickness:
       i) 2 cm ? ii) 3 cm ? iii) n cm ?

b) Show that the percent of light transmitted by a filter 0.5 cm thick is $100(0.9)^{0.5}$.

c) What percent of the light will pass through a filter of thickness: i) 0.7 cm ? ii) 1.3 cm ?

d) What thickness of filter transmits:
i) 75% of the light? ii) 50% of the light?

22. a) Three students discussed the meaning of the statement: $(2.3)^{4.7} \doteq 50.13$. Their discussion went as follows:
Andy: "It means 2.3 multiplied by itself 4.7 times is equal to about 50.13."
Jack: "In an expression like 2^4, 2 is multiplied by itself three times, not four. Therefore the statement means 2.3 multiplied by itself 3.7 times equals about 50.13."
Renée: "No! You can't multiply a number by itself a fractional number of times. $(2.3)^{4.7}$ may be written $(2.3)^{\frac{47}{10}}$. That is, 47 factors each equal to the tenth root of 2.3 multiplied together is about 50.13."
Which student is correct?

b) Find, and give the meaning:
i) $(3.8)^{2.6}$ ii) $\sqrt[3.2]{22.5}$

Exponents and the Scientific Calculator

A number of interesting investigations are associated with the use of rational exponents.

1. a) Find:
i) 3^7 ii) $(-3)^7$ iii) $(-4)^{\frac{1}{2}}$ iv) $(-243)^{\frac{1}{5}}$

b) Use a calculator or computer to find the expressions in (a) and compare the results.

2. Most scientific calculators can obtain square roots in two ways:
- by using the $\boxed{\sqrt{\ }}$ key;
- by using the sequence of keys $\boxed{y^x}\ \boxed{\cdot}\ \boxed{5}\ \boxed{=}$.

Find the square roots of different numbers by both methods and compare the results. Is there any difference in the time it takes to do the calculations?

3. The definition of a power with a rational exponent, $x^{\frac{m}{n}}$, gives two expressions: $(\sqrt[n]{x})^m$ and $\sqrt[n]{x^m}$. Find the following in these two ways and compare the results:
$(-64)^{\frac{2}{3}}$ $(-64)^{\frac{4}{6}}$

4. Write a report of your findings in the above investigations.

MATHEMATICS AROUND US

Measuring Air Pollution

The pollution generated by automobiles and industry in heavily populated areas occasionally becomes a danger to human health. It is therefore important to have a measure of the amount of air pollution so that appropriate authoritative action can be taken before serious health problems develop.

In Ontario, an Air Pollution Index (API) is determined for certain areas of the province. This index depends on two quantities which are constantly being monitored:

CoH—the coefficient of haze, a measure of the suspended particles in the air;

SO_2—the concentration of sulphur dioxide in parts per million.

Here is how the API is measured for three areas of Ontario:

Toronto: $0.2[30.5\ \text{CoH} + 126.0\ SO_2]^{1.35}$
Hamilton: $2.5[13.9\ \text{CoH} + 104.5\ SO_2]^{0.8}$
Sudbury: $1.84[11.0\ \text{CoH} + 161.0\ SO_2]^{0.87}$

To interpret the API, the following guide is used:

0 – 32	32 – 50	50 – 100	100 →
Acceptable Range	Warning Range	Sources of pollution may be ordered to curtail operations.	Sources of pollution will be ordered to curtail operations.

QUESTIONS

1. Calculate the API:
   a) Toronto:
      i) CoH 0.42 SO_2 0.13
      ii) CoH 1.3 SO_2 0.24
   b) Hamilton:
      i) CoH 1.84 SO_2 0.24
      ii) CoH 2.2 SO_2 0.18
   c) Sudbury:
      i) CoH 0.92 SO_2 0.36
      ii) CoH 1.6 SO_2 0.40
2. In Toronto, the highest API occurred at about the time of the Grey Cup game in 1962. Visibility on the playing field was so poor that it was necessary to complete the game on the following day. At the time, the values of CoH and SO_2 were about 2.7 and 0.44 respectively. Calculate the API for these values.
3. Suggest why there is a different formula for calculating the API for each city.

2-5 SIMPLIFYING EXPRESSIONS USING EXPONENT LAWS

The exponent laws may be used to simplify products, quotients, and roots involving powers with integral or rational exponents.

Example 1.

Simplify:

a) $3^{\frac{1}{2}} \times 3^{\frac{5}{2}}$ b) $(-2^{\frac{2}{3}} \times 5^{\frac{-1}{2}})^6$ c) $(\sqrt[3]{2^8})^{\frac{-1}{2}}$

Solution.

a) $3^{\frac{1}{2}} \times 3^{\frac{5}{2}} = 3^{\frac{1}{2}+\frac{5}{2}}$
$= 3^3$, or 27

b) $(-2^{\frac{2}{3}} \times 5^{\frac{-1}{2}})^6 = (-2^{\frac{2}{3}})^6(5^{\frac{-1}{2}})^6$
$= (-2)^4(5^{-3})$
$= \frac{16}{125}$

c) $(\sqrt[3]{2^8})^{-\frac{1}{2}} = (2^{\frac{8}{3}})^{-\frac{1}{2}}$
$= 2^{-\frac{4}{3}}$
$= \frac{1}{2^{\frac{4}{3}}}$, or $\frac{1}{(\sqrt[3]{2})^4}$

Example 2.

Simplify:

a) $\frac{x^2y^{\frac{1}{2}}}{x^{-3}y}$ b) $(xy^{\frac{1}{2}})^{-3}(x^{-2}y)^{\frac{1}{2}}$ c) $\sqrt{(12x^5y^{-3})(3xy^0)}$

Solution.

a) $\frac{x^2y^{\frac{1}{2}}}{x^{-3}y} = x^{2-(-3)}y^{\frac{1}{2}-1}$
$= x^5y^{\frac{-1}{2}}$, or $\frac{x^5}{y^{\frac{1}{2}}}$

b) $(xy^{\frac{1}{2}})^{-3}(x^{-2}y)^{\frac{1}{2}} = (x^{-3}y^{\frac{-3}{2}})(x^{-1}y^{\frac{1}{2}})$
$= x^{-4}y^{-1}$, or $\frac{1}{x^4y}$

c) $\sqrt{(12x^5y^{-3})(3xy^0)}$
$= (36x^6y^{-3})^{\frac{1}{2}}$
$= 6x^3y^{\frac{-3}{2}}$, or $\frac{6x^3}{y^{\frac{3}{2}}}$

Example 3.

Expand and simplify:

a) $(2^{\frac{1}{2}} + 3^{\frac{1}{2}})(2^{\frac{1}{2}} - 3^{\frac{1}{2}})$ b) $(\sqrt[3]{a} + \sqrt[3]{a^{-1}})(\sqrt[3]{a} - \sqrt{a^{-1}})$

Solution.

a) $(2^{\frac{1}{2}} + 3^{\frac{1}{2}})(2^{\frac{1}{2}} - 3^{\frac{1}{2}}) = 2^{\frac{1}{2}+\frac{1}{2}} - 2^{\frac{1}{2}} \times 3^{\frac{1}{2}} + 3^{\frac{1}{2}} \times 2^{\frac{1}{2}} - 3^{\frac{1}{2}+\frac{1}{2}}$
$= 2 - 6^{\frac{1}{2}} + 6^{\frac{1}{2}} - 3$
$= 2 - 3$, or -1

b) $(\sqrt[3]{a} + \sqrt[3]{a^{-1}})(\sqrt[3]{a} - \sqrt[3]{a^{-1}}) = (a^{\frac{1}{3}} + a^{\frac{-1}{3}})(a^{\frac{1}{3}} - a^{\frac{-1}{3}})$
$= a^{\frac{2}{3}} - a^{\frac{-2}{3}}$

EXERCISES 2-5

A

1. Simplify:
   a) $2^2 \times 2^{-3}$ b) $3^2 \div 3^{-2}$ c) $2^3 \div 2^7$
   d) $5^4 \times 5^{-6}$ e) $4^{-3} \div 4^{-6}$ f) $7^{-5} \div 7^{-3}$

2. Simplify:
   a) $6^{\frac{2}{3}} \times 6^{\frac{4}{3}}$ b) $2^{\frac{5}{2}} \div 2^{\frac{3}{2}}$ c) $7^{\frac{3}{4}} \div 7^{-\frac{5}{4}}$
   d) $(4)^{\frac{3}{2}} \times (4)^{\frac{9}{2}}$ e) $5^{-\frac{4}{3}} \div 5^{\frac{2}{3}}$ f) $10^{\frac{3}{5}} \times 10^{-\frac{8}{5}}$

3. Simplify:
   a) $(3^{\frac{1}{3}} \times 5^{\frac{-1}{2}})^6$ b) $(\sqrt[5]{3^{-4}})^{\frac{1}{2}}$ c) $(5^{\frac{9}{4}} \div 5^{-\frac{3}{4}})^{-\frac{1}{2}}$
   d) $(4^{\frac{-1}{2}} \times 3^{\frac{1}{4}})^{-4}$ e) $(\sqrt[3]{27^2})^{-\frac{1}{2}}$ f) $(\sqrt{16^3})^{-\frac{1}{6}}$

4. Simplify:
   a) $x^2 \div x^5$ b) $a^{\frac{1}{2}} \times a^{-\frac{1}{2}}$ c) $m^{\frac{2}{3}} \times m^{\frac{4}{3}}$
   d) $t^{\frac{3}{5}} \times t^{-\frac{8}{5}}$ e) $(n^{\frac{1}{2}})^{-6}$ f) $x^{-\frac{3}{2}} \div x^{-\frac{1}{4}}$

5. Simplify:
   a) $m^2n^5 \times m^3n^{-7}$ b) $a^{\frac{2}{3}}b^{\frac{2}{5}} \times a^{\frac{4}{3}}b^{-\frac{12}{5}}$ c) $(xy^{\frac{2}{3}})^6 \div (x^{\frac{1}{2}}y^{\frac{1}{4}})^8$
   d) $(9a^4b^{-2} \times 4a^2b^{-6})^{\frac{1}{2}}$ e) $12x^{\frac{-3}{4}}y^{-2} \div 4x^{\frac{3}{4}}y^{-2}$ f) $8m^{\frac{1}{3}}n^{\frac{-5}{3}}(-2m^{\frac{-2}{3}}n^{\frac{1}{3}})^{-4}$

B

6. Simplify:
   a) $2^5 \times 8^{-2}$ b) $27^{\frac{2}{3}} \div 9^{\frac{1}{2}}$ c) $16^{\frac{3}{4}} \times 4^{\frac{3}{2}}$
   d) $125^{-2} \div 5^{-7}$ e) $8^{-\frac{5}{3}} \times 4^{\frac{5}{2}}$ f) $9^{\frac{5}{2}} \div 81^{\frac{7}{4}}$

7. Simplify:
   a) $5^{\frac{3}{2}} \times 125^{\frac{1}{2}}$ b) $6^{\frac{3}{4}} \div 36^{-\frac{1}{3}}$ c) $8^{\frac{2}{5}} \times 16^{-\frac{2}{5}}$
   d) $125^{-\frac{2}{3}} \div (\sqrt{5})^{-3}$ e) $27^{-\frac{1}{2}} \times 9^{\frac{3}{4}}$ f) $(64)^{\frac{3}{5}} \div (4)^{\frac{3}{4}}$

8. Simplify:
   a) $\dfrac{2a^{\frac{1}{2}} \times a^{\frac{2}{3}}}{9a^{-\frac{5}{3}}}$ b) $(27x^2)^{\frac{1}{3}}(16x^{-2})^{\frac{1}{4}}$ c) $\sqrt{\dfrac{50x^2y^4}{5x^4y^7}}$
   d) $\dfrac{(4m^2n^{-3})^2}{(2m^{-1}n)^3}$ e) $\sqrt[4]{25x^2}$ f) $\dfrac{(x^2y)^{-\frac{5}{2}}}{(x^3y^{-3})^{\frac{1}{6}}}$

9. Simplify:
   a) $\left(\dfrac{a^{-2}b^3}{c^4}\right)^3$ b) $\dfrac{36x^{-2}y^3z^{-4}}{12xy^{-2}z^{-2}}$
   c) $\sqrt{\dfrac{32x^{-5}y^2 \times 18x^2y}{4xy^{-3}}}$ d) $(8c^{-2}d^6)^{\frac{2}{3}}(9c^{-3}d^9)^{\frac{1}{3}}$
   e) $\left(\dfrac{3x^{-2}y^3}{12xy^{-1}}\right)\left(\dfrac{10x^4y^{-2}}{5x^{-1}y^2}\right)$

10. Simplify:
   a) $\dfrac{x^a \cdot x^{3a}}{x^{-2a}}$ b) $\dfrac{m^{2n} \cdot m^{-3n} \cdot m^n}{m^{3-n}}$ c) $\dfrac{(m^{x-1})(m^{2x+5})}{m^{3x-1}}$
   d) $\dfrac{(c^{a+b})(c^{a-b})}{c^2}$ e) $\dfrac{(x^a)^2(x^b)^2}{(x^{a+b})(x^{a-b})}$ f) $\dfrac{x^{2a-b} \cdot x^{a-3b}}{(x^{3a+b})^{-2}}$

11. Simplify:

a) $3^{2x} \times 27^{x}$ b) $\dfrac{2^{n} \times 4^{n-1}}{8^{n-2}}$ c) $\dfrac{25^{3a+1} \times 5^{a-3}}{125^{a}}$

d) $\dfrac{8^{1-2x} \times 4^{2x+3}}{16^{2-3x}}$ e) $\dfrac{36^{a-2b} \times 6^{a+6}}{216^{2a-3b}}$ f) $\dfrac{16^{2m-n} \times 9^{m+3n}}{27^{m+n} \times 8^{m-n}}$

12. If $x = a^{-2}$ and $y = a^{\frac{2}{3}}$, write the following in terms of a:

a) $x^{-3}y^{3}$ b) $\dfrac{x^{2}}{y}$ c) $(x^{\frac{1}{2}}y^{\frac{2}{3}})^{2}$

d) $x^{\frac{2}{3}}y^{2}$ e) $x^{\frac{3}{5}}y^{\frac{1}{2}}$ f) $(x^{\frac{3}{4}} \div y^{\frac{-1}{2}})^{3}$

13. Expand and simplify:

a) $a^{\frac{1}{2}}(2a^{\frac{1}{2}} + a^{\frac{-3}{2}})$ b) $x^{\frac{2}{3}}(5x^{\frac{4}{3}} - 3x^{\frac{1}{3}})$ c) $3m^{\frac{3}{2}}(2m^{\frac{-1}{2}} - m^{\frac{1}{2}})$

d) $5^{\frac{1}{4}}(5^{\frac{3}{4}} + 5^{\frac{-5}{4}})$ e) $4x^{\frac{2}{3}}(7x^{6} + 3x^{\frac{4}{3}})$ f) $9^{\frac{2}{3}}(9^{\frac{-1}{6}} - 9^{\frac{-7}{6}})$

14. Expand and simplify:

a) $(5^{\frac{1}{2}} + 2^{\frac{1}{2}})(5^{\frac{1}{2}} - 2^{\frac{1}{2}})$ b) $(x^{\frac{3}{2}} - x^{\frac{7}{2}})(x^{\frac{3}{2}} + x^{\frac{7}{2}})$

c) $(\sqrt[4]{m} + \sqrt[3]{m})(\sqrt[4]{m} - \sqrt[3]{m})$ d) $(8^{\frac{2}{3}} - 5^{\frac{1}{2}})(8^{\frac{2}{3}} + 5^{\frac{1}{2}})$

e) $(2a^{\frac{5}{2}} - 7a^{\frac{1}{2}})(3a^{\frac{3}{2}} - a^{\frac{1}{2}})$ f) $(4x^{\frac{4}{3}} + 9x^{\frac{1}{3}})(3x^{\frac{5}{3}} - 2x^{\frac{2}{3}})$

Ⓒ

15. Simplify:

a) $(\sqrt{49y^{\frac{2}{m}}})^{\frac{-1}{n}}$ b) $\sqrt{8x^{a}y^{\frac{3}{a}}}$

c) $\dfrac{\sqrt[3]{a} \cdot b^{-\frac{1}{4}}}{\sqrt[4]{b} \cdot a^{\frac{-1}{3}}} \div \left(\dfrac{a^{\frac{1}{3}}}{\sqrt{b}}\right)^{-1}$ d) $\sqrt[3]{\dfrac{m^{\frac{1}{2}}\sqrt{mn}}{\dfrac{1}{\sqrt{n}}}}$

e) $\left(\dfrac{\sqrt[4]{a^{2n-1}} \times \sqrt[4]{a}}{\sqrt{a}}\right)^{2}$ f) $\dfrac{3x^{n} + 7x^{2n}}{3 + 7x^{n}} \div \sqrt{x^{2n}}$

2-6 SOLVING EXPONENTIAL EQUATIONS

The format of a ladies-singles tennis tournament is single elimination, that is, each competitor continues playing until she loses. If the tournament organizer received 64 entries, how many rounds must be played before a winner is declared?

The organizer found the number of rounds, n, by solving the equation:

$$2^{n}=64.$$

To solve the equation, she expressed 64 as a power of 2:

$$2^{n} = 2^{6}$$

Since the bases are the same, the exponents are equal.

$$n = 6$$

To declare a winner, six rounds of tennis must be played.

An equation such as $2^n = 64$ is called an exponential equation, since the unknown is the exponent or in the exponent. Other exponential equations are:

$$5^x = 625 \qquad 16^{3n-2} = 2$$

Such equations can be solved by expressing both sides as powers of the same base.

Example 1.

Solve: $3^x = 81$

Solution.

Write 81 as a power of 3: $3^x = 3^4$
When the powers are equal and the bases are the same, the exponents are equal.
Therefore, $x = 4$

Example 2.

Solve: a) $2^{x+3} = 16$ b) $9^{x-1} = 27$

Solution.

a) Write 16 as a power of 2: $2^{x+3} = 2^4$
Since the bases are the same, the exponents are equal.

$$x + 3 = 4$$
$$x = 1$$

b) Write both sides as powers of 3:
L.S.: $9^{x-1} = (3^2)^{x-1}$ R.S.: 3^3
$= 3^{2x-2}$
The equation becomes: $3^{2x-2} = 3^3$
Since the bases are the same, the exponents are equal.

$$2x - 2 = 3$$
$$2x = 5$$
$$x = 2.5$$

Example 3.

The number of insects in a colony doubles every month. If there are now 250 insects, about how long will it take for the colony to grow to 8000?

Solution.

Let n be the required number of months.
Then, $250 \times 2^n = 8000$

$$2^n = \frac{8000}{250}, \text{ or } 32$$
$$n = 5$$

In 5 months, the colony will number 8000 insects.

Example 4.

How long does it take money invested at 12% compounded annually to double in value?

Solution.

Let n denote the number of years for a sum of money to double.
Value of \$1 after n years: $\$1(1.12)^n$
The condition that the money doubles in n years is:

$$(1.12)^n = 2$$

We solve the equation by systematic trial, giving various values to n:

n	5	6	7
$(1.12)^n$	1.762	1.974	2.211

Since $1.974 \doteq 2$, $n \doteq 6$
Money invested at 12% compounded annually doubles in value in approximately 6 years.

EXERCISES 2-6

(A)

1. Solve:
   a) $2^x = 32$ b) $10^x = 100\,000$ c) $3^x = 81$
   d) $5^x = 625$ e) $(-2)^x = -128$ f) $4^x = 64$
   g) $9^x = 729$ h) $20^x = 8000$ i) $7^x = 2401$
2. Solve:
   a) $2^{x+1} = 4$ b) $2^{x-1} = 8$ c) $3^{x-5} = 9$
   d) $5^{x+3} = 25$ e) $10^{x+1} = 1000$ f) $4^{x+2} = 16$
3. Solve:
   a) $7^x = 1$ b) $6^x = \dfrac{1}{36}$ c) $5^x = 5$
   d) $10^x = 0.01$ e) $16^x = 2$ f) $27^x = 3$
4. How long does it take money invested at 9% compounded annually to double in value?
5. How long will it take \$1000 to triple if it is invested at 12% compounded annually?

(B)

6. Solve:
   a) $2^{2x+1} = 8$ b) $3^{2-x} = 9$ c) $5^{3x-2} = 25$
   d) $9^{x+1} = 1$ e) $4^x = 32$ f) $9^x = 27$
   g) $8^{x+2} = 16$ h) $9^{1-2x} = 81$ i) $16^{x-1} = 64$

7. Solve:

   a) $3 \times 2^x = 12$ b) $5 \times 2^x = 40$ c) $10 \times 3^x = 270$
   d) $10 \times 2^x = 640$ e) $6 \times 3^x = 162$ f) $4 \times 5^x = 500$
   g) $3 \times 6^x = 108$ h) $4 \times 7^x = 4$ i) $2 \times 4^x = 1$

8. The number of ants in a nest doubles every month. If there are now 600 ants, about how long will it take for their number to grow to 9600?

9. If the salt content of Lake Ontario continues to increase at the rate given in the news item,
   a) write an expression for the salt concentration after n years;
   b) in about how many years will the lake have the same salt concentration as the Dead Sea?

SALT HARMS ENVIRONMENT

TORONTO. Salt spread on roads in winter is finding its way into Lake Ontario and causing the lake's salt content to double every five years. The present level is about 25 parts per million. There is, however, no immediate danger of the lake becoming another Dead Sea which has a salt content of 10 000 parts per million.

(C)

10. Solve and check:

    a) $4^x + 4^{x+1} = 40$ b) $3^x - 3^{x-1} = \frac{2}{27}$
    c) $5 \times 2^x - 3 \times 2^{x-1} = 224$

11. Solve by systematic trial correct to two decimal places:

    a) $x^x = 2$ b) $2^x + x = 10$ c) $2^x + x^2 = 12$

Review Exercises

1. Express the first number as a power of the second:

   a) 81, 3 b) 1296, 6 c) −16 807, −7
   d) 0.000 32, 0.2 e) −3.375, −1.5 f) 39.0625, 2.5

2. If a cottage, originally bought for \$25 000, appreciates at the rate of 6% per year, what is it worth after:

   a) 3 years? b) 7 years? c) n years?

3. If a ball is dropped from a height of 3.0 m and allowed to bounce freely, the height, h, in metres, to which it bounces is given by the formula: $h = 3.0(0.9)^n$, where n is the number of bounces.
   a) What height does the ball reach after:
      i) the fourth bounce? ii) the seventh bounce?
   b) After what bounce does the ball reach a height of less than 1 m?
4. Simplify:
   a) $(x^a)^4(x^{2a+1})^3$ b) $(2^b)^4(2^{b+2})^2$ c) $(c^{3a})^2(c^{2a+1})^3$
   d) $\dfrac{(3t^{2u})(2t^{u+2})^4}{(6t^u)^2}$ e) $\dfrac{(w^{4x})^{3z}}{(w^{xz})^3}$ f) $\dfrac{(w^{3m}x^{b+2})^2}{w^{2m+1}x^b}$
5. If $x = a^3$ and $y = 3b^2$, express in terms of a and b:
   a) $4x^2y^3$ b) $(3x^3y^4)^3$ c) $\dfrac{4x^5y^3}{3x^3y^2}$ d) $\left(\dfrac{5x^6y^5}{10x^5y^3}\right)^3$
6. Simplify:
   a) $x^8 \times x^{-13}$ b) $w^5 \div w^7$
   c) $4b^{-4} \times 9b^{-6}$ d) $-21c^4d^4 \div 7c^5d^{-6}$
   e) $9u^{-5}y^8 \times 4u^7y^{-4}$ f) $\dfrac{13m^6n^{-3} \times 4m^{-10}n^6}{26m^4n^{-3}}$
7. What amount of money invested at 8% compounded annually will grow to \$5000 in 5 years?
8. There are 300 ants in a nest. The population doubles every month.
   a) Which of the following represents the number of ants after n months?
      i) $300 \times n^2$ ii) 300×2^n iii) 2×300^n iv) 600^n
   b) About how many ants were in the nest:
      i) 1 month ago? ii) 2 months ago? iii) 3 months ago?
9. Express as a power:
   a) $\sqrt[3]{19^2}$ b) $\sqrt{28^5}$ c) $\sqrt[5]{13^2}$
   d) $\sqrt{33^3}$ e) $\sqrt[3]{(-7)^{11}}$ f) $\sqrt[10]{43^3}$
10. The face of a cube has an area of A cm^2. Write the following as powers of A:
    a) the length of an edge b) the volume
11. Simplify:
    a) $100(1.05)^{2.7}$ b) $400(1.12)^{3.4}$ c) $1250(1.08)^{-4.2}$
    d) $60(0.9)^{3.1}$ e) $3500(1.1)^{-2.2}$ f) $265(0.85)^{-3.7}$
12. The number of insects in a colony doubles every month. If there are now 1000 insects in the colony:
    a) about how many insects will there be half a month from now?
    b) about how many insects were there half a month ago?
13. Simplify:
    a) $3^{\frac{3}{2}} \times 243^{\frac{1}{2}}$ b) $5^{\frac{3}{4}} \times 25^{\frac{-1}{3}}$ c) $9^{\frac{3}{5}} \times 18^{\frac{-3}{5}}$
    d) $343^{\frac{-2}{3}} \div (\sqrt{7})^3$ e) $8^{\frac{-1}{2}} \times 4^{\frac{3}{4}}$ f) $(-216)^{\frac{3}{5}} \div (-6)^{\frac{3}{4}}$

$1000(1.08)^n = 1500$

14. Simplify:
    a) $2^{3x} \times 8^x$ b) $\dfrac{3^{n+1} \times 9^{n-1}}{27^{n-3}}$ c) $\dfrac{4^{4a-1} \times 64^{2a+2}}{256^{2a}}$
    d) $\dfrac{25^{3-x} \times 5^{2x-1}}{125^{x+2}}$ e) $\dfrac{6^{2a-b} \times 36^{3b-a}}{216^{a+b}}$ f) $\dfrac{25^{x-2w} \times 7^{3x+w}}{49^{2x+3w} \times 5^{w-2x}}$
15. If $w = a^{\frac{3}{4}}$ and $x = a^{-3}$, write in terms of a:
    a) w^2x^{-2} b) $w^3 \div x^2$ c) $(w^{\frac{2}{3}}x^{\frac{1}{2}})^2$
    d) $x^{\frac{1}{4}}x^{\frac{3}{2}}$ e) $w^{\frac{5}{6}}x^{\frac{3}{4}}$ f) $(w^{\frac{2}{5}} \div x^{\frac{1}{3}})^3$
16. Solve:
    a) $2^x = 16$ b) $10^x = 1000$ c) $10^x = 0.1$
    d) $3^x = 1$ e) $4^x = 2$ f) $4^x = \dfrac{1}{2}$
17. Solve:
    a) $2^{x+1} = 8$ b) $3^{x-1} = 81$ c) $5^{x+2} = 25$
    d) $4^{x-3} = 16$ e) $2^{3x+1} = 32$ f) $6^{2x-1} = 1$
18. Solve:
    a) $3 \times 5^x = 75$ b) $10 \times 2^x = 160$ c) $4 \times 3^x = 324$
19. How long will it take \$1000 to grow to \$1500 when it is invested at 8% compounded annually?

Cumulative Review (Chapters 1 and 2)

1. Express as a product of prime factors:
   a) 234 b) 187 c) 420
2. Express as a repeating decimal:
   a) $0.\overline{6} + 4.\overline{3} - 1.\overline{15}$ b) $0.\overline{5} \times 1.\overline{3}$ c) $0.\overline{36} \times 1.2\overline{4}$
3. If $m = -3$, $n = \dfrac{2}{5}$, and $p = -\dfrac{4}{3}$, evaluate:
   a) $m(n - p)$ b) $\dfrac{10np + 3p}{2m}$ c) $\dfrac{4m^2p^2 - 5n^2}{mp}$
4. Solve:
   a) $4 - (7 + 2x) = 3(6 - x) - 5$ b) $\dfrac{3(w - 2)}{5} = \dfrac{5(2w - 1)}{6}$
   c) $5(x - 6) + (x - 3) = -2(3 - 4x) + 8$
5. Which of the following are rational and which irrational?
   a) $\sqrt{175}$ b) $-2.367\,676\,7\ldots$ c) $-\sqrt{289}$
   d) $\sqrt{169 - 36}$ e) $4.353\,153\,115\ldots$ f) $\sqrt{3.75}$
6. Simplify:
   a) $\sqrt{56}$ b) $3\sqrt{128}$ c) $3\sqrt{5} \times 4\sqrt{2} \times 3\sqrt{3}$
   d) $4\sqrt{8} \times 2\sqrt{2} \times 7$ e) $(-5\sqrt{3})(2\sqrt{5})(3\sqrt{6})$

7. Simplify:
   a) $3\sqrt{12} + 4\sqrt{27} - \sqrt{75}$ b) $\sqrt{32} - 2\sqrt{24} - 4\sqrt{18}$
   c) $4\sqrt{25} + 6\sqrt{169} - 3\sqrt{225}$ d) $2\sqrt{50} - 3\sqrt{40} + 4\sqrt{120}$
8. Simplify:
   a) $2\sqrt{5}(3\sqrt{7} + 8\sqrt{12})$ b) $(4\sqrt{3} - 2\sqrt{5})(4\sqrt{3} + 2\sqrt{5})$
   c) $(\sqrt{6} - 2\sqrt{3})(3\sqrt{8} + 4\sqrt{20})$ d) $(5\sqrt{2} + 3\sqrt{5})^2$
9. Simplify:
   a) $\dfrac{33\sqrt{6}}{3\sqrt{24}}$ b) $\dfrac{12}{5\sqrt{7}}$ c) $\dfrac{8\sqrt{2} - 6}{\sqrt{2}}$ d) $\dfrac{6\sqrt{5} + \sqrt{8}}{\sqrt{5}}$
10. Simplify: a) $4(3)^2 - 3(2)^4$ b) $(-4)^3 + (-3)^4$ c) $-5^4 + 6^3$
11. Express the first number as a power of the second:
   a) 243, 3 b) 4096, −4 c) −2048, −2 d) 0.03125, 0.5
12. In 1980, Panex stock was worth $13.00 per share. If the stock appreciates at the rate of 8% per year, what is a share worth in:
   a) 1990? b) 1998? c) 2010?
13. Simplify:
   a) $2a^4b \times 4a^3b^5$ b) $8c^5b^{-2} \times 3c^{-1}b^{-6}$ c) $18y^4h^5 \div 9yh^3$
   d) $24x^{-2}y^7 \div 8x^3y^{-4}$ e) $(4m^8n^{-2})^3$ f) $\dfrac{(x^{a+1})^2(x^{a-3})^3}{(x^3)^a}$
14. Simplify: a) $3^{2n} \times 27^{4n}$ b) $32^{4+n} \div 2^{3n+1}$ c) $\dfrac{(25^{2n})^3(125^n)^5}{(625)^{2n-2}}$
15. If $a = 3$ and $b = -2$, evaluate:
   a) $4a^3 \times 5a^{-3}$ b) $27a^{-3}b^7 \div 9a^{-5}b^5$ c) $(2^a)^4(2^b)^3$
   d) $(8a^b)^0 + \left(\dfrac{a}{b}\right)^a$ e) $2^{-a} + b^a$ f) $\dfrac{ab^0}{(a^{-2} + a^{-3})^{-1}}$
16. What amount of money invested at 9% compounded annually will grow to $7000 in 4 years?
17. Express as a power: a) $\sqrt[3]{17^4}$ b) $(\sqrt{19})^7$ c) $\dfrac{1}{\sqrt[5]{73}}$
18. Simplify:
   a) $4^{\frac{5}{2}}$ b) $\left(\dfrac{16}{625}\right)^{0.25}$ c) $81^{-\frac{3}{4}}$ d) $49^{\frac{1}{2}} - 64^{\frac{5}{6}}$ e) $8^{\frac{4}{3}} \times 27^{-\frac{2}{3}}$
19. Solve:
   a) $5^x = 3125$ b) $\left(\dfrac{4}{5}\right)^x = \dfrac{64}{125}$ c) $7^x = \dfrac{1}{343}$
   d) $3^x + 4 = 85$ e) $128 = 32^x$ f) $2(25^{x+1}) = 250$
20. The number of chinch bugs in a lawn doubles every month. If there are about 300 bugs now, how long will it take for their numbers to grow to 19 000?

3 Polynomials and Rational Expressions

Research scientists believe that by the year A.D. 2000 space colonies will be technically possible. One proposal is for a wheel-like colony 2000 m in diameter with an interior diameter of 200 m. How may the volume of the interior be found? (See *Example 5* in Section 3-5.)

3-1 OPERATIONS WITH MONOMIALS

Algebraic terms such as $-2a^2$ and $7x^2y$ are called **monomials**. Monomials may be added or subtracted by combining *like* terms.

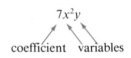

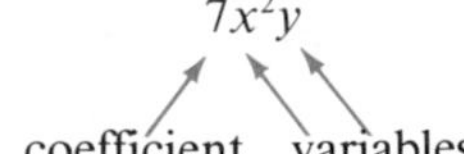

Example 1.

Simplify: $3x^2 - 5xy + 2y^2 - 2x - xy + 2x^2 - 3y^2$

Solution.

$$\begin{aligned} &3x^2 - 5xy + 2y^2 - 2x - xy + 2x^2 - 3y^2 \\ &= 3x^2 + 2x^2 - 5xy - xy + 2y^2 - 3y^2 - 2x \\ &= 5x^2 - 6xy - y^2 - 2x \end{aligned}$$

Group like terms.

Products and quotients of monomials can be found using the exponent laws.

Example 2.

Simplify: a) $(3ab^2)^3(2a^2b)$ b) $\dfrac{32x^4y^2}{8x^2y^3}$

c) $\dfrac{18x^3y}{10xy^2} \times \dfrac{15x^2y^2}{6x^4y}$

Solution.

a) $(3ab^2)^3(2a^2b) = 27a^3b^6 \times 2a^2b$
$= 54a^5b^7$

b) $\dfrac{32x^4y^2}{8x^2y^3} = 4x^2y^{-1}$

c) $\dfrac{18x^3y}{10xy^2} \times \dfrac{15x^2y^2}{6x^4y} = \dfrac{18 \times 15}{10 \times 6} \times \dfrac{x^5y^3}{x^5y^3}$
$= \dfrac{9}{2}$

Example 3.

A square is inscribed in a semicircle. Find the ratio of:

a) the diameter of the semicircle to the side of the square;

b) the area of the semicircle to the area of the square.

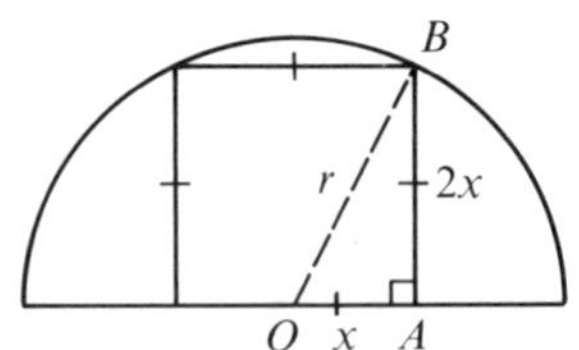

Solution.

a) Let the side of the square be $2x$.
Let the radius of the semicircle be r.
Then, in right $\triangle OAB$,

$$\begin{aligned} r^2 &= x^2 + (2x)^2 \\ &= 5x^2 \\ r &= \sqrt{5}x \end{aligned}$$

The ratio, $\dfrac{\text{diameter of semicircle}}{\text{side of square}}$, is: $\dfrac{2r}{2x} = \dfrac{2\sqrt{5}x}{2x}$, or $\dfrac{\sqrt{5}}{1}$.

b) $A_{semicircle} = \frac{1}{2}\pi r^2$

$= \frac{1}{2}\pi(\sqrt{5}x)^2$

$= \frac{5}{2}\pi x^2$

$A_{square} = (2x)^2$

$= 4x^2$

The ratio, $\frac{\text{area of semicircle}}{\text{area of square}}$, is $\frac{\frac{5}{2}\pi x^2}{4x^2}$, or $\frac{5\pi}{8}$.

EXERCISES 3-1

(A)

1. Simplify:
   a) $3x + 7 + 5x - 2$
   b) $2m - 11 - 9m + 4$
   c) $8a - 3b - 12a + 7b$
   d) $4x + 7y - 13x + 6y$
   e) $6a + 2b + 17a - 9b + 7a$
   f) $3x - 5y - 8y + 9x - 17x + 2y$
2. Simplify:
   a) $5a^2 - 3a + 2 - a^2 + 7a - 9$
   b) $12m^2 + 9m - 3 - 7m^2 - 4m + 6$
   c) $3x^2 - 7x - 4 + 5x^2 + 2x - 9$
   d) $11s^2 - 8 - 3s - 6s^2 + 17s - 4$
   e) $8x^2 - 12x - 15x^2 + 4 - 7x - 10$
   f) $a^2 - 6a + 4 - 7a^2 - 5a - 19$
3. Simplify:
   a) $4x^2 - 2xy + 5y^2 - 3x^2 + 7xy - 2y^2$
   b) $2a^2 + 7ab - 12b^2 - 8a^2 + 5b^2 - 10ab$
   c) $6x^2 - 4xy - 3y^2 - 19xy + 12y^2 + 11x^2$
   d) $18x^2 - 7xy + 5y^2 - 11x^2 + 15yx - 23y^2 + 2x^2$
   e) $16s^2t + 9 - 35st^2 - 12s^2t + 26t^2s - 41s^2t + 19 - 5t^2s$
   f) $15x^2y - 4xy^2 - 37yx^2 + 11 + 22xy^2 - 19xy^2 + 5y^2x - 18$
4. Simplify:
   a) $(7a^2b)(4a^2b^3)$
   b) $(4x^3y^2)(5x^2y^7)$
   c) $(-8m^5n^2)(3m^2n^6)$
   d) $(-9x^2y^3)(-6x^3y^7)$
   e) $(-12mn^3)(3m^5n^3)$
   f) $(6a^2b^4)(7a^2b^3)$
5. Simplify:
   a) $(3a^2b)^2(5a^2b^3)$
   b) $(2x^3y^2)^3(-7x^4y)$
   c) $(5mn^2)^2(-3m^3n)^2$
   d) $(-2x^2y)^3(3x^3y^5)^2$
   e) $(4a^5b^3)^3(3a^4b^2)^2$
   f) $(3xy^3)^2(-2x^4y^3)^5$

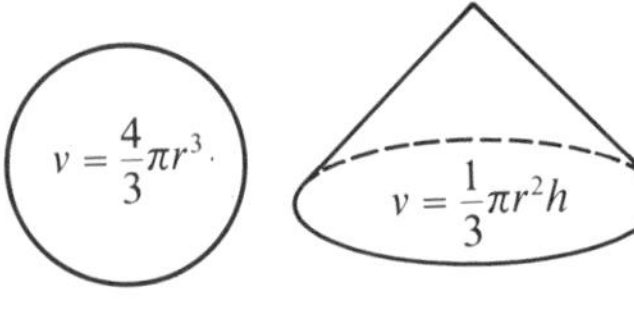

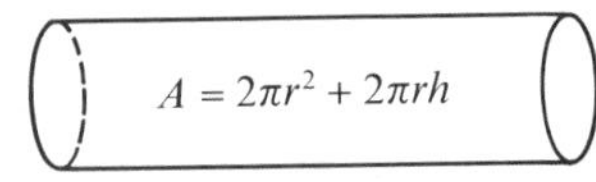

6. The formulas for the volumes of a sphere and a cone and the surface area of a cylinder are given in the diagram. Express V and A in terms of the diameter, d, instead of the radius, r.

7. Simplify:

   a) $\dfrac{24x^3y^8}{-6x^2y^2}$ b) $\dfrac{48m^6n^9}{3m^2n^3}$ c) $\dfrac{-51a^5b^3}{3a^2b^8}$

   d) $\dfrac{-36x^{10}y^4}{9x^4y^3}$ e) $\dfrac{85a^6b^3}{5a^2b^3}$ f) $\dfrac{87x^4y^6}{-3x^4y^4}$

8. The length of a rectangle is $12x^2y$ cm. Find the width if:

   a) the area is: i) $24x^3y^2$ cm^2, ii) $4xy^3$ cm^2;

   b) the perimeter is $30x^2y$ cm.

B

9. Simplify:

   a) $\dfrac{10x^4y}{27x^2y^3} \times \dfrac{18x^3y^2}{25xy^4}$

   b) $\dfrac{4x^3y^2}{7xy^5} \times \dfrac{28x^3y^4}{36x^2y^3}$

   c) $\dfrac{-12m^4n^2}{35m^3n^5} \times \dfrac{-15m^2n^6}{-48m^2n^2}$

   d) $\dfrac{(2x^2y)^3}{15x^3y^2} \times \dfrac{40x^3y^2}{6x^2y^7}$

   e) $\dfrac{14a^2b^5c^3}{45a^3b^2c} \times \dfrac{-18a^5b^2c}{21a^2b^2c^4}$

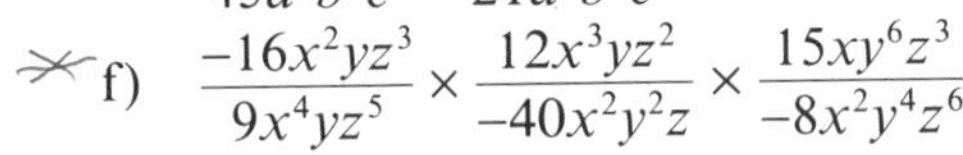

   f) $\dfrac{-16x^2yz^3}{9x^4yz^5} \times \dfrac{12x^3yz^2}{-40x^2y^2z} \times \dfrac{15xy^6z^3}{-8x^2y^4z^6}$

10. A square is inscribed in a circle. Find the ratio of:

    a) their areas; b) their perimeters.

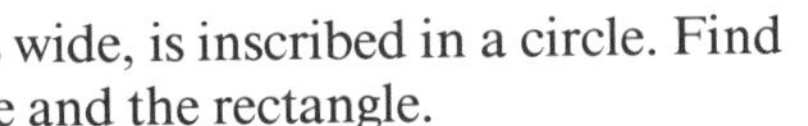

11. A rectangle, twice as long as it is wide, is inscribed in a circle. Find the ratio of the areas of the circle and the rectangle.

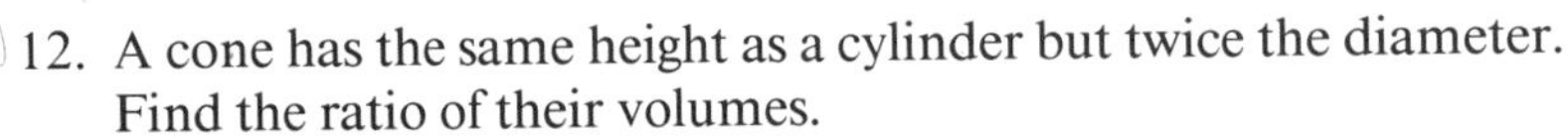

12. A cone has the same height as a cylinder but twice the diameter. Find the ratio of their volumes.

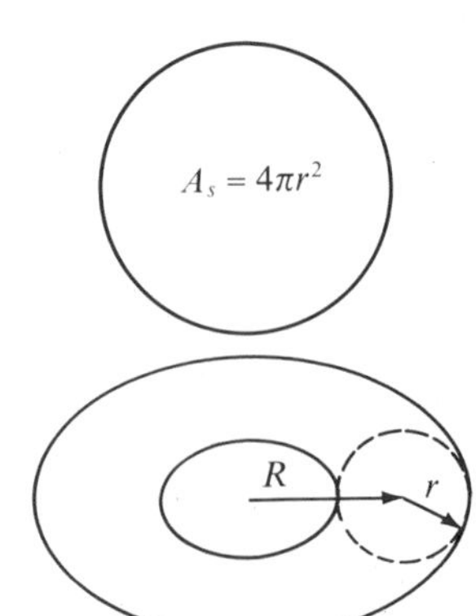

13. A closed cylinder, with a height equal to its diameter, has the same diameter as a sphere. Find the ratio of:

    a) their volumes; b) their surface areas.

14. The formula for the volume, V, of a torus is: $V = 2\pi^2Rr^2$. Find the volume if:

    a) $R = 2r$; b) $R = 6x^2y$ and $r = 2xy^2$.

C

15. A cylinder, with a height equal to its diameter, is inscribed in a sphere. Find the ratio of the volumes of the cylinder and the sphere.

3-2 OPERATIONS WITH POLYNOMIALS

Expressions formed by adding or subtracting monomials are called polynomials. Examples are:

$$2m + 3n \qquad x^2 - 6xy + 9y^2.$$

Polynomials are added or subtracted by combining like terms. To multiply a polynomial by a monomial, apply the distributive law.

Example 1.

Simplify: a) $(3m^2 - 8m + 9) - (5m^2 + 6m - 2)$
b) $5a(a^2 - 2ab - b^2) - 3b[a^2 + 2b(a - 4b)]$

Solution.

a) $(3m^2 - 8m + 9) - (5m^2 + 6m - 2)$
$= 3m^2 - 8m + 9 - 5m^2 - 6m + 2$
$= -2m^2 - 14m + 11$

b) $5a(a^2 - 2ab - b^2) - 3b[a^2 + 2b(a - 4b)]$
$= 5a^3 - 10a^2b - 5ab^2 - 3b[a^2 + 2ab - 8b^2]$
$= 5a^3 - 10a^2b - 5ab^2 - 3a^2b - 6ab^2 + 24b^3$
$= 5a^3 - 13a^2b - 11ab^2 + 24b^3$

To find the product of two polynomials, multiply each term of one polynomial by each term of the other polynomial.

Example 2.

Simplify: a) $(2x + y)(x - 3y)$
b) $(2x + y - 3)(x + y - 2)$
c) $3(2m - 5n)(m + 4n) - (3m - 2n)^2$

Solution.

a) $(2x + y)(x - 3y) = 2x(x - 3y) + y(x - 3y)$
$= 2x^2 - 6xy + xy - 3y^2$
$= 2x^2 - 5xy - 3y^2$

b) $(2x + y - 3)(x + y - 2)$
$= 2x(x + y - 2) + y(x + y - 2) - 3(x + y - 2)$
$= 2x^2 + 2xy - 4x + xy + y^2 - 2y - 3x - 3y + 6$
$= 2x^2 + 3xy + y^2 - 7x - 5y + 6$

c) $3(2m - 5n)(m + 4n) - (3m - 2n)^2$
$= 3(2m^2 + 3mn - 20n^2) - (9m^2 - 12mn + 4n^2)$
$= 6m^2 + 9mn - 60n^2 - 9m^2 + 12mn - 4n^2$
$= -3m^2 + 21mn - 64n^2$

Example 3.

If the radius, r, of a circle is increased by x, find the increase in: a) the circumference; b) the area.

Solution.

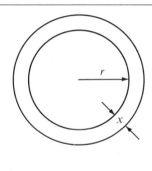

a) Circumference of original circle: $2\pi r$
Circumference of enlarged circle: $2\pi(r + x)$
Increase in circumference: $2\pi(r + x) - 2\pi r$
$= 2\pi r + 2\pi x - 2\pi r$
$= 2\pi x$
The increase in the circumference is $2\pi x$.

b) Area of original circle: πr^2
Area of enlarged circle: $\pi(r + x)^2$
Increase in area: $\pi(r + x)^2 - \pi r^2$
$= \pi(r^2 + 2rx + x^2) - \pi r^2$
$= \pi r^2 + 2\pi rx + \pi x^2 - \pi r^2$
$= 2\pi rx + \pi x^2$
The increase in area is $2\pi rx + \pi x^2$.

EXERCISES 3-2

(A)

1. Simplify:
   a) $(8a - 13b) - (12a + 4b)$
   b) $(5x^2 - 3y^2) - (7x^2 + y^2) + (3x^2 - 2y^2)$
   c) $(3m^2 - 8m + 9) - (5m^2 + 6m - 2)$
   d) $(5a^2 + 9ab - 3b^2) + (7a^2 - 16ab + 14b^2)$
   e) $(3ab + 7bc - 19ac) + (-11ab + 7ac - 32bc)$
   f) $(5m^2 + 3m - 9) + (8m^2 - 14m + 16) - (6m^2 - 11m + 4)$
2. Simplify:
   a) $4(2x + 7y) - 3(5x - 2y)$
   b) $7a(3a - 8) + 5a(6a + 4)$
   c) $14mn(3m - 2n) - 5mn(6m + 4n)$
   d) $2x(5x - 7y + 3) - 8x(2x + 3y - 1)$
   e) $7a(3a + 5b - 2) + 2a(5a - 11b + 17)$
   f) $5xy(2x - 3y - 7) + 2xy(8x - 13y + 21)$
3. Simplify:
   a) $3[5a - (2 - 4b)] + 5[2a - (7 + 3b)]$
   b) $4[2x - (6y + 3)] - 7[4x - (5y - 9)]$
   c) $2x[5x - (4 + 7y)] - 6x[3x - (2y - 5)]$
   d) $5a[2a + 3(4a - 9)] + 3a[a - 7(2a + 6)]$
   e) $3m[m - 4m(n - 5)] - 2m^2(3m - 2n + 7)$
   f) $8x[2x - 3y(x + 2)] - 5x[4x - 7y(2x - 9)]$

4. Simplify:
   a) $(3x + 7)(5x - 2)$
   b) $(2m + 9)(4m + 5)$
   c) $(7x - 3y)^2$
   d) $(8a - 5b)(7a - 11b)$
   e) $(4x + 3y)(4x - 3y)$
   f) $2(5x - 9y)(8x - 3y)$
5. A square has sides of length x. If each side is increased by an amount h, find the increase in area.
6. Simplify:
   a) $(3x + 7y)(2x + 5y) + (4x - 3y)(5x + 6y)$
   b) $(6a - 5b)(3a + 2b) - 2(2a + 7b)(4a - 3b)$
   c) $3(4m - 7n)(3m - 2n) - (7m - 5n)(7m + 5n)$
   d) $(6x - 2y)(4x + 7y) + (3x - 5y)^2$
   e) $(5x - 2y)^2 - (5x + 2y)^2$
   f) $(3a^2 + 8b)(2a^2 - 5b) - 3(4a^2 - 2b)^2$
7. Simplify:
   a) $3(2x - y)^2 - 2(x - 3y)^2$
   b) $4(2x - 3)^2 - 3(3x - 2)^2$
   c) $2(a - 3)^2 + 1$
   d) $5(2m + 7)^2 - 7(m - 3)(2m + 4)$
   e) $3(2x - 5)^2 - 14$
   f) $6(3a^2 + 2b)^2 + 3a^2(2a - 5b)^2$
8. Simplify:
   a) $(2m + 3)(5m^2 - 3m + 8)$
   b) $(3x - 7y)(2x - 4y - 5)$
   c) $(2a - 5b)(3a^2 + 2ab - b^2)$
   d) $3(x + 2y)(5x^2 - 2xy + 3y^2)$
   e) $(x^2 + 2x + 3)(2x^2 - 5x - 1)$
   f) $4a(2a^2 - 3ab + b^2)(3a^2 + ab - 2b^2)$
9. Simplify:
   a) $(x + 5)(x - 3)(x + 1)$
   b) $(2a - 1)(a + 5)(2a + 1)$
   c) $2(x - 3)^2(x - 1)$
   d) $(4m + 7n)(2m + 3n)(m - 5n)$
   e) $3(2a - 5b)(3a + 2b)(3a - 2b)$
   f) $5(2x - 7y)(4x + 3y)^2$

(B)

10. A cube has edges of length x. If each edge is increased by an amount h, find the increase in:
    a) surface area;
    b) volume.
11. Simplify:
    a) $2(3x - 4)(2x - 5) - 3(x + 3)(5x + 2) - (4x - 7)(2x + 5)$
    b) $3(2a + b)(5a - 2b) - 6(3a - 4b)^2 - (5a + 3b)(5a - 3b)$
    c) $(2m + 3)(3m^2 + 4m - 5) - (m - 2)(2m^2 + 3m - 8)$
    d) $(2x + 4y)(x - 2y + 1) - (3x - y)(5x + 3y - 4)$
    e) $(3a - 2b)(2a + 7b)^2 - (4a + 3b)^2(2a - 5b)$
    f) $3(4x - 2)(2x^2 + x + 6) - (2x - 3)(3x - 2)^2$

12. A shipping crate measures $(3x + 5)$ m by $(2x - 3)$ m by $(2x + 4)$ m.
    a) Find expressions for its volume and surface area.
    b) Evaluate the expressions in (a) for $x = 2.5$.
13. A cylinder has a radius of $(3x - 2)$ cm and a height of $(2x + 5)$ cm. Find expressions for its volume and surface area.
14. The stopping distance, d, in metres, for a car travelling at v km/h is given by the formula: $d = 0.20v + 0.15v^2$. Find the increase in stopping distance when v is increased by x km/h.
15. When an object of mass m is travelling at a speed v, its kinetic energy, E, is given by the formula: $E = \frac{1}{2}mv^2$. If the speed is increased by an amount x, find an expression to represent the change in kinetic energy.
16. A car brakes and decelerates uniformly. After t s, it has travelled a distance of d m where d is related to t by the formula: $d = 40t - 2t^2$, $t \leqslant 10$. How far does the car travel in the next second?
17. Find the volume of the unshaded portion of the rectangular prism shown below (left).

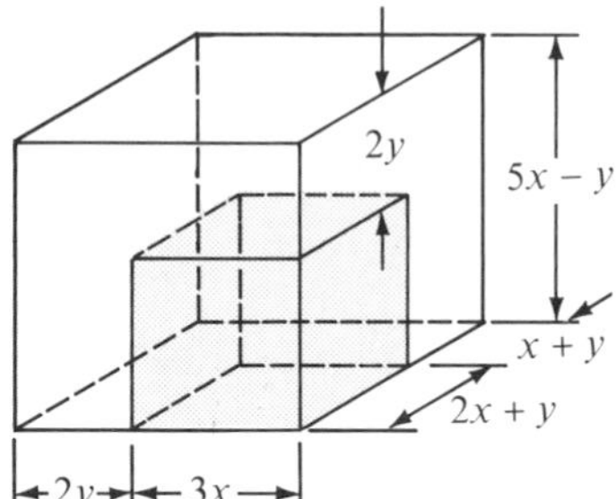

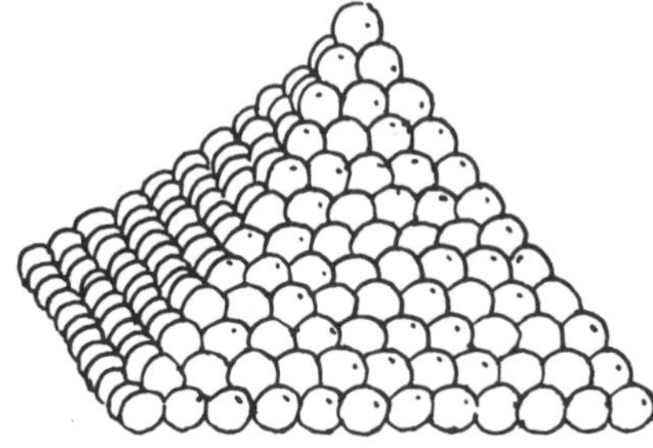

Ⓒ

18. When there are n coconuts in the bottom row of a square pyramid of coconuts (above, right), the total number of coconuts, N, is given by the formula: $N = \frac{1}{3}n^3 + \frac{1}{2}n^2 + \frac{1}{6}n$. How many additional coconuts would be needed to make a pyramid with one more layer?

INVESTIGATE

Verify that
$n(n + 1)(n + 2)(n + 3) + 1 = (n^2 + 3n + 1)^2$.
Substitute 1, 2, 3, 4, in turn, for n in this equation to obtain some interesting number patterns.

Patterns in Products

The product of two binomials such as $(x + 1)(x - 1)$ is significant because two terms of the product *add to zero*.

These products. . .these terms. . .add to zero.

$$(x + 1)(x - 1) = x^2 - x + x - 1$$
$$= x^2 - 1$$

Are there other products in which some of the terms add to zero? To answer this question, we could start with $(x + 1)(x - 1)$ and change one or both factors in a systematic way. For example, use higher powers of x and different combinations of signs. Here are a few of the many possibilities that could be considered.

- Changing one of the factors:

$(x + 1)(x^2 - x + 1)$	$(x - 1)(x^2 + x + 1)$
$(x + 1)(x^2 - x - 1)$	$(x - 1)(x^2 + x - 1)$
$(x + 1)(x^3 + x^2 - x - 1)$	$(x - 1)(x^3 + x^2 + x + 1)$
$(x + 1)(x^3 - x^2 + x - 1)$	$(x - 1)(x^3 + x^2 - x - 1)$

- Changing both factors:
  $(x^2 + x + 1)(x^2 + x - 1)$
  $(x^3 + x^2 + x + 1)(x^2 - x + 1)$

1. Using examples such as those above, try to arrange the powers and signs so that some of the terms of the product add to zero. Write the results in a systematic way that shows the underlying patterns.
2. Use the patterns in the results of Project 1 to factor the following expressions:

a) $x^3 + 1$	b) $8a^3 - 1$	c) $x^5 - 1$
d) $x^3 + y^3$	e) $x^4 + x^2 + 1$	f) $x^6 + x^4 - x^2 - 1$

3-3 FACTORING BY GROUPING

To factor a polynomial means to express it as a product. This can be done when all the terms share a common factor.

Example 1.

Factor: a) $4a^3b^2 - 8a^2b^2 + 12ab$

b) $-6x^4y + 15x^3y - 3x^2y$

Solution.

a) The greatest common factor is $4ab$.

$4a^3b^2 - 8a^2b^2 + 12ab = 4ab(a^2b - 2ab + 3)$

b) The greatest common factor is $3x^2y$.

$-6x^4y + 15x^3y - 3x^2y = 3x^2y(-2x^2 + 5x - 1)$

Some expressions have binomials or trinomials as common factors.

Example 2.

Factor: a) $2x(3x - 4y) + 5y(3x - 4y)$

b) $(a^2 + 3a + 1)\,a - 2(a^2 + 3a + 1)$

Solution.

a) $2x(3x - 4y) + 5y\,(3x - 4y) = (3x - 4y)(2x + 5y)$

b) $(a^2 + 3a + 1)a - 2(a^2 + 3a + 1) = (a^2 + 3a + 1)(a - 2)$

A factor may be common to only some of the terms of a polynomial, but sometimes these terms can be *grouped* so that the polynomial can be factored.

Example 3.

Factor: a) $ax + ay + bx + by$

b) $6x^2 + 2xy - 15x - 5y$

c) $6m^2n - 12mn^2 + 20n^2 - 10mn$

Solution.

a) The common factor of the first two terms is a; that of the last two terms is b.

$$\begin{aligned} ax + ay + bx + by &= a(x + y) + b(x + y) \\ &= (x + y)(a + b) \end{aligned}$$

b)
$$\begin{aligned} 6x^2 + 2xy - 15x - 5y &= 2x(3x + y) - 5(3x + y) \\ &= (3x + y)(2x - 5) \end{aligned}$$

Or, the order of the terms may be changed before grouping:

$$\begin{aligned} 6x^2 + 2xy - 15x - 5y &= 6x^2 - 15x + 2xy - 5y \\ &= 3x(2x - 5) + y(2x - 5) \\ &= (2x - 5)(3x + y) \end{aligned}$$

c)
$$\begin{aligned} &6m^2n - 12mn^2 + 20n^2 - 10mn \\ &= 2n(3m^2 - 6mn + 10n - 5m \\ &= 2n[3m(m - 2n) + 5(2n - m)] \\ &= 2n[3m(m - 2n) - 5(m - 2n)] \\ &= 2n(m - 2n)(3m - 5) \end{aligned}$$

$-5(m - 2n) = 5(2n - m)$

EXERCISES 3-3

(A)

1. Factor:
   a) $6x^2y + 15xy^2 - 27xy$
   b) $35m^3n^3 - 21m^2n^2 + 56m^2n$
   c) $12a^3b^2 + 28a^2b^3 - 44ab^4$
   d) $36s^4t^2 - 45s^2t^3 - 18st^4$
   e) $20x^3y^3 + 45x^2y^4 - 35xy^5$
   f) $42a^2b^3 - 18a^3b + 48ab^2$
2. Factor:
   a) $12x^3y^2 - 18x^2y^3 + 24x^2y^2$
   b) $28a^3b^2 - 12a^2b^3 - 48ab^4$
   c) $45m^4n + 30m^3n^2 - 75m^2n^3$
   d) $39x^3y^5 - 65x^3y^4 - 26x^5y^3$
   e) $54a^3b^3c^2 - 36a^3bc^3 + 63a^3b^2c - 81a^2bc^3$
   f) $24x^3y^3z^2 + 80x^3yz^3 + 88x^2y^2z^2 - 8x^2yz^2$
3. Factor:
   a) $3x(2a - 7) + 5y(2a - 7)$
   b) $9x^2(4x + 3y) - 8y(4x + 3y)$
   c) $4a^2(2a - 5b) - 7b^2(5b - 2a)$
   d) $5m^2(3m - 7n + 2) + 9n^2(3m - 7n + 2)$
   e) $12x^2(4x^2 - 7x + 9) - 5xy\,(4x^2 - 7x + 9) - (4x^2 - 7x + 9)$
   f) $4x^2(7x - 2y) - 5xy(7x - 2y) + (7x - 2y) + 11y^2\,(2y - 7x)$
4. Factor:
   a) $5x^2y\,(3x^2 - 11y^2) + 4(3x^2 - 11y^2)$
   b) $2m^2(5m^2 + 3) - 7n^2(5m^2 + 3)$
   c) $6x^2(4x - 7y) - 2y^2(7y - 4x)$
   d) $6x^2(4x^2 + 5xy - 3y^2) - 11y^2(4x^2 + 5xy - 3y^2)$
   e) $3a^2(2a^2 + 9ab - 5b^2) + 4ab(2a^2 + 9ab - 5b^2) - 2b^2(2a^2 + 9ab - 5b^2)$
   f) $2m^2(5m^2 - 2mn + 3n^2) + 7mn(5m^2 - 2mn + 3n^2) - 13n^2(5m^2 - 2mn + 3n^2)$
5. Factor:
   a) $xm - xn + ym - yn$
   b) $10ax + 4ay - 15x - 6y$
   c) $9am + 3bm + 6an + 2bn$
   d) $14ax - 63x - 10ay + 45y$
   e) $28x^2 - 16xy + 21x - 12y$
   f) $48x^2 - 56x - 30xy + 35y$
6. Factor:
   a) $x^2 - xz - xy + yz$
   b) $x^3 + x^2 + x + 1$
   c) $21x^3 + 2y - 6x^2y - 7x$
   d) $1 + ab + a + b$
   e) $2x^3 - 3x^2 + 3 - 2x$
   f) $(x + y)^2 - x - y$
7. Factor:
   a) $x^3 + x^2 + 2x + 2$
   b) $2ac + 3ad - 2bc - 3bd$
   c) $a^3 - 3a + 3 - a^2$
   d) $(x + y)^2 + 4x + 4y$
   e) $a + ab - ac - abc$
   f) $a(a - b)^2 - a + b$

(B)

8. A rectangle has a perimeter P and a length x. Find expressions in terms of P and x for the width and the area.

9. Find the surface area of the washer shown below (left).

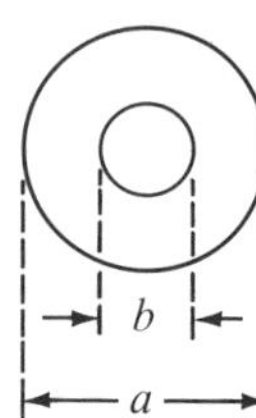

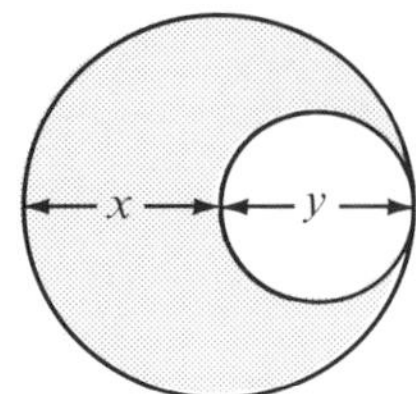

10. In the diagram above (right), find:
    a) the circumference of the larger circle;
    b) the area of the shaded region.
11. A circular cylinder has a radius r and a height h.
    a) If the radius is increased by x, the height staying the same, find the increase in: i) surface area; ii) volume.
    b) If the height is increased by y, the radius staying the same, find the increase in: i) surface area; ii) volume.
12. Factor:
    a) $a^4 - 2a^3 - a^3b + 2a^2b$
    b) $x^3y + x^2y^2 - 3x^2y - 3xy^2$
    c) $3m^3 + 12m^2 + 12mn + 3m^2n$
    d) $6a^3b^2 - 6a^2b^3 + 4a^2b^2 - 4ab^3$
    e) $10m^4 - 10m^3n - 15m^3 + 15m^2n$
    f) $24x^4y - 8x^3y^2 - 36x^3y + 12x^2y^2$

Ⓒ

13. Prove that the difference between a 3-digit number and the number formed by reversing its digits is divisible by 99.
14. Prove that a 3-digit number is divisible by 9 if, and only if, the sum of its digits is divisible by 9.
15. A rectangle of length l and width w is inscribed in a circle. Semicircles are drawn on each side, as shown. Prove that the total shaded area is equal to the area of the rectangle.

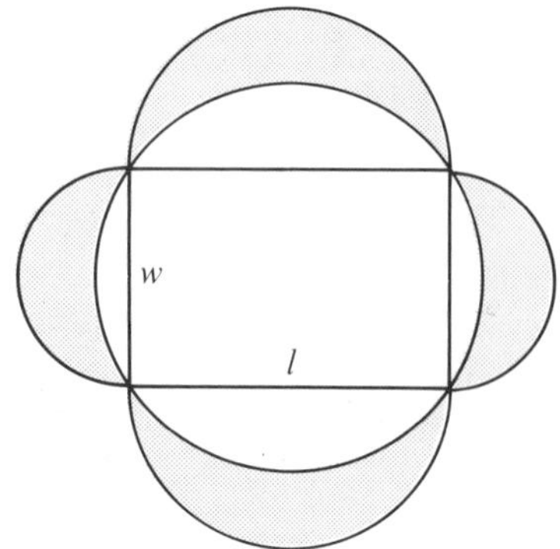

3-4 FACTORING TRINOMIALS

A method of factoring a trinomial of the form $ax^2 + bx + c$ is suggested by the way the product of two binomials is obtained.

The integers -10 and 7 have a sum -3 and a product -70—the same as the product of 2 and -35.

$$\begin{aligned}(2x + 7)(x - 5) &= 2x(x - 5) + 7(x - 5)\\ &= 2x^2 - 10x + 7x - 35\\ &= 2x^2 - 3x - 35\end{aligned}$$

This indicates that a trinomial of the form $ax^2 + bx + c$ can be factored if two integers can be found with a sum b and a product ac.

Example 1.

Factor: $6x^2 + 11x - 10$

Solution

What two integers have a sum 11 and a product -60?

$$6x^2 + 11x - 10$$

The integers are 15 and -4. The trinomial can be factored by first writing the second term as $15x - 4x$ and then grouping the terms to find a common factor.

The second term could also be written: $-4x + 15x$.

$$\begin{aligned}6x^2 + 11x - 10 &= 6x^2 + 15x - 4x - 10\\ &= 3x(2x + 5) - 2(2x + 5)\\ &= (2x + 5)(3x - 2)\end{aligned}$$

Example 2.

Factor: a) $10x^2 - 23xy + 12y^2$ b) $12a^3 - 94a^2 - 16a$

Solution.

a) $$\begin{aligned}10x^2 - 23xy + 12y^2 &= 10x^2 - 15xy - 8xy + 12y^2\\ &= 5x(2x - 3y) - 4y(2x - 3y)\\ &= (2x - 3y)(5x - 4y)\end{aligned}$$

Extract the common factor first.

b) $$\begin{aligned}12a^3 - 94a^2 - 16a &= 2a(6a^2 - 47a - 8)\\ &= 2a(6a^2 + a - 48a - 8)\\ &= 2a[a(6a + 1) - 8(6a + 1)]\\ &= 2a(6a + 1)(a - 8)\end{aligned}$$

EXERCISES 3-4

(A)

1. Factor:
   a) $x^2 + 5x + 6$ b) $m^2 - 9m + 20$ c) $a^2 + 5a - 14$
   d) $m^2 - 5m - 24$ e) $x^2 - 15x + 54$ f) $x^2 + 5x - 84$
2. Factor:
   a) $2m^2 + 7m + 3$ b) $5x^2 - 7x + 2$ c) $3a^2 - 10a + 3$
   d) $4x^2 + x - 3$ e) $3s^2 - s - 2$ f) $2m^2 + 5m - 7$
3. Factor:
   a) $3x^2 + 7xy + 2y^2$ b) $2m^2 - 5mn + 3n^2$
   c) $3a^2 + 5ab - 2b^2$ d) $5m - 3mn - 2n^2$
   e) $21x^2 - 10xy + y^2$ f) $3x^2 - 16xy + 5y^2$

4. Factor:
   a) $6s^2 + 11s - 10$ b) $6m^2 - m - 40$
   c) $10a^2 + 51a + 27$ d) $8x^2 + 38x + 45$
   e) $24m^2 - 38m + 15$ f) $21x^2 + 10x - 16$

5. Factor:
   a) $5p^2 + pq - 18q^2$ b) $8m^2 - 2mn - 21n^2$
   c) $15x^2 - 34xy + 15y^2$ d) $32s^2 - 92st + 45t^2$
   e) $24p^2 + 2pq - 15q^2$ f) $-6x^2 - 17xy + 14y^2$

6. Factor:
   a) $36x^2 - 48x - 20$ b) $14x^2 + 77x - 147$
   c) $48x^2 - 200x + 200$ d) $24m^3 + 68m^2 + 48m$
   e) $10a^3b - 85a^2b + 105ab$ f) $-45mn + 66m^2n - 24m^3n$

B

7. Factor:
   a) $m^4 + 6m^2 - 16$ b) $3x^4 - 16x^2y^2 + 5y^4$
   c) $2a^4 - a^2 - 15$ d) $12x^4 - 5x^2y^2 - 2y^4$
   e) $20m^4 - 47m^2n^2 + 24n^4$ f) $8x^4 - 22x^2y^2 - 21y^4$

8. Factor:
   a) $6a^4 - 21a^2 - 45$ b) $2x^5 + 14x^3 + 20x$
   c) $15m^5 - 115m^3 + 70m$ d) $16s^5 - 64s^3t^2 + 60st^4$
   e) $30p^5 + 52p^3q^2 + 16pq^4$ f) $48x^5y - 56x^3y^3 - 40xy^5$

9. Factor:
   a) $(5x)^2 + 7(5x) + 12$ b) $2(3x)^2 - 9(3x) + 4$
   c) $15(7m)^2 - 14(7m) - 8$ d) $6(a + b)^2 + 17(a + b) + 5$
   e) $8(2p + q)^2 - 10(2p + q) + 3$
   f) $10(3x^2 + 2y)^2 - 29(3x^2 + 2y) - 21$

10. Factor:
   a) $(x^2 + 3x)^2 - 2(x^2 + 3x) - 8$
   b) $(x^2 + 4x)^2 + 7(x^2 + 4x) + 12$
   c) $(a^2 + 2a)^2 - 2(a^2 + 2a) - 3$
   d) $(y^2 - 2y)^2 - 11(y^2 - 2y) + 24$
   e) $(2a^2 + 5a)^2 - 10(2a^2 + 5a) - 24$
   f) $(3x^2 - 2x)^2 - 13(3x^2 - 2x) + 40$

11. Factor:
   a) $3(x - y)^2 + 2x^2 - 2xy$ b) $5(2m - n)^2 + 6m^2 - 3mn$
   c) $(a - 1)^2 + 2(a^2 + 4a - 5)$ d) $(2x + y)^2 + 3(6x^2 - xy - 2y^2)$
   e) $2(3s + 2t)^2 - 4(3s^2 - st - 2t^2)$
   f) $3(2x - 5y)^2 + 6x^2 + 9xy - 60y^2$

C

12. In how many ways can the following trinomials be factored?
   a) $5x^2 + 20x + 20$ b) $5x^2 + 5x - 10$
   c) $4x^2 + 16x + 16$ d) $4x^2 + 4x - 8$
   e) $6x^2 + 24x + 24$ f) $6x^2 + 6x - 12$

COMPUTER POWER

Factoring Trinomials

Factoring trinomials in which the coefficients are very large numbers can be tedious and time-consuming. In such cases a computer can be of assistance.

The sequence of steps in factoring a trinomial of the form $Ax^2 + Bx + C$ has been written into the program below. The computer searches for two integers with a product AC and a sum B. If they are found, the coefficients of the two factors are printed. If there are no such integers, the computer indicates that there are no factors of the form $Px + Q$, where P and Q are integers.

```
100 REM *** FACTORING TRINOMIALS ***
110 INPUT "WHAT ARE THE COEFFICIENTS? ";A,B,C:PRINT
120 M=INT(SQR(ABS(A*C)))
130 FOR X =-M TO M
140 IF X=0 THEN 160
150 IF X+A*C/X=B THEN 180
160 NEXT X
170 PRINT "THERE ARE NO LINEAR FACTORS.":GOTO 230
180 P=ABS(A):Q=ABS(X)
190 R=P-INT(P/Q)*Q:REM *** FIND GCF OF A AND X ***
200 IF R=0 THEN 220
210 P=Q:Q=R:GOTO 190
220 PRINT "FACTORS: (";A/Q;" ";X/Q;")(";Q;" ";C*Q/X;")"
230 END
```

When the program was used to factor the trinomial $40x^2 - 114x + 54$, the following output was obtained:

WHAT ARE THE COEFFICIENTS? 40, −114, 54
FACTORS: (5 −3)(8 −18)

This shows that $40x^2 - 114x + 54 = (5x - 3)(8x - 18)$.

The program does not remove common factors. If there is a common factor, it can usually be seen in the second bracket of the result. In the above example, there is a common factor of 2 in $8x - 18$. Therefore, a complete factorization of the trinomial is:

$$40x^2 - 114x + 54 = 2(5x - 3)(4x - 9)$$

1. Factor:
   a) $10x^2 + 21x + 8$
   b) $8a^2 - 42a + 27$
   c) $12x^2 - 25xy - 75y^2$
   d) $24 + 26t - 15t^2$
2. Factor completely:
   a) $12x^2 + 78x + 90$
   b) $50x^2 - 155xy - 70y^2$
   c) $162a^2 - 567ab + 360b^2$
   d) $128 - 448m + 392m^2$
3. Investigate how the program can give a complete factorization of:
   a) $884x^2 + 1003x - 306$;
   b) $2024x^2 + 3657x + 1495$.

3-5 FACTORING A DIFFERENCE OF SQUARES AND A TRINOMIAL SQUARE

A polynomial in the form $x^2 - y^2$ is called a **difference of squares**, and is factored:

$$x^2 - y^2 = (x - y)(x + y).$$

Using the above identity, we can express a difference of squares as a product. As always, look for a common factor first.

Example 1.

Factor: a) $81x^2 - 64y^2$ b) $12a^3 - 27a$

Solution.

a) $81x^2 - 64y^2 = (9x - 8y)(9x + 8y)$

b) $12a^3 - 27a = 3a(4a^2 - 9)$
$= 3a(2a - 3)(2a + 3)$

Example 2.

Factor: a) $m^4 - 16$ b) $(2x - 3)^2 - (y + 2)^2$

Solution.

a) $m^4 - 16 = (m^2 - 4)(m^2 + 4)$
$= (m - 2)(m + 2)(m^2 + 4)$

b) $(2x - 3)^2 - (y + 2)^2$
$= [(2x - 3) - (y + 2)][(2x - 3) + (y + 2)]$
$= (2x - y - 5)(2x + y - 1)$

When a binomial is squared, the result is called a **trinomial square**.

$$(x + y)^2 = x^2 + 2xy + y^2$$
$$(x - y)^2 = x^2 - 2xy + y^2$$

These identities can be used to recognize and factor trinomial squares.

Example 3.

Factor: a) $x^2 - 14x + 49$ b) $-2z^2 + 20z - 50$

Solution.

a) Since x^2 and 49 are the squares of x and -7, and since $-14x$ is double the product of x and -7, $x^2 - 14x + 49$ is a trinomial square.

$$x^2 - 14x + 49 = (x - 7)^2$$

b) $-2z^2 + 20z - 50 = -2(z^2 - 10z + 25)$
$= -2(z - 5)^2$

Example 4.

Factor: a) $x^2 - 8x + 16 - y^2$
b) $4a^2 - 9b^2 - c^2 + 6bc$

Solution.

a) $x^2 - 8x + 16 - y^2 = (x^2 - 8x + 16) - y^2$
$= (x - 4)^2 - y^2$
$= [(x - 4) - y][(x - 4) + y]$
$= (x - 4 - y)(x - 4 + y)$

b) $4a^2 - 9b^2 - c^2 + 6bc$
$= 4a^2 - (9b^2 - 6bc + c^2)$
$= 4a^2 - (3b - c)^2$
$= [2a - (3b - c)]\,[2a + (3b - c)]$
$= (2a - 3b + c)\,(2a + 3b - c)$

Example 5.

Research scientists believe that by the year A.D. 2000 space colonies will be technically possible. One proposal is for a wheel-like colony 2000 m in diameter with an interior diameter of 200 m. The volume of the interior, V, is given by: $V = \frac{1}{4}\pi^2(a^3 - a^2b - ab^2 + b^3)$, where a and b are the external and internal radii.

a) Express V as a product of algebraic factors.
b) What is the volume of the space colony?

Solution.

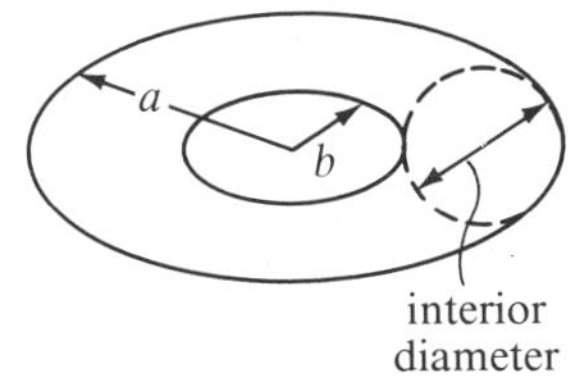

a) $V = \frac{1}{4}\pi^2(a^3 - a^2b - ab^2 + b^3)$
$= \frac{1}{4}\pi^2[a^2(a - b) - b^2(a - b)]$
$= \frac{1}{4}\pi^2(a^2 - b^2)(a - b)$
$= \frac{1}{4}\pi^2(a - b)^2(a + b)$

b) From the data, $a = 1000$ and $b = 800$. Substituting these values in the formula:

$V = \frac{1}{4}\pi^2\,(1000 - 800)^2(1000 + 800)$
$= \frac{1}{4}\pi^2(40\ 000)(1800)$
$= 18\ 000\ 000\ \pi^2$, or approximately 178 000 000

The volume of the space colony is about 178 000 000 m^3.

EXERCISES 3-5

(A)

1. Factor:
   a) $4x^2 - 25$ b) $16m^2 - 81n^2$ c) $36a^2 - 121$
   d) $9s^2 - 49t^2$ e) $64x^2 - 169y^2$ f) $400a^2 - 81b^2$
2. Factor:
   a) $48a^2 - 147b^2$ b) $50m^3 - 18m$ c) $20x^3 - 405xy^2$
   d) $63a^3 - 112ab^2$ e) $100x^3y^2 - 324xy^4$ f) $54y - 384x^2y$
3. Factor:
   a) $x^4 - 81$ b) $12m^4 - 75n^4$ c) $32a^4 - 1250b^4$
   d) $9s^4t - \frac{1}{4}t^3$ e) $\frac{16}{25}x^2y^2 - \frac{36}{49}y^4$ f) $256x^8 - y^8$
4. Factor:
   a) $(5x - 2)^2 - 49$ b) $4m^2 - (6m - 7)^2$
   c) $16(3x - y)^2 - 81y^2$ d) $(2x - 7y)^2 - (3x + 2y)^2$
   e) $(5m + 2)^2 - (3m - 8)^2$ f) $9(2a + 5b)^2 - 4(7a - 3b)^2$
5. Factor:
   a) $(a^2 + 2a)^2 - 64$ b) $(2x^2 - 6x)^2 - 1296$
   c) $(2x^2 + 3xy)^2 - 4y^4$ d) $36n^4 - (3m^2 + 7mn)^2$
   e) $(a^2 - 13a)^2 - 900$ f) $2(x^2 - 10xy)^2 - 1152y^4$
6. Factor:
   a) $x^2 + 10x + 25$ b) $m^2 - 14m + 49$ c) $4a^2 + 12a + 9$
   d) $x^2 - 18xy + 81y^2$ e) $36x^2 + 132xy + 121y^2$

(B)

7. Factor:
   a) $49m^2 + 70m + 25$ b) $12a^2 - 108a + 243$
   c) $16s^2 + 88s + 121$ d) $-32x^2 + 48xy - 18y^2$
   e) $9m^2 - 60mn + 100n^2$ f) $45x^2 - 210xy + 245y^2$
8. Factor:
   a) $m^2 + 6m + 9 - n^2$ b) $4x^2 - 20x + 25 - 16y^2$
   c) $9a^2 - 12a + 4 - 49b^2$ d) $x^2 + 8xy + 16y^2 - 81$
   e) $4s^2 - 20st + 25t^2 - 9$ f) $25x^2 - 80x + 64 - 64y^2$
9. Factor:
   a) $a^2 - b^2 + 8bc - 16c^2$ b) $x^2 - y^2 - 14yz - 49z^2$
   c) $25 - m^2 - 12mn - 36n^2$ d) $4s^2 - 9t^2 - 12t - 4$
   e) $x^2 - a^2 - y^2 - 2ay$ f) $a^2 - 2a + 1 - b^2 + 2bc - c^2$
10. Factor:
    a) $x^2 + 9y^2 - 25z^2 - 6xy$ b) $9m^2 - 49p^2 - 4n^2 - 28np$
    c) $x^3 + x^2 - x - 1$ d) $a^2 + 2a + 1 - b^2 + 6b - 9$
    e) $a^{2n} - b^{2n}$ f) $2x^4 - 20x^2 + 18$
11. A cylinder of length h has outside radius R and inside radius r. Find an expression for the total surface area of the cylinder (including the ends) and write it as a product of algebraic factors.

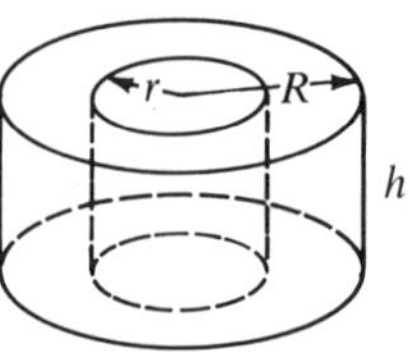

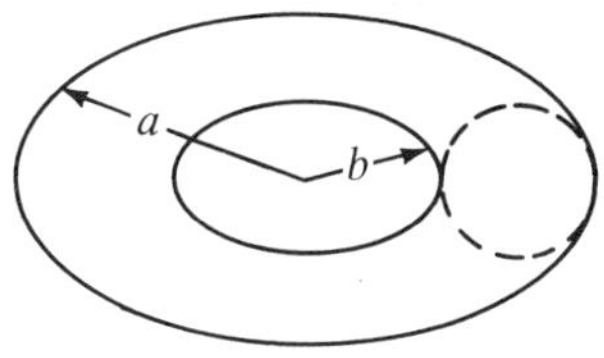

12. The surface of a torus-shaped subway tunnel of external radius a units and internal radius b units is to be lined with a strengthening material. The surface area, A, of the tunnel is given by:

$$A = \pi^2 a^2 - \pi^2 b^2.$$

   a) Express A as a product of algebraic factors.
   b) If the diameter of the tunnel is 10 m and the external diameter of the subway is 15 km, what is the surface area in square metres?

Ⓒ

13. Astronomers calculate the temperature, T, of a star from the equation: $E = kT^4$, where k is a constant and E is the energy radiated by the star. If the temperature increases by an amount, x, find an expression to represent the increase in energy radiated by the star, and write it as a product of factors.

14. a) Find if possible, a positive integer, n, such that $m^2 - n^2$ is a prime number when: i) $m = 7$; ii) $m = 8$.
   b) For what values of m is it possible to find a positive integer, n, such that $m^2 - n^2$ is prime?

SIDE TRIP **Counting Methods II**

The counting rule says that if there are m ways of doing one thing and n ways of doing another, there are $m \times n$ ways of doing them together. Furthermore, we know that this rule can be extended to any number of things.

1. How many six-letter "words" can be made using all the letters in FACTOR?
2. How many four-digit numbers can be formed using the digits 1, 2, 3, 4: a) if no repetition is allowed? b) if repetition is allowed?
3. a) Use a calculator to determine the number of arrangements possible using all the letters in MANUSCRIPT.
   b) If you could write one of these arrangements every six seconds and could work around-the-clock, how many days would it take to complete the list?
4. A province decides its licence plates shall consist of:

   a digit—a letter—a four-digit numeral.

   However, the first digit cannot be zero, and the letters O, I, and Z are excluded. How many different licence plates can it issue?

   Why do you suppose O, I, and Z are excluded?

PROVINCE
2-B-0175

1. 720 2) a) 24 b) 256 3. a) 3 628 800 b) 252 4. 2 070 000

3-6 FACTORING THE SUM AND DIFFERENCE OF CUBES

Only a *difference* of squares, not the sum, can be expressed as the product of two factors. However, both the sum *and* difference of two cubes can be factored, using the following identities. They may be easily verified by expansion.

$$x^3 - y^3 = (x - y)(x^2 + xy + y^2)$$
$$x^3 + y^3 = (x + y)(x^2 - xy + y^2)$$

Example.

Factor: a) $x^3 - 64$ b) $8y^3 + 27$ c) $27x^3 - 8y^3$

Solution.

a) $x^3 - 64 = x^3 - 4^3$
$= (x - 4)(x^2 + 4x + 16)$

b) $8y^3 + 27 = (2y)^3 + 3^3$
$= (2y + 3)[(2y)^2 - 6y + 9]$
$= (2y + 3)(4y^2 - 6y + 9)$

c) $27x^3 - 8y^3 = (3x)^3 - (2y)^3$
$= (3x - 2y)(9x^2 + 6xy + 4y^2)$

EXERCISES 3-6

(A)

1. Factor:
   a) $z^3 - 27$ b) $y^3 + 1$ c) $8x^3 - 64$
   d) $a^3 - 8b^3$ e) $8x^3 + 27y^3$ f) $64x^3 + 1$

(B)

2. Express as a product and simplify all factors:
   a) $(x + 1)^3 - 1$ b) $(2x)^3 + 1$ c) $(x + 2)^3 - x^3$
   d) $(2x + 1)^3 + (2y)^3$ e) $(a + 2b)^3 - (a - 2b)^3$
   f) $(x + y)^3 + (x - y)^3$ g) $(x + 3)^3 + (x - 3)^3$
3. Factor:
   a) $x^6 - y^6$ b) $x^6 + y^6$ c) $64a^6 - 1$
   d) $1 + 64y^6$ e) $(x + y)^6 - (x - y)^6$ f) $(x + y)^6 + (x - y)^6$

(C)

4. The volume, V, of the frustrum of a right circular cone of radii a, b and height h is given by:

$$V = \frac{1}{3}\pi h\left(\frac{b^3 - a^3}{b - a}\right).$$

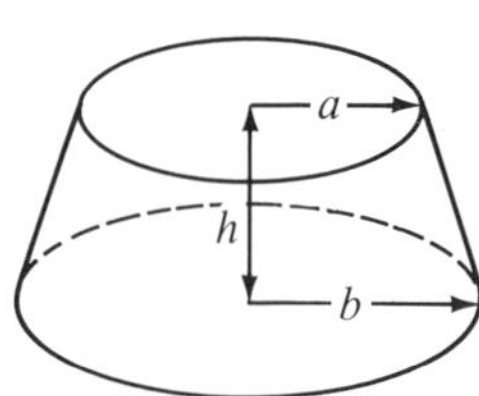

   a) Express V as a polynomial in a and b.
   b) Show that when $a = b$ the formula becomes: $V = \pi a^2 h$.

3-7 SIMPLIFYING RATIONAL EXPRESSIONS

The development of rational numbers arose naturally from the concept of the quotient of two integers. Similarly, the concept of the quotient of two polynomials led to the development of rational expressions.

> Any algebraic expression that can be written as the quotient of two polynomials is called a rational expression.

These are rational expressions:

$$\frac{x-1}{2x+3} \qquad \frac{2x^2-9xy+7y^2}{5xy} \qquad 17x^2-6$$

These are not rational expressions:

$$\frac{1+\sqrt{a}}{\sqrt{a^2+1}} \qquad \frac{x^2+6}{\sqrt{x}} \qquad \sqrt{x}+3$$

Rational expressions, like rational numbers in the $\frac{m}{n}$ form, can be reduced to lower terms by dividing numerator and denominator by any non-zero factor common to both.

Example 1.

Reduce to lowest terms:

a) $\frac{15x^2y}{6xy^2}$ b) $\frac{x^2-9x+20}{2x-10}$ c) $\frac{m^3-mn^2}{mn-m^2}$

Solution.

a) $$\frac{15x^2y}{6xy^2} = \frac{\cancel{(3xy)}(5x)}{\cancel{(3xy)}(2y)} = \frac{5x}{2y}$$

b) $$\frac{x^2-9x+20}{2x-10} = \frac{\cancel{(x-5)}(x-4)}{2\cancel{(x-5)}} = \frac{x-4}{2}$$

c) $$\frac{m^3-mn^2}{mn-m^2} = \frac{m(m^2-n^2)}{m(n-m)} = \frac{\cancel{(m-n)}(m+n)}{-\cancel{(m-n)}} = \frac{m+n}{-1}, \text{ or } -(m+n)$$

$n - m = -(m - n)$

When a rational expression is reduced to lowest terms, the result can be checked by substituting a convenient value for the variable. For example, in *Example 1b* we showed that:

$$\frac{x^2 - 9x + 20}{2x - 10} = \frac{x - 4}{2}$$

To check this, substitute 3 for x:

L.S.: $\frac{3^2 - 9(3) + 20}{2(3) - 10} = \frac{2}{-4}$, or $-\frac{1}{2}$ R.S.: $\frac{3 - 4}{2} = -\frac{1}{2}$

The result is correct.

But, if 5 is substituted for x:

L.S.: $\frac{5^2 - 9(5) + 20}{2(5) - 10}$ This reduces to $\frac{0}{0}$, which is not defined.

R.S.: $\frac{5 - 4}{2} = \frac{1}{2}$

The fact that the L.S. does not equal the R.S. shows that $\frac{x^2 - 9x + 20}{2x - 10} = \frac{x - 4}{2}$ is *not* true when $x = 5$. The reason is that 5 is a value of x for which the denominator of the given rational expression equals 0. Since division by 0 is not defined, the rational expression is not defined when $x = 5$.

> A rational expression is not defined when its denominator is equal to 0.

Example 2.

For what values of the variable is the expression undefined?

a) $\frac{2x^2 + 10x}{2x - 6}$ b) $\frac{-7y}{y^2 + y}$ c) $\frac{z^2 + 4z + 3}{z^2 + 5z + 6}$

Solution.

In each case, let the denominator equal zero.

a) Let $2x - 6 = 0$

$x = 3$

The expression $\frac{2x^2 + 10x}{2x - 6}$ is undefined when $x = 3$.

b) Let $y^2 + y = 0$

$y(y + 1) = 0$

$y = 0$ or $y = -1$

The expression $\frac{-7y}{y^2 + y}$ is undefined when $y = 0$ or $y = -1$.

c) Let $z^2 + 5z + 6 = 0$

$$(z + 2)(z + 3) = 0$$

$$z = -2 \text{ or } z = -3$$

The expression $\dfrac{z^2 + 4z + 3}{z^2 + 5z + 6}$ is undefined when $z = -2$ or $z = -3$.

When a rational expression is simplified, the result is true only for values of the variables for which the expression is defined.

Example 3.

Given: a) $\dfrac{x^2 - 5x + 4}{3x - 12}$ b) $\dfrac{x + 5}{x^2 - 25}$

i) Simplify each expression;
ii) For what values of x is the result true?

Solution.

a) i) $\dfrac{x^2 - 5x + 4}{3x - 12} = \dfrac{(x - 4)(x - 1)}{3(x - 4)}$

$$= \frac{x - 1}{3}$$

ii) $\dfrac{x^2 - 5x + 4}{3x - 12}$ is undefined when $3x - 12 = 0$, or $x = 4$. This means that $\dfrac{x^2 - 5x + 4}{3x - 12} = \dfrac{x - 1}{3}$ is true for all real values of x except 4.

b) i) $\dfrac{x + 5}{x^2 - 25} = \dfrac{x + 5}{(x + 5)(x - 5)}$

$$= \frac{1}{x - 5}$$

ii) $\dfrac{x + 5}{x^2 - 25}$ is undefined when $x^2 - 25 = 0$

$$(x + 5)(x - 5) = 0$$

$$x = -5 \text{ or } x = 5$$

This means that $\dfrac{x + 5}{x^2 - 25} = \dfrac{1}{x - 5}$ is true for all real values of x except -5 and 5.

When working with rational expressions, it is usually inconvenient to write the restrictions on the variable for every expression. Therefore, when no restriction is stated, it is assumed that the expression is defined for all values of the variable for which the denominator is *not* equal to zero.

EXERCISES 3-7

Ⓐ

1. Reduce to lowest terms:

a) $\dfrac{24m^2n}{15mn^2}$ b) $\dfrac{-25a^2b^3c}{40a^3bc^2}$ c) $\dfrac{18st^3}{54s^2t}$

d) $\dfrac{45x^2y^2}{-72xy^3}$ e) $\dfrac{-85m^6n^2}{-34mn^5}$ f) $\dfrac{39x^3y}{65xy}$

2. Reduce to lowest terms:

a) $\dfrac{6x^2 - 15xy}{9x^2 + 12x}$ b) $\dfrac{20m^2n - 24mn}{8m^2 + 12m}$ c) $\dfrac{7a^3 - 14a^2b}{14a^3 - 7a^2b}$

d) $\dfrac{6x^2 - 4xy}{-2x^2 + 2xy}$ e) $\dfrac{12m^2n^2 - 9n^4}{15mn^2 + 6n^3}$ f) $\dfrac{4x^2y - 6xy + 14y}{16y - 6xy}$

Ⓑ

3. Simplify:

a) $\dfrac{m^2 + mn - 2n^2}{3m^2 - 3mn}$ b) $\dfrac{x^2 - xy - 6y^2}{2x^2y + 4xy^2}$

c) $\dfrac{2a^2 + 11ab + 15b^2}{-4a^2 - 12ab}$ d) $\dfrac{10s^3t + 15s^2t^2}{4s^2 + 12st + 9t^2}$

e) $\dfrac{6x^2 - 23xy + 20y^2}{14x^2y - 35xy^2}$ f) $\dfrac{9mn^2 - 12m^2n}{8m^2 - 26mn + 15n^2}$

4. Simplify:

a) $\dfrac{x^2 + 5xy + 6y^2}{x^2 - 4y^2}$ b) $\dfrac{2m^2 - 9mn + 10n^2}{m^2 - 5mn + 6n^2}$

c) $\dfrac{6a^2 + 7ab - 3b^2}{4a^2 + 16ab + 15b^2}$ d) $\dfrac{y^2 - 16x^2}{8x^2 + 14xy + 3y^2}$

e) $\dfrac{15m^2 - 26mn - 21n^2}{6m^2 - 5mn - 21n^2}$ f) $\dfrac{15x^2 - 46xy + 16y^2}{25x^2 - 4y^2}$

5. For what values of the variable(s) are the following undefined?

a) $\dfrac{9x^3y}{15x}$ b) $\dfrac{8y}{y^2 - 2y}$

c) $\dfrac{3x^2 + 5x - 2}{5x - 20}$ d) $\dfrac{x^2 + 6x + 9}{x^2 + 7x - 8}$

6. For what values of the variable(s) are the following undefined?

a) $\dfrac{32ab^3}{10b^2}$ b) $\dfrac{m^2 - 25}{2m + 10}$

c) $\dfrac{x^2 + 7x + 6}{x^2 - 6x - 7}$ d) $\dfrac{y^2 - 16}{y^2 - 8y + 16}$

7. Simplify, and state the values of the variable for which the result is true:

a) $\dfrac{28x^2}{10x}$ b) $\dfrac{2x^2 + 5x - 3}{6x - 3}$ c) $\dfrac{m^2 + 7m + 10}{m^2 + 10m + 25}$

d) $\dfrac{8a^2b - 24ab}{a^2 - 9}$ e) $\dfrac{x^3 - x^2}{x^3 + x^2}$ f) $\dfrac{6x^3 + 4x^2}{2x^2 + 14}$

Ⓒ

8. Simplify:

a) $\dfrac{10x^2 + 25xy - 15y^2}{2x^2 + 12xy + 18y^2}$ b) $\dfrac{12m^3 - 44m^2n + 24mn^2}{14m^2n - 63mn^2 + 63n^3}$

c) $\dfrac{6x^2y + xy - y}{4x^2 + 8x + 3}$ d) $\dfrac{2x^3 - 22x^2 + 56x}{4x^2 - 64}$

e) $\dfrac{5x^4y^2 - 80y^2}{3x^3 - 6x^2 + 12x - 24}$ f) $\dfrac{18a^2b^2 + 48ab^3 + 32b^4}{45a^2b - 80b^3}$

3-8 MULTIPLYING AND DIVIDING RATIONAL EXPRESSIONS

The same procedures are used to multiply and divide rational expressions as are used to multiply and divide rational numbers.

Example 1.

Simplify:

a) $\dfrac{12a^2b}{15} \times \dfrac{5ab}{8b^2}$ b) $\dfrac{6(x - 5y)}{xy^2} \div \dfrac{9(x - 5y)}{y(x + 3y)}$

Solution.

a) $\dfrac{12a^2b}{15} \times \dfrac{5ab}{8b^2} = \dfrac{\overset{4}{\cancel{12}}a^2b}{\underset{5}{\cancel{15}}} \times \dfrac{\cancel{5}ab}{\underset{2}{\cancel{8}}b^2}$

$= \dfrac{a^3}{2}$

b) $\dfrac{6(x - 5y)}{xy^2} \div \dfrac{9(x - 5y)}{y(x + 3y)} = \dfrac{\overset{2}{\cancel{6}}\cancel{(x - 5y)}}{xy^2} \times \dfrac{\cancel{y}(x + 3y)}{\underset{3}{\cancel{9}}\cancel{(x - 5y)}}$

$= \dfrac{2(x + 3y)}{3xy}$

Multiply by the reciprocal.

Sometimes, the numerator or denominator must be factored before the expression can be simplified.

Example 2.

Simplify:

a) $\dfrac{2x + 6}{x^2 + 7x + 10} \times \dfrac{x^2 + 3x - 10}{x^2 - 4}$

b) $\dfrac{a^2 + 5a - 14}{a^2 + 8a + 7} \div \dfrac{a^2 - 4a + 4}{3a^2 - 6a}$

Solution.

a) $$\frac{2x+6}{x^2+7x+10} \times \frac{x^2+3x-10}{x^2-4}$$

$$= \frac{2(x+3)}{(x+2)\cancel{(x+5)}} \times \frac{\cancel{(x+5)}\cancel{(x-2)}}{(x+2)\cancel{(x-2)}}$$

$$= \frac{2(x+3)}{(x+2)^2}$$

b) $$\frac{a^2+5a-14}{a^2+8a+7} \div \frac{a^2-4a+4}{3a^2-6a}$$

$$= \frac{a^2+5a-14}{a^2+8a+7} \times \frac{3a^2-6a}{a^2-4a+4}$$

$$= \frac{\cancel{(a+7)}\cancel{(a-2)}}{\cancel{(a+7)}(a+1)} \times \frac{3a\cancel{(a-2)}}{\cancel{(a-2)}\cancel{(a-2)}}$$

$$= \frac{3a}{a+1}$$

Example 3.

The kinetic energy, E, of an object is given by the formula: $E = \frac{1}{2}mv^2$, where m is its mass and v its velocity. Find the ratio of the kinetic energies of two racing cars if the ratio of their masses is 2 : 3 and the ratio of their velocities is 5 : 4.

Solution.

	Car 1	Car 2
Mass (units	$2x$	$3x$
Velocity (units)	$5y$	$4y$
Kinetic energy, E	$\frac{1}{2}(2x)(5y)^2$	$\frac{1}{2}(3x)(4y)^2$

$$\frac{E_1}{E_2} = \frac{\frac{1}{2}(2x)(5y)^2}{\frac{1}{2}(3x)(4y)^2}$$

$$= \frac{25}{24}$$

The ratio of their kinetic energies is 25 : 24.

EXERCISES 3-8

(A)

1. Simplify:

a) $\frac{8m^2}{3mn} \times \frac{6mn^2}{4m}$ b) $\frac{15a^2b}{28a^3} \times \frac{-21b^2}{10ab}$

c) $\frac{12xy^3}{25x^2y^2} \div \frac{18x^2y}{15xy^2}$ d) $\frac{35st}{-24s^2t^3} \times \frac{-42st^2}{56s^3t}$

e) $\frac{-52xy^2}{32xy} \div \frac{-39x^3y}{-48y^2}$ f) $\frac{63a^3bc^2}{40ab^2} \div \frac{27a^2bc^4}{-15ab^3c}$

2. If $x = 2k$ and $y = 3k$, express the following in terms of k:

a) $3x^2y$ b) $\frac{9x^3}{10y^2}$ c) $\frac{(4x^2y)^2}{3xy}$ d) $(5x^3y^2)(2xy^3)$

3. If $x = 5a$ and $y = \frac{1}{2b}$, express the following in terms of a and b:

a) $4xy^2$ b) $(3x^2y)(2xy)$ c) $\frac{12x^2y}{25y^2}$ d) $\frac{(2xy^2)^2}{5xy}$

4. Simplify:

a) $\frac{5(2x - y)}{-3xy^2} \times \frac{6x^3y}{x(2x - y)}$

b) $\frac{4m(m - 2n)}{7(m + 3n)} \times \frac{3(m + 3n)}{6m^2(2m - n)}$

c) $\frac{8a(2a + 5b)}{-6ab^2} \div \frac{-2(2a + 5b)}{a^2b(a - 3b)}$

d) $\frac{4(x^2 - 3y)}{25x(x + 2y)} \times \frac{15y(x + 2y)}{12(x^2 - 3y)}$

e) $\frac{6s(3s + 7)}{35(2s - t)} \div \frac{15s^2(3s + 7)}{-42(2s + t)}$

f) $\frac{4xy^2(8x - 3y)}{25x^3(5x^2 + 3y)} \times \frac{10x(5x^2 + 3y)}{2y(3y - 8x)}$

5. Simplify:

a) $\frac{4x^2 - 10}{x + 3y} \times \frac{2x^2 - 18y^2}{6x^2 - 15}$

b) $\frac{9a^2 - 16b^2}{4a^2 + 12ab} \div \frac{9a^2 - 12ab}{8a + 24b}$

c) $\frac{6mn^2}{6m - 9} \times \frac{2m - 3}{-18m^2n}$

d) $\frac{3x^2 - 6xy}{4x + 20y} \div \frac{9x^2 - 18xy}{3xy + 15y^2}$

e) $\frac{8mn}{m^2 - 4n^2} \div \frac{4n^2}{3(m - 2n)^2}$

f) $\frac{20ab - 4a^2}{3ab} \times \frac{6ab + 6a^2}{5ab - 25b^2}$

Ⓑ

6. Simplify:

   a) $\dfrac{a^2 + 4a - 21}{a^2 - 8a + 15} \div \dfrac{a^2 + 6a - 7}{a^2 - 4a - 5}$

   b) $\dfrac{x^2 + 11xy + 28y^2}{x^2 + 12xy + 32y^2} \div \dfrac{x^2 + 9xy + 14y^2}{x^2 + 6xy - 16y^2}$

   c) $\dfrac{x^2 - 16y^2}{x^2 - 2xy} \times \dfrac{x^2 - 4xy}{x^2 - 6xy + 8y^2} \div \dfrac{x^2 + 4xy}{x - 2y}$

   d) $\dfrac{3m^2 - 30mn + 48n^2}{m^2 + 3mn - 10n^2} \times \dfrac{m^2 + 8mn + 15n^2}{2m^2 - 128n^2}$

   e) $\dfrac{6s^3 - 13s^2t - 5st^2}{6s^2 - st - t^2} \times \dfrac{6s^2 + 5st - 4t^2}{8s^2 - 50t^2}$

   f) $\dfrac{9x^4 - 49x^2y^2}{18x^2 + 69xy + 60y^2} \div \dfrac{12x^2y + 19xy^2 - 21y^3}{12x^2 + 7xy - 12y^2}$

7. The resistance, R, of a wire to an electric current is given by the formula: $R = \dfrac{kl}{A}$, where k is a constant, l is the length, and A is the cross-sectional area of the wire. Find the ratio of the resistances of two wires of the same material having lengths in the ratio 3 : 8 and cross-sectional areas in the ratio 1 : 4.

8. Two cylinders have radii in the ratio 6 : 5 and heights in the ratio 7 : 9. Find the ratio of:

   a) their volumes; b) their surface areas.

9. In house construction, the safe load, m, in kilograms, on a floor joist l m long is given by the formula $m = \dfrac{4th^2}{l}$, where t is the thickness and h the height of the joist in centimetres. By what factor are these joists stronger than a 5 × 10 cm joist?

   a) 5 × 15 cm b) 5 × 20 cm

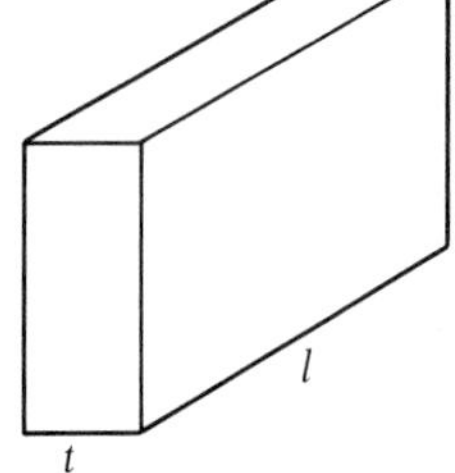

Ⓒ

10. For any triangle of side lengths a, b, and c, the radii of the inscribed circle and the circumcircle, r and R respectively, are given by the formulas:

$$r^2 = \frac{(-a + b + c)(a - b + c)(a + b - c)}{4(a + b + c)}$$

$$R^2 = \frac{a^2b^2c^2}{(a + b + c)(-a + b + c)(a - b + c)(a + b - c)}$$

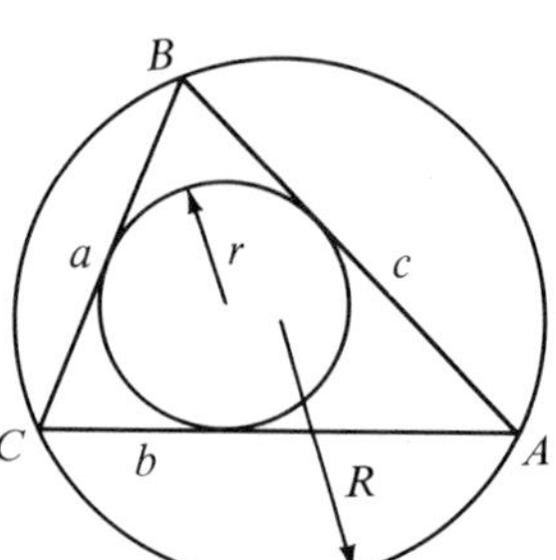

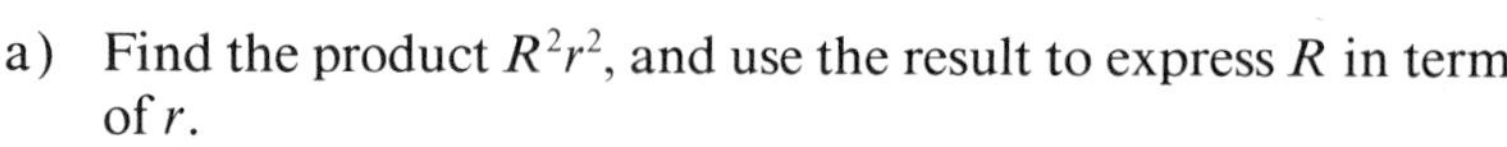

   a) Find the product R^2r^2, and use the result to express R in terms of r.

   b) Find expressions for R and r if $\angle B$ is 90°.

3-9 ADDING AND SUBTRACTING RATIONAL EXPRESSIONS

To add or subtract rational expressions it is necessary, as with rational numbers, to raise them to higher terms in order to obtain the lowest common denominator (l.c.d.).

Example 1.

Simplify: a) $\frac{1}{x^2} + \frac{5}{xy}$ b) $\frac{2}{5mn} - \frac{3n + m^2}{2m^2} + 3$

c) $\frac{x+5}{x-3} - \frac{x-2}{x+1}$

Solution.

a) The l.c.d. is x^2y.

$$\frac{1}{x^2} + \frac{5}{xy} = \frac{1}{x^2} \times \frac{y}{y} + \frac{5}{xy} \times \frac{x}{x}$$
$$= \frac{y}{x^2y} + \frac{5x}{x^2y}$$
$$= \frac{y + 5x}{x^2y}$$

b) The l.c.d. is $10m^2n$.

$$\frac{2}{5mn} - \frac{3n + m^2}{2m^2} + 3$$
$$= \frac{2}{5mn} \times \frac{2m}{2m} - \left(\frac{3n + m^2}{2m^2}\right) \times \frac{5n}{5n} + 3 \times \frac{10m^2n}{10m^2n}$$
$$= \frac{4m}{10m^2n} - \frac{(15n^2 + 5m^2n)}{10m^2n} + \frac{30m^2n}{10m^2n}$$
$$= \frac{4m - 15n^2 - 5m^2n + 30m^2n}{10m^2n}$$
$$= \frac{4m - 15n^2 + 25m^2n}{10m^2n}$$

c) The l.c.d. is $(x - 3)(x + 1)$.

$$\frac{x+5}{x-3} - \frac{x-2}{x+1} = \frac{x+5}{x-3} \times \frac{x+1}{x+1} - \frac{x-2}{x+1} \times \frac{x-3}{x-3}$$
$$= \frac{(x^2 + 6x + 5) - (x^2 - 5x + 6)}{(x-3)(x+1)}$$
$$= \frac{11x - 1}{(x-3)(x+1)}$$

Frequently, the denominators of rational expressions must be factored in order to determine the l.c.d.

Example 2.

Simplify: a) $\frac{1}{2x-6} - \frac{x}{x^2-9}$ b) $\frac{x+5}{x^2-2x-15} + \frac{5x-2}{x^2-5x}$

Solution.

a) $\frac{1}{2x-6} - \frac{x}{x^2-9}$

$= \frac{1}{2(x-3)} - \frac{x}{(x-3)(x+3)}$

$= \frac{1}{2(x-3)} \times \frac{x+3}{x+3} - \frac{x}{(x-3)(x+3)} \times \frac{2}{2}$

$= \frac{-x+3}{2(x-3)(x+3)}$

$= \frac{-(x-3)}{2(x-3)(x+3)}$

$= \frac{-1}{2(x+3)}$

b) $\frac{x+5}{x^2-2x-15} + \frac{5x-2}{x^2-5x}$

$= \frac{x+5}{(x-5)(x+3)} + \frac{5x-2}{x(x-5)}$

$= \frac{x+5}{(x-5)(x+3)} \times \frac{x}{x} + \frac{5x-2}{x(x-5)} \times \frac{x+3}{x+3}$

$= \frac{x^2+5x+5x^2+13x-6}{x(x-5)(x+3)}$

$= \frac{6x^2+18x-6}{x(x-5)(x+3)}$, or $\frac{6(x^2+3x-1)}{x(x-5)(x+3)}$

Real world problems often involve the addition or subtraction of rational expressions.

Example 3.

Water has an unusual property: at temperatures below 4°C, it expands as it cools. At 4°C, the density of water is 1 kg/L. If 1 kg of water, cooling from 4°C, increases in volume by x L, by how much does its density decrease?

$\text{Density} = \frac{\text{Mass}}{\text{Volume}}$

Solution.

At 4°C, volume of 1 kg of water: 1 L
density of 1 kg of water: 1 kg/L

At a lower temperature,
volume of 1 kg of water: $(1+x)$ L
density of 1 kg of water: $\frac{1}{(1+x)}$ kg/L

Temperature °C	Mass kg	Volume L	Density kg/L
4	1	1	1
<4	1	$1 + x$	$\frac{1}{1+x}$

Decrease in density, in kilograms per litre:

$$1 - \frac{1}{1+x} = \frac{1+x}{1+x} - \frac{1}{1+x}$$
$$= \frac{x}{1+x}$$

The decrease in density of 1 kg of water which increases in volume by x L is $\frac{x}{1+x}$ kg/L.

EXERCISES 3-9

1. Simplify:

a) $\frac{2}{x} + \frac{3}{y}$ b) $\frac{8}{x} - \frac{5}{x^2}$ c) $\frac{4}{x^2} + \frac{11}{xy}$

d) $\frac{7}{xy^2} - \frac{15}{x^2y}$ e) $\frac{12}{xy} - \frac{9}{yz}$ f) $\frac{6}{x^2} + \frac{19}{y^2}$

2. Simplify:

a) $\frac{5m}{n} - \frac{3n}{m}$ b) $\frac{17a}{bc} + \frac{5b}{ac}$ c) $\frac{8y}{x} + \frac{13x}{y^2}$

d) $\frac{2s}{t^2} - \frac{11s}{t}$ e) $\frac{15n^2}{m} + \frac{11n}{m^2}$ f) $\frac{23x}{y^2} - \frac{16y}{x}$

3. Simplify:

a) $\frac{3x}{y^2} + \frac{2x - 5y}{xy}$ b) $\frac{2a}{b^2} - \frac{6a + 11}{ab}$

c) $\frac{7x - 2y}{xy^2} - \frac{12x - 5y}{x^2y}$ d) $\frac{4a}{3b} + \frac{2a - 9b}{4a}$

e) $\frac{9s - 5t}{4t} + \frac{3t}{5s}$ f) $\frac{8x - 3y}{7x} - \frac{2x + 5y}{4y}$

4. Simplify:

a) $\frac{3x}{10y} + \frac{8x - 7}{4x}$ b) $\frac{5m + 9}{8m} - \frac{5m}{6n}$ c) $\frac{2a - 5}{4a} - \frac{7a + 2}{6b}$

d) $\frac{6x - 11y}{9x} + \frac{3x - 16y}{6y}$ e) $\frac{12m - 5n}{6m} - \frac{4m + 9n}{10n}$

5. Simplify:

a) $\frac{2}{3xy} + \frac{7x^2 - 4y}{5x^2} + 1$ b) $\frac{3a + b^2}{4b^2} - \frac{7}{5ab} - 2$

c) $\frac{9m}{7n^2} + \frac{3m^2 - 8n}{4mn^2} + \frac{5}{n}$ d) $\frac{2x + 3y^2}{8xy} - 3 - \frac{5x^2 - 2y}{6x^2}$

6. Simplify:

a) $\frac{5}{m+3}+\frac{7}{m+4}$ b) $\frac{2a}{3a-4}+\frac{7a}{5a-2}$ c) $\frac{9m}{3m-7}-\frac{2m}{5m-3}$

d) $\frac{x+3}{x+5}+\frac{x-2}{x+4}$ e) $\frac{5x+2}{3x-2}-\frac{3x-7}{2x+5}$ f) $\frac{2m+9}{5m-4}-\frac{3m+1}{2m-3}$

7. Simplify:

a) $\frac{7a}{2a-10}+\frac{4a}{3a-15}$ b) $\frac{9x}{x^2-4}-\frac{3}{x+2}$

c) $\frac{3x}{4x^2-10x}-\frac{x}{14x-35}$ d) $\frac{7m}{6m^2-15m}+\frac{12m}{4m^2-25}$

e) $\frac{2a}{a^2-6a+8}+\frac{7a}{a^2-a-12}$ f) $\frac{7x}{x^2-x-12}-\frac{4x}{x^2+2x-3}$

(B)

8. Simplify:

a) $\frac{x-3}{x^2-9x+20}+\frac{2x-1}{x^2-7x+12}$ b) $\frac{3x+2}{x^2-36}-\frac{x-4}{x^2-8x+12}$

c) $\frac{a-2}{a^2-4a-32}-\frac{a-1}{a^2-2a-48}$ d) $\frac{2m+5}{m^2-6m+5}+\frac{4m-3}{m^2-5m+4}$

e) $\frac{x-6}{x^2-11x+28}-\frac{x-5}{x^2-8x+7}$ f) $\frac{3a+2}{a^2+10a+21}+\frac{5a-4}{a^2-2a-15}$

9. The time, t, to travel a distance, d, at a constant speed, v, can be obtained from the formula: $d = vt$. If the speed is increased by x, find an expression to represent the decrease in time to travel the same distance.

10. The volume, v, in litres, of a sample of hydrogen chloride gas is given by the formula: $pv = 280$, where p is the pressure in kilopascals. If p is increased by x kPa, what is the corresponding decrease in volume?

11. The intensity of light, I, reaching a screen from a light source r m away is given by the formula: $I = \frac{k}{r^2}$, where k is a constant. Find an expression for the change in I when the light source is moved x m farther from the screen.

12. It is 160 km from Camden to Newport. How much time is saved on the trip by increasing an average speed of 80 km/h by x km/h?

(C)

13. What value of k makes each equation a true statement?

a) $\frac{5}{8m}-\frac{7m}{6}=\frac{k}{24m}$ b) $\frac{3}{x-5}-\frac{k}{x+2}=\frac{46-5x}{(x-5)(x+2)}$

c) $\frac{k}{8a}-\frac{5}{12a}=\frac{53}{24a}$ d) $\frac{2a+4}{2a-1}-\frac{k}{a+5}=\frac{21a+17}{(2a-1)(a+5)}$

3-10 APPLICATIONS OF RATIONAL EXPRESSIONS

Many problems in engineering and science involve rational expressions. The expressions are almost always simpler than those worked with earlier in the chapter.

Example 1.

A rectangular poster is to have an area of 6000 cm^2. If w, l, and P represent its width, length, and perimeter respectively, write an expression in terms of w for:

a) the length; b) the perimeter;

c) the change in length when the width is increased by 1 cm.

Solution.

a) $wl = 6000$

$$l = \frac{6000}{w}$$

b) $P = 2(l + w)$

$$= 2\left(\frac{6000}{w} + w\right)$$

$$= 2\left(\frac{6000 + w^2}{w}\right)$$

c) When w increases to $w + 1$, l decreases to $\frac{6000}{(w+1)}$.

Change in length: $\frac{6000}{w} - \frac{6000}{w+1} = \frac{6000w + 6000 - 6000w}{w(w+1)}$

$$= \frac{6000}{w(w+1)}$$

Example 2.

Car A leaves town travelling east at 80 km/h. Car B leaves 10 min later travelling at v km/h and overtakes car A after t hours.

a) Find the distance, in terms of v and t, that each car travels until B overtakes A.

b) Express t in terms of v and draw a graph.

c) How fast would car B have to travel to overtake car A in 30 min?

Solution.

Car	Distance km	Time h	Average speed km/h
A	$80\left(t + \frac{10}{60}\right)$	$t + \frac{10}{60}$	80
B	vt	t	v

a) At the moment of overtaking:
car B has travelled for t hours
and covered a distance of vt km;
car A has travelled for t hours + 10 min
and covered a distance of $80\left(t + \frac{10}{60}\right)$ km,
or $\left(80t + \frac{40}{3}\right)$ km.

b) Since both cars have covered the same distance:

$$vt = 80t + \frac{40}{3}$$

To solve for t we write: $vt - 80t = \frac{40}{3}$

$$t(v - 80) = \frac{40}{3}$$

$$t = \frac{40}{3(v - 80)}$$

v	t
85	2.67
90	1.33
95	0.89
100	0.67
105	0.53
110	0.44
115	0.38
120	0.33

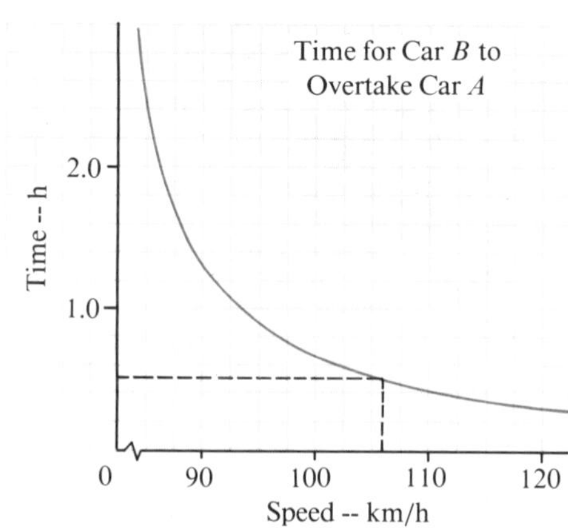

b) From the graph, $v \doteq 106$ km/h when $t = 30$ min. For a more accurate value, substitute $\frac{1}{2}$ for t in the equation above.

$$\frac{1}{2} = \frac{40}{3(v - 80)}$$

$$3v - 240 = 80$$

$$3v = 320$$

$$v = \frac{320}{3}, \text{ or approximately } 107$$

Car B would have to travel at approximately 107 km/h to overtake car A in 30 min.

EXERCISES 3-10

Ⓐ

1. In *Example 1*, express the change in the perimeter of the poster in terms of the width if the width is increased by 1 cm.
2. A rectangular board has an area of 6000 cm^2 and a width of w cm.
   a) Write an expression for the length of the board.
   b) If the width is increased by x cm, write an expression for:
      i) the decrease in length;
      ii) the change in perimeter.

3. In *Example 2*, assume that car B's speed is 100 km/h.
   a) How long will it take car B to overtake car A?
   b) By how much is the time to overtake lessened if car B's speed is increased by x km/h?
   c) Graph the relation formed in (b).
   d) Interpret the above results if $x < 0$.

4. Gordana starts out on a snowmobile trail and travels at 30 km/h. Heidi leaves 5 min later travelling at v km/h and overtakes Gordana after t hours.
   a) Express t in terms of v and draw the graph.
   b) How fast would Heidi have to travel to overtake Gordana in 20 min?

5. In *Example 2*, by how many minutes would the time for car B to overtake car A be shortened if car B's speed is increased by x km/h?

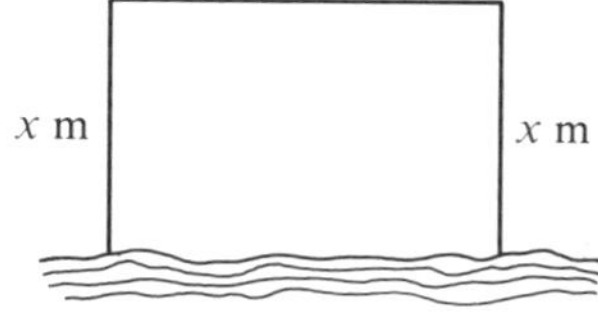

6. A rectangular lot with an area of 2000 m^2 is to be fenced on three sides, the fourth side being a stream. The sections of fence opposite each other are x m long.
   a) Express the total length of fencing, L, in terms of x and draw the graph.
   b) Use the graph to estimate the dimensions of the lot requiring the least amount of fencing.

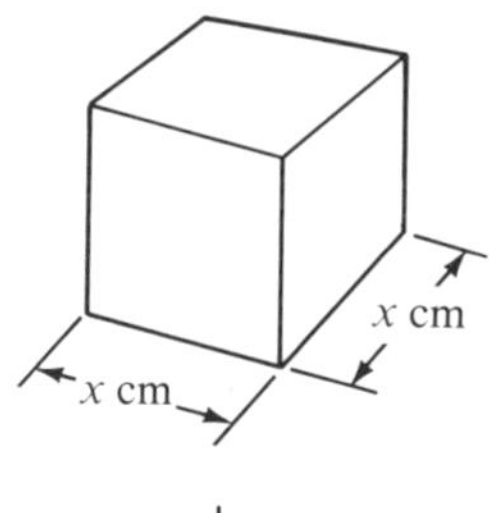

7. An open cardboard box with a square base with a side of x cm has a volume of 100 cm^3.
   a) Express in terms of x:
      i) the height of the box, h; ii) the area of cardboard, A.
   b) From a graph of A against x, estimate the dimensions of the box that has the least amount of cardboard.

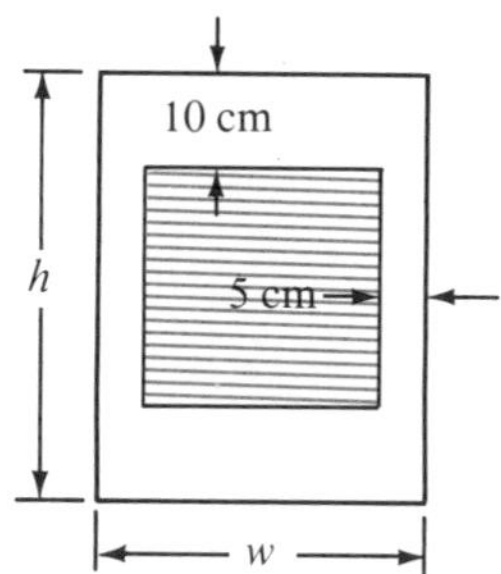

8. A poster is to have 400 cm^2 of printed matter with margins of 10 cm at the top and bottom and 5 cm at each side. The width, height, and area of the poster are w, h, and A respectively.
   a) Express h in terms of w.
   b) Express A in terms of w, and draw the graph.

9. When two resistances, r and s, are connected in parallel, their combined resistance, R, can be obtained from the formula: $\frac{1}{R} = \frac{1}{r} + \frac{1}{s}$. If r is increased by x units and s decreased by x units, what is the change in the combined resistance?

Ⓒ

10. A sailor falls overboard fom a ship in a convoy travelling at 10 km/h. 2 min later a ship travels back from the convoy at 20 km/h for the rescue. It takes 1 min to pick the sailor up and then the rescue ship returns at 20 km/h to the convoy which has continued on its way at a steady 10 km/h.
    a) How much time elapses from the sailor falling overboard to the ship rejoining the convoy?
    b) If the speed of the rescue ship is v, express the rescue time, t, in terms of v, and draw the graph for reasonable values of v.
    c) From the graph, find t when v is: i) 12 km/h; ii) 15 km/h.
    d) From the graph, find v when t is 6 min.

MATHEMATICS PROJECT

Investigating the Equation $x^n + y^n = z^n$

The equation $x^n + y^n = z^n$ is one of the most famous equations in mathematics. Solutions of the equations depend on the value of n.

When $n = 2$, the equation becomes $x^2 + y^2 = z^2$, and x, y, and z can represent the sides of a right triangle. Positive integers which satisfy the equation, such as 3, 4, 5, or 5, 12, 13, are called **Pythagorean triples**.

1. Find other examples of Pythagorean triples.

- When n is an integer greater than 2, the equation $x^n + y^n = z^n$ becomes the subject of a famous unsolved problem called *Fermat's Last Theorem*. Over three hundred years ago, the French mathematician Pierre de Fermat stated that the equation has no solution for $n > 2$. No proof of Fermat's theorem has ever been given, but neither has it ever been disproved, even with the aid of powerful computers.

- When $n = -1$, the equation becomes $x^{-1} + y^{-1} = z^{-1}$, or $\frac{1}{x} + \frac{1}{y} = \frac{1}{z}$
- When $n = \frac{1}{2}$, the equation becomes $x^{\frac{1}{2}} + y^{\frac{1}{2}} = z^{\frac{1}{2}}$, or $\sqrt{x} + \sqrt{y} = \sqrt{z}$

2. Can you find any positive integers x, y, z satisfying these equations?
3. Try to find integral solutions of $x^n + y^n = z^n$ for other values of n.
4. Write a report of your findings.

Review Exercises

1. Simplify:
   a) $9m^2 + 3mn - 4n^2 - 5m^2 - 14mn - 11n^2$
   b) $-5s^2 - 3st + 16t^2 + 9st - 3s^2 - 8t^2$
   c) $a^2 - 5b^2 + 3ab - 7b^2 - 8ab - 4a^2$
   d) $29m^2n^3 + 19m^2n^2 - 41mn^3 - 13n^2m^2 + 17mn^3 - 15m^2n^3$

2. Simplify:
   a) $(8ab)(7a^2b^3)$ b) $(-9a^3b)(7ab^3)$ c) $(-13x^5y)(-12x^5y^4)$
   d) $(14m^3n^3)(-13nm^2)$ e) $(3x^2y)(8x^3y)$
   f) $(17s^6t^3)(-6s^5t^4)$ g) $(3xy^2z)^3(x^2y^3z)^2$

3. Simplify:
   a) $\dfrac{14x^3y^2}{35xy} \times \dfrac{39x^4y^3}{2x^3y^4}$ b) $\dfrac{-15ab^2}{75a^2b} \times \dfrac{50a^3b}{ab^4}$
   c) $\dfrac{(3x^2y)^2}{27x^3y} \times \dfrac{63xy^2}{(4xy)^3}$ d) $\dfrac{7abc}{63a^2bc} \times \dfrac{27a^3b^2c^3}{3ab^2c^2}$

4. Simplify:
   a) $(x + 2y)(x + 3y) + (2x + y)(3x + y)$
   b) $(a - 2b)(a + 3b) - (2a - b)(3a + b)$
   c) $(3m + 2n)^2 - 2(2m - n)^2$
   d) $(11x - 2y)(11x + 2y) + (2x - 11y)(11y + 2x)$

5. Factor:
   a) $2ax - ay + 4bx - 2by$ b) $6sm + 9tm - 4sn - 6tn$
   c) $18ax + 24x - 3ay - 4y$ d) $35x^2 - 20xy - 42x + 24y$

6. Factor:
   a) $4x^2 - 31x + 21$ b) $12w^2 - 29w + 15$
   c) $9x^2 + 12x + 4$ d) $24m^2 - 31m - 15$

7. Factor:
   a) $6m^2 - 7mn + 2n^2$ b) $4a^2 - ab - 3b^2$
   c) $15a^2 + 29ab - 14b^2$ d) $-2x^2 + 13x - 15$

8. Factor:
   a) $(3x + 4)^2 - (2x - 3)^2$ b) $81m^2 - (9m + 3)^2$
   c) $4x^2 + 20x + 25$ d) $9x^2 - 24x + 16$
   e) $a^2 - 2ab + b^2 + a - b$ f) $9x^2 - 25y^2 + 10y - 1$

9. For what values of the variable(s) are the following undefined?
   a) $\dfrac{x^2 + 10x + 11}{x^2 - 121}$ b) $\dfrac{m^2 + 8m + 12}{m^2 + 12m + 36}$
   c) $\dfrac{4s^2 + st + t^2}{10st + 15t}$ d) $\dfrac{2a^2 + 5ab - 3b^2}{9a^2 - 25b^2}$
   e) $\dfrac{3cd^2}{6c^2 - cd - 12d^2}$ f) $\dfrac{r^2s + 3rs^2 + 2s^3}{12r^3 - 7r^2s - 12rs^2}$

10. Simplify:

a) $\dfrac{x^2 - 25}{2x^2 - 6x} \times \dfrac{x^2 - 7x + 12}{x^2 + x - 20}$

b) $\dfrac{6m^2 - 18mn}{m^2 - 5mn + 6n^2} \times \dfrac{m^2 + 2mn - 8n^2}{8m^2 + 32mn}$

c) $\dfrac{2a^2 + 7ab + 3b^2}{3a^2 + 13ab + 12b^2} \div \dfrac{4a^2 + 4ab + b^2}{3a^2 - 2ab - 8b^2}$

d) $\dfrac{x^4y^2 - x^2y^4}{x^2 + 2xy + y^2} \div \dfrac{(x - y)^2}{3x^2 + 3xy}$

11. Simplify:

a) $\dfrac{8m - 5}{m^2} + \dfrac{7}{mn}$

b) $\dfrac{9x^2 + 4x}{xy^2} - \dfrac{3}{xy}$

c) $\dfrac{5s^2}{t^2} - \dfrac{2s - 9}{s^2t}$

d) $\dfrac{6m - 2}{5m} - \dfrac{3m}{2n}$

e) $\dfrac{5x}{3y} - \dfrac{8x + 2y}{7x}$

f) $\dfrac{2m + 11n}{5m} - \dfrac{6m - 9n}{3n}$

12. Simplify:

a) $\dfrac{3}{x - y} - \dfrac{2x}{x^2 - y^2}$

b) $\dfrac{x^2 + 3x + 2}{x^2 - 1} - \dfrac{2x}{x + 1}$

c) $\dfrac{5x^2 - 10x}{x^2 - 4} - \dfrac{x^2 + 4x + 4}{(x + 2)(x - 3)}$

d) $\dfrac{x^2 + 4x + 3}{x^2 + 5x + 4} - \dfrac{x^2 - 9}{x^2 - 6x + 9}$

e) $\dfrac{x^2 - 49}{x^2 - 8x + 7} - \dfrac{2x - 2}{x^2 - 1}$

f) $\dfrac{2a + 4}{a^2 - 4} - \dfrac{3a - 2}{a - 2}$

13. When two thin lenses with focal lengths a and b are in contact, the focal length, F, of the combination can be obtained from the formula: $\frac{1}{F} = \frac{1}{a} + \frac{1}{b}$. The focal length of a combination of two identical lenses is 50 mm. If one lens is replaced by another having a focal length x mm less than the one it replaces, by how much does the focal length of the combination change?

4 Quadratic Equations

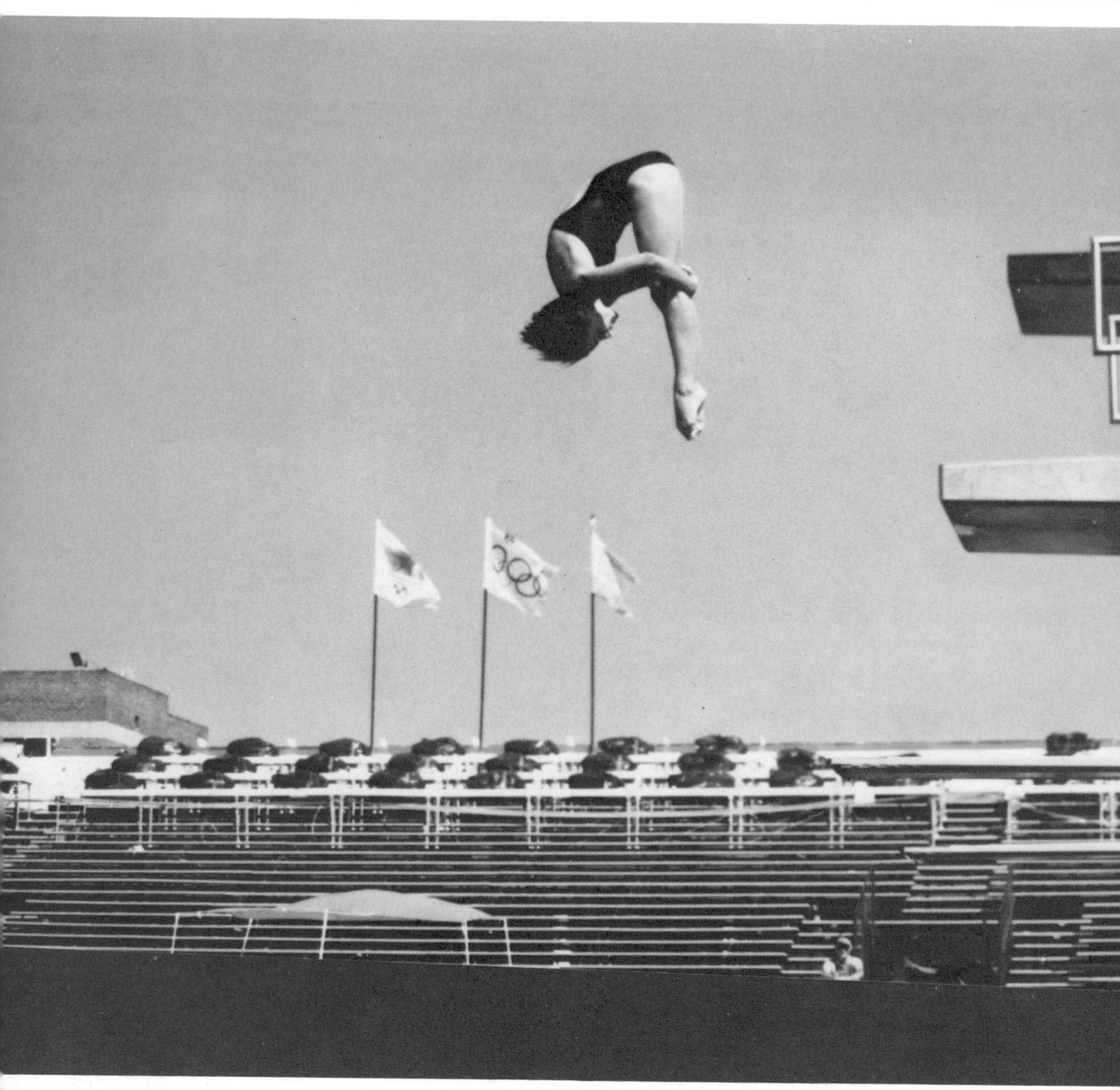

In the 1984 Summer Olympics, the Canadian diver, Sylvie Bernier, won a gold medal in springboard diving. After she leaves the board, how long does it take her to reach the water? (See *Example 3* in Section 4-5.)

4-1 QUADRATIC EQUATIONS

Daring divers in Acapulco, Mexico, dive into the sea from high on the cliffs. The time, t, it takes them to reach the water is given by an equation such as:

$$4.9t^2 - t - 35 = 0$$

This is an example of a **quadratic equation.**

> An equation that can be written in the form
> $$ax^2 + bx + c = 0, \text{ where } a \neq 0,$$
> is called a **quadratic equation.**

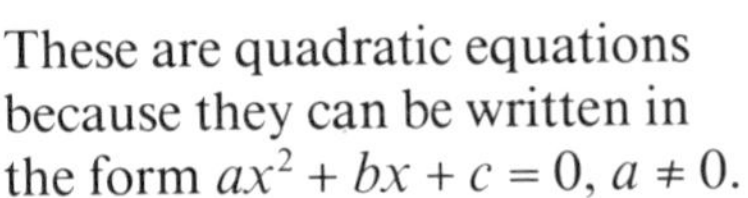

These are quadratic equations because they can be written in the form $ax^2 + bx + c = 0$, $a \neq 0$.

$$\begin{cases} (x-5)(x+2) = 0 \\ 1 + \sqrt{3}x - x^2 = 0 \\ 9y - 0.6y^2 = 0 \\ 5x^2 - 4 = 41 \end{cases}$$

These are *not* quadratic equations because they cannot be written in the form $ax^2 + bx + c = 0$, $a \neq 0$.

$$\begin{cases} 2x - 3 = 6x + 9 \\ x^3 + 2x^2 - 3x - 6 = 0 \\ (x+1)(x-4)(x+2) = 0 \end{cases}$$

The terms of a quadratic equation are named as follows:

$$ax^2 + bx + c = 0$$

quadratic term	linear term	constant term

In the equation $5x^2 - 4 = 41$, there is no linear term. Such an equation is solved by reducing it to the form $x^2 = c$, then taking the square root of both sides. Two solutions are obtained:

$$x = \sqrt{c} \quad \text{and} \quad x = -\sqrt{c}, \ c > 0.$$

Example 1.

Solve:

a) $5x^2 - 4 = 41$

b) $19 - 3x^2 = 4$

c) $x^2 + 12 = 3$

d) $ax^2 + b = c \quad (a \neq 0)$

Solution.

a) $5x^2 - 4 = 41$
$5x^2 = 45$
$x^2 = 9$
$x = \pm 3$

b) $19 - 3x^2 = 4$
$15 = 3x^2$
$5 = x^2$
$x = \pm\sqrt{5}$

c) $x^2 + 12 = 3$
$x^2 = -9$

There is no solution in the set of real numbers.

d) $ax^2 + b = c$
$ax^2 = c - b$
$x^2 = \frac{c-b}{a}$
$x = \pm\sqrt{\frac{c-b}{a}}, \quad \frac{c-b}{a} \geqslant 0$

The solutions of many problems involve quadratic equations without a linear term.

Example 2.

The distance, d, in metres, that an object falls from rest in t seconds is given by the formula $d = 4.9t^2$.

a) How far does an object fall from rest in 3 s?
b) How long does it take an object to fall 200 m?

Solution.

a) Substitute 3 for t in the formula: $d = 4.9 \times 3^2$
$= 44.1$
In 3 s, an object will fall about 44 m.

b) Substitute 200 for d in the formula: $200 = 4.9 \times t^2$
$t = \pm\sqrt{\frac{200}{4.9}}$
$\doteq \pm 6.4$
Since $t > 0$, the negative root is rejected. It takes about 6.4 s to fall 200 m.

EXERCISES 4-1

(A)

1. Solve.
 a) $m^2 - 5 = 11$ b) $4x^2 - 9 = 0$ c) $2a^2 + 1 = 51$
 d) $3s^2 + 29 = 2$ e) $74 - 5t^2 = -6$ f) $9c^2 - 17 = 32$
2. Find the length of the side of a square if its area is:
 a) $12\ cm^2$; b) $32\ m^2$; c) $1.5\ km^2$.
3. Use the formula in *Example 2* to determine:
 a) how far an object falls in 5.2 s;
 b) how long it takes an object to fall 500 m.

(B)

4. Solve and check:
 a) $2x^2 + 3 = 7$ b) $5a^2 - 8 = 42$
 c) $6(s^2 + 6) = 5 - 2s^2$ d) $15(m^2 - 4) = 4(m^2 + 7)$
 e) $4(x^2 + 3) - 28 = 2(x^2 - 5)$ f) $7(2a^2 - 9) = 3(a^2 + 5) - 1$

5. Solve:
   a) $(x + 1)(2x + 4) = (x + 2)(x + 4)$
   b) $(x + 4)(2x + 1) = (x + 5)(x + 4)$
   c) $(x + 2)(4x + 1) = (x + 3)(2x + 3)$
   d) $(2x - 3)(x - 5) = (x - 6)(x - 7)$
   e) $(2x + 1)(x + 7) = (x + 7)(x + 8)$
   f) $(2x + 7)(2x - 5) = (2x - 8)(x + 6)$
6. The maximum distance a lighthouse beam can be seen, d, in kilometres, is given by the formula $d^2 = 13h$, where h is the height of the light, in metres, above water level.
   a) Calculate the maximum distance of visibility for a height of:
      i) 50 m; ii) 100 m.
   b) Calculate the height required for a maximum distance of visibility of:
      i) 30 km; ii) 60 km.
7. Solve for the variable(s) indicated:
   a) $a^2 + b^2 = c^2$ a, b, c
   b) $v^2 = u^2 + 2as$ v, u
   c) $A = \pi r^2$ r
   d) $V = \pi r^2 h$ r
8. Calculate the radius of a circle that has an area of:
   a) 100 cm^2; b) 1.5 m^2; c) $9\pi \text{ km}^2$.
9. The surface area, A, of a ball of radius r is given by the formula $A = 4\pi r^2$.
   a) Find the surface area of a ball of radius:
      i) 4 cm; ii) 12.5 cm.
   b) Find the radius of a ball that has a surface area of:
      i) 296 cm^2; ii) 1348 cm^2.
10. The volume, V, of a cone is given by the formula $V = \frac{1}{3}\pi r^2 h$.

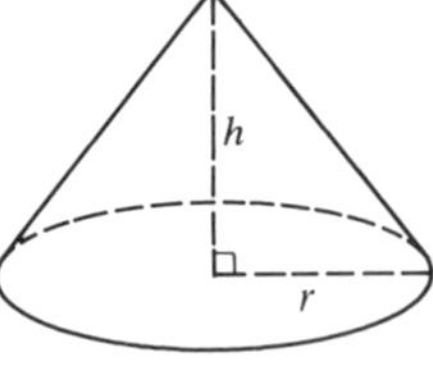

   a) Find the volume of a cone with radius 15 m and height 12 m.
   b) Solve the formula for r.
   c) What is the radius of a conical pile of sand with volume $425\ 000 \text{ m}^3$ and height:
      i) 45 m? ii) 60 m?
11. Mario, the manager of Paisano Pizza, determines the approximate selling price, C, in dollars, of a basic pizza by the formula $C = \frac{d^2 + 337.5}{275}$, where d is the diameter in centimetres.
   a) Solve the formula for d.
   b) What is the diameter of a pizza that costs:
      i) \$3.50? ii) \$4.50?
   c) How much should Mario charge for a pizza 40 cm in diameter?

12. The kinetic energy, E, in joules, of a mass of m kilograms moving with a velocity of v metres per second is given by the formula $E = \frac{1}{2}mv^2$.
    a) Calculate the kinetic energy of a 2000 kg car travelling at:
        i) 50 km/h; ii) 100 km/h.
    b) Calculate the velocity of a 2000 kg car when its kinetic energy is:
        i) 10^2 kJ; ii) 10^3 kJ.

Ⓒ

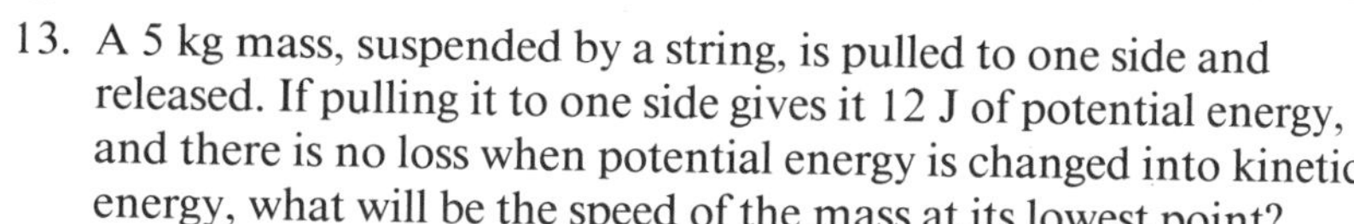

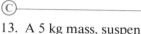

13. A 5 kg mass, suspended by a string, is pulled to one side and released. If pulling it to one side gives it 12 J of potential energy, and there is no loss when potential energy is changed into kinetic energy, what will be the speed of the mass at its lowest point?

14. The diagram shows a storage shed being constructed from equilateral triangles. The area, A, of an equilateral triangle with sides of length x is given by the formula $A = \frac{\sqrt{3}}{4}x^2$.

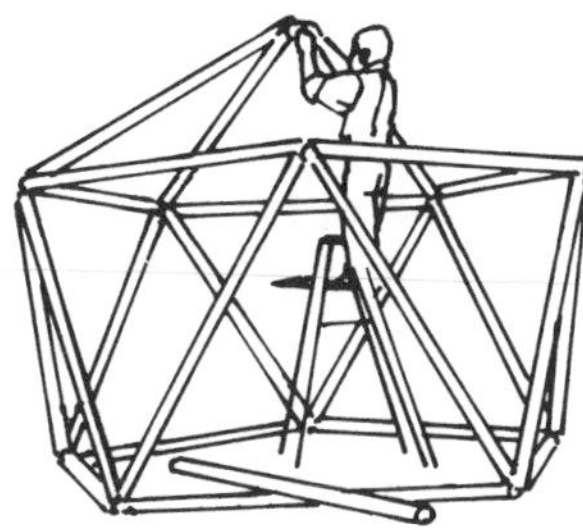

    a) How many equilateral triangles will there be in the finished shed?
    b) If the sides of each triangle are 2.5 m long, find the total outside area of the shed.
    c) How long should the sides of each triangle be for the shed to have an outside area of 100 m^2?

4-2 SOLVING QUADRATIC EQUATIONS BY GRAPHING

Quadratic equations with a linear term, such as $4x^2 - 12x - 7 = 0$, first appeared in problems which were studied by the ancient Babylonians and Egyptians about 2000 B.C. Since then, various techniques have been developed to solve such equations.

About 350 years ago, the French mathematician, René Descartes, introduced the idea of plotting points on a grid. When a quadratic expression is plotted on a grid, the expression equals zero where its graph crosses the x-axis. Solving a quadratic equation is finding those values of x.

Example 1.

Solve by graphing: $4x^2 - 12x - 7 = 0$.

Solution

Let $y = 4x^2 - 12x - 7$. Make a table of values for various values of x, plot the ordered pairs (x, y) on a grid, and draw a smooth curve through them.

x	y
−2	33
−1	9
0	−7
1	−15
2	−15
3	− 7
4	9
5	33

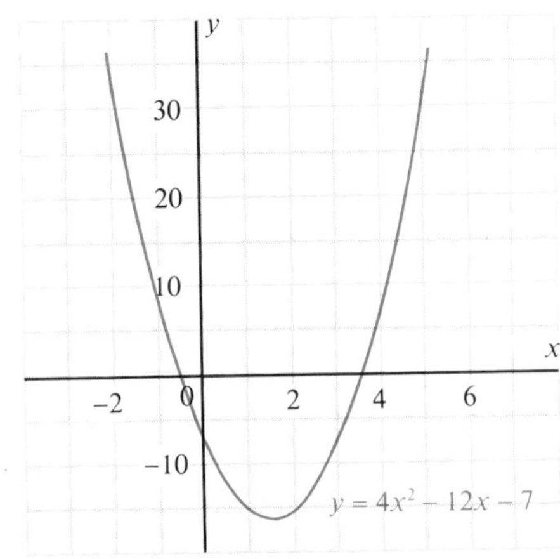

This curve is called a **parabola**. Parabolas occur when a ball is thrown, bounced, or hit, and have properties used in the design of telescopes, antennas, and solar furnaces.

The expression is equal to 0 where the graph crosses the x-axis. The roots of the equation $4x^2 - 12x - 7 = 0$ are about −0.5 and 3.5.

Check.

When $x = -0.5$,

$$\text{L.S.} = 4(-0.5)^2 - 12(-0.5) - 7 = 1 + 6 - 7, \text{ or } 0 \qquad \text{R.S.} = 0$$

When $x = 3.5$,

$$\text{L.S.} = 4(3.5)^2 - 12(3.5) - 7 = 49 - 42 - 7 \text{ or } 0 \qquad \text{R.S.} = 0$$

The roots −0.5 and 3.5 are correct.

The equation in *Example 1* has two different roots. But not all quadratic equations have two different roots.

Example 2.

Solve graphically:

a) $4x^2 - 12x + 9 = 0$ b) $4x^2 - 12x + 25 = 0$

Solution

The tables of values and graphs for each equation are shown below:

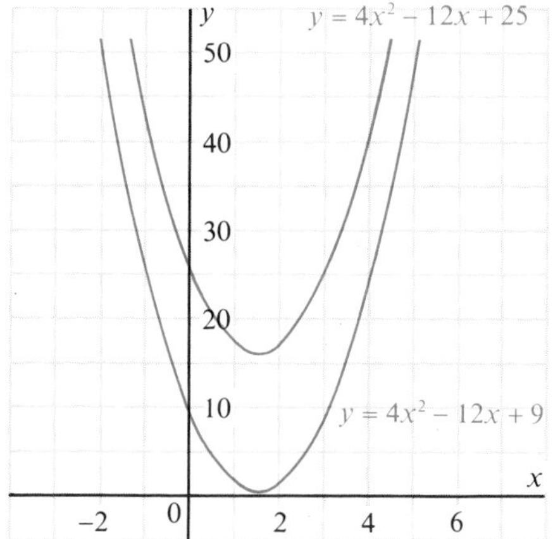

a)

x	y
−2	49
−1	25
0	9
1	1
2	1
3	9
4	25
5	49

b)

x	y
−2	65
−1	41
0	25
1	17
2	17
3	25
4	41
5	65

a) $4x^2 - 12x + 9 = 0$ has two equal roots, 1.5.
Check L.S. $= 4(1.5)^2 - 12x + 9$ R.S. $= 0$
$= 9 - 18 + 9$, or 0

b) $4x^2 - 12x + 25 = 0$ has no solution in the set of real numbers.

The exact values of roots of quadratic equations can seldom be read from a graph, though they can be estimated. The two preceding mples suggest that a quadratic equation may have two different ts, two equal roots, or, in the set of real numbers, no roots.

RCISES 4-2

rom the graph, estimate the roots of the equation it represents:

ı)

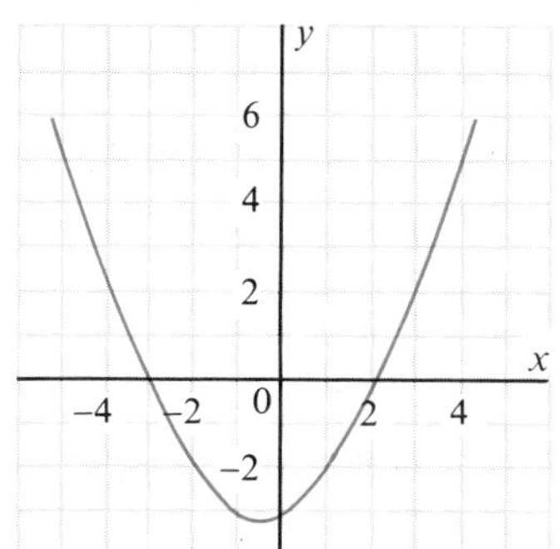

b)

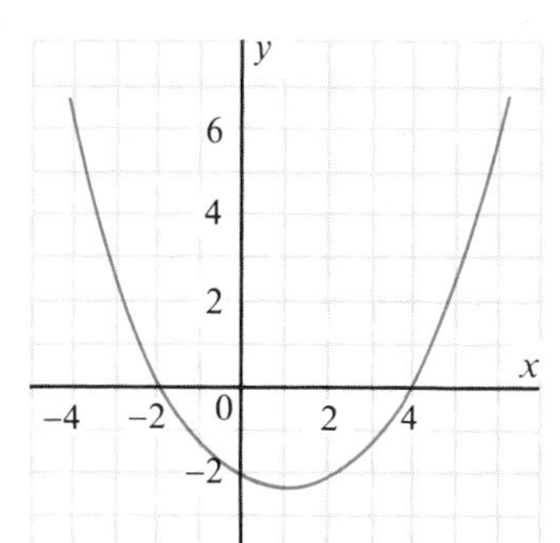

c)

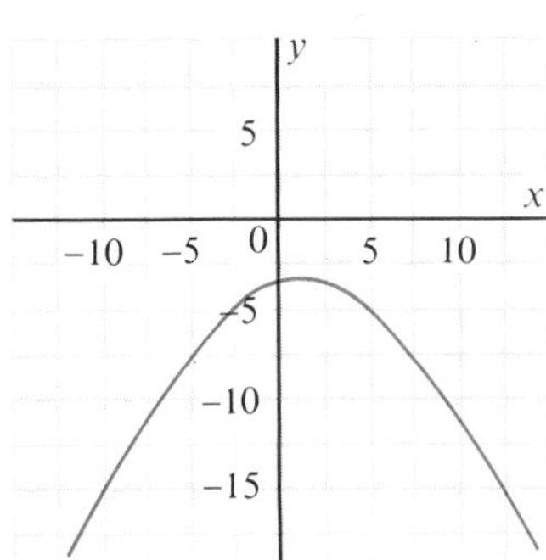

d)

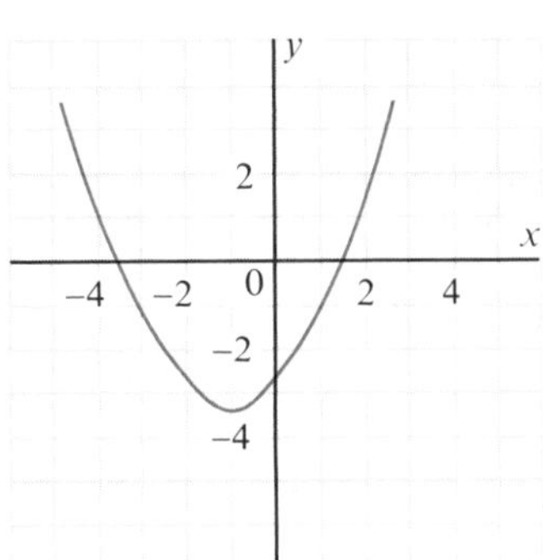

2. Solve graphically:
   a) $2x^2 - 13x + 20 = 0$
   b) $4x^2 + 16x - 9 = 0$
   c) $4x^2 + 8x + 3 = 0$
   d) $6x^2 + x - 15 = 0$
   e) $4x^2 - 20x + 25 = 0$
   f) $6x^2 - 5x + 2 = 0$

(B)

3. Solve graphically:
   a) $6x^2 - 5x - 6 = 0$
   b) $6x^2 + 5x - 21 = 0$
   c) $4x^2 + 8x - 45 = 0$
   d) $x^2 + 4x - 3 = 0$
   e) $8x^2 + 22x + 9 = 0$
   f) $x^2 - 8x + 13 = 0$
4. Solve graphically and check:
   a) $2x^2 - 7x + 3 = 0$
   b) $4x^2 + 4x - 15 = 0$
   c) $3x^2 - 2x + 2 = 0$
   d) $2x^2 + 15x + 28 = 0$
   e) $4x^2 + 28x + 49 = 0$
   f) $4x^2 - 4x - 3 = 0$
5. If $4x^2 - 20x + 25 = 0$ has two equal roots, which of the following has two different roots? no roots?
   a) $4x^2 - 20x + 30 = 0$
   b) $4x^2 - 20x + 20 = 0$

(C)

6. x_1 and x_2 are the roots of $x^2 - 8x + 13 = 0$, and x_3 and x_4 are the roots of $x^2 - 8x + 10 = 0$. If $x_1 < x_2$ and $x_3 < x_4$, which of the following statements is true?
   a) $x_1 < x_2 < x_3 < x_4$
   b) $x_1 < x_3 < x_2 < x_4$
   c) $x_3 < x_1 < x_2 < x_4$
   d) $x_1 < x_3 < x_4 < x_2$
7. If $x^2 - 8x + 13 = 0$ has roots x_1 and x_2, and $x_1 < x_2$, for what range of values of k will $x^2 - 8x + k = 0$ have roots x_3 and x_4, $x_3 < x_4$, such that:
   a) $x_3 < x_1 < x_2 < x_4$
   b) $x_1 < x_3 < x_4 < x_2$

Solving Quadratic Equations With Calculators or Computers

Quadratic equations can be solved in many different ways. The methods suggested here are simple in concept but involve a considerable amount of arithmetic. They are therefore appropriate for calculators or computers. Consider the equation:

$$x^2 + 3x - 15 = 0$$

Solving by Systematic Trial

$x^2 + 3x - 15 = 0$ can be written: $x(x + 3) = 15$. Find a value of x that, when substituted in $x(x + 3)$, gives a result as close to 15 as possible. Since $2(2 + 3) = 10$, and $3(3 + 3) = 18$, there must be a root between 2 and 3.

Try 2.6: $(2.6)(2.6 + 3) = 14.56$ 2.6 is too small.
Try 2.7: $(2.7)(2.7 + 3) = 15.39$ 2.7 is too great.

Therefore, the root is between 2.6 and 2.7. By trying numbers between 2.6 and 2.7, we can find the root to as many decimal places as desired.

Solving by Using an Expression for x

$x^2 + 3x - 15 = 0$ can be written: $x(x + 3) = 15$

$$x = \frac{15}{x + 3}$$

Now, by systematic trial, try to find a value of x such that both sides of this equation are equal.

Try 2.6: $\frac{15}{2.6 + 3} \doteq 2.679$ 2.6 is too small.

Try 2.7: $\frac{15}{2.7 + 3} \doteq 2.632$ 2.7 is too great.

This shows that the root is between 2.6 and 2.7, and we can find the root as accurately as desired by continuing the process.

1. Find the other root of $x^2 + 3x - 15 = 0$ correct to three decimal places by either of the above methods.
2. Find another way of rearranging $x^2 + 3x - 15 = 0$ so that x is equal to an expression containing x. Then find the roots to three decimal places, as before.
3. Write a report outlining the advantages and disadvantages of these methods for solving quadratic equations.

4-3 SOLVING QUADRATIC EQUATIONS BY FACTORING

Solving quadratic equations by graphing is time-consuming and does not always give exact roots. It is therefore important to develop algebraic methods of solving them.

Some quadratic equations can be solved by factoring. This method depends on the following important property of real numbers:

> If $A \cdot B = 0$, then $A = 0$, or $B = 0$, or both.

Example 1.

Solve and check:

a) $x^2 - 3x + 2 = 0$

b) $4x^2 + 12y + 9 = 0$

Solution.

a)
$$x^2 - 3x + 2 = 0$$
$$(x - 1)(x - 2) = 0$$
Either $x - 1 = 0$
or $x - 2 = 0$
That is, $x = 1$ or $x = 2$

b)
$$4y^2 + 12y + 9 = 0$$
$$(2y + 3)(2y + 3) = 0$$
That is, $2y + 3 = 0$
$$y = -\frac{3}{2}$$

Check.

If $x = 1$,
$x^2 - 3x + 2$
$= 1 - 3 + 2$
$= 0$

If $x = 2$,
$x^2 - 3x + 2$
$= 4 - 6 + 2$
$= 0$

Both solutions are correct.

If $y = -\frac{3}{2}$,
$4y^2 + 12y + 9$
$= 4\left(\frac{9}{4}\right) + 12\left(-\frac{3}{2}\right) + 9$
$= 9 - 18 + 9$, or 0
The solution is correct.

When a quadratic expression has two equal factors, as in *Example 1b*, it is customary to say that the corresponding quadratic equation has *two equal roots*.

Example 2.

Solve:

a) $3x(x - 4) = 2(x + 1) + 3$

b) $2a + \frac{5}{2} = \frac{3}{a}$

Solution.

a) $3x(x - 4) = 2(x + 1) + 3$
$3x^2 - 12x = 2x + 5$
$3x^2 - 14x - 5 = 0$
$(3x + 1)(x - 5) = 0$
Either $3x + 1 = 0$ or $x - 5 = 0$
$x = -\frac{1}{3}$ or $x = 5$

The roots of the equation are $-\frac{1}{3}$ and 5.

b) $2a + \frac{5}{2} = \frac{3}{a}$

Multiply both sides by $2a$. $a \neq 0$.

$4a^2 + 5a = 6$

$4a^2 + 5a - 6 = 0$

$(4a - 3)(a + 2) = 0$

Either $4a - 3 = 0$ or $a + 2 = 0$

$a = \frac{3}{4}$ or $a = -2$

The roots of the equation are $\frac{3}{4}$ and -2.

Example 3.

A rectangle, 3 cm longer than it is wide, has a diagonal 15 cm long. Find the dimensions of the rectangle.

Solution.

Let the width of the rectangle be x and its length $x + 3$. By the Pythagorean theorem:

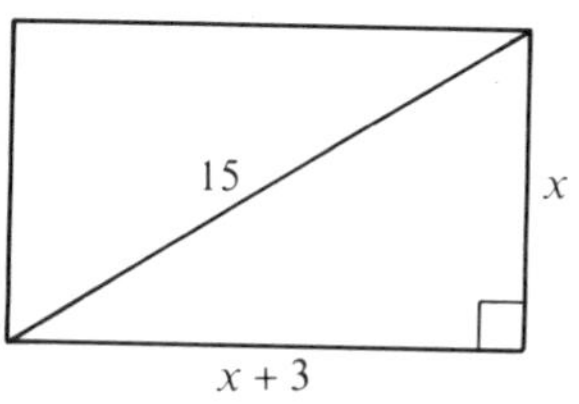

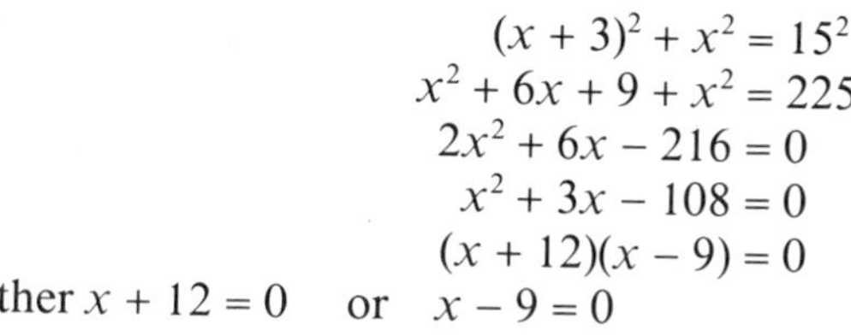

$$(x + 3)^2 + x^2 = 15^2$$
$$x^2 + 6x + 9 + x^2 = 225$$
$$2x^2 + 6x - 216 = 0$$
$$x^2 + 3x - 108 = 0$$
$$(x + 12)(x - 9) = 0$$

Either $x + 12 = 0$ or $x - 9 = 0$

$x = -12$ or $x = 9$

Since the dimensions cannot be negative, the only admissible solution is $x = 9$. The dimensions of the rectangle are 9 cm by $(9 + 3)$ cm, or 12 cm.

If the roots of a quadratic equation are known, the equation can always be formed. This is a result of the following property of real numbers:

If $A = 0$, or $B = 0$, then $A \cdot B = 0$.

Example 4.

Write a quadratic equation with roots:

a) 3 and -7;

b) $\frac{3}{4}$ and $-\frac{2}{3}$.

Solution.

a) If $x = 3$, $x - 3 = 0$. If $x = -7$, $x + 7 = 0$

A quadratic equation with roots 3 and -7 is:

$$(x - 3)(x + 7) = 0$$
$$x^2 + 4x - 21 = 0$$

b) If $x = \frac{3}{4}$, $x - \frac{3}{4} = 0$. If $x = -\frac{2}{3}$, $x + \frac{2}{3} = 0$

$4x - 3 = 0$ $\qquad$ $3x + 2 = 0$

A quadratic equation with roots $\frac{3}{4}$ and $-\frac{2}{3}$ is:

$$(4x - 3)(3x + 2) = 0$$
$$12x^2 - x - 6 = 0$$

EXERCISES 4-3

(A)

1. Solve:
   a) $x^2 - 4x + 3 = 0$
   b) $y^2 + 8y + 15 = 0$
   c) $m^2 - m - 56 = 0$
   d) $2a^2 + a - 15 = 0$
   e) $x^2 - 64 = 0$
   f) $9m^2 - 12m + 4 = 0$
2. Solve and check:
   a) $x^2 + 3x - 10 = 0$
   b) $m^2 - 12m + 35 = 0$
   c) $a^2 - 5a - 6 = 0$
   d) $y^2 - 11y = 0$
   e) $4c^2 - 49 = 0$
   f) $2x^2 - 7x - 15 = 0$
3. Solve:
   a) $y^2 - 10y = 2y - 36$
   b) $m^2 + 8m = 3m + 24$
   c) $x(x - 6) = 2(x - 8)$
   d) $a(a - 9) = 2(a - 14)$
   e) $3c(c - 3) = c(c - 2) + 15$
   f) $6x(x + 3) + 5 = 2(x^2 - x - 10)$
4. Write a quadratic equation with roots:
   a) $5, -2$;
   b) $3, 3$;
   c) $4, -3$;
   d) $-\frac{7}{3}, \frac{3}{4}$;
   e) $-7, 7$;
   f) $\frac{1}{6}, \frac{5}{8}$.

(B)

5. Solve:
   a) $5x^2 - x - 18 = 0$
   b) $6z^2 - 5z - 4 = 0$
   c) $3y^2 + 15y - 18 = 0$
   d) $6x^2 + 17x - 14 = 0$
   e) $2t^2 - 24t + 72 = 0$
   f) $25m^2 - 36 = 0$
6. Solve:
   a) $2m(m + 3) = 5(3 + m)$
   b) $3v(v + 2) = 2(v^2 - 4)$
   c) $x(x + 3) = -2(3x + 10)$
   d) $3a(a - 4) - 5 = 2(a - 3) - 7$
   e) $(2x - 1)(x - 3) = (x + 1)(x - 2)$
   f) $3(x - 2)(x + 2) + 5x = 2x(x + 4) + 16$
7. Solve:
   a) $6x(x - 2) - 3 = 2(x - 2)(x + 2) - 4$
   b) $3(c - 1)^2 - 2 = (c - 4)(c + 1) + 7$
   c) $(2y + 1)(2y - 3) + 5 = (y + 8)(y - 5) + 48$
   d) $(2p - 1)^2 - 3 = (p - 2)(p - 1)$
   e) $2(x - 1)(x - 2) = (x - 5)(x + 4) + 5x$
   f) $(2x - 1)(x - 3) = (x + 2)(x + 3) - x(2x - 1) + 7$

8. Find two consecutive integers with a product: a) 56; b) 156.
9. What number and its square differ by: a) 20? b) 30?
10. The sum of the squares of two consecutive integers is 145. Find the integers.
11. The sum of the squares of three consecutive integers is 149. Find the integers.
12. The hypotenuse of a right triangle is 29 cm. If the other two sides differ by 1 cm, what are their lengths?
13. Show that, if k is any real number, the equation $x^2 + (k + 1)x + k = 0$ always has real roots. For what value of k are the roots equal?
14. Solve:

a) $x - \frac{7}{2} = \frac{2}{x}$ b) $3a - \frac{17}{5} = -\frac{4}{5a}$ c) $y + \frac{12}{5} = \frac{32}{5y}$

d) $m + \frac{7}{3} = \frac{2}{m}$ e) $2s - \frac{14}{3s} = -\frac{17}{3}$ f) $2x + \frac{27}{4x} = \frac{15}{2}$

Ⓒ

15. Find the ratio $x{:}y$.

a) $x^2 - 5xy + 6y^2 = 0$ b) $x^2 + 7xy + 12y^2 = 0$
c) $2x^2 + 9xy - 5y^2 = 0$ d) $6x^2 + 11xy - 10y^2 = 0$
e) $6x^2 - xy - 15y^2 = 0$ f) $8x^2 - 38xy + 35y^2 = 0$

16. If one root is 5, find the value of k and the other root:

a) $x^2 - 3x + k = 0$ b) $x^2 + kx + 40 = 0$
c) $x^2 + kx + 25 = 0$ d) $2x^2 - 13x + k = 0$

17. Solve for x:

a) $x^2 + a = 0$ b) $x^2 - ax = 0$ c) $ax^2 - b = 0$
d) $\frac{a}{x} + bx = 0$ e) $x^2 - (a + b)x + ab = 0$

18. Solve:

a) $x^4 - 16 = 0$ b) $x^4 - 10x^2 + 9 = 0$
c) $x^3 - 4x = 0$ d) $2x^3 - x^2 - 15x = 0$
e) $4a^4 - 20a^2 + 16 = 0$ f) $8a^5 - 74a^3 + 18a = 0$

19. The product of the squares of two consecutive integers is 17 424. Find the integers.
20. Solve for x:

a) $x^2 + ax = ab + bx$ b) $2x^2 - 4bx = ax - 2ab$
c) $x^2 - 2pq = p^2 + q^2$ d) $x^2 - 3ax + 2a^2 = ab + b^2$

Solving Quadratic Equations

When quadratic equations are difficult or impossible to solve by factoring, a computer can be programmed to solve them. The technique is essentially *systematic trial*, an approach well-suited to the computer.

The following program directs the computer to display a table of values for the expression $Ax^2 + Bx + C$. Input the coefficients A, B, and C and an estimated initial and final value for x. Where the value of the expression changes sign, a root occurs. By refining the initial and final values, the root can be found to any desired degree of accuracy. The other root can be found by estimating a new interval for x.

```
100 REM *** QUADRATIC EQUATIONS ***
110 INPUT "WHAT ARE THE COEFFICIENTS? ";A,B,C
120 INPUT "WHAT IS THE INITIAL VALUE OF X? ";X1
130 INPUT "WHAT IS THE FINAL VALUE OF X? ";X2
140 PRINT:PRINT "X", "EXPRESSION":PRINT
150 FOR X=X1 TO X2 STEP (X2-X1)/10
160 PRINT X,(A*X+B)*X+C
170 NEXT X:PRINT
180 PRINT:INPUT "PRESS S TO STOP, RETURN TO REPEAT ";Y$
190 PRINT:IF Y$<>"S" THEN 120:END
```

When the program was used to solve $2x^2 - 7x - 6 = 0$, this was the display:

```
RUN QUADRATIC EQUATIONS

WHAT ARE THE COEFFICIENTS? 2, -7, -6
WHAT IS THE INITIAL VALUE OF X? 3
WHAT IS THE FINAL VALUE OF X? 5

X              EXPRESSION

3              -9
3.2            -7.92
3.4            --6.68
3.6            -5.28
3.8            -3.71999999
4              -2
4.2            -.120000007
4.4            1.91999999
4.6            4.11999998
4.8            6.47999996
5              8.99999995

PRESS S TO STOP, RETURN TO REPEAT
```

For greater accuracy, the values for x_1 and x_2 could be changed to 4.2 and 4.22. Use the program to find another root between −2 and 0.

1. Solve:
   a) $10x^2 + 11x - 153 = 0$ b) $2x^2 - 9x + 3 = 0$
   c) $32x^2 - 60x - 27 = 0$ d) $x^2 - x - 1 = 0$
2. The sum of two numbers is 10. The square of one number is double the square of the other. Find the numbers.

4-4 SOLVING QUADRATIC EQUATIONS BY COMPLETING THE SQUARE

During the period A.D. 700 to A.D. 1100, Arab and Hindu mathematicians gradually developed formal rules for solving quadratic equations. These rules were often taught orally and in verse. The methods used were equivalent to the method developed in this section. It can be used to solve any quadratic equation, including those that cannot be solved by factoring, and it depends on recognizing the form of a trinomial which is a perfect square.

Example 1.

Which of the following trinomials are perfect squares?
a) $x^2 + 10x + 25$ b) $x^2 - 8x + 9$

Solution.

a) This trinomial is a perfect square, since:

$$x^2 + 10x + 25 = (x + 5)^2$$

The constant term, 25, is the square of $\frac{1}{2}(10)$.

b) This trinomial is not a perfect square since the constant term, 9, is not the square of $\frac{1}{2}(-8)$.

As *Example 1* suggests, the constant term of a perfect-square trinomial of the form $x^2 + 2ax + a^2$ is the square of half the coefficient of x.

Example 2.

What constant term must be added to the following expressions to make them perfect squares?

a) $x^2 - 8x$ b) $x^2 + 14x$ c) $x^2 + 3x$

Solution.

a) The constant term needed is the square of $\frac{1}{2}(-8)$, or 16.

$x^2 - 8x + 16$ is a perfect square.

b) The constant term needed is the square of $\frac{1}{2}(14)$, or 49.

$x^2 + 14x + 49$ is a perfect square.

c) The constant term needed is the square of $\frac{1}{2}(3)$, or $\frac{9}{4}$.

$x^2 + 3x + \frac{9}{4}$ is a perfect square.

The next example shows how to solve any quadratic equation using the method of **completing the square**.

Example 3.

Solve: a) $x^2 + 14x + 40 = 0$; b) $x^2 - 10x + 23 = 0$.

Solution.

a)
$$x^2 + 14x + 40 = 0$$

Isolate the constant term: $x^2 + 14x = -40$

Add the square of $\frac{1}{2}(14)$ to both sides:

$$x^2 + 14x + 49 = -40 + 49$$
$$(x + 7)^2 = 9$$

Take the square root of both sides: $x + 7 = \pm 3$

$$x = -7 \pm 3$$
$$= -4 \text{ or } -10$$

The roots of the equation are -4 and -10.

b)
$$x^2 - 10x + 23 = 0$$

Isolate the constant term: $x^2 - 10x = 23$

Add the square of $\frac{1}{2}(-10)$ to both sides:

$$x^2 - 10x + 25 = -23 + 25$$
$$(x - 5)^2 = 2$$

Take the square root of both sides: $x - 5 = \pm\sqrt{2}$

$$x = 5 \pm \sqrt{2}$$

The roots of the equation are $5 + \sqrt{2}$ and $5 - \sqrt{2}$.

If the second-degree term has a coefficient other than 1, both sides of the equation should be divided by the coefficient.

Example 4.

Find the roots of $2x^2 - 10x + 11 = 0$ correct to two decimal places.

Solution.

Divide both sides by 2:

$$2x^2 - 10x + 11 = 0$$
$$x^2 - 5x + \frac{11}{2} = 0$$
$$x^2 - 5x = -\frac{11}{2}$$

Add the square of $\frac{1}{2}(-5)$ to both sides:

$$x^2 - 5x + \frac{25}{4} = -\frac{11}{2} + \frac{25}{4}$$
$$\left(x - \frac{5}{2}\right)^2 = \frac{3}{4}$$

Take the square root of both sides:

$$x - \frac{5}{2} = \frac{\pm\sqrt{3}}{2}$$
$$x = \frac{5 \pm \sqrt{3}}{2}$$
$$\doteq 3.37 \text{ or } 1.63$$

The roots are approximately 3.37 and 1.63.

EXERCISES 4-4

(A)

1. Determine if the trinomial is a perfect square:
   a) $x^2 + 6x + 9$ b) $x^2 - 4x + 4$ c) $x^2 + 10x - 25$
   d) $x^2 - 9x + 81$ e) $x^2 - 14x + 49$ f) $x^2 - 3x + \frac{9}{4}$

2. What constant term must be added to make the expression a perfect square?
   a) $x^2 + 6x$ b) $x^2 - 2x$ c) $x^2 - 20x$
   d) $x^2 + 7x$ e) $x^2 - 3x$ f) $x^2 + x$
   g) $x^2 - 11x$ h) $x^2 + 2ax$ i) $x^2 + bx$

3. Solve by completing the square:
   a) $x^2 + 4x - 12 = 0$ b) $x^2 + 8x - 33 = 0$
   c) $x^2 - 6x + 7 = 0$ d) $x^2 - 16x + 50 = 0$
   e) $x^2 - 3x + 1 = 0$ f) $x^2 + 5x + 3 = 0$

4. Solve:
   a) $x^2 + 12x - 8 = 0$ b) $x^2 - 18x + 20 = 0$
   c) $x^2 - 3x - 5 = 0$ d) $x^2 - x - 1 = 0$
   e) $x^2 + 9x + 16 = 0$ f) $x^2 + 5x - 3 = 0$

(B)

5. Solve:
   a) $2x^2 + 8x + 5 = 0$
   b) $3y^2 - 12y + 5 = 0$
   c) $2k^2 - 12k + 3 = 0$
   d) $3d^2 + 6d + 2 = 0$
6. Solve:
   a) $a^2 - 6a - 9 = 0$
   b) $2x^2 + x - 5 = 0$
   c) $2r^2 - 7r + 1 = 0$
   d) $2t^2 - 10t + 3 = 0$
   e) $2x^2 + 3x - 3 = 0$
   f) $5c^2 - 2c - 6 = 0$
7. Find the roots correct to two decimal places:
   a) $m^2 + 2m - 9 = 0$
   b) $x^2 + 9x - 12 = 0$
   c) $2s^2 - 3s - 6 = 0$
   d) $3c^2 + 5c - 11 = 0$
   e) $2y^2 + 7y + 2 = 0$
   f) $5x^2 - 20x + 3 = 0$

Show that one root of $x^2 - 12x + 32 = 0$ is double the other.

Find other quadratic equations in which one root is double the other. What patterns can you find?

THE MATHEMATICAL MIND

The Algebra of Al-Khowarizmi

The first systematic treatment of algebra was given in the ninth century A.D. by the Arab mathematician al-Khowarizmi in his work "Al-jabr w'al muqabala". The word, al-jabr, in the title means "restoration", and refers to the fact that equality is restored when the same number is added to or subtracted from both sides of an equation. It is from this word that our word "algebra" is derived.

The word was used in a non-mathematical sense in medieval Europe. There, an "algebrista" was a person who restored broken bones. This was often the barber who, in addition to cutting hair, administered the simpler medical treatments as a sideline. Red and white striped signs, still seen today, indicated that such services were available.

Al-Khowarizmi gave geometrical rules for solving such equations as $x^2 + 10x = 39$. In the diagram, the unshaded part is $x^2 + 10x$. To complete the square he added 25. Then 25 had to be added to the right side of the equation to restore the equality.

$$x^2 + 10x + 25 = 39 + 25$$
$$(x + 5)^2 = 64$$
$$x + 5 = \pm 8$$
$$x = 3 \text{ or } -13$$

The negative root is not admissible.

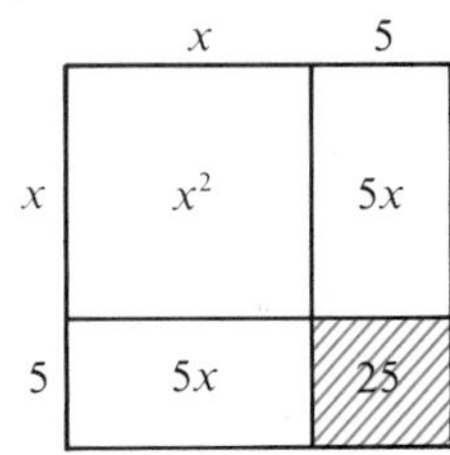

1. Solve $x^2 + 6x = 91$ by completing the square, and illustrate the solution with a diagram.
2. a) Solve $x^2 + px = q$ by completing the square, and illustrate with a diagram.
   b) Suggest why al-Khowarizmi would have difficulty solving an equation such as $x^2 - 4x = 45$ by this method. Can you find a geometrical method of illustrating the solution of this equation by completing the square?

4-5 SOLVING QUADRATIC EQUATIONS BY USING A FORMULA

For many centuries, mathematicians considered only equations with numerical coefficients. This meant repeating the whole process of calculation for each equation. Moreover, as they did not recognize negative numbers—they would not, for instance, write $x^2 = 8x + 20$ in the form $x^2 - 8x = 20$—a totally different type of calculation was needed for each type of equation.

About 1550, the French mathematician, François Vieta, introduced the idea of using letters to represent the coefficients of an equation. By that time, negative numbers were becoming accepted. The combination of the two ideas meant that all quadratic equations could be written in the form $ax^2 + bx + c = 0$, and it was possible to develop a single formula that could be used to solve any one of them.

To obtain a formula, we solve the equation, written in the general form, by completing the square.

Consider the general equation: $ax^2 + bx + c = 0, \quad a \neq 0$

Divide both sides by a:

$$x^2 + \frac{b}{a}x + \frac{c}{a} = 0$$

$$x^2 + \frac{b}{a}x = -\frac{c}{a}$$

Add the square of $\frac{1}{2}\left(\frac{b}{a}\right)$ to both sides:

$$x^2 + \frac{b}{a}x + \frac{b^2}{4a^2} = \frac{b^2}{4a^2} - \frac{c}{a}$$

$$\left(x + \frac{b}{2a}\right)^2 = \frac{b^2 - 4ac}{4a^2}$$

Take the square root of both sides:

$$x + \frac{b}{2a} = \frac{\pm\sqrt{b^2 - 4ac}}{2a}, \quad b^2 - 4ac \geqslant 0$$

$$x = \frac{-b \pm \sqrt{b^2 - 4ac}}{2a}$$

The roots of the equation: $ax^2 + bx + c = 0, a \neq 0$, are:

$\dfrac{-b + \sqrt{b^2 - 4ac}}{2a}$ and $\dfrac{-b - \sqrt{b^2 - 4ac}}{2a}$, where $b^2 - 4ac \geqslant 0$.

Example 1.

Solve and check:

a) $3x^2 - 5x + 2 = 0$ b) $z^2 - 6z + 7 = 0$

Solution.

a) $x = \dfrac{-b \pm \sqrt{b^2 - 4ac}}{2a}$ $a = 3$, $b = -5$, $c = 2$

$$x = \frac{-(-5) \pm \sqrt{(-5)^2 - 4(3)(2)}}{2(3)}$$
$$= \frac{5 \pm \sqrt{1}}{6}$$
$$= 1 \text{ or } \frac{2}{3}$$

The roots of the equation are 1 and $\frac{2}{3}$.

Check.

When $x = 1$, L.S. $= 3(1)^2 - 5(1) + 2$ R.S. $= 0$

$= 3 - 5 + 2$

$= 0$

When $x = \frac{2}{3}$, L.S. $= 3\left(\frac{2}{3}\right)^2 - 5\left(\frac{2}{3}\right) + 2$ R.S. $= 0$

$= \frac{4}{3} - \frac{10}{3} + 2$

$= 0$

The solution is correct.

b) $z = \dfrac{-b \pm \sqrt{b^2 - 4ac}}{2a}$ $a = 1$, $b = -6$, $c = 7$

$$z = \frac{(-6) \pm \sqrt{(-6)^2 - 4(1)(7)}}{2(1)}$$
$$= \frac{6 \pm \sqrt{36 - 28}}{2}$$
$$= \frac{6 \pm 2\sqrt{2}}{2}, \text{ or } 3 \pm \sqrt{2}$$

The roots of the equation are $3 + \sqrt{2}$ and $3 - \sqrt{2}$.

Check.

When $x = 3 + \sqrt{2}$, L.S. $= (3 + \sqrt{2})^2 - 6(3 + \sqrt{2}) + 7$ R.S. $= 0$

$= 9 + 6\sqrt{2} + 2 - 18 - 6\sqrt{2} + 7$

$= 0$

When $x = 3 - \sqrt{2}$, $\quad$ L.S. $= (3 - \sqrt{2})^2 - 6(3 - \sqrt{2}) + 7$ $\qquad$ R.S. $= 0$

$$= 9 - 6\sqrt{2} + 2 - 18 + 6\sqrt{2} + 7$$
$$= 0$$

The solution is correct.

Example 2.

Solve: $5x - \dfrac{1}{x+1} = 3$

Solution.

$$5x - \frac{1}{x+1} = 3$$

Multiply both sides by $(x + 1)$:

$$5x(x + 1) - 1 = 3(x + 1)$$
$$5x^2 + 5x - 1 = 3x + 3$$
$$5x^2 + 2x - 4 = 0$$

$$x = \frac{-b \pm \sqrt{b^2 - 4ac}}{2a} \qquad a = 5,\ b = 2,\ c = -4$$

$$x = \frac{-2 \pm \sqrt{2^2 - 4(5)(-4)}}{2(5)}$$
$$= \frac{-2 \pm \sqrt{84}}{10}$$
$$= \frac{-2 \pm 2\sqrt{21}}{10}, \text{ or } \frac{-1 \pm \sqrt{21}}{5}$$

The roots are $\dfrac{-1 + \sqrt{21}}{5}$ and $\dfrac{-1 - \sqrt{21}}{5}$.

Example 3.

Sylvie does a reverse $2\frac{1}{2}$ somersault dive from a 3 m springboard.

Her height above the water, h, in metres, t seconds after she leaves the board is given by: $h = -4.9t^2 + 8.8t + 3$. How long is it until she reaches the water?

Solution.

Substitute 0 for h: $0 = -4.9t^2 + 8.8t + 3$ or, $4.9t^2 - 8.8t - 3 = 0$

$$t = \frac{-b \pm \sqrt{b^2 - 4ac}}{2a} \qquad a = 4.9,\ b = -8.8,\ c = -3$$

$$t = \frac{-(-8.8) \pm \sqrt{(-8.8)^2 - 4(4.9)(-3)}}{2(4.9)}$$
$$= \frac{8.8 \pm \sqrt{136.24}}{9.8}$$
$$\doteq 2.09 \text{ or } -0.29$$

Since the time is positive, the negative root is rejected. She reaches the water in about 2.1 s.

EXERCISES 4-5

A

1. Solve:
   a) $2x^2 - 5x + 2 = 0$ b) $2x^2 + 7x + 3 = 0$
   c) $3x^2 - 11x - 14 = 0$ d) $4x^2 - 9x + 5 = 0$
   e) $5x^2 + 7x + 2 = 0$ f) $6x^2 + 7x - 20 = 0$
2. Solve and check:
   a) $6m^2 - 7m + 2 = 0$ b) $2c^2 - 25c + 77 = 0$
   c) $6t^2 - t - 1 = 0$ d) $2p^2 - p - 45 = 0$
   e) $2x^2 - 5x - 12 = 0$ f) $6x^2 - x - 2 = 0$
3. Find the roots correct to two decimal places:
   a) $2b^2 - 13b + 10 = 0$ b) $2z^2 - 7z + 4 = 0$
   c) $3x^2 - x - 5 = 0$ d) $2a^2 - 9a - 1 = 0$
   e) $5t^2 - 3t - 1 = 0$ f) $2y^2 + 5y + 1 = 0$
4. Find the roots correct to two decimal places:
   a) $5x^2 + 6x - 1 = 0$ b) $2c^2 - 6c - 1 = 0$
   c) $3m^2 + 2m - 7 = 0$ d) $4r^2 + 2r - 3 = 0$
   e) $3p^2 - 6p + 1 = 0$ f) $2a^2 - 6a + 1 = 0$
5. An Acapulco diver dives into the sea from a height of 35 m. His height, h, in metres, t seconds after leaving the cliff is given by: $h = -4.9t^2 + t + 35$. How long is it until he reaches the water?

6. Solve:
   a) $3x^2 - 4x = 0$ b) $12m^2 - 192 = 0$
   c) $25c^2 + 70c + 49 = 0$ d) $\frac{5}{2}y^2 - \frac{3}{2}y - \frac{1}{4} = 0$
   e) $0.2s^2 - s - 3.2 = 0$ f) $\sqrt{2}x^2 - 5x + \sqrt{8} = 0$
7. Solve and check:
   a) $4m^2 - 17m + 4 = 0$ b) $6a^2 - 11a + 4 = 0$
   c) $12x^2 - x - 6 = 0$ d) $3y^2 + 16y - 99 = 0$
   e) $5t^2 - 13t - 6 = 0$ f) $15s^2 + 7s - 2 = 0$

8. Solve:
   a) $2x^2 + 8x - 5 = 0$ b) $3x^2 + 10x - 8 = 0$
   c) $x^2 - 7x + 4 = 0$
   d) $(x + 3)(5x + 1) = (2x + 1)(x + 7)$
   e) $(2x - 1)(3x + 5) = (x + 2)(2x - 1)$
   f) $(5x + 1)(x + 2) = 5x - (2x + 1)(2x + 2)$
9. Solve:
   a) $\frac{x^2 + 6}{3} - \frac{7}{2} = \frac{x + 10}{2}$ b) $(x + 6)(x - 1) + x^2 = 10x + 9$
   c) $\frac{4}{x} + \frac{x}{4} = \frac{5}{2}$ d) $\frac{50}{x} - \frac{40}{x + 10} = 1$
   e) $\frac{3}{x + 2} = \frac{1}{4} - \frac{1}{x - 4}$
   f) $(x - 2)(x + 3) = x(5x - 9) - 2$
10. Solve:
    a) $24a^2 - 46a + 21 = 0$ b) $4x^2 - 75x - 79 = 0$
    c) $575t^2 - 2t - 1 = 0$ d) $27x^2 - 24x - 16 = 0$
    e) $32m^2 - 50m + 17 = 0$ f) $30s^2 - 17s - 450 = 0$
11. The approximate stopping distance, d, in metres, of a car travelling at v kilometres per hour is given by the formula $d = 0.0066v^2 + 0.14v$.
    a) What is the stopping distance for a car travelling at:
       i) 80 km/h? ii) 100 km/h?
    b) Find the highest speed at which a car can be stopped in
       i) 35 m; ii) 95 m.
12. The surface area, A, of a closed cylinder of radius r is given by the formula $A = 6.28r^2 + 47.7r$.
    a) Find the area if the radius is:
       i) 6 cm; ii) 25 cm.
    b) Find the radius if the surface area is:
       i) 291.28 cm^2; ii) 2128.5 cm^2.

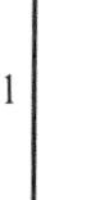

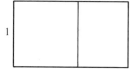

13. A rectangle of unit width is divided into a square and a rectangle. What is the length of the original rectangle if the smaller rectangle has the same length-to-width ratio?
14. What number differs from its reciprocal by:
    a) 1? b) −1?

15. Solve for x:
    a) $px^2 + qx + r = 0$ b) $3x^2 + nx - 5 = 0$
    c) $\frac{k}{x} - x = 3$ d) $x^2 + 4px - p^2 = 0$
    e) $\frac{3x}{a} + \frac{1}{a} = \frac{1}{3x}$ f) $x^2 + (3m - 2n)x = 6mn$

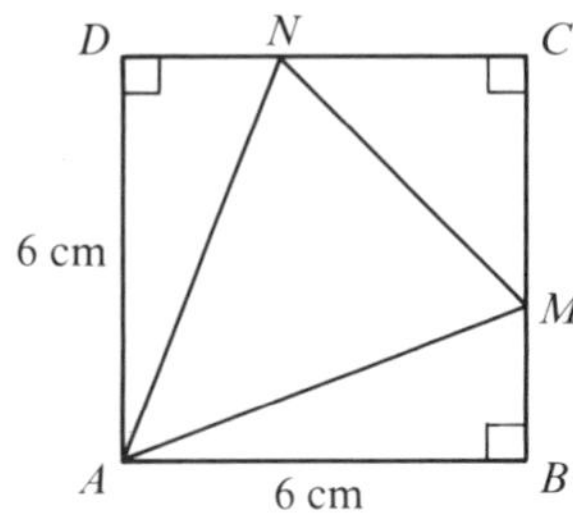

16. Square $ABCD$ has sides of length 6 cm. M and N are points on sides BC and DC such that the areas of $\triangle ABM$, $\triangle MCN$, and $\triangle ADN$ are all equal. Find the lengths of BM and DN.

17. a) Solve:
    i) $x^2 - 5x + 7 = 0$ ii) $-3x^2 + 7x - 11 = 0$
    iii) $2x^2 + 5x + 6 = 0$ iv) $3x^2 - 7x + 10 = 0$
    b) Under what conditions will a quadratic equation have no real roots?
    c) Which of the following have no real roots?
    i) $5x^2 + 4x + 1 = 0$ ii) $3x^2 - 8x + 7 = 0$
    iii) $6x^2 - 5x - 3 = 0$ iv) $12x^2 - 19x + 7 = 0$

18. a) Solve:
    i) $x^2 - x - 1 = 0$ ii) $x^2 - x - 2 = 0$
    iii) $x^2 - x - 3 = 0$ iv) $x^2 - x - 4 = 0$
    b) For what values of n does the equation: $x^2 - x - n = 0$ have integral roots?

19. a) Find the sum and product of the roots of the equation:
    i) $x^2 + 4x - 45 = 0$ ii) $4x^2 + 20x + 21 = 0$
    iii) $6x^2 - 29x + 35 = 0$ iv) $5x^2 - 6x - 3 = 0$
    b) From the results of (a), make a conjecture concerning the sum and product of the roots of $ax^2 + bx + c = 0$

20. Find the condition that must be satisfied by a, b, and c if the roots of the equation $ax^2 + bx + c$ are in the ratio:
    a) 2:3; b) $m:n$.

INVESTIGATE

Write a report comparing the different methods of solving quadratic equations presented in this chapter. What are the advantages and disadvantages of each?

LEADERS IN MATHEMATICS

Emmy Noether

Emmy Noether was born over 100 years ago in Erlangen, Germany. Her father was a professor of mathematics at the university.

Although in those days it was unusual for a woman to seek a university education, Emmy Noether was accepted as an undergraduate by the University of Erlangen in 1900 and obtained her Ph. D. in 1907.

Emmy Noether is famous for her work in both physics and mathematics. "Noether's Theorem" in physics was acknowledged by Einstein to be one of the cornerstones of general relativity, as well as elementary particle physics. Her work in modern algebra, the theory of rings and ideals, is perhaps her greatest contribution.

She was very popular as a teacher and has been acknowledged by most scholars as an outstanding mathematician. Many of her students became great contributors to mathematics in their own right.

Amalie Emmy Noether
23 March 1882–14 April 1935

4-6 THE NATURE OF THE ROOTS OF A QUADRATIC EQUATION

In the previous section we developed the formula $x = \dfrac{-b \pm \sqrt{b^2 - 4ac}}{2a}$ for the roots of the general quadratic equation $ax^2 + bx + c = 0$, $a \neq 0$. Consider how the formula applies to the three equations:

$x^2 - 6x + 5 = 0$, $x^2 - 6x + 9 = 0$, and $x^2 - 6x + 13 = 0$

$$x^2 - 6x + 5 = 0$$

$$x = \frac{6 \pm \sqrt{36 - 20}}{2}$$

$$= \frac{6 \pm \sqrt{16}}{2}$$ Positive

The roots are: $\dfrac{6 + 4}{2} = 5$ and $\dfrac{6 - 4}{2} = 1$

Two different real roots

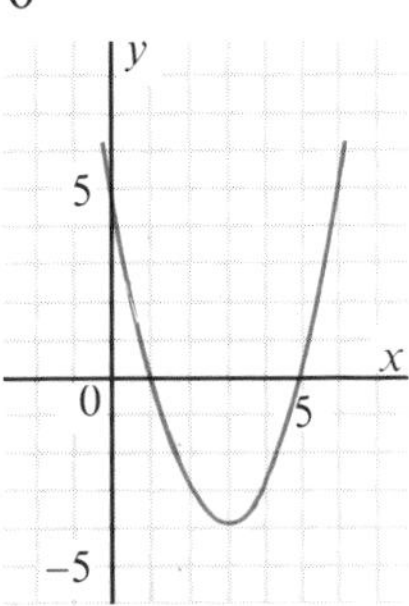

Parabola crosses the x-axis at two points.

$$x^2 - 6x + 9 = 0$$

$$x = \frac{6 \pm \sqrt{36 - 36}}{2}$$

$$= \frac{6 \pm \sqrt{0}}{2}$$ Zero

The roots are: $\dfrac{6 + 0}{2} = 3$ and $\dfrac{6 - 0}{2} = 3$

Two equal real roots

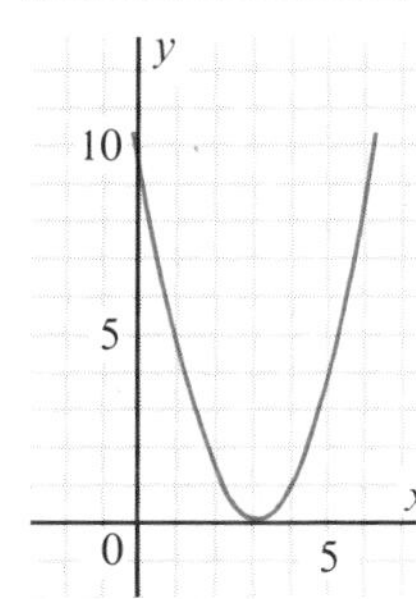

Parabola touches the x-axis at one point.

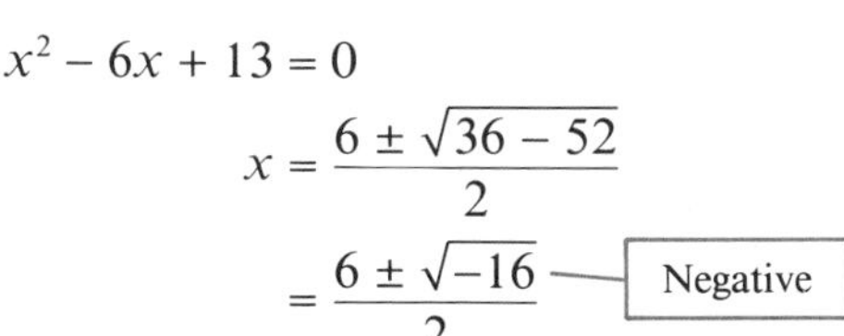

$$x^2 - 6x + 13 = 0$$

$$x = \frac{6 \pm \sqrt{36 - 52}}{2}$$

$$= \frac{6 \pm \sqrt{-16}}{2}$$ Negative

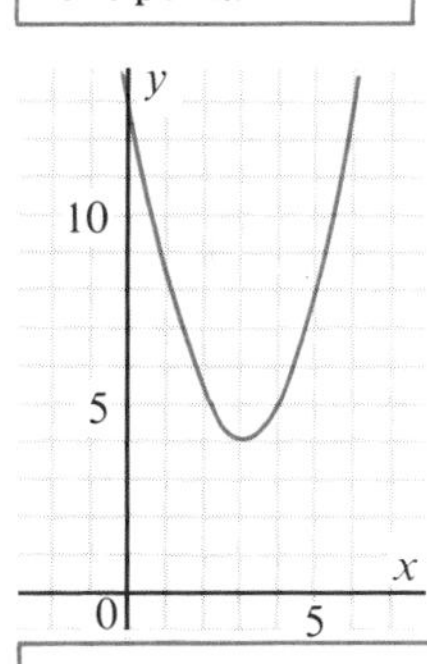

The roots are undefined.

No real roots

Parabola does not intersect the x-axis.

We can see that the expression under the radical sign plays an important role in the calculation of the roots. This expression enables us to determine the *nature of the roots* without solving the equation.

By the nature of the roots we mean:

- whether or not the equation has real roots;
- if there are real roots, whether they are different or equal.

The above examples suggest the following conclusions about the nature of the roots of $ax^2 + bx + c = 0$.

> If $b^2 - 4ac > 0$, there are two different real roots.
> If $b^2 - 4ac = 0$, there are two equal real roots.
> If $b^2 - 4ac < 0$, there are no real roots.

The expression $b^2 - 4ac$ is called the **discriminant** of $ax^2 + bx + c = 0$ because it discriminates among the three cases that can occur.

Example 1.

Without solving the equation, determine the nature of the roots:

a) $4x^2 - 12x + 9 = 0$ b) $2x^2 + 5x - 1 = 0$

c) $x^2 - 2x + 3 = 0$

Solution.

The nature of the roots is determined by the value of the discriminant, $b^2 - 4ac$.

a) $4x^2 - 12x + 9 = 0 \qquad a = 4, b = -12, c = 9$

$$\begin{aligned} b^2 - 4ac &= (-12)^2 - 4(4)(9) \\ &= 144 - 144 \\ &= 0 \end{aligned}$$

There are two equal real roots.

b) $2x^2 + 5x - 1 = 0 \qquad a = 2, b = 5, c = -1$

$$\begin{aligned} b^2 - 4ac &= 25 - 4(2)(-1) \\ &= 33 \end{aligned}$$

Since $33 > 0$, there are two different real roots.

c) $x^2 - 2x + 3 = 0 \qquad a = 1, b = -2, c = 3$

$$\begin{aligned} b^2 - 4ac &= (-2)^2 - 4(1)(3) \\ &= -8 \end{aligned}$$

Since $-8 < 0$, the equation has no real roots.

Example 2.

Find the values of k for which the equation $x^2 + kx + 9 = 0$ has:

a) equal roots; b) two different real roots.

Solution.

$x^2 + kx + 9 = 0 \qquad a = 1, b = k, c = 9$

$$\begin{aligned} b^2 - 4ac &= k^2 - 4(1)(9) \\ &= k^2 - 36 \end{aligned}$$

a) For equal roots, $k^2 - 36 = 0$

$$k^2 = 36$$
$$k = \pm 6$$

The equation has equal roots when $k = 6$ or -6.

b) For two different real roots,

$$k^2 - 36 > 0$$
$$k^2 > 36$$
$$k > 6 \text{ or } k < -6$$

The equation has two different real roots when $k > 6$ or $k < -6$.
This may also be written: $|k| > 6$.

EXERCISES 4-6

1. Find the value of the discriminant:
   a) $x^2 + 11x + 24 = 0$ b) $x^2 - 4x + 2 = 0$
   c) $4x^2 - 20x + 25 = 0$ d) $2x^2 - 5x + 8 = 0$
   e) $3x^2 + 13x - 10 = 0$ f) $7x^2 + 12x + 6 = 0$
2. Which of the equations in Exercise 1 have:
   a) two different real roots? b) two equal real roots?
   c) no real roots?
3. Determine the nature of the roots of these equations:
   a) $x^2 - 9x + 7 = 0$ b) $4x^2 + 36x + 81 = 0$
   c) $6x^2 + 22x + 20 = 0$ d) $2x^2 - 7x - 5 = 0$
   e) $5x^2 - 8x + 4 = 0$ f) $49x^2 - 70x + 25 = 0$

4. a) Solve: i) $x^2 - 2x - 3 = 0$ ii) $x^2 - 2x + 1 = 0$
   iii) $x^2 - 2x + 5 = 0$
   b) Graph the expressions in (a) on the same grid, and explain the results of (a) in terms of the graphs.
5. What is the condition that $px^2 + qx + r = 0$ has:
   a) two real roots? b) no real roots?
6. For what values of k does the equation have two different real roots?
   a) $x^2 + kx + 1 = 0$ b) $kx^2 + 4x - 3 = 0$
   c) $3x^2 + kx + 2 = 0$
7. For what values of m does the equation have two equal real roots?
   a) $x^2 + mx + 7 = 0$ b) $(2m + 1)x^2 - 8x + 6 = 0$
   c) $x^2 - 15 = 2m(x - 4)$
8. For what values of p does the equation have no real roots?
   a) $x^2 - px - 4 = 0$ b) $px^2 - 8x + 9 = 0$
   c) $px^2 - 5x + p = 0$

9. Which of the following have real roots for the values of k indicated?
   a) $kx^2 - 2x + 3 = 0, k < \frac{1}{3}$
   b) $3x^2 + kx + 2 = 0, |k| < 2\sqrt{6}$
   c) $(2k - 3)x^2 - 7x + 1 = 0, k < 7.5$
10. For what values of k will $x^2 + kx - k + 8 = 0$ have:
    a) equal roots?
    b) real roots?
    c) no real roots?
11. When a projectile is fired, the vertical component of its initial velocity is such that its height h, in metres, t seconds after firing is given by $h = 250t - 4.9t^2$. Is it possible for the projectile to reach a height of 2.75 km? 4.0 km?
12. A small change in the value of the constant term of some quadratic equations has a significant effect on the roots.
    a) Illustrate the truth of this statement by solving:
       $x^2 + 50x + 624 = 0, x^2 + 50x + 625 = 0, x^2 + 50x + 626 = 0.$
    b) Explain why in terms of the graphs of the equations.
13. Show that, if k is any real number, each of the following equations always has real roots:
    a) $kx^2 + (3k + 2)x + (2k + 3) = 0$
    b) $(k + 1)x^2 + 2kx + (k - 1) = 0$
14. Show that there are no real numbers x and y such that:
    $$\frac{1}{x+y} = \frac{1}{x} + \frac{1}{y}, \quad (x, y \neq 0).$$
15. If the coefficients of $ax^2 + bx + c = 0, (a \neq 0)$, are integers, determine which of the following statements are:
    i) always true; ii) never true; iii) sometimes true.
    a) One root is an integer and the other is rational.
    b) One root is rational and the other is irrational.
    c) If the roots are equal, then they are real.
    d) If $ac > 0$, there are no real roots.
    e) If $ac < 0$, the roots are real.

INVESTIGATE

Using the numbers 2, 3, and −8 as coefficients, how many different quadratic equations can be formed?

Is it possible to find three different integers such that for all possible arrangements of the coefficients, the equation will have integral roots?

Ⓒ

16. Consider the equation $x^2 - 12x + (36 - 4k) = 0$
    a) If k is an integer, for what values of k will the equation have rational roots?
    b) List some values of k and the roots of the corresponding equations. What patterns can you find? Do the results seem to be related to the coefficients?
    c) If k is a rational number, for what values of k will the equation have rational roots?
17. Show that the product of two consecutive natural numbers can never be a perfect square.

INVESTIGATE

Show that $x^2 + 4x - 5 = 0$ and $x^2 - 5x + 4 = 0$ have a common real root.

What conditions must be satisfied by p and q for the following equations to have a common real root?

$x^2 + px + q = 0$
$x^2 + qx + p = 0$

Other Ways of Solving Quadratic Equations

Three other ways of solving quadratic equations developed by mathematicians in times past are as follows.

1. About A.D. 250, the Greek mathematician Diophantus, solved quadratic equations of the form $ax^2 + bx + c = 0$ by the method of completing the square. But instead of his first step being the division of both sides by a, he multiplied both sides by a.
2. About A.D. 1050, the Hindus developed a way of solving quadratic equations, the first step of which was the multiplication of both sides by a number equal to four times the coefficient of x^2.
3. In the 16th century, the French mathematician François Vieta solved quadratic equations by a novel substitution method. To solve an equation such as $x^2 + 6x + 7 = 0$ he substituted $y + k$ for x, where k was a number to be determined. He then rearranged the equation as a quadratic in y and chose a value for k so that the coefficient of the linear term was zero. It was then an easy matter to solve for y, and by adding the chosen value of k, the roots of the original equation were obtained.

1. Solve the following using the above methods:
   a) $x^2 + 6x + 7 = 0$ b) $3x^2 + x - 2 = 0$
2. Use the above methods to solve $ax^2 + bx + c = 0$ $(a \neq 0)$.

4-7 COMPLEX NUMBERS

Prior to the middle of the seventeenth century, when mathematicians encountered quadratic equations with negative discriminants they dismissed them as impossible or absurd. They considered that the equations had no roots because no meaning was given to square roots of negative numbers. They did not realize that meaning could be given to these quantities by extending the number system.

The idea of extending a number system to include all formally derived roots of equations was one of the important advances in mathematical thinking. Consider these examples:

- The equation $x + 3 = 0$ has no solution in the set of natural numbers. But it does have a solution, -3, in the set of integers.
- The equation $2x + 1 = 0$ has no solution in the set of integers. But it does have a solution, $-\frac{1}{2}$, in the set of rational numbers.
- The equation $x^2 - 2 = 0$ has no solution in the set of rational numbers. But it does have two solutions, $\pm\sqrt{2}$, in the set of real numbers.

Similarly, an equation such as $x^2 + 1 = 0$ has no solution in the set of real numbers. But by extending the number system, we can give meaning to the solution of this equation. We do this by defining the number, i, with the property that:

$$i^2 = -1, \text{ or } i = \sqrt{-1}.$$

With this definition of i, $x^2 + 1 = 0$ has two roots, i and $-i$.

When $x = i$,

$$\begin{aligned} \text{L.S.} &= i^2 + 1 \qquad\qquad \text{R.S.} = 0 \\ &= -1 + 1, \text{ or } 0 \end{aligned}$$

When $x = -i$,

$$\begin{aligned} \text{L.S.} &= (-i)^2 + 1 \qquad\qquad \text{R.S.} = 0 \\ &= i^2 + 1 \\ &= -1 + 1, \text{ or } 0 \end{aligned}$$

Since there is no real number with the property that its square is negative, the number i is not a real number. It cannot be expressed as a decimal, and it cannot be represented by a point on the number line. For these reasons, the square roots of negative numbers were called *imaginary* numbers. This is an unfortunate name because it suggests that these numbers are somehow less valid than the real or decimal numbers to which we have become accustomed. All numbers are imaginary in the sense that they are abstractions.

Once mathematicians had learned to understand and work with this new kind of number, they found that the numbers had many applications in science, engineering, and electronics.

The number i can be used to define the square root of any negative number.

Since $\sqrt{-16} = \sqrt{16 \times (-1)}$,
we can define $\sqrt{-16} = \sqrt{16} \times \sqrt{-1}$
$= 4 \times i$, or $4i$

Similarly, if $k > 0$, we define:

$$\sqrt{-k} = \sqrt{k} \times \sqrt{-1}$$
$$= \sqrt{k}i$$

This definition permits us to solve quadratic equations with a negative discriminant.

Example 1.

Solve and check: $x^2 - 6x + 13 = 0$

Solution.

Using $x = \dfrac{-b \pm \sqrt{b^2 - 4ac}}{2a}$ $\qquad a = 1$, $b = -6$, $c = 13$

$$x = \frac{-(-6) \pm \sqrt{(-6)^2 - 4(1)(13)}}{2(1)}$$
$$= \frac{6 \pm \sqrt{-16}}{2}$$
$$= \frac{6 \pm 4i}{2}, \text{ or } 3 \pm 2i$$

The roots of the equation are $3 + 2i$ and $3 - 2i$.

Check.

When $x = 3 + 2i$,

L.S. $= (3 + 2i)^2 - 6(3 + 2i) + 13$ $\qquad$ R.S. $= 0$
$= 9 + 12i + 4i^2 - 18 - 12i + 13$
$= 9 + 12i - 4 - 18 - 12i + 13$
$= 0$

When $x = 3 - 2i$,

L.S. $= (3 - 2i)^2 - 6(3 - 2i) + 13$ $\qquad$ R.S. $= 0$
$= 9 - 12i - 4 - 18 + 12i + 13$
$= 0$

The solution is correct.

The numbers $3 + 2i$ and $3 - 2i$, which are the roots of the equation in *Example 1*, are examples of **complex numbers**.

An expression of the form $a + bi$, where a and b are real numbers, and $i = \sqrt{-1}$, is called a **complex number**.

Example 2.

Write as a complex number:

a) $\sqrt{-9}$ b) $\sqrt{-32}$ c) $(2 + i) + (5 - 3i)$

d) $i(4 - 5i)$ e) i^6 f) $(1 + 2i)(1 - 2i)$

Solution.

a) $\sqrt{-9} = \sqrt{9 \times (-1)}$
$= 3 \times \sqrt{-1}$
$= 3i$

b) $\sqrt{-32} = \sqrt{32 \times (-1)}$
$= 4\sqrt{2} \times \sqrt{-1}$
$= 4\sqrt{2}i$

c) $(2 + i) + (5 - 3i) = 2 + i + 5 - 3i$
$= 7 - 2i$

d) $i(4 - 5i) = 4i - 5i^2$
$= 4i - 5(-1)$
$= 4i + 5$, or $5 + 4i$

e) $i^6 = (i^2)^3$
$= (-1)^3$
$= -1$

f) $(1 + 2i)(1 - 2i)$
$= 1 - 2i + 2i - 4i^2$
$= 1 - 4i^2$
$= 1 - 4(-1)$, or 5

Examples 2e and *2f* show that operations with complex numbers sometimes result in real numbers.

Example 3.

Solve: $x^2 + 4x + 7 = 0$

Solution.

$$x = \frac{-b \pm \sqrt{b^2 - 4ac}}{2a} \qquad a = 1,\ b = 4,\ c = 7$$

$$x = \frac{-4 \pm \sqrt{4^2 - 4(1)(7)}}{2(1)}$$

$$= \frac{-4 \pm \sqrt{-12}}{2}$$

$$= \frac{-4 \pm 2\sqrt{3}\,i}{2}, \text{ or } -2 \pm \sqrt{3}\,i$$

The roots of the equation are $-2 + \sqrt{3}\,i$ and $-2 - \sqrt{3}\,i$.

Example 4.

Find two numbers with a sum of 10 and a product of 40.

Solution.

Let the numbers be x and $10 - x$.
Since their product is 40: $x(10 - x) = 40$

$$10x - x^2 = 40$$
$$x^2 - 10x + 40 = 0$$

$$x = \frac{-b \pm \sqrt{b^2 - 4ac}}{2a} \qquad a = 1,\ b = -10,\ c = 40$$

$$x = \frac{10 \pm \sqrt{(-10)^2 - 4(40)}}{2}$$
$$= \frac{10 \pm \sqrt{-60}}{2}$$
$$= 5 \pm \sqrt{-15}, \text{ or } 5 \pm \sqrt{15}\, i$$

The numbers are $5 + \sqrt{15}\, i$ and $5 - \sqrt{15}\, i$

Check.

$$5 + \sqrt{15}\, i + 5 - \sqrt{15}\, i = 10$$
$$(5 + \sqrt{15}\, i)(5 - \sqrt{15}\, i) = 25 - 15i^2$$
$$= 25 + 15, \text{ or } 40$$

The solution is correct.

EXERCISES 4-7

1. Write as a complex number:
   a) $\sqrt{-5}$ b) $\sqrt{-49}$ c) $(3 + 2i) - (1 + 5i)$
   d) $i(8 + 3i)$ e) $(2 + i)(5 - 3i)$ f) $(7 - 4i)^2$
2. Show that both i and $-i$ are roots of the equation $x^2 + 1 = 0$.
3. Show that $2 + \sqrt{2}\, i$ and $2 - \sqrt{2}\, i$ satisfy the equation $x^2 - 4x + 6 = 0$.
4. Show that $\frac{-3 + i}{2}$ and $\frac{-3 - i}{2}$ are the roots of the equation $2x^2 + 6x + 5 = 0$.
5. Solve and check:
   a) $x^2 + 4 = 0$ b) $x^2 + 9 = 0$ c) $x^2 + 25 = 0$
   d) $x^2 + 12 = 0$ e) $x^2 + 18 = 0$ f) $x^2 - 2x + 2 = 0$

(B)

6. Write as a complex number:
   a) $2i(3 - 5i)$ b) $(5 - 3i)(5 + 3i)$
   c) $(2 - 7i) + (5 + 3i)$ d) $(7 + 2i)(5 - 4i)$
   e) $2i(3i^2 - 4i - 5)$ f) $3i(2 + 5i)^2$

7. Solve and check:
   a) $x^2 + 3x + 5 = 0$ b) $x^2 - 4x + 5 = 0$
   c) $x^2 + x + 2 = 0$ d) $x^2 - 2x + 3 = 0$
   e) $x^2 - 5x + 7 = 0$ f) $2x^2 + 3x + 2 = 0$
8. Solve:
   a) $3x^2 - 4x + 2 = 0$ b) $3x^2 - 2x + 2 = 0$
   c) $x^2 + \sqrt{2}x + \frac{1}{2} = 0$ d) $x^2 - 2x + 5 = 0$
   e) $7x^2 - 4x + 2 = 0$ f) $-7 + 4x + x^2 = 0$
9. Find two numbers which have a sum of 2 and a product of 2.

4-8 THE SUM AND PRODUCT OF THE ROOTS OF A QUADRATIC EQUATION

There are simple relations between the roots of a quadratic equation and its coefficients. Let the equation $ax^2 + bx + c = 0$, $a \neq 0$, have the roots:

$$m = \frac{-b + \sqrt{b^2 - 4ac}}{2a} \quad \text{and} \quad n = \frac{-b - \sqrt{b^2 - 4ac}}{2a}$$

Then the sum of the roots is:

$$\begin{aligned} m + n &= \frac{-b + \sqrt{b^2 - 4ac}}{2a} + \frac{-b - \sqrt{b^2 - 4ac}}{2a} \\ &= -\frac{2b}{2a}, \text{ or } -\frac{b}{a} \end{aligned}$$

And the product of the roots is:

$$\begin{aligned} mn &= \left(\frac{-b + \sqrt{b^2 - 4ac}}{2a}\right)\left(\frac{-b - \sqrt{b^2 - 4ac}}{2a}\right) \\ &= \frac{b^2 - (b^2 - 4ac)}{4a^2} \\ &= \frac{4ac}{4a^2}, \text{ or } \frac{c}{a} \end{aligned}$$

For the general quadratic equation $ax^2 + bx + c = 0$, $a \neq 0$, the sum and product of the roots are given by the formulas:

$$m + n = -\frac{b}{a} \quad \text{and} \quad mn = \frac{c}{a}$$

Since these formulas involve only the coefficients a, b, and c, both the sum and product of the roots of any quadratic equation can be found without having to solve the equation.

Example 1.

Find the sum and product of the roots of the equation $3x^2 + 7x - 6 = 0$.

Solution.

For this equation, $a = 3$, $b = 7$, $c = -6$.

The sum of the roots, $-\frac{b}{a} = -\frac{7}{3}$

The product of the roots, $\frac{c}{a} = -\frac{6}{3}$, or -2.

Example 2.

One root of $4x^2 - 7x - 15 = 0$ is 3. Find the other root.

Solution.

The sum of the roots, $-\frac{b}{a} = \frac{-(-7)}{4}$, or $\frac{7}{4}$

Since one root is 3, the other root is: $\frac{7}{4} - 3 = -\frac{5}{4}$

The formulas for the sum and product of the roots provide a convenient check for the solutions of quadratic equations.

Example 3.

Check that 5 and $-\frac{7}{2}$ are the roots of $2x^2 - 3x - 35 = 0$.

Solution.

For this equation, $a = 2$, $b = -3$, $c = -35$.
We compare the sum and product of the proposed roots with the sum and product of the roots of the equation.

Sum: $5 + \left(-\frac{7}{2}\right) = \frac{3}{2}$ and $-\frac{b}{a} = -\frac{(-3)}{2}$, or $\frac{3}{2}$

Product: $5\left(-\frac{7}{2}\right) = -\frac{35}{2}$ and $\frac{c}{a} = -\frac{35}{2}$

Therefore, 5 and $-\frac{7}{2}$ are the correct roots.

EXERCISES 4-8

(A)

1. Find the sum and product of the roots of:
   a) $x^2 + 5x - 8 = 0$;
   b) $2x^2 - 9x - 17 = 0$;
   c) $3x^2 - 8x - 12 = 0$;
   d) $5x^2 - 23x + 12 = 0$;
   e) $2x^2 + 10x + 15 = 0$;
   f) $7x^2 + 20x - 14 = 0$;
2. Given one root, m, find the other root of:
   a) $2x^2 + 7x - 15 = 0$; $m = -5$
   b) $3x^2 - x - 14 = 0$; $m = \frac{7}{3}$
   c) $4x^2 + 24x + 27 = 0$; $m = -\frac{9}{2}$
   d) $6x^2 + 17x - 88 = 0$; $m = \frac{8}{3}$
   e) $10x^2 + 37x + 7 = 0$; $m = -\frac{7}{2}$
   f) $15x^2 - 34x + 15 = 0$; $m = \frac{3}{5}$
3. Determine if the two numbers given are the roots of:
   a) $x^2 - 10x - 39 = 0$; -3 and 13
   b) $2x^2 + 19x + 35 = 0$; $-\frac{5}{2}$ and -7
   c) $3x^2 - 8x + 12 = 0$; $-\frac{5}{3}$ and 1
   d) $6x^2 + x - 40 = 0$; $-\frac{8}{3}$ and $\frac{5}{2}$
   e) $2x^2 + 11x + 12 = 0$; $-\frac{3}{2}$ and 4
   f) $10x^2 - 31x - 63 = 0$; $\frac{7}{5}$ and $-\frac{9}{2}$

(B)

4. Find which of the five equations given have roots with:
   a) a sum of:
      i) $\frac{11}{2}$, ii) -10, iii) -6;
   b) a product of:
      i) 6, ii) $\frac{16}{3}$, iii) $-\frac{15}{2}$.

   1) $2x^2 - 11x + 12 = 0$
   2) $3x^2 - 18x - 32 = 0$
   3) $3x^2 + 30x + 16 = 0$
   4) $2x^2 + 12x - 15 = 0$
   5) $4x^2 - 22x - 30 = 0$
5. Find expressions for the sum and product of the roots of:
   a) $px^2 + qx - pq = 0$;
   b) $(c + d)x^2 + 3cx - 2c - d = 0$;
   c) $fx^2 + (3f - 1)x + f^2 + 2f = 0$;
   d) $(a - b)x^2 - (a^2 - b^2)x + a^2 - ab = 0$.
6. Given: $kx^2 + (2k + 5)x + (3 - k) = 0$. Find the value of k if:
   a) the sum of the roots is 3;
   b) the product of the roots is 0;
   c) one of the roots is 1.

7. Given: $3dx^2 - (2d - 3)x - (5d + 2) = 0$. Find the value of d if:
   a) the sum of the roots is $\frac{4}{3}$;
   b) the product of the roots is $-\frac{3}{4}$;
   c) one of the roots is $\frac{3}{2}$.

8. If the coefficients of $ax^2 + bx + c = 0$ $(a \neq 0)$ are integers, which of the following statements are: i) always true? ii) never true? iii) sometimes true?
   a) If the roots are irrational, then the sum and product of the roots are also irrational.
   b) The sum and product of the roots are rational numbers.
   c) The roots are rational numbers.

9. Show that any quadratic equation can be written in the form: $x^2 - (\text{sum of the roots})x + (\text{product of the roots}) = 0$.

10. Find the quadratic equation with roots:
    a) 3 and 2;
    b) $\frac{1}{2}$ and $-\frac{3}{2}$;
    c) $1 + \sqrt{5}$ and $1 - \sqrt{5}$;
    d) $1 + \sqrt{2}i$ and $1 - \sqrt{2}i$.

Ⓒ

11. a) Determine how the roots of $ax^2 + bx + c = 0$ and $cx^2 + bx + a = 0$ are related $(a, c \neq 0)$.
    b) Find an equation with roots that are the negative reciprocals of the roots of $ax^2 + bx + c = 0$.

12. If m and n represent the roots of $2x^2 - 4x - 3 = 0$, find the value of:
    a) $(m + n)^2$
    b) $m^2 + n^2$
    c) $\frac{1}{m} + \frac{1}{n}$
    d) $\frac{m}{n} + \frac{n}{m}$
    e) $(m - n)^2$
    f) $m^2 - n^2$

13. Without solving the equation $6x^2 + x - 15 = 0$, find;
    a) the sum of the squares of the roots;
    b) the sum of the reciprocals of the roots.

14. If $ax^2 + bx + c = 0$, find an expression in terms of a, b, and c for:
    a) the difference of the roots;
    b) the quotient of the roots;
    c) the sum of the squares of the roots;
    d) the sum of the reciprocals of the roots.

15. Find the quadratic equation with roots which are the squares of the roots of $x^2 - 5x - 3 = 0$

4-9 SOLVING PROBLEMS USING QUADRATIC EQUATIONS

A variety of problems lead to quadratic equations. The example and the exercises give some idea of this variety.

Example.

Biathlon skiing combines cross-country ski racing with rifle shooting. At Olympic Games and world championships, competitors start singly at one-minute intervals. Frank Ullrich, who is scheduled to start immediately following Anatole Alyabiev, feels that no matter how fast Anatole skis, he can ski 1 km/h faster. What is the average speed of each skier if Frank overtakes Anatole at the first shooting range, which is 4 km from the start?

Solution.

Let x be Anatole's speed in kilomètres per hour. The data is organized in this table:

Skier	Distance km	Average speed km/h	Time h
Anatole	4	x	$\frac{4}{x}$
Frank	4	$x + 1$	$\frac{4}{x+1}$

Since Frank started 1 min, or $\frac{1}{60}$ h, after Anatole:

$$\frac{4}{x} - \frac{4}{x+1} = \frac{1}{60}$$

$$\frac{4x + 4 - 4x}{x(x+1)} = \frac{1}{60}$$

$$x(x + 1) = 240$$

The equation may be solved using the formula.

$$x^2 + x - 240 = 0$$

$$(x - 15)(x + 16) = 0$$

$$x = 15 \text{ or } -16$$

The negative solution is rejected because the speed must be positive. Anatole's speed is 15 km/h and Frank's is 16 km/h.

EXERCISES 4-9

(A)

1. Write algebraic equivalents for these verbal expressions:
   a) Two consecutive numbers
   b) Two consecutive odd numbers
   c) Two numbers which differ by 3
   d) The sum of the squares of two numbers which differ by 3
   e) The product of two consecutive even numbers
   f) The sum of the squares of a number and its reciprocal
2. Write algebraic equivalents for these verbal expressions:
   a) The time required to travel 80 km at $(x - 12)$ km/h
   b) The dimensions of a frame for a picture 40 cm by 60 cm with a border x cm wide
   c) The length-to-width ratio of a rectangle with a length 5 units longer than the width
   d) The area of a rectangle with a length 8 units less than three times the width
   e) The profit on each radio when x radios are bought for \$15 000 and $x - 2$ are sold for \$16 000
   f) The volume of acid in a solution if x litres of a 30% acid solution are added to 20 L of a 25% acid solution

(B)

3. Chris cuts half a rectangular lawn, 40 m by 30 m, by mowing strips of equal width around the perimeter. Jerri cuts the small rectangle left. How wide a strip does Chris cut so that they share the work equally?
4. Students sent flowers costing \$20 to a sick classmate. There were four fewer students contributing than was planned, requiring each of the others to give 25¢ more. How many students contributed to the gift?
5. Three pieces of rod measure 20 cm, 41 cm, and 44 cm. If the same amount is cut off each piece, the remaining lengths can be formed into a right triangle. What length is cut off?
6. Dieter makes a journey of 430 km, travelling 160 km by bus and 270 km by car. If the car averages 10 km/h faster than the bus and the whole journey takes 5 h, what is the speed of the car?
7. A storeowner buys a quantity of balls for \$600. If they had each cost \$0.25 less, she would have had 10 more for the same money. How much did she pay for each ball?
8. The edges of three cubes are consecutive odd integers. If the cubes are stacked on a desk, as shown, the total exposed surface area is 381 cm^2. Find the lengths of the sides of the cubes.

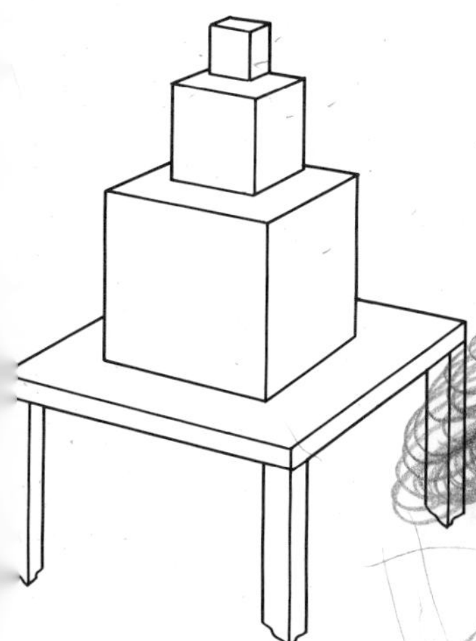

9. When a car reduces its speed by 18 km/h, its wheels, 200 cm in circumference, take 1 s longer to make 50 revolutions. What was the car's original speed?
10. If a bus travelled 10 km/h faster, it would take 2 h less time to make a 315 km trip. What is its speed?
11. Over a distance of 120 km, the average speed of a train is 40 km/h faster than that of a car. If the train covers the distance in 30 min less time, find its average speed.
12. To save fuel on the 240 km trip to their cottage, the Nakamura family reduce their usual average speed by 20 km/h. This lengthens the journey time by 1 h. What is the slower average speed?
13. Antonella bought some calculators for a total of $240. She kept one for herself and sold the rest for $300 making a profit of $5 on each calculator. How many calculators did she buy?

Ⓒ

14. Brendan buys a block of shares of Laser Technology for $1875. When the share price increases by $4/share, he sells all but 15 of them for $1740. How many shares did he buy?
15. When a ball is thrown upward, its height, h, in metres, is given by: $h = 1.5 + 19.6t - 4.9t^2$, where t is the number of seconds after it is thrown. For what length of time is the ball higher than 16.2 m?
16. Two taps turned on together can fill a tank in 15 min. By themselves, one takes 16 min longer than the other to fill the tank. Find the time taken to fill the tank by each tap on its own.
17. Car A leaves Toronto for Montreal, 500 km away, at an average speed of 80 km/h. Car B leaves Montreal for Toronto on the same highway 2 h later at 100 km/h. How far are they from Toronto when they pass?

Review Exercises

1. Solve:
   a) $(x + 7)(x - 3) = (x + 7)(5 - x)$
   b) $(3x - 9)(x + 2) = (x - 3)(2x + 1)$
   c) $(x + 4)(x - 4) = -9(x + 1)(x - 1)$
   d) $(x + 5)(2x - 3) = (x + 3)(x + 4)$
2. Calculate the radius of a circle that has an area of:
   a) $169\ \text{cm}^2$; b) $1772\ \text{mm}^2$; c) $16\pi\ \text{km}^2$.
3. Solve graphically:
   a) $2x^2 + 11x - 6 = 0$ b) $2x^2 - 5x - 12 = 0$
   c) $4x^2 - 25 = 0$ d) $16x^2 + 8x - 143 = 0$
4. Write a quadratic equation with roots:
   a) $7, -1$; b) $0, \frac{11}{2}$; c) $\frac{4}{3}, -\frac{3}{4}$; d) $1.125, -5.875$.
5. Solve.
   a) $x^2 - 5x - 14 = 0$ b) $m^2 + 4m - 32 = 0$
   c) $3v^2 - 2v - 1 = 0$ d) $6t^2 - 11t - 10 = 0$
6. Solve:
   a) $x^2 - 3x - 22 = 4(x - 1)$ b) $7v(v - 1) = 5(v^2 - 1.2)$
   c) $2(x - 3)(x + 3) + 5x = 0$
   d) $(z - 4)(3z + 2) = (z - 5)(2z + 1) - 1$
7. One side of a right triangle is 2 cm shorter than the hypotenuse and 7 cm longer than the third side. Find the lengths of the sides of the triangle.
8. The height, h, in metres, of an infield fly ball t seconds after being hit is given by the formula: $h = 30t - 5t^2$. How long is the ball in the air?
9. The length of a rectangular picture is 5 cm greater than the width. Find the dimensions of the picture if its area is:
   a) $150\ \text{cm}^2$; b) $300\ \text{cm}^2$.
10. Solve by completing the square:
    a) $x^2 - 8x - 30 = 0$ b) $x^2 + 6x - 90 = 0$
    c) $x^2 - 5x + 2 = 0$ d) $x^2 + 15x + 25 = 0$
11. Solve by completing the square:
    a) $2x^2 + 9x + 3 = 0$ b) $6x^2 + 2x - 5 = 0$
    c) $7x^2 - 16x + 5 = 0$ d) $10x^2 + 7x - 10 = 0$
12. Solve:
    a) $5x^2 + 11x - 12 = 0$ b) $3x^2 + 10x - 32 = 0$
    c) $5x^2 - 15x + 11 = 0$ d) $9x^2 - 6x - 143 = 0$
    e) $12x^2 - 29x + 14 = 0$ f) $20x^2 + x - 12 = 0$
13. The surface area, A, of a closed cylinder of radius r is given by the formula: $A = 6.28r^2 + 92.1r$. Find the radius of the cylinder if the surface area is:
    a) $1138.72\ \text{cm}^2$; b) $1772.98\ \text{cm}^2$.

14. A uniform border on a framed photograph has the same area as the photograph. What are the outside dimensions of the border if the dimensions of the photograph are 25 cm by 20 cm?

15. For what values of m will $x^2 - 2mx + m + 12 = 0$ have:
   a) equal roots? b) real roots? c) no real roots?

16. If m is a positive number less than 4, which of the following equations has equal roots?
   a) $x^2 + mx + 1 = 0$
   b) $mx^2 + 3x - 5 = 0$
   c) $3x^2 + 2mx + 7 = 0$

17. A grappling iron is thrown vertically to catch on a ledge 7.5 m above the thrower. If its height, h, in metres, t seconds after being thrown is given by $h = -4.9t^2 + 11t + 1.5$, will it reach the ledge?

18. Write as a complex number:
   a) $3i(2 + 3i)$
   b) $(3 + 2i)(3 - 2i)$
   c) $(3 + i) + (4 - 3i)$
   d) $7i(1 - 2i)^2$

19. Solve:
   a) $x^2 - x + 3 = 0$
   b) $3x^2 - 7x + 7 = 0$
   c) $2x^2 + 3x + 4 = 0$
   d) $10x^2 - 2x + 1 = 0$

20. Given one root, m, find the other root of:
   a) $8x^2 + x - 30 = 0$; $m = -2$
   b) $3x^2 - 22x + 35 = 0$; $m = 5$
   c) $6x^2 - x - 22 = 0$; $m = 2$
   d) $4x^2 + 17x - 15 = 0$; $m = \frac{3}{4}$

21. Given: $kx^2 + (k + 3)x + (3 - 4k) = 0$. Find the value of k if:
   a) the sum of the roots is: -2;
   b) the product of the roots is: -7;
   c) one of the roots is: 2.

22. A storeowner sold a number of dresses for \$75 each. Her percent profit was numerically the same as the cost of each dress. What was the cost of each dress?

23. A rectangular field has a perimeter 500 m and an area 14 400 m^2. Find the lengths of its sides.

24. C is a point on line segment AB such that $AB \cdot BC = AC^2$. If AB is 6 cm, find the length of BC to the nearest millimetre.

25. The perimeter of a square exceeds that of another square by 100 m. The area of the larger square exceeds three times that of the smaller by 325 m^2. Find the lengths of the sides of the squares.

26. Two taps turned on together can fill a tank in 30 min. By themselves, one takes 25 min longer than the other to fill the tank. Find the time taken to fill the tank by each tap on its own.

Cumulative Review (Chapters 3 and 4)

1. Simplify:
   a) $4m^2n - 3mn^2 + m^2n - 5mn^2$
   b) $(2ab)(-4a^2b^3)$
   c) $(x^4y^3)^5(xy^2)^3$
   d) $\dfrac{c^4d^5}{cd^3} \times \dfrac{c^6d}{c^2d^2}$
   e) $\dfrac{-16m^5r}{30m^2r^7} \times \dfrac{-27mr^6}{-24m^4r^3}$
2. A cone is four times as tall as a sphere but has half the radius. Find the ratio of their volumes.
3. Simplify:
   a) $6(2x + 4y - 5z) - (7x - 2y - 3z)$
   b) $(x - 2y)(x + 2y) + 5(x + y)(2x - y)$
   c) $4(a - b)^2 - (a + 2b)^2$
4. The slant height, s, of a right circular cone is given by the formula: $s = \sqrt{r^2 + h^2}$, where r is the radius of the base and h is the altitude. Find an expression for the slant height if the altitude is 4 units longer than the radius.
5. Factor completely:
   a) $-4x^2y^3 + 12x^3y^2 - 20x^3y^3$
   b) $a^2x + b^2y + b^2x + a^2y$
   c) $15x^3y^3 - 12x^3y^2 - 10x^2y^3 + 8x^2y^2$
   d) $8a^2 + 22a + 5$
   e) $24b^2 - 26bc + 5c^2$
   f) $4a^2 - 28a + 49$
   g) $9z^2 - 144r^2$
   h) $y^2 - m^2 + 10mc - 25c^2$
   i) $y^3 - 125$
   j) $27a^3 + 8d^3$
6. For what values of the variable is the expression undefined?
   a) $\dfrac{3x - 5}{4x}$
   b) $\dfrac{y^2 - y - 2}{2y + 5}$
   c) $\dfrac{b^2 - 11b + 24}{b^2 - 3b - 40}$
7. Simplify:
   a) $\dfrac{a^2 - 4a}{a^2 + 12a + 36} \times \dfrac{a^2 - 36}{a^2 - 10a + 24}$
   b) $\dfrac{x^4 - y^4}{x^2 + xy - 2y^2} \div \dfrac{x^2 + 2xy + y^2}{x^2 + 10xy + 16y^2}$
   c) $\dfrac{5}{2y} + \dfrac{y - 6}{y - 3}$
   d) $\dfrac{9}{x^2 - 2x - 3} - \dfrac{7}{x^2 - 10x + 21}$
   e) $\dfrac{4}{x^2} + \dfrac{2x^2 - 10x}{x^2 - 5x} \times \dfrac{x^2 - x - 20}{2x^2 + 9x + 4}$
8. A garbage disposal bin with a volume of 80 m^3 has a square base, w m by w m. Write an expression in terms of w for:
   a) the height of the bin, h;
   b) the change in height when each side of the base is decreased by 1 m.

9. Solve:
   a) $6b^2 - 5 = 7$ b) $3(2c^2 - 1) - 2 = 4(2c^2 - 3)$
   c) $(a - 3)(a - 7) = (a - 2)(3a - 4)$
10. Solve graphically:
    a) $2x^2 - 11x - 40 = 0$ b) $4x^2 + 12x + 9 = 0$
11. Write a quadratic equation with roots:
    a) 3, -7 b) -2, 0 c) $\frac{3}{5}, \frac{1}{8}$
12. Solve:
    a) $a^2 - 2a - 15 = 0$ b) $4y^2 + 20y - 24 = 0$
    c) $5x^2 - 42x + 16 = 0$ d) $4x^2 + 25x - 21 = 0$
    e) $16b^2 - 25 = 0$ f) $2(b + 3)(b + 1) = b(2b - 1)$
13. Solve:
    a) $4c^2 - 2c - 5 = 0$ b) $4x^2 + 7x - 6 = 0$
    c) $3x^2 + 7x + 2 = 0$ d) $3x^2 + 2x = 11$
    e) $\frac{5}{x} + \frac{6}{x + 2} = 5$ f) $(x + 6)(x - 1) = 5x(x - 2) + 6$
14. Determine the nature of the roots:
    a) $4a^2 - 3a - 7 = 0$ b) $2x^2 - 7x + 3 = 0$
    c) $-4a^2 + 4a = 1$ d) $3b^2 = 2b - 9$
15. For what values of k does the equation have two different real roots?
    a) $x^2 + kx - 4 = 0$ b) $kx^2 + 3x - 3 = 0$
16. For what values of p does the equation have no real roots?
    a) $x^2 + px + 9 = 0$ b) $px^2 - 3x + 3 = 0$
17. Write as a complex number:
    a) $(i - 4)(2i + 5)$ b) $3i(4 - 2i)^2$
18. Solve:
    a) $x^2 - 6x + 13 = 0$ b) $3x^2 - x + 7 = 0$
19. Find the sum and product of the roots of:
    a) $x^2 - 11x - 7 = 0$ b) $3x^2 + 2x - 1 = 0$ c) $6x - 4 = 9x^2$
20. Given: $wx^2 + (2w - 6)x + (w - 10) = 0$. Find the value of w if:
    a) the sum of the roots is 4; b) the product of the roots is 3;
    c) one of the roots is -2.
21. A framed picture has a border the same area as the picture. If the picture is 12 cm by 17 cm, find the width of the border.
22. A metal strip, 40 cm long, is cut in two and each piece bent to form a square. If the sum of the areas of the squares is 58 cm², how long is each piece of strip?

5 Ratio and Proportion

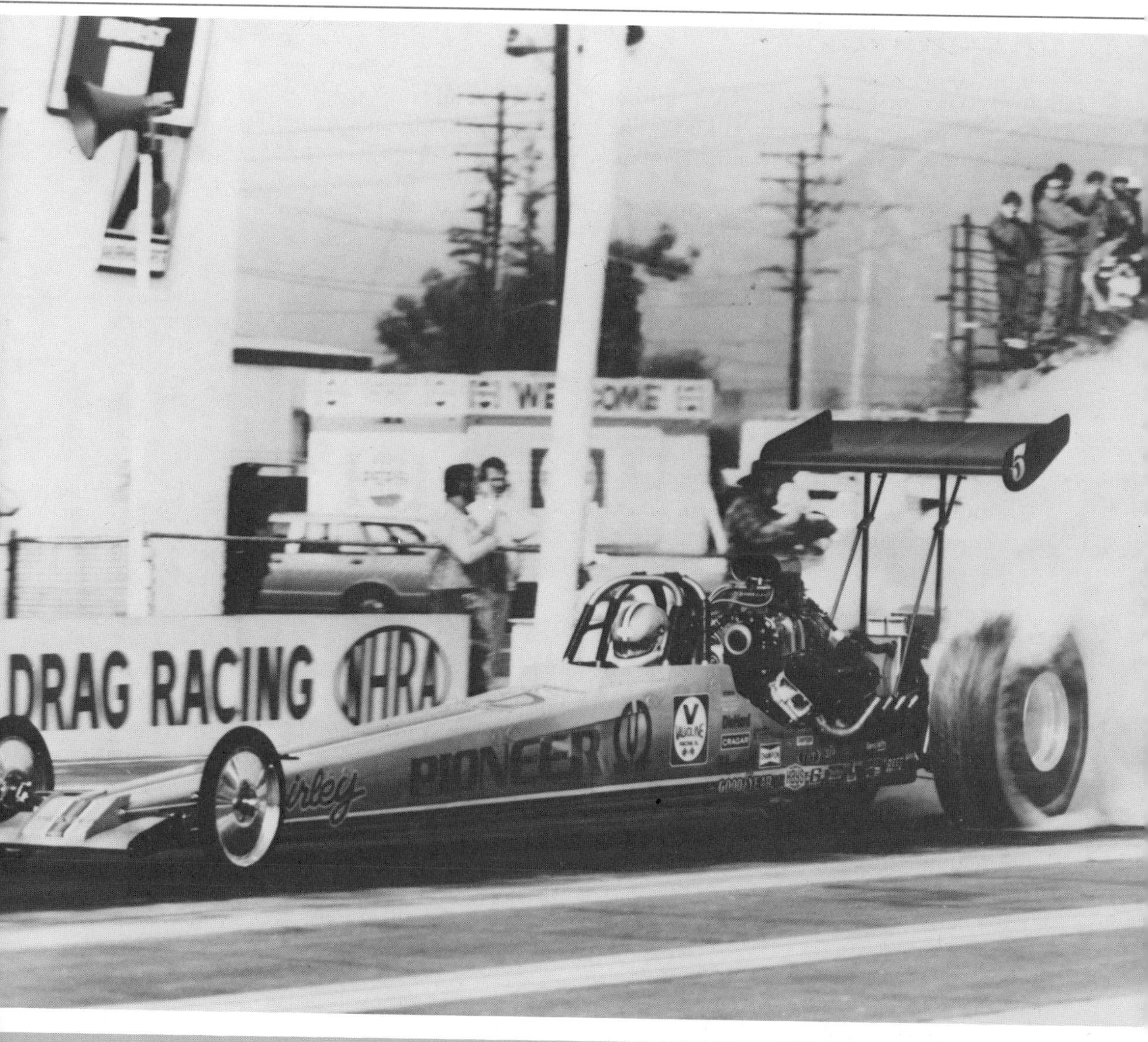

In a drag race, cars accelerate from a standing start towards a finish line a fixed distance away. How would you calculate the speed of the car at any moment during the race? (See *Example 2* in Section 5-3.)

5-1 TWO-TERM RATIOS

For nearly a century, the relationship between brain mass and body mass among mammals has been studied. The study shows that the mass of the human brain is about $\frac{1}{45}$ of the total body mass.

The relationship between brain mass, b, and total body mass, t, for human beings may be written as follows:

i) In fraction notation:

$$\frac{b}{t} = \frac{1}{45}$$

ii) In ratio notation:

$$b:t = 1:45$$

Fraction notation cannot be used if the denominator is 0.

The ratio $b:t$ is used to compare the masses of the brain and body. We say: "The ratio of brain mass to body mass is 1 to 45."

Multiplying or dividing each term of a ratio by the same non-zero number produces equivalent ratios.

These are equivalent ratios: $2:90 \quad 3:135 \quad 1:45$

or $\frac{2}{90} \quad \frac{3}{135} \quad \frac{1}{45}$

The ratio $1:45$ is in lowest terms because its terms have no common factor.

Example 1.

Write in lowest terms:

a) $65:85$

b) $12a^3b:8ab^2$

c) $(3x+6):(4x+8)$

Solution:

a) Divide both terms by 5, the g.c.f. (greatest common factor) of 65 and 85.
$65:85 = 13:17$

b) Divide both terms by $4ab$. ($a \neq 0$, $b \neq 0$)
$12a^3b:8ab^2 = 3a^2:2b$

c) Since $3x+6 = 3(x+2)$ and $4x+8 = 4(x+2)$, divide both terms by $(x+2)$.
$(3x+6):(4x+8) = 3:4$ $(x \neq -2)$

If x and y are two numbers in the ratio $a:b$, then there is a number k such that $x = ak$ and $y = bk$.

Example 2.

Find two numbers in the ratio 2 : 5 that have:

a) a sum of 63:

b) 261 as the sum of their squares.

Solution.

a) Let the two numbers be represented by $2k$ and $5k$. Since the sum of the numbers is 63:

$$2k + 5k = 63$$
$$7k = 63$$
$$k = 9$$

The numbers are: 2(9), or 18, and 5(9), or 45.

b) Since the sum of the squares of the numbers is 261,

$$(2k)^2 + (5k)^2 = 261$$
$$4k^2 + 25k^2 = 261$$
$$29k^2 = 261$$
$$k^2 = 9$$
$$k = 3 \text{ or } -3$$

The numbers are: 6 and 15, or −6 and −15.

Example 3.

To make a certain shade of orange paint 5 parts of red paint are mixed with 3 parts of yellow paint. What volumes of red and yellow paint are required to make 500 mL of orange paint?

Solution.

Let the volume of red paint, in millilitres, be $5k$. Let the volume of yellow paint, in millilitres, be $3k$.

Then, $5k + 3k = 500$

$$8k = 500$$
$$k = 62.5$$

The volume of red paint is 312.5 mL and the volume of yellow paint is 187.5 mL.

EXERCISES 5-1

(A)

1. Write in lowest terms:

a) $12:18$ b) $75:45$ c) $54:72$

d) $8x^2y : 10xy^2$ e) $15m^2n : 35mn$ f) $42a^3b^2 : 28ab^3$

g) $(2x - 4):(5x - 10)$ h) $(12a^2 + 28b):(9a^2 + 21b)$

2. The composition of three alloys is given. Express each as a ratio in lowest terms.

Bronze: Copper 90%, Tin 10%

Brass: Copper 60%, Zinc 40%

Pewter: Tin 75%, Lead 25%

3. Write a ratio in lowest terms for each of the following:
   a) Gina and Terry buy a $10 lottery ticket. Gina paid $6 and Terry $4.
   b) Of every 10 people alive today, 4 live in India or China.
   c) In Middletown High School, there are 40 teachers and 700 students.
   d) By the end of this century, 12% of the Canadian population will be retired.
   e) Only 22% of those who join the Canadian Armed Forces enlist for more than 5 years.
   f) The average adult has 30 kg of muscles and 1.5 kg of brains.

(B)

4. The ratio of silver to copper in sterling silver is 37 : 3.
   a) What percent of a sterling silver spoon is pure silver?
   b) How many grams of copper are there in 1 kg of sterling silver?
5. Two positive numbers are in the ratio 3 : 4. If the sum of their squares is 100, find the numbers.
6. Find two numbers in the ratio 8 : 3 that have:
   a) a sum of 77; b) a product of 216;
   c) 1825 as the sum of their squares.
7. Find two numbers in the ratio 5 : 9 that have:
   a) a sum of 252; b) a difference of 44; c) a product of 720;
   d) 424 as the sum of their squares.
8. A chainsaw motor is lubricated by adding 60 mL of oil to every litre of gasoline.
   a) Write the gasoline-to-oil ratio in lowest terms.
   b) What volumes of gasoline and oil are in 10 L of the mixture?
9. A microbe 0.002 mm long, seen under a microscope, appears to be 4 mm long. What is the magnifying power of the microscope?
10. An airplane travelling at twice the speed of sound is said to be travelling at Mach 2. At an altitude where the speed of sound is 1150 km/h, find:
    a) the Mach number corresponding to a speed of 3680 km/h;
    b) the speed corresponding to Mach 2.8.
11. a) Segment AB is 10 cm long. C is a point on AB such that $AC : CB = 3 : 4$. Find the lengths of AC and CB.
    b) Segment AB is x cm long. C is a point on AB such that $AC : CB = a : b$. Find the lengths of AC and CB.
12. In $\triangle ABC$, $\angle B = 90°$. If $AB : BC = 2 : 1$, find:
    a) $AB : AC$; b) $BC : AC$.

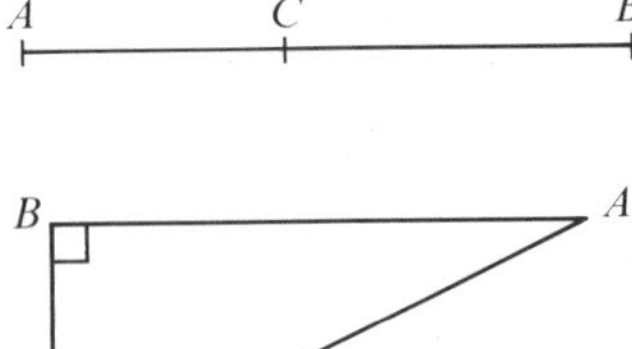

13. The length and width of a rectangle are in the ratio 3 : 2. Find the ratio:
    a) length : perimeter; b) length : diagonal;
    c) perimeter : diagonal.

14. The length and width of a rectangle are in the ratio 4 : 3. Find the length and width if:
    a) the perimeter is 182 cm;
    b) the area is 108 m^2;
    c) the length of a diagonal is 30 mm.

15. In an isosceles triangle, the two different sizes of angles are in the ratio 4 : 7. What are the angles?

16. If $x : y = 2 : 3$, evaluate:
    a) $\dfrac{4x - y}{x + y}$
    b) $\dfrac{5x - y}{x + 2y}$
    c) $\dfrac{x^2 - y^2}{x^2 + y^2}$

17. Find the ratio of x to y:
    a) $3x = 4y$
    b) $2x - 5y = 0$
    c) $7x + 2y = 0$
    d) $x^2 - 4y^2 = 0$

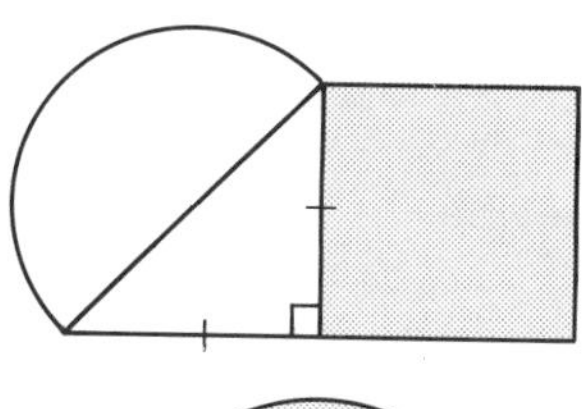

18. A semicircle is drawn on the hypotenuse of an isosceles right triangle. Find the ratio of the area of the semicircle to the area of the shaded square.

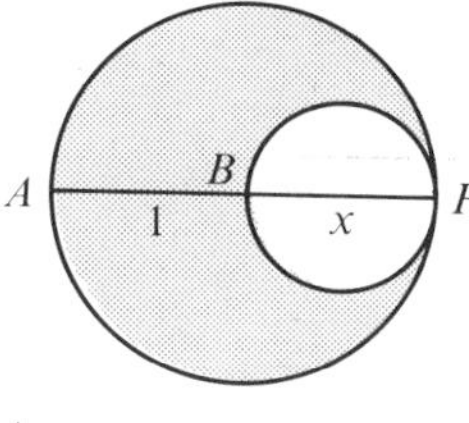

19. In the diagram, AP and BP are diameters of the two circles. If $AB = 1$ and $BP = x$,
    a) find the ratio of the unshaded area to the shaded area:
    b) for what value of x is the shaded area equal to the unshaded area?

20. Line segments AE and AF trisect the area of square $ABCD$. Find the ratios $BE : EC$ and $CF : FD$.

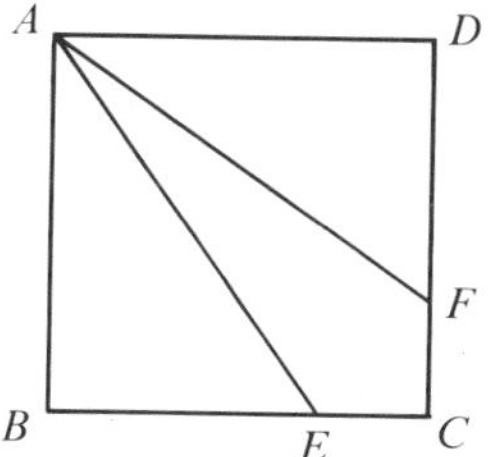

Ⓒ

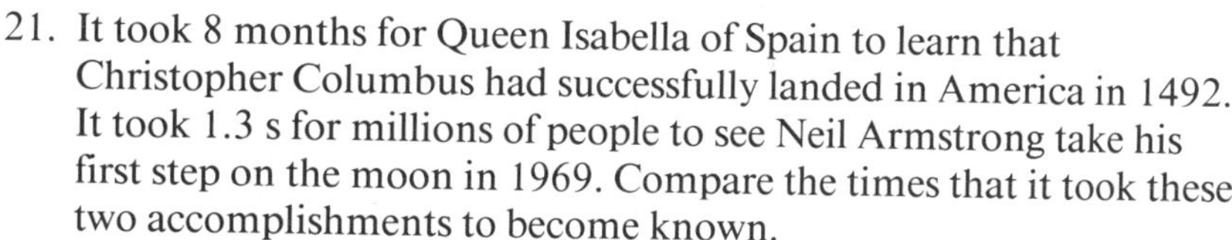

21. It took 8 months for Queen Isabella of Spain to learn that Christopher Columbus had successfully landed in America in 1492. It took 1.3 s for millions of people to see Neil Armstrong take his first step on the moon in 1969. Compare the times that it took these two accomplishments to become known.

22. a) Find the ratio of the sides of a rectangle that can be divided, as shown, into five squares.
    b) Is there any other way to divide a rectangle into five squares? If so, what is the ratio of its sides?

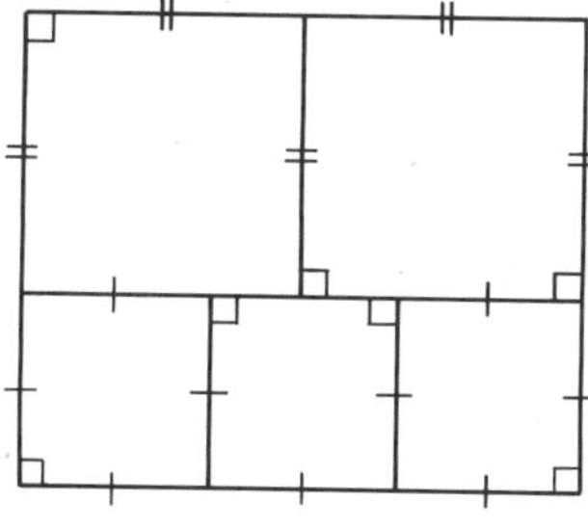

5-2 PROPORTIONS

The summit of Mt. Logan in the Yukon Territory is the highest point in Canada. An idea of its height can be obtained from the following statement.

The height of Mt. Logan compared to the height of Niagara Falls is the same as the height of a tall adult compared to the diameter of a dime.

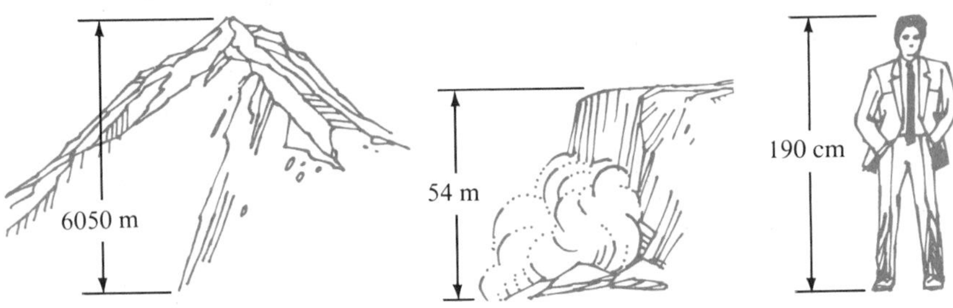

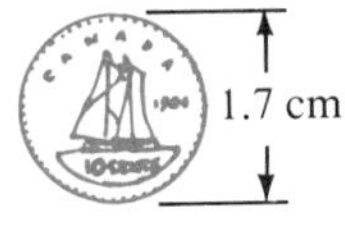

The above statement can be checked by evaluating the appropriate ratios.

$$\frac{\text{Height of Mt. Logan}}{\text{Height of Niagara Falls}} = \frac{6050 \text{ m}}{54 \text{ m}} \doteq 112$$

$$\frac{\text{Height of adult}}{\text{Diameter of dime}} = \frac{190 \text{ cm}}{1.7 \text{ cm}} \doteq 112$$

Since the values of the two ratios are approximately equal, the statement is correct.

A statement that two ratios are equivalent is called a **proportion**. A proportion may be written in two ways.

i) In ratio notation:

$a : b = c : d$

ii) In fraction notation:

$\frac{a}{b} = \frac{c}{d}\ (b \neq 0, d \neq 0)$

Either form leads to the equation: $ad = bc$. If three terms of this equation are known, the fourth can be found.

Example 1.

Find the unknown term:

a) $\frac{9}{16} = \frac{x}{24}$ b) $\frac{21}{a} = \frac{14}{45}$

Solution.

a)
$$\frac{9}{16} = \frac{x}{24}$$
$$16x = 9 \times 24$$
$$x = \frac{9 \times 24}{16}$$
$$x = 13.5$$

b)
$$\frac{21}{a} = \frac{14}{45}$$
$$14a = 21 \times 45$$
$$a = \frac{21 \times 45}{14}$$
$$a = 67.5$$

Example 2.

The ratio of the speed of sound in water to its speed in air is about 17 : 4. How fast does sound travel in water if its speed in air is 340 m/s?

Solution.

Let the speed of sound in water be w m/s.
Let the speed of sound in air be a m/s.

Then, $$\frac{w}{a} = \frac{17}{4}$$

Since $a = 340$, $$\frac{w}{340} = \frac{17}{4}$$

$$w = \frac{17 \times 340}{4}, \text{ or } 1445$$

The speed of sound in water is about 1445 m/s.

Example 3.

What number must be added to each term of the ratio 2 : 5 so that the result is equivalent to 3 : 4?

Solution.

Let the required number be x.

Then, $$\frac{2 + x}{5 + x} = \frac{3}{4}$$
$$4(2 + x) = 3(5 + x)$$
$$8 + 4x = 15 + 3x$$
$$x = 7$$

If 7 is added to each term of the ratio 2 : 5, the result is 9 : 12, which is equivalent to 3 : 4.

EXERCISES 5-2

Ⓐ

1. Find the missing term:

   a) $\frac{7}{12} = \frac{28}{x}$ b) $\frac{5}{8} = \frac{a}{40}$ c) $\frac{9}{20} = \frac{m}{50}$

   d) $\frac{14}{y} = \frac{63}{36}$ e) $\frac{c}{18} = \frac{11}{24}$ f) $\frac{15}{n} = \frac{24}{45}$

2. In a photograph, the length and mast height of a sailboat are 56 mm and 75 mm respectively. If the mast height is actually 12 m, how long is the boat?

3. On a map drawn to a scale of 1 : 1 500 000, two towns are 8 cm apart. What is the actual distance between the towns?

4. A section of a cell appears to be 8 mm long when viewed through an electron microscope with a magnifying power of 50 000 : 1. What is the section's actual length?

5. Air is a mixture of nitrogen and oxygen in the approximate ratio of 19 : 5 by volume. If a sample of air contains 323 m^3 of nitrogen, what volume of oxygen does it contain?

6. The table gives the lengths of some of the world's longest rivers. If the Nile River is represented by a segment 20 cm long, what would be the lengths of the segments representing the other rivers?

River	Length km
Nile	6650
Amazon	6275
Yangtze	5520
Mackenzie	4240
Volga	3690

7. What number must be subtracted from each term of the ratio 3 : 4 so that the result is equal to the ratio 1 : 2?

8. What number must be added to each term of the ratio 5 : 8 so that the result is equal to the ratio 4 : 5?

9. In a school, the ratio of the number of grade 11 students to the number of grade 12 students is 4 : 3. If there were 2 fewer students in grade 11 and 2 more students in grade 12, the ratio would be 5 : 4. How many students are in each grade?

Ⓑ

10. Find the ratio $x : y$:

    a) $5x = 2y$ b) $3x + 4y = 0$

    c) $3x - y = 5y$ d) $2x + 3y = x + 4y$

    e) $7x - 2y = 3y - 2x$ f) $ax + by = cx + dy$

11. An amoeba is a tiny, one-celled animal about 0.5 mm long. The length of an amoeba compared to the height of a Labrador Retriever is the same as the length of a bacterium compared to the height of a flea. Use the information in the illustration to find the approximate length of a bacterium.

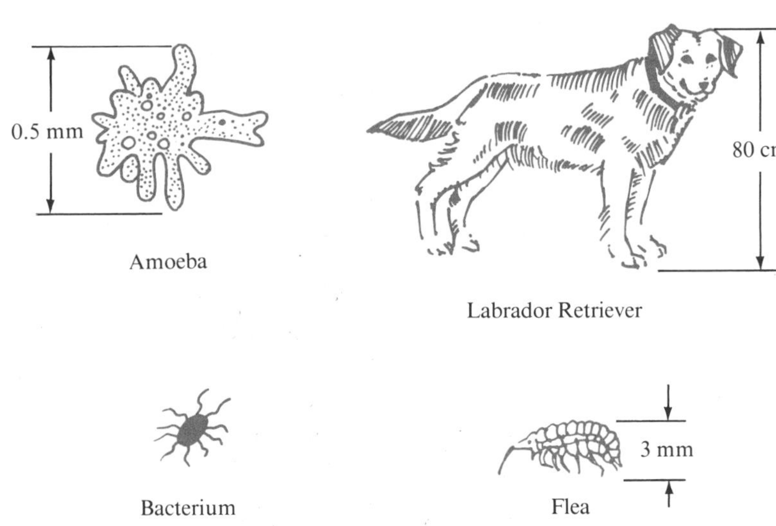

12. Canada's tallest totem pole is at Alert Bay, N.W.T. The height of the totem pole compared to the height of a 2 m door is the same as the height of an adult (170 cm) compared to the width of a playing card (6.3 cm). How high is the totem pole?
13. If Canada's coastline were straightened out and represented by the width of this page, then, on the same scale, the distance from Victoria, B.C. to St. John's, Nfld. would be represented by this dash—. If the distance from Victoria to St. John's is 5240 km, about how long is Canada's coastline?

Ⓒ

14. If $a:b = 2:3$ and $b:c = 4:5$, find $a:c$.
15. If $x:y = 2:5$ and $x:z = 3:2$, find $y:z$.

Properties of Proportions

For any given proportion $\frac{a}{b} = \frac{c}{d}$, $ad = bc$.

Given: $\frac{5}{3} = \frac{20}{12}$, then $5 \times 12 = 3 \times 20$.

From any proportion, many related proportions can be written. Some of these are shown below.

1. If $\frac{5}{3} = \frac{20}{12}$, then $\frac{3}{12} = \frac{5}{20}$.

   If $\frac{a}{b} = \frac{c}{d}$, then $\frac{b}{a} = \frac{d}{c}$.

2. If $\frac{5}{3} = \frac{20}{12}$, then $\frac{5}{20} = \frac{3}{12}$.

   If $\frac{a}{b} = \frac{c}{d}$, then $\frac{a}{c} = \frac{b}{d}$.

3. $\frac{5}{3} = \frac{20}{12}$, then $\frac{5+3}{3} = \frac{20+12}{12}$.

   If $\frac{a}{b} = \frac{c}{d}$, then $\frac{a+b}{b} = \frac{c+d}{d}$.

4. If $\frac{5}{3} = \frac{20}{12}$, then $\frac{5 + 2 \times 3}{3} = \frac{20 + 2 \times 12}{12}$.

   If $\frac{a}{b} = \frac{c}{d}$, then $\frac{a+2b}{b} = \frac{c+2d}{d}$.

5. If $\frac{5}{3} = \frac{20}{12}$, then $\frac{5+3}{5-3} = \frac{20+12}{20-12}$.

   If $\frac{a}{b} = \frac{c}{d}$, then $\frac{a+b}{a-b} = \frac{c+d}{c-d}$.

6. If $\frac{5}{3} = \frac{20}{12}$, then $\frac{5^2+3^2}{5^2-3^2} = \frac{20^2+12^2}{20^2-12^2}$

   If $\frac{a}{b} = \frac{c}{d}$, then $\frac{a^2+b^2}{a^2-b^2} = \frac{c^2+d^2}{c^2-d^2}$

We can verify any of the above proportions. One way is to start with something we know to be true.

For 2: If $\frac{a}{b} = \frac{c}{d}$, then $ad = bc$.

$$\text{and } \frac{ad}{cd} = \frac{bc}{cd}, \quad \text{dividing by } cd$$

$$\frac{a}{c} = \frac{b}{d}.$$

For 3: If $\frac{a}{b} = \frac{c}{d}$, then $ad = bc$,

and $ad + bd = bc + bd$ adding bd to both sides

$$d(a + b) = b(c + d)$$

$$\frac{a + b}{b} = \frac{c + d}{d} \quad \text{dividing by } bd$$

1. Try to verify properties 1, 4, 5, and 6.
2. Try to verify:
   a) If $\frac{a}{b} = \frac{c}{d}$, then $\frac{a + 2b}{a - 2b} = \frac{c + 2d}{c - 2d}$.
   b) If $\frac{a}{b} = \frac{c}{d}$, then $\frac{a + c}{b + d} = \frac{a}{b}$.
3. By examining the patterns in the above properties, find and verify other properties of proportions.

5-3 DIRECT VARIATION

If a car travels at a steady speed of 80 km/h, the amount of fuel consumed is related to the distance travelled. The table and the graph show this relationship.

Distance, d km	Fuel Consumed, f L
10	0.8
20	1.6
30	2.4
40	3.2

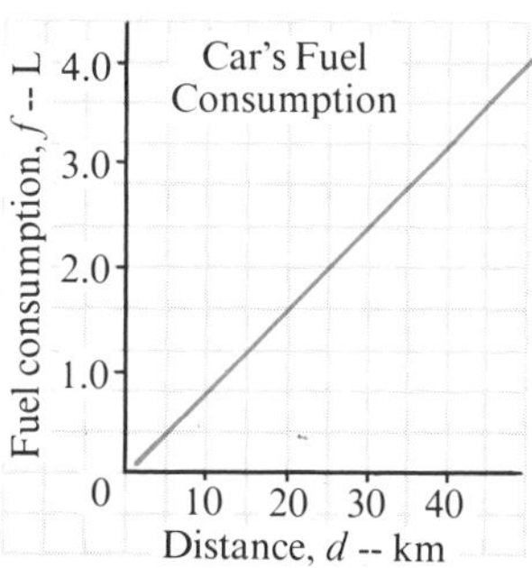

The table and graph show that when d is doubled, f is doubled; when d is tripled, f is tripled, and so on. Since ratios of corresponding values of f and d are constant:

$$\frac{f_1}{d_1} = \frac{f_2}{d_2}$$

This means that f is **directly proportional** to d, or f **varies directly** as d.

Example 1.

y is directly proportional to x. When $x = 12$, $y = 16$.

a) Find y when $x = 5$.

b) Find x when $y = 30$.

Solution.

Since y is directly proportional to x, $\frac{y_1}{x_1} = \frac{y_2}{x_2}$

a) Substitute 12 for x_1, 16 for y_1, and 5 for x_2:

$$\frac{16}{12} = \frac{y_2}{5}$$
$$12y_2 = 5 \times 16$$
$$y_2 = \frac{5 \times 16}{12}, \text{ or } 6.\overline{6}$$

b) Substitute 12 for x_1, 16 for y_1, and 30 for y_2:

$$\frac{16}{12} = \frac{30}{x_2}$$
$$16x_2 = 30 \times 12$$
$$x_2 = \frac{30 \times 12}{16}, \text{ or } 22.5$$

Some variation problems may involve powers or roots of the variables.

Example 2.

In a drag race, cars accelerate from a standing start towards a finish line a fixed distance away. Elapsed time and final speed are recorded. Shirley Muldowney once dragged a record 411.2 km/h in 5.56 s. If the speed at any moment varies directly as the square of the elapsed time:

a) calculate the speed after 4.00 s;

b) calculate the elapsed time when the car reaches a speed of 100 km/h.

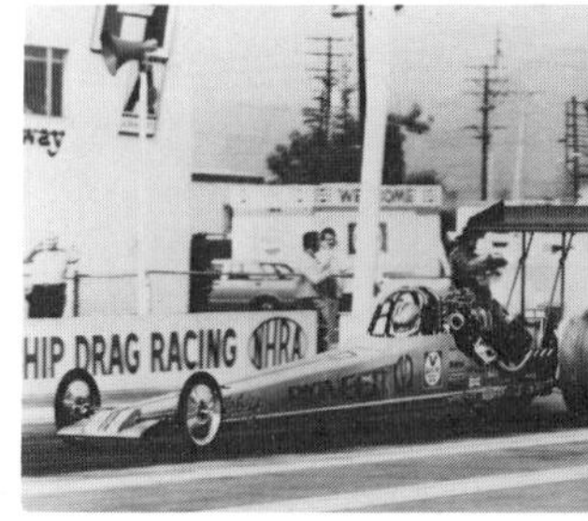

Solution.

Let v represent the speed in kilometres per hour, and t the elapsed time in seconds. Since v varies directly as t^2:

$$\frac{v_1}{t_1^2} = \frac{v_2}{t_2^2}$$

a) Substitute 411.2 for v_1, 5.56 for t_1, 4.00 for t_2:

$$\frac{411.2}{(5.56)^2} = \frac{v_2}{(4.00)^2}$$
$$v_2 = \frac{16 \times 411.2}{(5.56)^2}$$
$$\doteq 212.8$$

The speed after 4.00 s is 212.8 km/h.

b) Substitute 411.2 for v_1, 5.56 for t_1, 100 for v_2:

$$\frac{411.2}{(5.56)^2} = \frac{100}{t_2^2}$$

$$t_2^2 = \frac{(5.56)^2 \times 100}{411.2}$$

$$\doteq 7.52$$

$$t_2 \doteq \sqrt{7.52}, \text{ or } 2.74$$

The speed is 100 km/h after approximately 2.74 s.

One variable may vary directly as the product of two or more variables.

Example 3.

The stopping distance of a vehicle on an icy road is directly proportional to the product of its speed and the square of its mass. A 2 t car travelling at 50 km/h stops in a distance of 150 m. What is the stopping distance of a 3 t truck travelling at 60 km/h?

Solution.

Let the stopping distance of a vehicle of mass m t travelling at a speed of s km/h be d m. Since d varies directly with s and m^2:

$$\frac{d_1}{s_1 m_1^2} = \frac{d_2}{s_2 m_2^2}$$

Substitute 2 for m_1, 50 for s_1, 150 d_1, 3 for m_2, 60 for s_2:

$$\frac{150}{50 \times 4} = \frac{d_2}{60 \times 9}$$

$$d_2 = \frac{150 \times 60 \times 9}{50 \times 4}$$

$$= 405$$

A 3 t truck travelling at 60 km/h needs 405 m to stop.

EXERCISES 5-3

(A)

1. y is directly proportional to x. When $x = 12$, $y = 8$.
   a) Find y when $x = 21$.
   b) Find x when $y = 15$.
2. y varies directly as x. When $x = 15$, $y = 24$.
   a) Find y when $x = 4$.
   b) Find x when $y = 18$.
3. If y varies directly as x, find the missing numbers:

a)

x		3	5	7	13
y	−4		−10		

b)

x	2		15	45	
y		8		18	22

4. y is directly proportional to x^2. When $x = 5$, $y = 75$.
   a) Find y when $x = 4$.
   b) Find x when $y = 12$.

5. If y varies directly as x^2, find the missing numbers:

a)

x	2	3	4		7
y		13.5		54	

b)

x	−2	4			12
y		8	12.5	32	

6. A supertanker travelling at 25 km/h needs 5 km to come to a complete stop. If stopping distance is directly proportional to speed, what distance will it need to stop from a speed of 15 km/h?

7. The mass of a diamond varies directly as the cube of its diameter. A diamond with a mass of 1 carat has a diameter of 5 mm.
   a) What is the mass of a diamond with a diameter of 10 mm?
   b) What is the diameter of a 2 carat diamond?

(B)

8. It is estimated that the volume of blood in the human body varies directly as the body mass. If an 80 kg person has a blood volume of 6 L, find the blood volume of a 60 kg person.

9. The surface area of a sphere is directly proportional to the square of its diameter. If a baseball with a diameter of 7.4 cm has a surface area of 172 cm^2, find the surface area of a soccer ball, which has a diameter of 22.2 cm.

10. The volume of a sphere is directly proportional to the cube of its diameter. If a tennis ball with a diameter of 6.6 cm has a volume of 150 cm^3, find the volume of a basketball, which has a diameter of 24.4 cm.

11. At a constant oven temperature, the time to cook a turkey is directly proportional to the square root of its mass. If it takes 4.25 h to cook a 5 kg turkey, how long would it take to cook one weighing 8 kg?

12. On level ground, the distance to the horizon varies directly as the square root of the observer's height above the ground. If the distance to the horizon from a height of 100 m is 36 km,
    a) how far can you see from the top of Mount Royal, 234 m?
    b) from what height would the distance to the horizon be 400 km?

13. The volume of wood in a tree varies directly as the product of its height and the square of the average diameter of its trunk. A 15 m tree with an average trunk diameter of 50 cm contains about 2 m^3 of wood. How much wood is in a 25 m tree with an average trunk diameter of 75 cm?

14. In chemistry, Charles' Law states that if the pressure is kept constant, the volume of a gas varies directly with its absolute temperature. A balloon contains 2 L of helium at 10°C.
    a) What is its volume when the temperature is 30°C? 0°C?
    b) What is the temperature if its volume is 4 L? 1 L?

Absolute temperature is °C + 273°

15. If the pressure of a gas is kept constant, what happens to its volume if the absolute temperature is:
    a) doubled? b) tripled? c) divided by 2?

16. The mass of a cylindrical rod varies directly as the product of the length, the square of the radius, and the density of the material. A 3 m cylindrical rod of radius 2 cm and density 7.9 g/cm^3 has a mass of 29.8 kg.
    a) Find the mass of a 4 m rod of radius 3 cm and density:
       i) 7.9 g/cm^3; ii) 2.7 g/cm^3.
    b) Find the density of the material of a 4 m rod of radius 3 cm and mass 9.6 kg.

Ⓒ

17. For any planet, its year is the time that it takes to circle the sun once. Kepler's Third Law in astronomy states that, for any planet, the square of the number of Earth days in its year varies directly with the cube of its mean distance from the sun. Find the number of Earth days in the year of each of these planets:

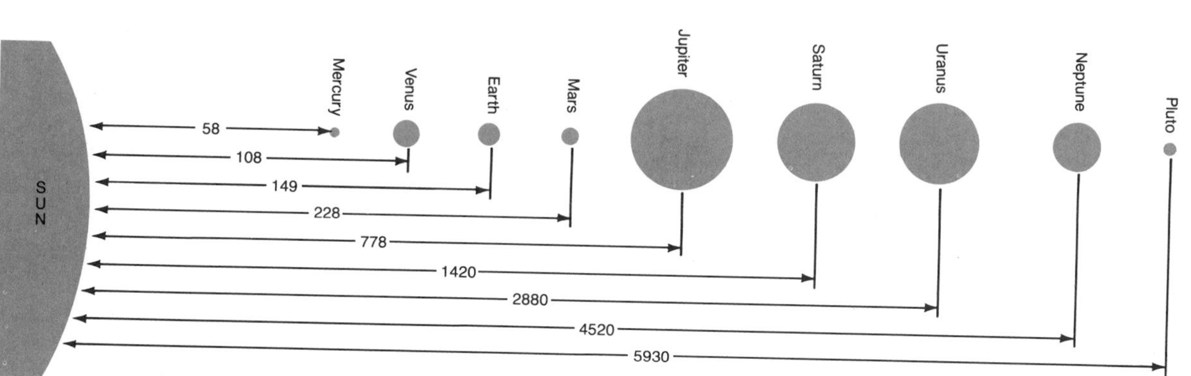

5-4 INVERSE VARIATION

The time it takes to ride, run, or walk a given distance is related to the average speed. The following table and graph show the variation of time with speed over a distance of 100 m.

Time, t s	Average Speed, v m/s
5	20.0
10	10.0
15	6.7
20	5.0
25	4.0
30	3.3

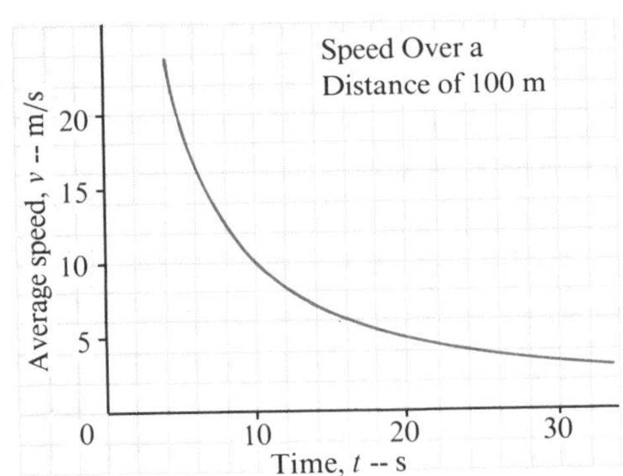

The table and graph show that when t is doubled, v is divided by 2; when t is tripled, v is divided by 3, and so on. That is, the product of v and t is constant:

$$v_1 t_1 = v_2 t_2$$

This means that v is **inversely proportional** to t, or v **varies inversely** as t.

Example 1.

y is inversely proportional to x. When $x = 3$, $y = 8$.
a) Find y when $x = 12$. b) Find x when $y = 4$.

Solution.

Since y is inversely proportional to x, $y_1 x_1 = y_2 x_2$.

a) Substitute 3 for x_1, 8 for y_1, and 12 for x_2:

$$(8)(3) = (y_2)(12)$$
$$12y_2 = 24$$
$$y_2 = 2$$

When $x = 12$, $y = 2$.

b) Substitute 3 for x_1, 8 for y_1, and 4 for y_2:

$$(8)(3) = (4)(x_2)$$
$$x_2 = 6$$

When $y = 4$, $x = 6$.

Example 2.

The number of trees that can be planted at a Christmas-tree farm varies inversely as the square of the average distance between the trees. When this distance is 3 m, about 1000 trees can be planted. How many more trees can be planted if the average distance between the trees is reduced to 2.5 m?

Solution.

Let n represent the number of trees, and d, in metres, represent the average distance between them. Since n varies inversely as d^2:

$$n_1d_1^2 = n_2d_2^2$$

Substitute 1000 for n_1, 3 for d_1, and 2.5 for d_2:

$$(1000)(3)^2 = (n_2)(2.5)^2$$
$$9000 = 6.25n_2$$
$$n_2 = \frac{9000}{6.25}, \text{ or } 1440$$

If the average distance is reduced to 2.5 m, about 1440 trees can be planted. This is 440 more than before.

Some variation problems involve both direct and inverse variation.

Example 3.

The pressure exerted on the floor by the heel of a shoe varies directly with the wearer's mass and inversely with the square of the width of the heel. A 75 kg man wearing shoes with heels 6 cm wide exerts a pressure of 200 kPa. Find the pressure exerted by a 50 kg woman wearing shoes with heels 2 cm wide.

Solution.

Let the pressure exerted on the floor by a person of mass m kg in shoes with a heel width of x cm be p kPa. Since p varies directly with m and inversely with x^2:

$$\frac{p_1x_1^2}{m_1} = \frac{p_2x_2^2}{m_2}$$

Substitute 200 for p_1, 6 for x_1, 75 for m_1, 2 for x_2, 50 for m_2:

$$\frac{(200)(36)}{75} = \frac{(p_2)(4)}{50}$$
$$p_2 = \frac{(50)(200)(36)}{(75)(4)}, \text{ or } 1200$$

A 50 kg woman with heels 2 cm wide exerts a pressure of 1200 kPa on the floor.

EXERCISES 5-4

1. y is inversely proportional to x. When $x = 8$, $y = 5$.
   a) Find y when $x = 4$. b) Find x when $y = 20$.
2. y varies inversely as x. When $x = 10$, $y = 6$.
   a) Find y when $x = 30$. b) Find x when $y = 12$.

3. Find the missing numbers:

a) y varies inversely as x.

x	2		6	12	15
y		20		5	

b) y varies inversely as x.

x	−3		2	4	
y		24	−6		−60

c) y varies inversely as x^2.

x	5	15		20	
y		4	9		144

d) y varies inversely as $\sqrt{x}$.

x	36	144		64	
y	8		12		96

4. The time required to fly from Quebec City to Vancouver is inversely proportional to the average speed. When the average speed is 350 km/h, the flying time is 11 h.
   a) How long does the trip take at an average speed of 550 km/h?
   b) What is the average speed if the time taken is 4.25 h?

5. The intensity of illumination of a screen is inversely proportional to the square of its distance from a projector. When the distance is 80 m, the intensity is 9 units.
   a) Find the intensity when the distance is:
      i) 60 m; ii) 100 m.
   b) What distance results in an intensity of:
      i) 12 units? ii) 36 units?

(B)

6. Boyle's Law states that if the temperature is kept constant, the volume of a gas varies inversely as the pressure. A tank contains 10 L of hydrogen at a pressure of 500 kPa. If the hydrogen is released into the atmosphere where the pressure is 100 kPa, what volume would it occupy?

7. If the temperature of a gas is kept constant, what happens to the volume when the pressure is:
   a) doubled? b) tripled? c) divided by 2?

8. The number of years required for an investment to double varies inversely as the interest rate. At 12% compound interest, an investment will double in about 6 years.
   a) How many years does it take for an investment to double at 8%? at 18%?
   b) At what interest rate will the investment double in 5 years?

9. The volume of a gas varies directly with the absolute temperature and inversely with the pressure. 25 L of oxygen at 10 000 kPa pressure and 5°C is released into the atmosphere where the pressure and temperature are 100 kPa and 25°C. What volume does it occupy?

10. In house construction, the safe load that can be supported by a horizontal joist varies directly with its thickness, t, the square of its height, h, and inversely with its length, l. The safe load of a 4 m joist of thickness 5 cm and height 20 cm is 2000 kg. What is the safe load of the joist if it is turned so that the thickness is 20 cm and the height 5 cm?

11. The electrical resistance of a wire varies directly with its length and inversely with the square of its cross section. If 500 m of 3 mm diameter wire have a resistance of 35 Ω (ohms), what is the resistance of 12 km of 5 mm wire of the same material?

12. The front sprockets of a ten-speed bicycle have 39 and 52 teeth. The back sprockets have 14, 17, 20, 24, and 28 teeth. The speed of the bicycle varies directly with the number of teeth on the front sprocket, inversely with the number of teeth on the rear sprocket, and directly with the rate of pedalling in revolutions per minute (r/min). With the 39-tooth front spocket engaged with the 20-tooth rear sprocket and the pedalling rate 45 r/min, the bicycle's speed is about 10 km/h.
    a) At a constant rate of pedalling, what gear selection gives:
       i) the highest speed? ii) the lowest speed?
    b) If the maximum rate of pedalling is 120 r/min, what is the top speed?

Ⓒ

13. The speed of a satellite varies inversely as the square root of its distance from Earth's centre. When the space shuttle is in orbit at an altitude of 200 km, its speed is 28 000 km/h. If the radius of Earth is 6370 km, find:
    a) the speed of the shuttle at an altitude of 500 km;
    b) the speed of the moon, which is about 384 700 km from Earth.

THE MATHEMATICAL MIND

Measuring the Earth

How would you determine the distance around Earth? This problem was first tackled by the ancient Greeks over two thousand years ago.

Eratosthenes (c. 276–192 B.C.) was the director of the great library at Alexandria. He was also an expert mathematician, astronomer, and geographer.

Eratosthenes knew that at noon, on the longest day of summer at the town of Syene, 5000 "stades" to the south of Alexandria, vertical objects had no shadows. This meant that the sun was directly overhead. But he also knew that at the same time in Alexandria, vertical objects did have shadows. He measured the inclination of the sun's rays and found them to be 7.5° to the vertical.

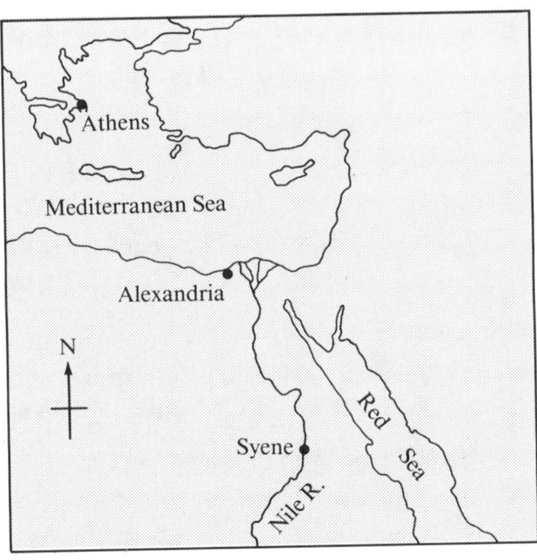

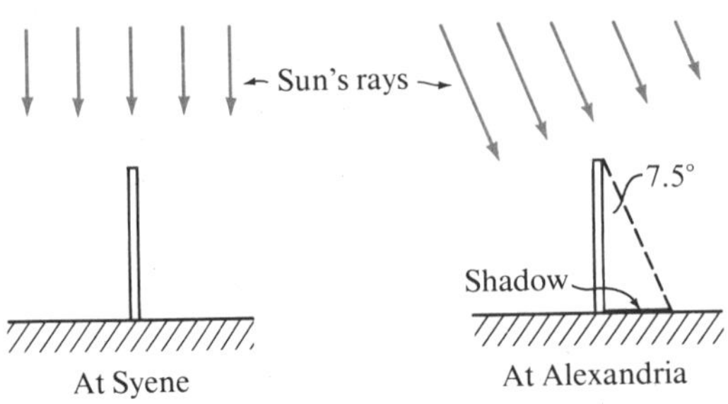

How is it possible that, at the same time, there are shadows at Alexandria but none at Syene? Eratosthenes realized that the only possible answer was that Earth is round. Further, the inclination of the sun's rays at Alexandria was the key to calculating the circumference.

Eratosthenes assumed that the sun was so far away that its rays at Syene and Alexandria are parallel, and drew a cross section of Earth.

If O is the centre of Earth, then

$\angle SOA = \angle OAB$ . . . alternate angles
$= 7.5°$

This is $\frac{7.5}{360}$, or $\frac{1}{48}$, of a complete rotation. Therefore, the distance from Syene to Alexandria is $\frac{1}{48}$ of the circumference of Earth. That is, the circumference is 48×5000, or 240 000 stades.

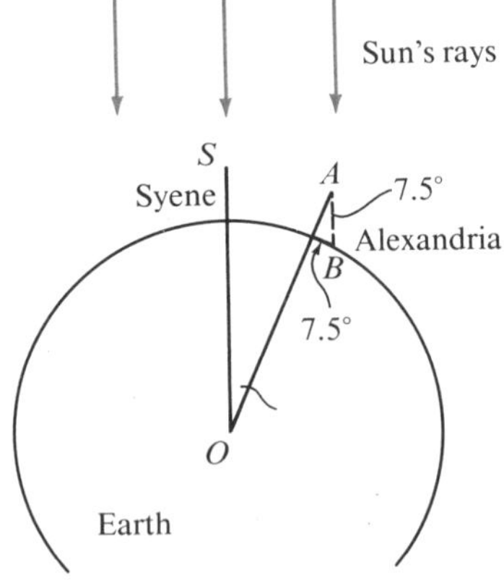

Although Eratosthenes did not know it, his estimate was surprisingly close to the correct value. This was a remarkable achievement, accomplished over two thousand years ago, using only simple instruments and a clever idea.

1. It is believed that 1 stade was about 157 m. Calculate, to the nearest kilometre, Eratosthenes' estimate of Earth's:
   a) circumference; b) radius.
2. The radius of Earth is about 6370 km. By what percent did Eratosthenes's estimate differ from the correct value?
3. What assumptions are involved in Eratosthenes' method?
4. Suggest how Eratosthenes was able to determine information about shadows in two widely separated locations on the same day of the year.

5-5 MULTI-TERM RATIOS

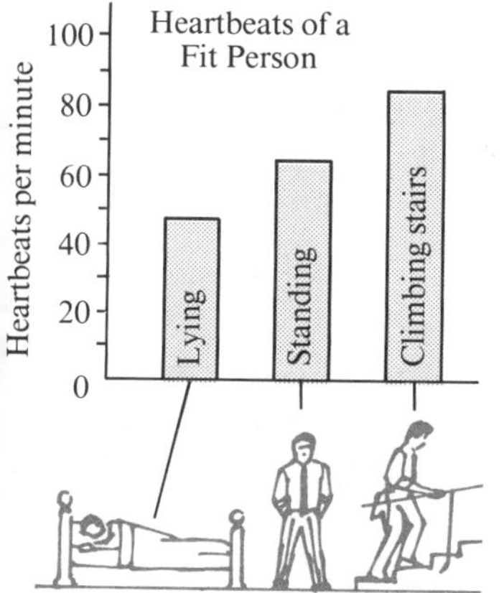

If l, s, and c represent the number of heartbeats per minute when a physically fit person is lying, standing, and climbing, then:

$$l : s : c = 48 : 65 : 85$$

The expression $l : s : c$ is an example of a 3-term ratio. As with 2-term ratios:

> Multiplying or dividing each term of a ratio by the same non-zero number produces equivalent ratios.

Example 1.

Write in lowest terms:

a) $36:24:54$ b) $12a^3:9a:6a^2$

Solution.

a) Since the g.c.f. of 36, 24, and 54 is 6,

$$36:24:54 = 6:4:9.$$

b) Since the g.c.f. of the three terms is $3a$,

$$12a^3:9a:6a^2 = 4a^2:3:2a \qquad (a \neq 0)$$

If $a:b:c = x:y:z$, there is a number k such that $a = kx$, $b = ky$, and $c = kz$. That is,

$$\frac{a}{x} = \frac{b}{y} = \frac{c}{z} = k$$

Example 2.

Solve for x and y:

a) $x:4:6 = 27:14:y$ b) $75:x:y = 30:9:12$

Solution.

a) From the given proportion,

$$\frac{x}{27} = \frac{4}{14} = \frac{6}{y}$$

Since $\frac{x}{27} = \frac{4}{14}$,

$$14x = 27 \times 4$$
$$x = \frac{27 \times 4}{14}$$
$$x = \frac{54}{7}$$

Since $\frac{4}{14} = \frac{6}{y}$,

$$4y = 14 \times 6$$
$$y = \frac{14 \times 6}{4}$$
$$y = 21$$

b) In lowest terms, $75:x:y = 10:3:4$.

$$\frac{75}{10} = \frac{x}{3} = \frac{y}{4}$$

Since $\frac{75}{10} = \frac{x}{3}$,

$$10x = 75 \times 3$$
$$x = 22.5$$

Since $\frac{75}{10} = \frac{y}{4}$,

$$10y = 75 \times 4$$
$$y = 30$$

Example 3.

A commemorative coin contains silver, copper, and nickel in the ratio $8:9:3$. How many grams of silver are there in the coin if it contains 4.2 g of nickel?

Solution.

If s is the number of grams of silver in the coin and c the number of grams of copper, then:

$$s:c:4.2 = 8:9:3.$$
$$\frac{s}{8} = \frac{4.2}{3}$$
$$3s = 8 \times 4.2$$
$$s = 11.2$$

There are 11.2 g of silver in the coin.

Example 4.

If $a:b = 7:2$ and $b:c = 3:4$, find:

a) $a:c$; b) $a:b:c$.

Solution.

a) Since $a:b = 7:2$, $\frac{a}{b} = \frac{7}{2}$

$$a = \frac{7}{2}b$$

Since $b:c = 3:4$, $\frac{b}{c} = \frac{3}{4}$

$$c = \frac{4}{3}b$$

Therefore, $\frac{a}{c} = \left(\frac{7}{2}b\right) \div \left(\frac{4}{3}b\right)$

$= \frac{7b}{2} \times \frac{3}{4b}$, or $\frac{21}{8}$

$a:c = 21:8$

b) From (a): When $a = 21$, $c = 8$

Since $\frac{a}{b} = \frac{7}{2}$, then $a = 21$, $b = 6$

Therefore, $a:b:c = 21:6:8$

EXERCISES 5-5

(A)

1. Write in lowest terms:
   a) $24:32:56$ b) $75:45:120$ c) $57:95:76$
   d) $15m^2n:40m^2n^2:25mn^2$ e) $18xy^2z^3:12xy^3z^2:21xy^2z^2$
   f) $28a^4b^2:42a^3b^3:63a^2b^4$ g) $153a^2b:51ab^2:102a^2b^2$
2. If $a:b:c = 15:12:18$, write in lowest terms:
   a) $a:b$; b) $b:c$; c) $a:c$.
3. If $x:y:z = 32:60:24$, write in lowest terms:
   a) $x:y$; b) $y:z$; c) $x:z$.
4. Solve for x and y:
   a) $8:11:x = 24:y:45$ b) $18:x:y = 54:75:36$
   c) $39:x:104 = y:10:16$ d) $12:9:18 = 30:x:y$
   e) $x:25:40 = 12:y:30$ f) $42:x:y = 28:45:65$
5. Solve for a and b:
   a) $20:18:a = b:12:10$ b) $36:57:75 = 18:a:b$
   c) $14:25:a = 35:b:120$ d) $a:23:30 = 2:46:b$
   e) $2a:7:15 = 10:14:3b$ f) $7:5a:17 = 14:10:6b$

(B)

6. Sheila, Murray, and Evelyn contribute \$12.50, \$8.00, and \$4.50 respectively to buy five \$5 lottery tickets. One of their tickets wins a prize of \$100 000. How should the money be divided?
7. If three people invest \$24 000, \$15 000, and \$6000 to set up a business, how should a profit of \$120 600 be divided?
8. If $\frac{a}{6} = \frac{b}{12} = \frac{c}{9}$, write in lowest terms:
   a) $a:b$; b) $b:c$; c) $a:c$; d) $a:b:c$.
9. If $2x = 3y = 4z$, write in lowest terms:
   a) $x:y$; b) $y:z$; c) $x:z$; d) $x:y:z$.
10. A punch recipe calls for lemonade, orange juice, and ginger ale in the ratio of $3:5:12$. If 15 L of punch are needed, what quantity of each ingredient is required?

11. The sides of a triangle are in the ratio 3:6:7. If the perimeter of the triangle is 128 cm, find its dimensions.
12. The angles of a triangle are in the ratio 3:4:5. What are their measures?
13. The angles of a quadrilateral are in the ratio 3:4:5:6. What are their measures?
14. The volume of a rectangular box is 7500 cm^3. If its dimensions are in the ratio 3:4:5, what are they?
15. If $x:y:z = 36:50:22$, find:
    a) $\frac{x}{y}$; b) $\frac{z}{y}$; c) $\frac{z}{x}$.
16. If $a:b = 3:2$ and $b:c = 4:3$, find:
    a) $a:c$; b) $a:b:c$.
17. If $x:y = 5:6$ and $x:z = 2:3$, find:
    a) $y:z$; b) $x:y:z$.
18. In 1976, the Royal Canadian Mint produced a 14*K* \$100 gold coin. Each coin contained gold, copper, zinc, and silver in the ratio 583:313:64:40, and had a mass of 13.337 g. If gold is priced at \$15/g, what is the value of its gold content?

19. The gravities on Mars, Earth, and Neptune are in the approximate ratio 5:14:18. How many times heavier would you be on Neptune than on Earth?

Ⓒ

20. If $\frac{a}{b} = \frac{b}{c} = \frac{c}{a}$, show that $a = b = c$.
21. Chemical fertilizers contain nitrogen, phosphorus, and potassium and the amount of each nutrient present is expressed as a percent of the total mass of fertilizer in a three-term ratio in that order.
    a) A 6:12:24 fertilizer is used to dress a field with 900 kg of potassium. How much nitrogen and phosphorus does the field receive?
    b) A field receives 320 kg of phosphorus in 14:4:8 fertilizer. How much fertilizer is used?
    c) How much nitrogen is contained in 700 kg of 21:7:7 fertilizer?
22. In a basketball game, Jean, Katherine, and Lorna score a total of 72 points. If the points scored by Jean and Katherine are in the ratio 2:7 and those scored by Katherine and Lorna are in the ratio 7:3, how many points did each score?

5-6 RATIO AND PROPORTION IN GEOMETRY

The first of these two pictures of a windsurfer is a 1.5x enlargement of the second. To check this, we measure the lengths of the corresponding sides of the triangular sails and compare their ratios.

$$\frac{AB}{DE} = \frac{5.0 \text{ cm}}{3.3 \text{ cm}} = 1.5$$
$$\frac{BC}{EF} = \frac{4.5 \text{ cm}}{3.0 \text{ cm}} = 1.5$$
$$\frac{AC}{DF} = \frac{2.7 \text{ cm}}{1.8 \text{ cm}} = 1.5$$

Since corresponding sides have the same ratio, we say that $\triangle ABC$ is *similar* to $\triangle DEF$, and write: $\triangle ABC \sim \triangle DEF$.

If we measure corresponding angles of $\triangle ABC$ and $\triangle DEF$, we find:

$$\angle A = 72^\circ \qquad \angle D = 72^\circ$$
$$\angle B = 35^\circ \qquad \angle E = 35^\circ$$
$$\angle C = 73^\circ \qquad \angle F = 73^\circ$$

Corresponding angles of the two triangles are equal. This is a property of similar triangles.

If the ratios of corresponding sides of two triangles are equal, the triangles are similar and corresponding angles are equal.

In triangles ABC and DEF,

if $\frac{AB}{DE} = \frac{BC}{EF} = \frac{AC}{DF}$, then

$\triangle ABC \sim \triangle DEF$, and $\angle A = \angle D$
$\angle B = \angle E$
$\angle C = \angle F$

A B C D E F

Conversely, it can be shown that:

If corresponding angles of two triangles are equal, the triangles are similar and corresponding sides have the same ratio.

In triangles ABC and DEF,

if $\begin{cases} \angle A = \angle D \\ \angle B = \angle E, \\ \angle C = \angle F \end{cases}$ then $\triangle ABC \sim \triangle DEF$

and $\frac{AB}{DE} = \frac{BC}{EF} = \frac{AC}{DF}$

A B C D E F

Example 1.

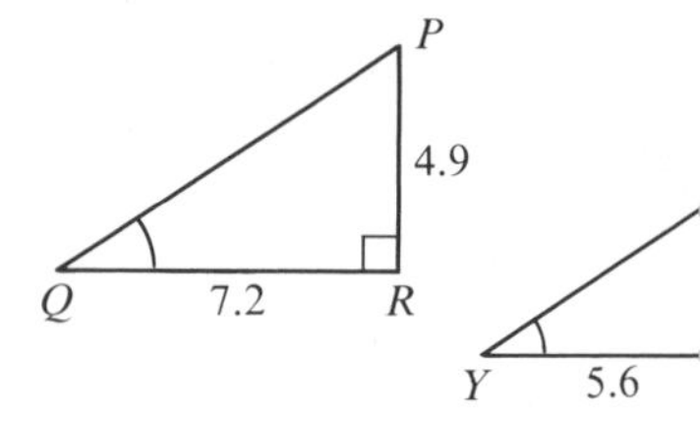

In right triangles PQR and XYZ, $\angle Q = \angle Y$.

a) Explain why $\triangle PQR \sim \triangle XYZ$.

b) Find the lengths of XZ and XY.

Solution.

a) Since $\angle Q = \angle Y$ and $\angle R = \angle Z$, $\angle P = \angle X$. Corresponding angles of the triangles are equal. $\triangle PQR \sim \triangle XYZ$

b) Since $\triangle PQR \sim \triangle XYZ$, $\dfrac{PQ}{XY} = \dfrac{QR}{YZ} = \dfrac{PR}{XZ}$

Substitute the given lengths for QR, PR, and YZ:

$$\frac{7.2}{5.6} = \frac{4.9}{XZ}$$

$$XZ = \frac{5.6 \times 4.9}{7.2}, \text{ or approximately 3.8 units}$$

$$\begin{aligned} XY &= \sqrt{YZ^2 + XZ^2} \\ &= \sqrt{(5.6)^2 + (3.8)^2} \\ &= \sqrt{45.8}, \text{ or approximately 6.8 units} \end{aligned}$$

Example 2.

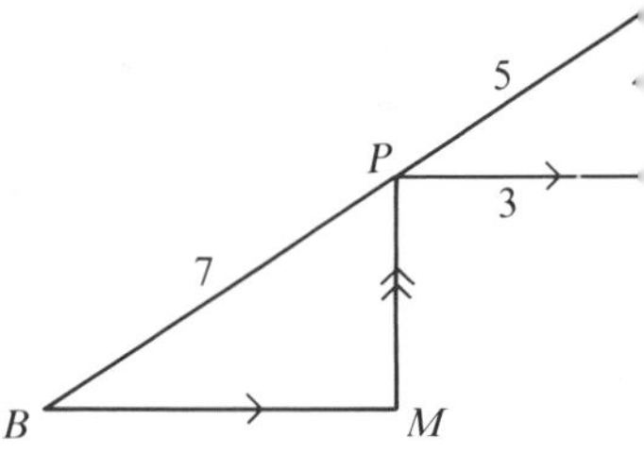

In the diagram, P is a point on line segment AB. $PN \| BM$ and $PM \| AN$. Find the length of BM.

Solution.

Since $PN \| BM$, $\angle PBM = \angle APN$
Since $PM \| AN$, $\angle BPM = \angle PAN$
Therefore, $\angle M = \angle N$
and, $\triangle BPM \sim \triangle PAN$

and, $$\frac{BP}{PA} = \frac{BM}{PN}$$

Substitute the given lengths for BP, PA, and PN:

$$\frac{7}{5} = \frac{BM}{3}$$

$$BM = \frac{21}{5}, \text{ or } 4.2$$

The length of BM is 4.2 units.

Example 3.

How can the distance from a tree on a sandy beach to an offshore lighthouse be determined?

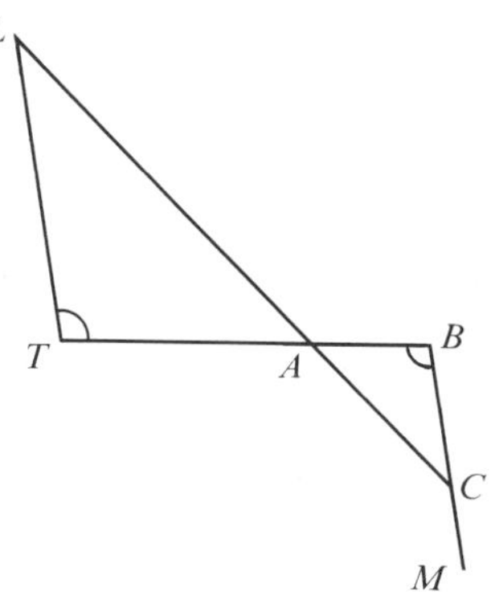

Solution.

From tree T, walk along the beach and place a marker at a suitable point B. At B, locate direction BM such that $\angle T = \angle B$. From any suitable point, C, on BM sight the lighthouse and place marker A where the line of sight intersects TB.

Since $\angle T = \angle B$, $\angle TAL = \angle BAC$, and $\angle L = \angle C$,

$$\triangle LTA \sim \triangle CBA$$

$$\text{and} \quad \frac{LT}{CB} = \frac{TA}{BA}$$

$$\text{Therefore,} \quad LT = \frac{CB \times TA}{BA}$$

By measuring the distances CB, TA, and BA on the beach and substituting in the above expression, the distance, LT, from the tree to the lighthouse can be determined.

EXERCISES 5-6

1. Write the ratios of corresponding sides:

a)

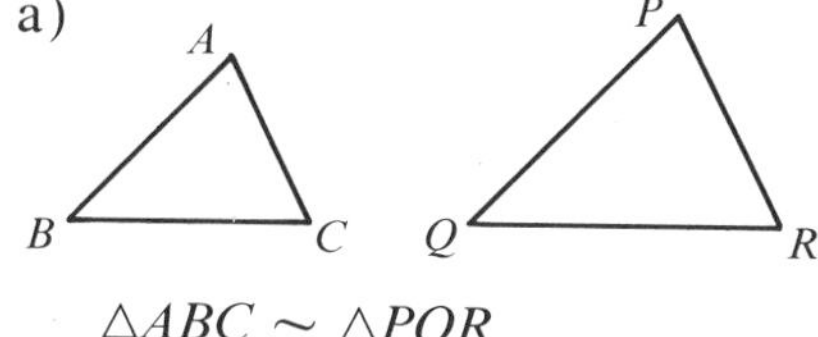

$\triangle ABC \sim \triangle PQR$

b)

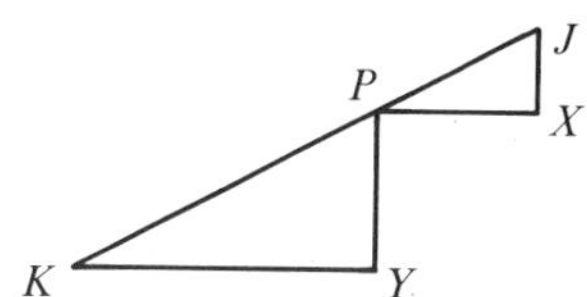

$\triangle JPX \sim \triangle PKY$

c)

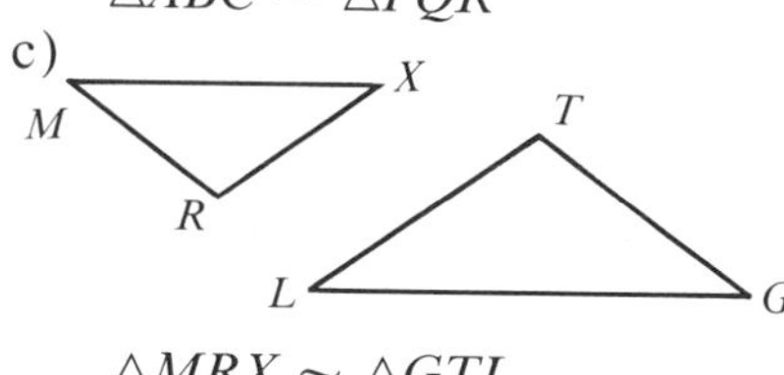

$\triangle MRX \sim \triangle GTL$

d)

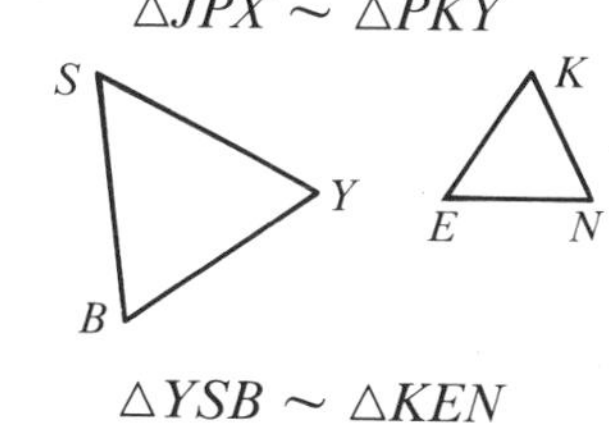

$\triangle YSB \sim \triangle KEN$

2. Find the value of x and y:

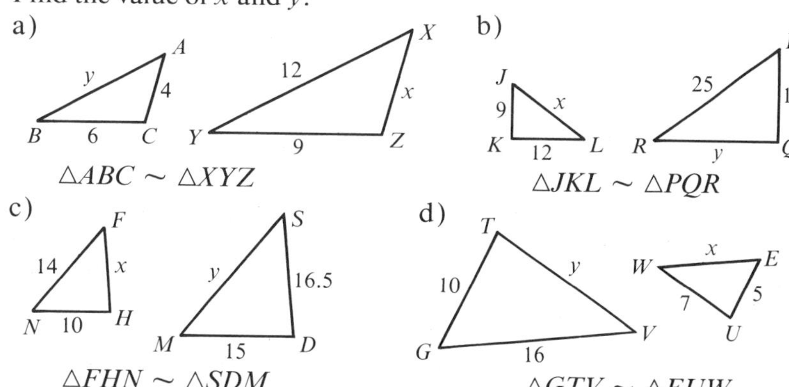

a) $\triangle ABC \sim \triangle XYZ$

b) $\triangle JKL \sim \triangle PQR$

c) $\triangle FHN \sim \triangle SDM$

d) $\triangle GTV \sim \triangle EUW$

3. a) Use ruler and compasses to construct:
   i) $\triangle PQR$ with sides of 6.0 cm, 8.0 cm, and 5.0 cm;
   ii) $\triangle XYZ$ with sides of 9.0 cm, 12.0 cm, and 7.5 cm.
   b) Determine the ratios of corresponding sides. Are the triangles similar?
   c) Measure the angles in each triangle. Are corresponding angles equal?
4. A tree 6 m tall casts a shadow 8 m long. How tall is a tree that casts a shadow 12 m long?

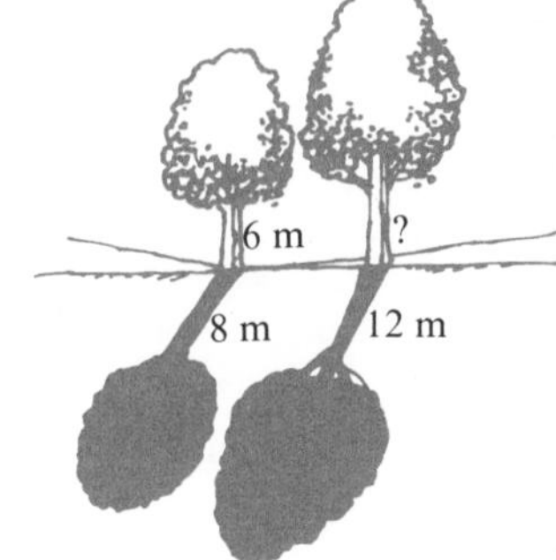

5. In *Example 3*, if $CB = 64.5$ m, $TA = 107.6$ m, and $AB = 4.9$ m, find the distance from the tree to the lighthouse.
6. A metre stick held vertically casts a shadow 1.5 m long. How tall is a building that casts a shadow 90 m long?

(B)

7. Find the values of x and y:
   a)

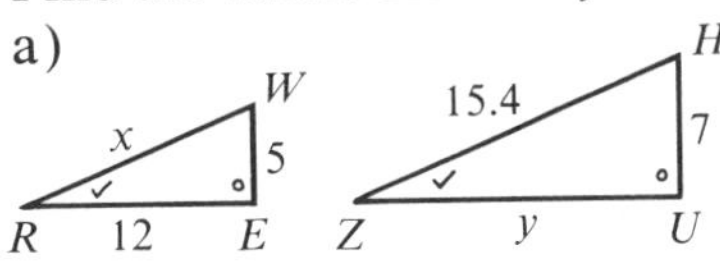

   b)

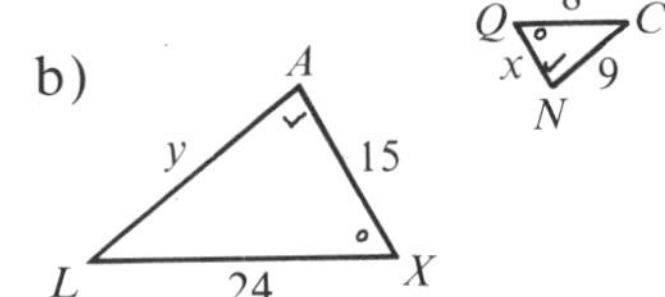

   c)

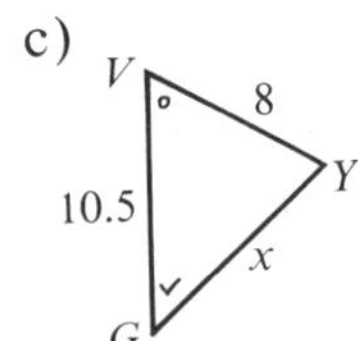

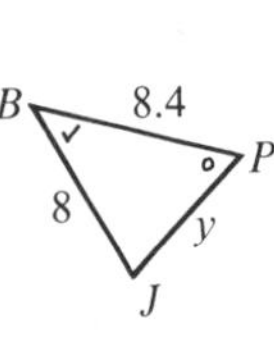

   d)

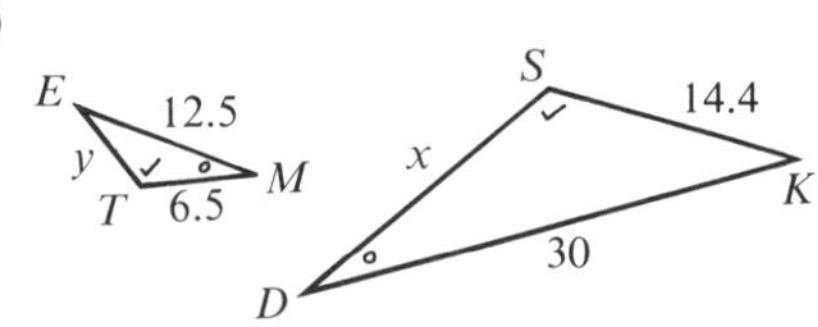

8. Find the value of x:
   a)

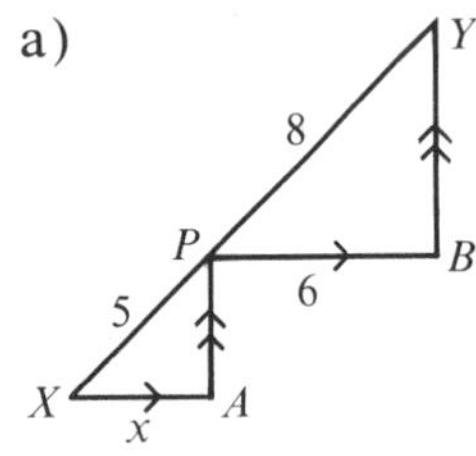

   b)

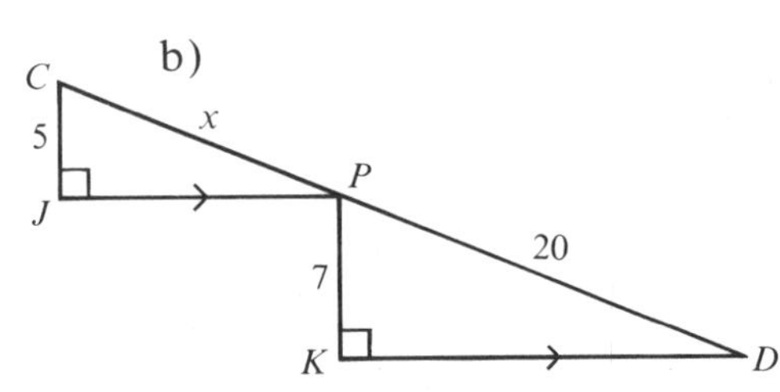

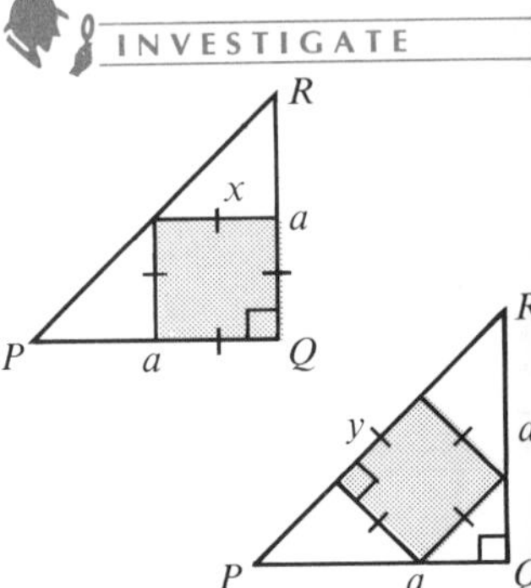

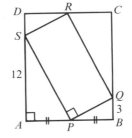

The diagrams show two ways of inscribing a square in a right isosceles triangle. Express x and y in terms of a.
Investigate similar problems with other right triangles.

9. In the diagram, $ABCD$ and $PQRS$ are rectangles. Find:
   i) the length of AP;
   ii) the ratio $PS:PQ$.

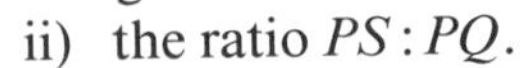

   a)

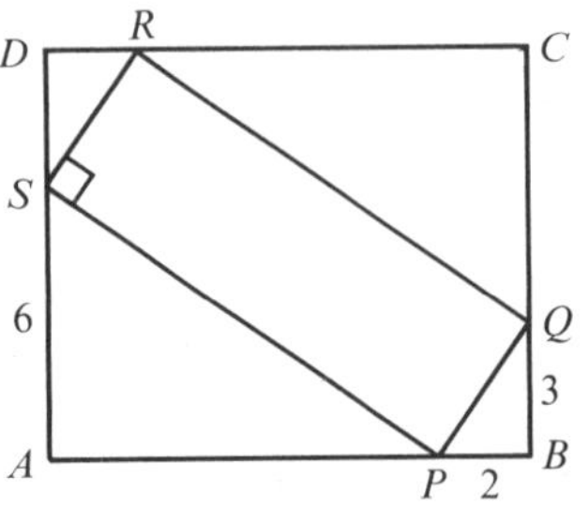

   b)

D R C S 12 Q 3 A P B

INVESTIGATE

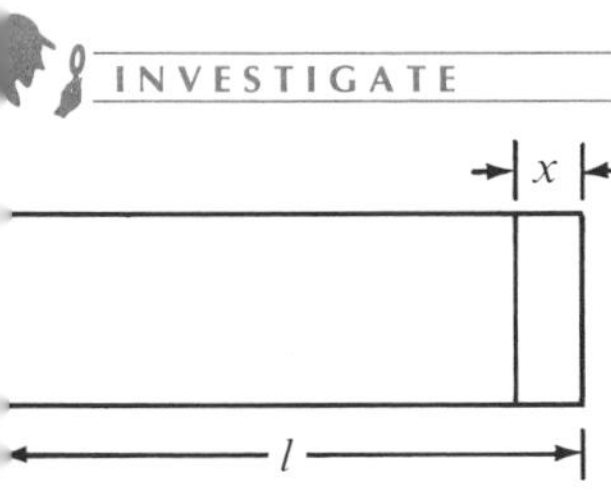

he diagram shows a rectangle hich is divided into two simi- r rectangles. Express x in rms of l.

10. $\triangle ABC$ (below left) is a right triangle with $AC = 6$ cm, $BC = 3$ cm. and $\angle C = 90°$. Find the side length of square $CDEF$.

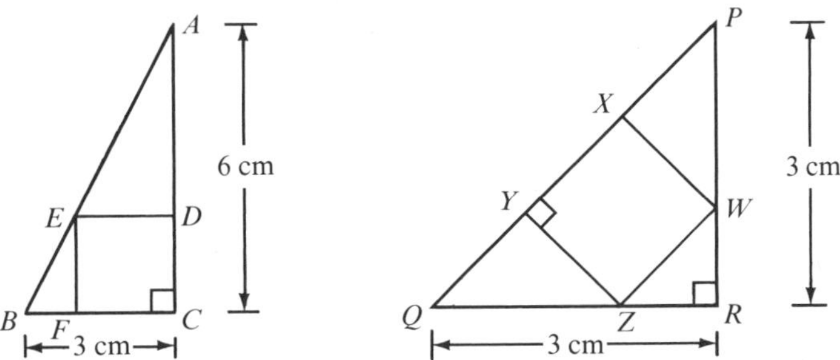

11. $\triangle PQR$ (above, right) is an isosceles right triangle with $PR = QR =$ 3 cm.
    a) Find the side length of square $WXYZ$.
    b) What is the ratio of the area of the square to the area of $\triangle PQR$?

12. P is a point on side BC of rectangle $ABCD$ (below, left) such that $\triangle ABP \sim \triangle PCD$. If $BP = 16$ cm and $DC = 12$ cm,
    a) find the lengths of PC, PA, and PD;
    b) show that $\triangle ABP \sim \triangle DPA$.

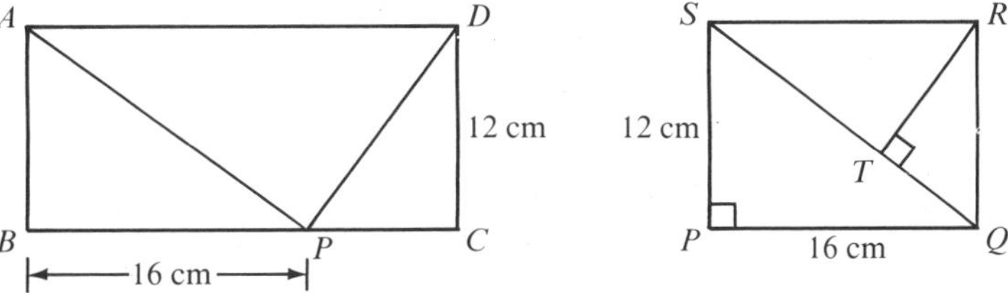

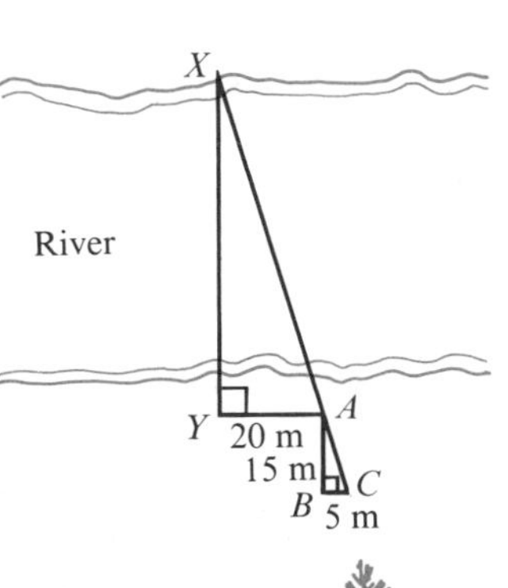

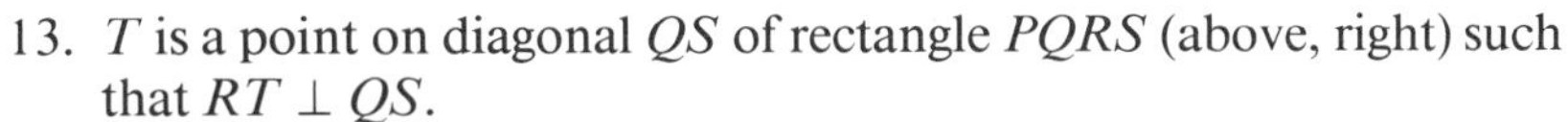

13. T is a point on diagonal QS of rectangle $PQRS$ (above, right) such that $RT \perp QS$.
    a) Show that the triangles PQS, TSR, and TQR are all similar.
    b) If $PQ = 16$ cm and $PS = 12$ cm, find the lengths of RT, ST, and QT.

14. Use the information in the diagram to determine the distance, XY, across the river.

15. To measure the distance across a pond, Gerry marks two trees, X and Y, and drives a stake at S. She finds points A and B which line up with the stake and the trees such that $\angle A = \angle Y$. If $SY = 120$ m, $AS = 15$ m, and $AB = 24$ m, find the distance, XY, across the pond.

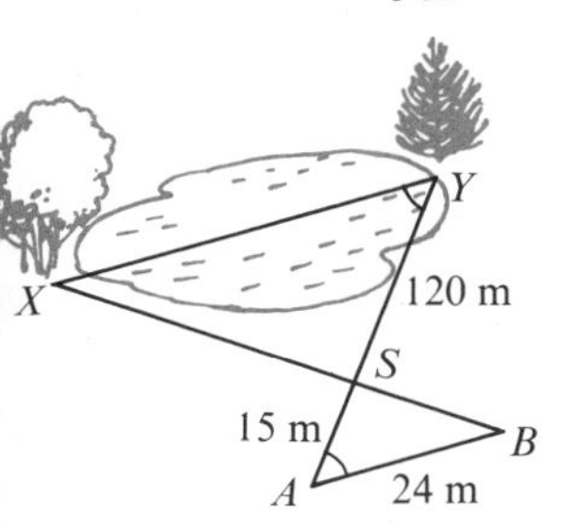

Ⓒ

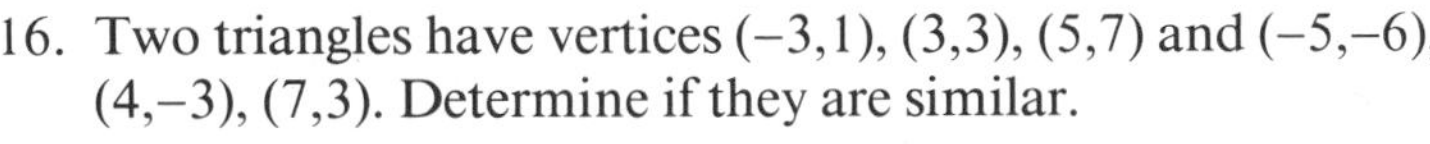

16. Two triangles have vertices $(-3,1)$, $(3,3)$, $(5,7)$ and $(-5,-6)$, $(4,-3)$, $(7,3)$. Determine if they are similar.

MATHEMATICS AROUND US

The Terrestrial Year

Scientists estimate that planet Earth is about 4 billion years old. If we imagine that this time is compressed into a single year, we can express events that occurred in the past as dates or times in this "terrestrial" year.

For example, the dinosaurs appeared on Earth about 200 million years ago. This is illustrated on the diagram below.

The date during the terrestrial year corresponding to the appearance of the dinosaurs can be calculated from the proportion:

$$\frac{\text{age in terrestrial year}}{\text{days in terrestrial year}} = \frac{\text{actual age}}{\text{age of Earth}}$$

$$\frac{x}{365} = \frac{200 \times 10^6}{4 \times 10^9}$$

$$x = 18.25$$

The dinosaurs appeared about 18 days before December 31, that is, on December 13 during the terrestrial year.

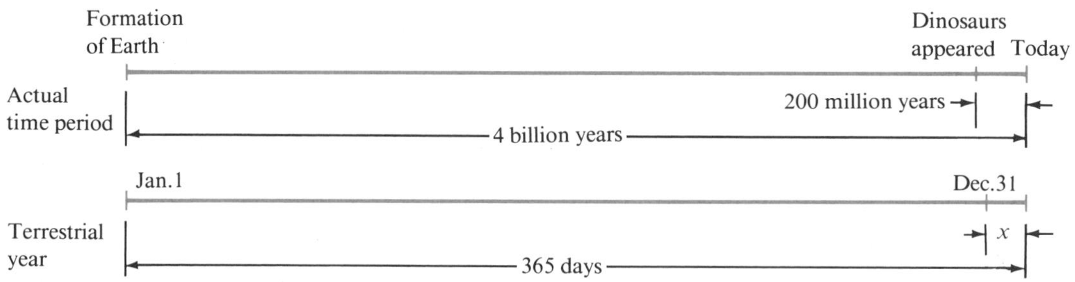

QUESTIONS

1. There are 365 days in a year. Express this time in
   a) hours; b) minutes; c) seconds.
2. About how many years are represented by the following time intervals in the terrestrial year?
   a) 1 month b) 1 week c) 1 h
   d) 1 min e) 1 s
3. Determine, approximately, when these events would occur during the terrestrial year.

Event	Estimated time ago
Oldest fossils	3 billion years
Extinction of dinosaurs	65 million years
First humans appeared	3 million years
End of the last ice age	10 000 years
Beginning of recorded history	5000 years
Canadian confederation	120 years

Review Exercises

1. Write in lowest terms:
   a) 78 : 169 b) $51a : 119ab$ c) $(3x+9):(2x+6)$
2. Find two numbers in the ratio 3 : 7 that have:
   a) a sum of 70; b) a product of 4116;
   c) 9802 as the sum of their squares.
3. Passengers and crew carried by the *Mayflower* numbered about 130. Passengers and crew of the *Queen Elizabeth 2* number 2930. Compare the numbers aboard the two ships.
4. Find x:
   a) $\frac{27}{39} = \frac{x}{26}$ b) $\frac{76}{32} = \frac{57}{x}$
5. The ratio of the speed of sound at sea level to the speed of sound at 10 500 m is approximately 8 : 7. If the speed of sound at sea level is 340 m/s, what is it at 10 500 m?
6. What number must be added to each term of the ratio 5 : 7 so that the result is equivalent to the ratio 10 : 11?
7. In a school the ratio of the number of grade 11 students to the number of grade 12 students is 4 : 3. If there were 5 fewer students in grade 11 and 3 more students in grade 12, the ratio would be 7 : 6. How many students are in each grade?
8. If y varies directly as x, find the missing numbers:

a)

x	3			−2.5
y		−6	4	10

b)

x		−10	−2	4
y	8		$-\frac{1}{2}$	

9. The value of a certain type of diamond is directly proportional to the square of its mass. One of these diamonds has a mass of 2 carats and is worth \$3000.
   a) What is the value of a 3 carat diamond of the same type?
   b) What is the mass of a diamond worth \$1000?
10. Find the missing numbers:

a) t varies directly as $\sqrt{x}$.

t		18	24	30
x	4			25

b) x varies directly as the product yz^2.

x	6		144	24
y	16	2		$\frac{1}{4}$
z	$\frac{1}{2}$	2	6	

11. The mass of a cylinder varies directly as the product of the length, the square of the radius, and the density of the material. A cylinder of length 50 cm, radius 3.0 cm, and density 2.7 g/cm^3 has a mass of 3.8 kg.
    a) Find the mass of a cylinder 75 cm long, with radius 2.5 cm, and density: i) 2.7 g/cm^3; ii) 7.9 g/ cm^3.
    b) Find the density of the material of a cylinder 90 cm long, 3.5 cm radius, with mass 32.73 kg.

12. Find the missing numbers:
    a) y varies inversely as x.

x		-9		18
y	-2		12	8

    b) y varies inversely as x^2.

x		2		$\frac{1}{2}$
y	3	12	$\frac{1}{3}$	

13. The time taken to drive from Ottawa to Toronto is inversely proportional to the average speed. When the average speed is 80 km/h the driving time is 5 h.
    a) How long does it take at 75 km/h?
    b) What is the average speed if the time taken is 4 h 10 min?

14. Find the missing numbers:
    a) w varies inversely as $\sqrt{x}$.

w	5		2	$1.\overline{6}$
x		16	25	

    b) l varies directly as m^2 and inversely as n.

l	16	40	2	
m	0.4		0.5	0.8
n		25	125	32

15. Solve for x and y:
    a) $x:8:12=9:18:y$ b) $65:x:y=5:2:6$

16. The angles of a triangle are in the ratio $8:9:13$. What are their measures?

17. The angles of a quadrilateral are in the ratio $7:10:13:15$. What are their measures?

18. The volume of a rectangular box is 13 440 cm^3. If its dimensions are in the ratio $5:6:7$, what are they?

19. A vertical metre stick casts a shadow 1.25 m long. How tall is a building that casts a shadow 88 m long?

20. Use the information in the diagram to find the distance, XY, across the river.

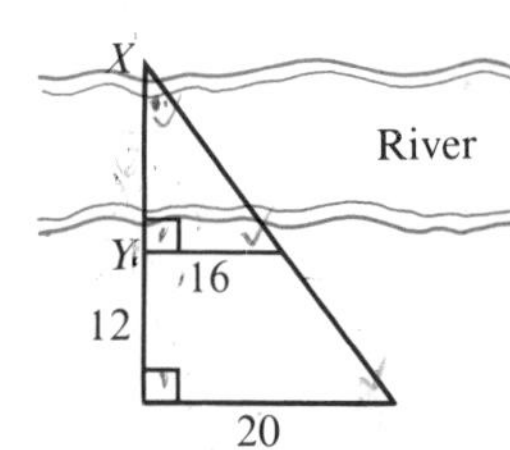

6 Analytic Geometry: Lines and Circles

How would you find the radius of a highway tunnel, which is an arc of a circle, if you know its width and maximum height? (See *Example 2* in Section 6-10.)

6-1 LENGTH AND MIDPOINT OF A LINE SEGMENT

In the Cartesian coordinate system, the positions of points in the plane are represented by ordered pairs (x, y). One advantage of this system is that the distance between any two points is easily found.

Length of a Line Segment

In the Hibernia Oil Fields off the coast of Newfoundland, the Canadian Coast Guard sights an iceberg on a possible collision course with an oil rig. On a map, the navigator uses ordered pairs to plot the positions of the rig, R, and iceberg, I. If the units are kilometres, how far is the iceberg from the oil rig?

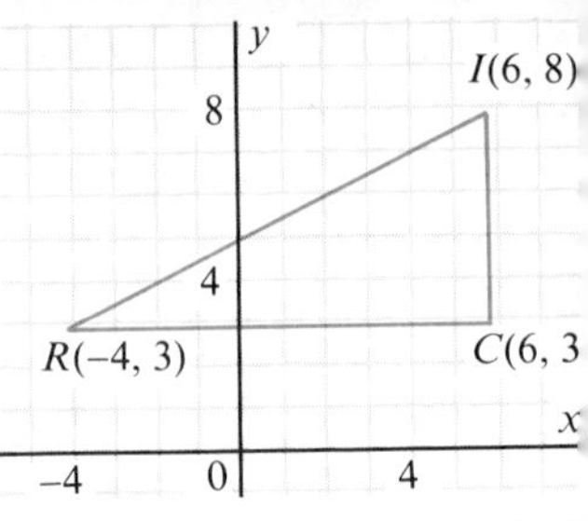

On the grid, line segments RC and IC are parallel to the x- and y-axes respectively. Therefore,

$$RC = |6 - (-4)| = 10 \quad \text{and} \quad IC = |8 - 3| = 5$$

The length of RI is found by the Pythagorean theorem:

$$\begin{aligned} RI^2 &= RC^2 + IC^2 \\ &= 10^2 + 5^2 \\ &= 125 \\ RI &= \sqrt{125} \\ &\doteq 11.2 \end{aligned}$$

The negative root is ignored since distances cannot be negative.

The iceberg is about 11.2 km from the oil rig.

The distance between any two points $P_1(x_1, y_1)$ and $P_2(x_2, y_2)$ is given by the formula:

$$P_1P_2 = \sqrt{(x_2 - x_1)^2 + (y_2 - y_1)^2}$$

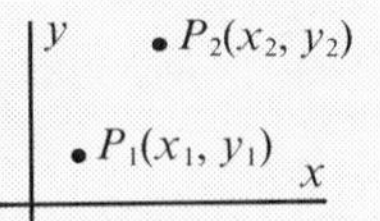

Example 1.

A triangle has vertices $R(-2, 4)$, $S(4, 1)$, and $T(2, -3)$.

a) Graph $\triangle RST$ and find the lengths of its sides correct to one decimal place.

b) Determine if $\triangle RST$ is a right triangle.

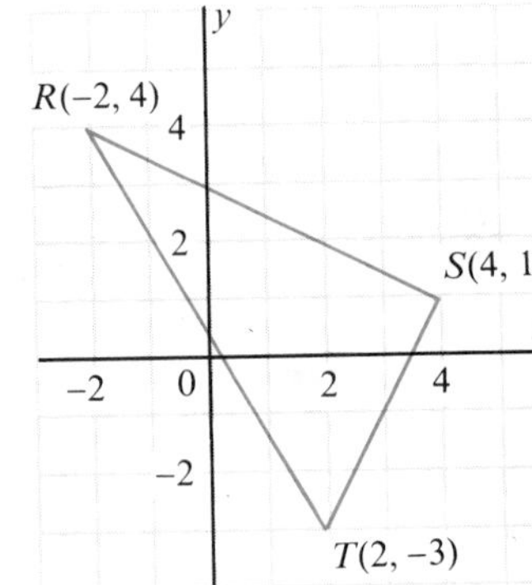

Solution.

a) $$\begin{aligned} RS &= \sqrt{[4 - (-2)]^2 + (1 - 4)^2} \\ &= \sqrt{45} \\ &\doteq 6.7 \\ ST &= \sqrt{(2 - 4)^2 + (-3 - 1)^2} \\ &= \sqrt{20} \\ &\doteq 4.5 \\ RT &= \sqrt{[2 - (-2)]^2 + (-3 - 4)^2} \\ &= \sqrt{65} \\ &\doteq 8.1 \end{aligned}$$

b) If $\triangle RST$ is a right triangle, the longest side, RT, will be the hypotenuse and $RT^2 = RS^2 + ST^2$.

$$RT^2 = (\sqrt{65})^2 \qquad RS^2 + ST^2 = (\sqrt{45})^2 + (\sqrt{20})^2$$
$$= 65 \qquad\qquad = 45 + 20, \text{ or } 65$$

Since $RT^2 = RS^2 + ST^2$, $\triangle RST$ is a right triangle.

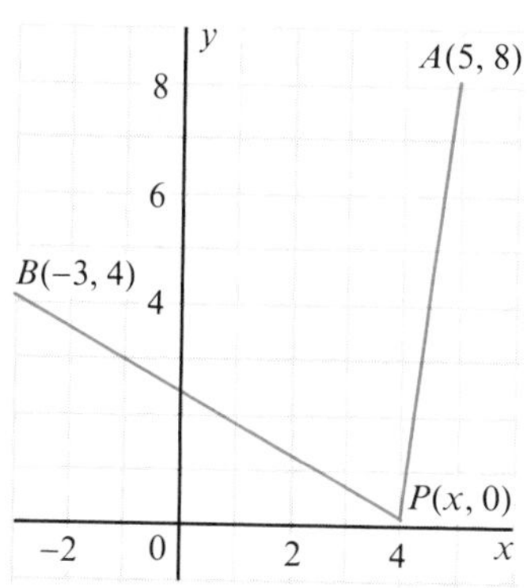

Example 2.

Find the coordinates of the point on the x-axis which is equidistant from $A(5, 8)$ and $B(-3, 4)$.

Solution.

Let $P(x, 0)$ be the required point.

$PA = \sqrt{(5 - x)^2 + (8 - 0)^2}$ and $PB = \sqrt{(-3 - x)^2 + (4 - 0)^2}$

Since P is equidistant from A and B, $PA = PB$.

$$\sqrt{(5 - x)^2 + (8 - 0)^2} = \sqrt{(-3 - x)^2 + (4 - 0)^2}$$

Square both sides:

$$(5 - x)^2 + 64 = (-3 - x)^2 + 16$$
$$25 - 10x + x^2 + 64 = 9 + 6x + x^2 + 16$$
$$\text{Therefore,} \quad x = 4$$

The point $(4, 0)$ is equidistant from $A(5, 8)$ and $B(-3, 4)$.

Check.

$PA = \sqrt{65}$ and $PB = \sqrt{65}$. The solution is correct.

Midpoint of a Line Segment

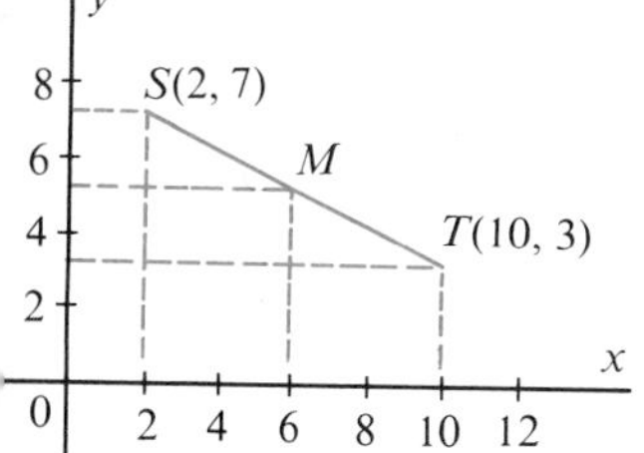

The Coast Guard sights another iceberg, M, halfway between two other oil rigs, S and T. If the coordinates of S and T are as shown, what are the coordinates of M?

M is the midpoint of line segment ST. Perpendiculars are drawn from T, M, and S to the axes. It appears that the coordinates of M are the means of the coordinates of S and T.

x-coordinate of M: $\dfrac{2 + 10}{2} = 6$

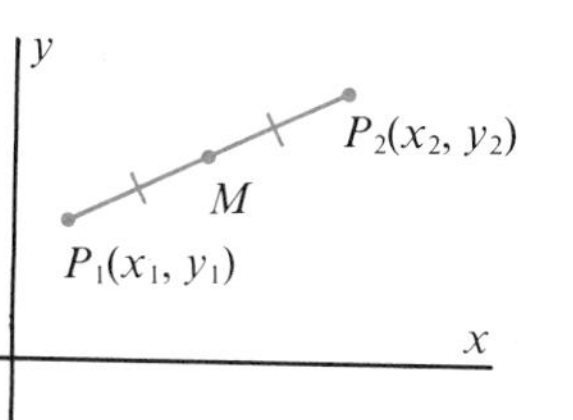

y-coordinate of M: $\dfrac{7 + 3}{2} = 5$

If M is the midpoint of a line segment with endpoints $P_1(x_1, y_1)$ and $P_2(x_2, y_2)$, the coordinates of M are: $\left(\dfrac{x_1 + x_2}{2}, \dfrac{y_1 + y_2}{2}\right)$. That is, the coordinates of M are the average of the coordinates of P_1 and P_2.

Example 3.

A triangle has vertices $D(7, 5)$, $E(1, -3)$, and $F(9, -1)$. The midpoints of DE and EF are M and N respectively.

a) Find the coordinates of M and N.

b) Compare the lengths of MN and DF.

Solution.

a) The coordinates of M are: $\left(\frac{7+1}{2}, \frac{5-3}{2}\right)$, or $(4, 1)$.

The coordinates of N are: $\left(\frac{1+9}{2}, \frac{-3-1}{2}\right)$, or $(5, -2)$.

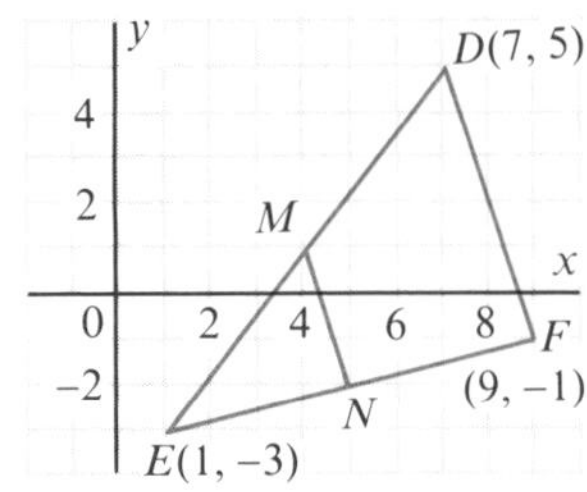

b) $$\begin{aligned} MN &= \sqrt{(5-4)^2 + (-2-1)^2} \\ &= \sqrt{10} \\ DF &= \sqrt{(9-7)^2 + (-1-5)^2} \\ &= \sqrt{40}, \text{ or } 2\sqrt{10} \end{aligned}$$

DF is twice as long as MN.

EXERCISES 6-1

(A)

1. Plot each pair of points and find the distance between them:
   a) $(3, 1), (9, 9)$ b) $(-2, 4), (7, -1)$
   c) $(-5, -2), (10, 6)$ d) $(-2, 5), (-4, -3)$
   e) $(8, 4), (2, -7)$ f) $(-3, 5), (7, -3)$

2. Find the length of the line segment with endpoints:
   a) $(7, 12), (-1, 3)$; b) $(-9, 5), (6, -2)$;
   c) $(-4, -8), (1, -13)$; d) $(6, -7), (-5, 8)$;
   e) $(-3, -1), (4, -11)$; f) $(14, 9), (-6, -6)$.

3. Find the coordinates of the midpoint of the line segment with endpoints:
   a) $(4, 2), (-8, -6)$; b) $(5, 6)(13, -4)$;
   c) $(-6, 3), (4, -5)$; d) $(4, 2), (12, -7)$;
   e) $(-3, 7), (6, 2)$; f) $(-4, -3), (10, 9)$.

4. A triangle has vertices $A(-2, 8)$, $B(2, -6)$, $C(6, 2)$.
   a) Find the coordinates of the midpoints, D, E, F, of the sides.
   b) Compare the lengths of the sides of $\triangle DEF$ with those of $\triangle ABC$.

5. A triangle has vertices $P(-1, -3)$, $Q(1, -1)$, $R(-5, 5)$. Show that:
   a) The triangle is a right triangle;
   b) the midpoint of the hypotenuse is equidistant from all three vertices.

6. Find the coordinates of the point on i) the x-axis, ii) the y-axis which is equidistant from:
   a) (5, 5) and (4, –4);
   b) (2, –6) and (–5, –1);
   c) (7, 5) and (3, 8);
   d) (–4, 2) and (9, –6).

(B)

7. The coordinates of the vertices of a triangle are given. Graph the triangle and classify it as scalene, isosceles, or equilateral. State whether it is a right triangle.
   a) (7, –3), (2, 6), (–2, 2)
   b) (0, –3), (5, 2), (–1, 0)
   c) (2, –3), (6, 2), (0, 3)
   d) (–6, 6), (–3, –3), (6, 0)
   e) (1, –2), (9, 5), (–3, 3)
   f) (–3, –1), (6, –4), (6, 2)
8. The coordinates of the vertices of a rectangle are given. Find:
   i) the lengths of the sides,
   ii) the lengths of the diagonals,
   iii) the perimeter,
   iv) the area:
   a) (–3, 3), (–2, –1), (6, 1), (5, 5)
   b) (8, 5), (–4, –1), (–2, –5), (10, 1)
   c) (2, 1), (6, –5), (12, –1), (8, 5)
   d) (6, 10), (3, 9), (6, 0), (9, 1)
9. The coordinates of the endpoints of a line segment are given. Find the coordinates of the three points that divide the segment into four equal parts.
   a) (–6, 4), (10, –4)
   b) (2, 9), (–14, –3)
   c) (–7, 5), (11, 9)
   d) (–4, –9), (9, –1)
10. M is the midpoint of line segment AB. Find the coordinates of B if those of A and M are:
    a) $A(-2, 4)$, $M(3, 1)$;
    b) $A(-5, -2)$, $M(6, 3)$;
    c) $A(4, 7)$, $M\left(-\frac{3}{2}, 2\right)$;
    d) $A(8, -3)$, $M\left(-\frac{1}{2}, \frac{5}{2}\right)$.
11. P is the point (9, 3) and Q is a point on the y-axis. If the midpoint, M, of PQ is on the x-axis, find the coordinates of Q and M.
12. The vertices of a parallelogram are (–4, –1), (5, –6), (11, –3), (2, 2). Show that the diagonals bisect each other.
13. A triangle has vertices (–4, 3), (2, –5), (6, 5). Find the lengths of its three medians.
14. A triangle has vertices $P(3, 6)$, $Q(-5, 0)$, $R(3, -4)$.
    a) Classify the triangle according to the lengths of its sides.
    b) If the median from P meets QR at S, what is the measure of $\angle PSR$?
    c) What is the area of $\triangle PQR$?

15. Boats in a regatta are required to sail a triangular course with vertices on a map grid (25, –25), (100, 150), and (200, 25). If the units are kilometres, how long is the course?

16. A fishing boat sends out a distress signal giving its location by the grid reference (–50, 175). A yacht at (100, –400) and a freighter at (225, 100) hear and respond. If the yacht travels twice as fast as the freighter, which arrives first?

17. Three booster transmitters are to be located equally spaced between two towers at grid references (–240, –160) and (560, 800). Find the positions of the booster transmitters.

Ⓒ

18. Two vertices of a triangle are (3, 4) and (6, –2). Find the possible coordinates of the third vertex if its distances from the given vertices are 5 units and $\sqrt{40}$ units.

19. A quadrilateral has vertices (–5, 5), (11, –5), (7, 7), (–1, 9). Show that the segments joining the midpoints of opposite sides:
   a) bisect each other;
   b) bisect the line segment joining the midpoints of the diagonals.

SIDE TRIP Counting Methods III

Lynne has five reference books to arrange on her bookshelf—a dictionary, a thesaurus, a style manual, an atlas, and a book of quotations. She wondered how many possible arrangements there are.

She reasoned that any one of the 5 books can be placed first. Any one of the remaining 4 books can be placed next. There are 5×4 ways two books can be placed. For each of these ways, there are 3 ways the next book can be placed. Reasoning this way, five books can be placed, on the shelf, in $5 \times 4 \times 3 \times 2 \times 1$, or 120 ways.

Products such as $5 \times 4 \times 3 \times 2 \times 1$ occur often in mathematics. To save space, they are denoted by a special symbol.

$5 \times 4 \times 3 \times 2 \times 1$ is written 5!, and is read: "five factorial."

$n \times (n-1) \times \ldots \times 2 \times 1 = n!$ Read, "n factorial."

1. Compute: a) 6! b) 4! c) 7!
2. Using a calculator, find: a) 8! b) 9! c) 10!
3. Without using a calculator, find: a) $\frac{10!}{7!}$ b) $\frac{20!}{18!}$ c) $\frac{100!}{98!}$
4. If Lynne wants the dictionary to be in the centre of her five books, how many ways can she arrange them?
5. 10! = 3 628 800. It ends with two zeros. How many zeros do the following end with? a) 20! b) 30! c) 40! d) 50!

1. a) 720 b) 24 c) 5040
2. a) 40 320 b) 362 880 c) 3 628 800
3. a) 720 b) 380 c) 9900
4. 24
5. a) 4 b) 7 c) 9 d) 12

6-2 INTERNAL DIVISION OF A LINE SEGMENT

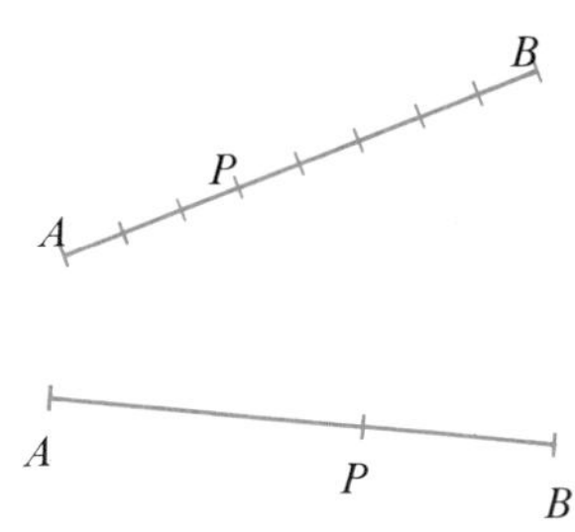

The coordinates of the midpoint of a line segment can be found by averaging the coordinates of the endpoints. In this section, we show how to find the coordinates of other points on a line segment when the coordinates of the endpoints are known.

In the diagram, P is a point on line segment AB such that $AP = 3$ and $PB = 5$. We say that P divides AB *internally* in the ratio $3:5$, and we write: $AP:PB = 3:5$.

In general, if P is a point on a line segment AB, the ratio in which P divides AB is:

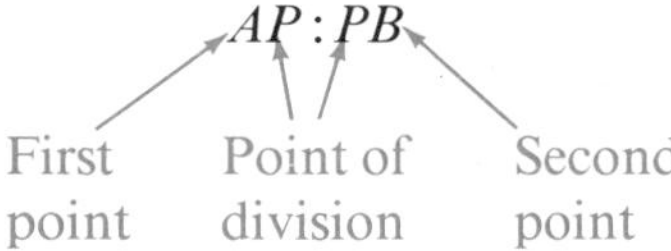

In this definition, order is important. The first term of the ratio is the length of the line segment from the first endpoint to the point of division; the second term is the length of the line segment from the point of division to the second endpoint.

Example 1.

C and D are points on segment AB as shown. State the ratio in which:

a) C divides AB; b) C divides BA;
c) C divides AD; d) D divides CB.

Solution.

a) $AC:CB = 5:7$ b) $BC:CA = 7:5$
c) $AC:CD = 5:3$ d) $CD:DB = 3:4$

Example 2.

A line segment has endpoints $R(-2, 12)$ and $S(8, -3)$. Find the ratio in which it is divided by point $P(4, 3)$.

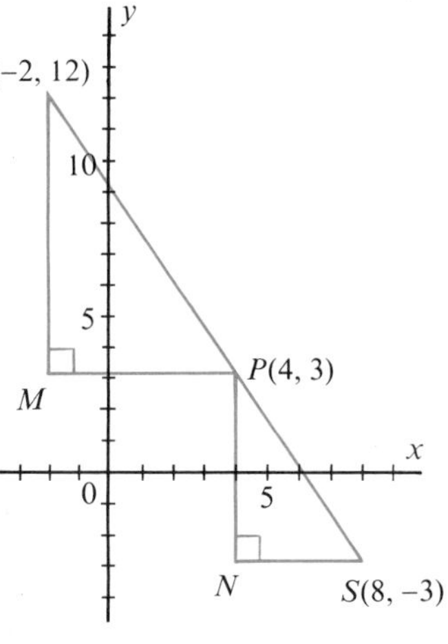

Solution.

Draw right triangles RMP and PNS as shown.

Since $MP \| NS$, $\angle RPM = \angle S$, and since $RM \| PN$, $\angle R = \angle NPS$

$$\angle M = \angle N$$

Therefore, $\triangle RPM \sim \triangle PSN$

and $$\frac{RP}{PS} = \frac{MP}{NS}$$

Since segments MP and NS have lengths 6 and 4 respectively,

$$\frac{RP}{PS} = \frac{6}{4}, \text{ or } \frac{3}{2}$$

That is, P divides RS in the ratio $3:2$.

Example 3.

A line segment has endpoints $A(3, 2)$ and $B(13, 8)$. Find the coordinates of the point that divides it in the ratio 1 : 4.

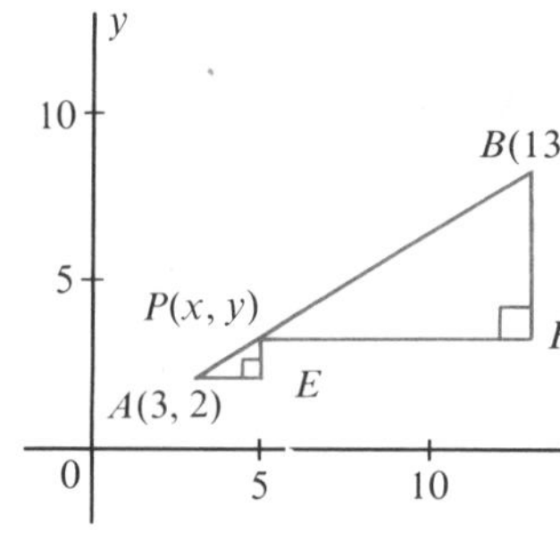

Solution.

Let $P(x, y)$ be the point of division. On the graph, since $\triangle AEP \sim \triangle PFB$:

$$\frac{AE}{PF} = \frac{AP}{PB} = \frac{EP}{FB}$$

That is, $\dfrac{x-3}{13-x} = \dfrac{1}{4} = \dfrac{y-2}{8-y}$

$$\frac{x-3}{13-x} = \frac{1}{4} \qquad \frac{y-2}{8-y} = \frac{1}{4}$$

$$4x - 12 = 13 - x \qquad 4y - 8 = 8 - y$$

$$5x = 25 \qquad 5y = 16$$

$$x = 5 \qquad y = 3.2$$

The coordinates of the point of division are (5, 3.2).

EXERCISES 6-2

(A)

1. State the ratio in which P divides AB:

a)

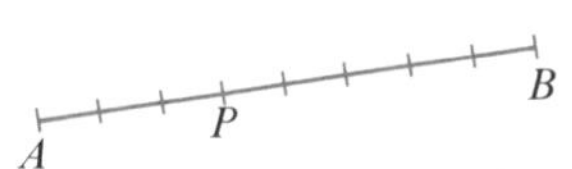

b)

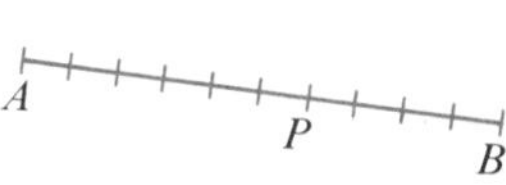

c)

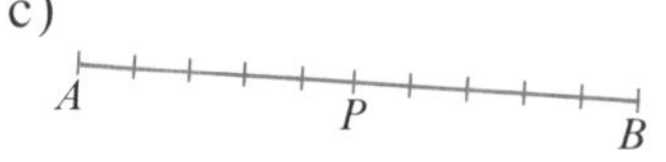

d)

2. State the ratio in which P divides each line segment:

a)

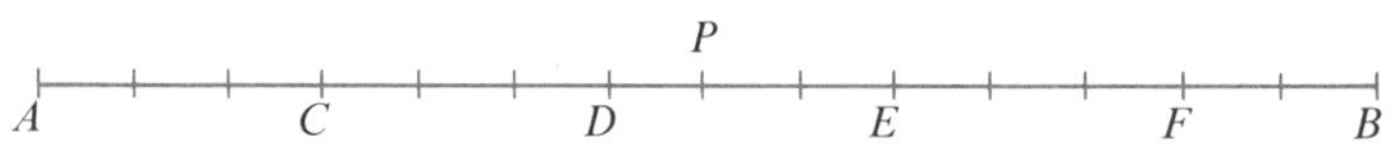

3. In each of the following, P is a point on line segment AB. State the ratio in which P divides AB.

a) $AP = 4, AB = 10$ b) $AP = 8, AB = 12$

c) $AP = 2, AB = 7$ d) $PB = 12, AB = 15$

4. P divides line segment AB in the ratio 3 : 4. If $AB = 21$, find the lengths of AP and PB.

5. A line segment has endpoints $(-5, -1)$ and $(7, 5)$. In what ratio does point $(3, 3)$ divide it?

6. A line segment has endpoints (–6, 7) and (4, 2). Find the coordinates of the point that divides it in the ratio $\frac{2}{3}$.
7. A line segment has endpoints (–9, –2) and (6, 8). Find the ratio in which it is divided by:
   a) the x-axis; b) the y-axis.
8. A line segment has endpoints $O(0, 0)$ and $A(12, 10)$. Find the coordinates of the point that divides OA in the ratio:
   a) 3:1; b) 2:3.

(B)

9. Line segment AB is divided by point P in the ratio given. State whether P is closer to A or closer to B.
   a) $\frac{1}{4}$ b) $\frac{4}{1}$ c) $\frac{3}{2}$ d) $\frac{3}{8}$
10. In Exercise 9, in which case is P closest to A? closest to B?
11. A is a point on the x-axis and B is a point on the y-axis. If point $P(6, -2)$ divides line segment AB in the ratio $\frac{1}{2}$, find the coordinates of A and B.
12. A line segment has endpoints $A(-7, -3)$ and $B(13, 4)$. Find the coordinates of the point, P, that divides it in the ratio $\frac{7}{3}$. Check your answer by calculating the lengths of AP and PB using the distance formula.
13. A line segment with endpoints (8, 1) and (2, 7) is intersected by the line $y = mx$. Find the value of m for the point of intersection that divides the segment in the ratio: a) 1:2; b) 5:1.
14. A parallelogram has vertices $A(4, -4)$, $B(16, 2)$, $C(10, 4)$, $D(-2, -2)$.
    a) If E and F are the midpoints of BC and AD respectively, show that DE and BF trisect AC.
    b) If G and H are the trisection points of AC with G adjacent to C, calculate the ratio:
       i) $\frac{EG}{GD}$; ii) $\frac{BH}{HF}$.

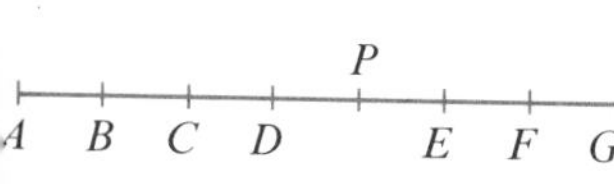

15. a) In the diagram, how many different line segments contain the point P between their endpoints?
    a) State the ratio in which P divides each segment in (a).
16. Line segment PQ is trisected by points M and N which lie on the coordinate axes. If the coordinates of P are (6, 4), find the possible coordinates of Q.

17. Find the coordinates of the points that trisect the line segment with endpoints:
    a) (–5, 5) and (7, 2); b) (1, 3) and (10, 7).
18. Points P and Q trisect line segment AB. Find the possible coordinates of B if the coordinates of A and P are:
    a) $A(3, 6), P(7, 4)$; b) $A(11, 7), P(5, 3)$.
19. Point P divides line segment AB in the ratio 3 : 1. Find the coordinates of B if the coordinates of A and P are:
    a) $A(2, 8), P(11, 2)$; b) $A(-5, 2), P(1, -7)$;
    c) $A(-4, -6), P(2, -2)$; d) $A(8, 10), P(-1, 2.5)$

Ⓒ

20. Line segment AB is divided by point P in the ratio $\frac{1}{2}$, and by point Q in the ratio $\frac{3}{1}$. What is the ratio in which:
    a) P divides AQ? b) Q divides PB?
21. A line segment has endpoints $A(x_1, y_1)$ and $B(x_2, y_2)$. Develop a formula for the coordinates of the point that divides AB in the ratio $a:b$.

Internal and External Division of a Line Segment

In the examples and exercises of this section, the point P which divided a line segment AB was always between A and B. We say that P divides AB *internally* in the ratio $AP:PB$. Try to extend the definition to the cases where P is not between A and B. You should provide for the two possibilities of *external* division shown—P could be on the extension of BA, or it could be on the extension of AB.

Write a report of your findings, and include some examples.

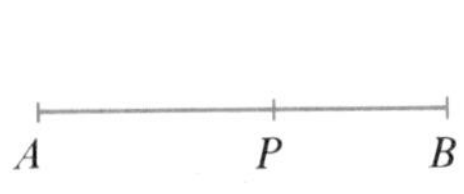

Internal division

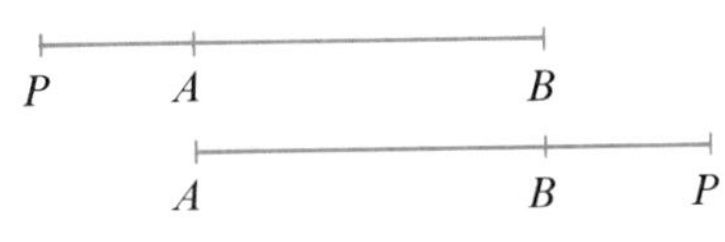

Two possible cases of external division

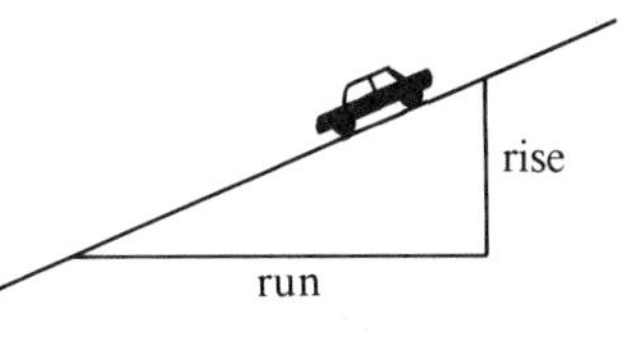

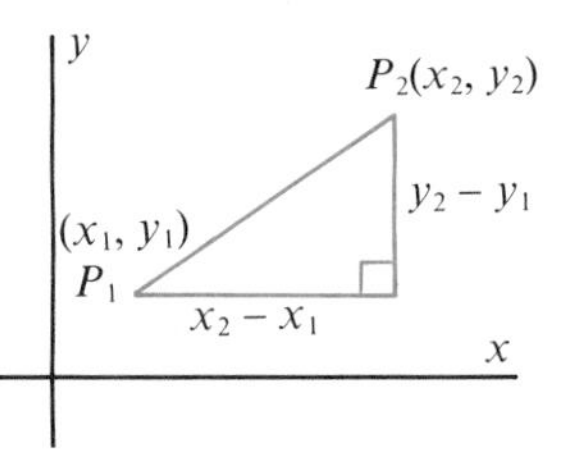

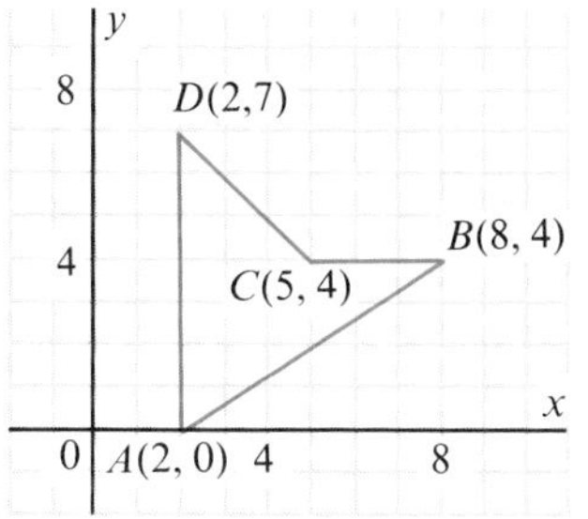

6-3 SLOPE OF A LINE SEGMENT

The steepness or gradient of a hill is an example of a mathematical concept called slope.

$$\text{slope} = \frac{\text{rise}}{\text{run}}$$

In a coordinate system the slope, m, of a line segment joining any two points $P_1(x_1, y_1)$ and $P_2(x_2, y_2)$ is defined as:

$$m = \frac{y_2 - y_1}{x_2 - x_1} \qquad (x_2 \neq x_1)$$

Example 1.

Quadrilateral $ABCD$ has vertices $A(2, 0)$, $B(8, 4)$, $C(5, 4)$, and $D(2, 7)$. Find the slope of each side.

Solution.

Slope of AB: $\dfrac{4 - 0}{8 - 2} = \dfrac{2}{3}$

Slope of BC: $\dfrac{4 - 4}{5 - 8} = 0$

Slope of CD: $\dfrac{7 - 4}{2 - 5} = -1$

Slope of AD: $\dfrac{7 - 0}{2 - 2}$. Since the denominator equals 0 and division by 0 is undefined, the slope of AD is undefined.

Example 1 illustrates these properties of slope:

- Lines rising to the right have positive slope.
- Lines rising to the left have negative slope.
- The slope of any horizontal line is zero.
- The slope of any vertical line is undefined.

The Constant Slope Property

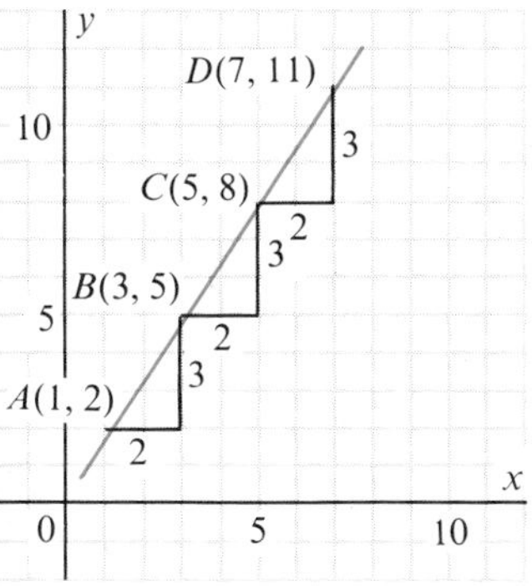

Starting at $A(1, 2)$ on the line shown in the diagram, move 2 units to the right and 3 units up to point B on the line. As the diagram shows, points C and D can be reached by again moving in each case 2 units to the right and 3 up. Choose any two segments of the line, say BC and AD.

Slope of BC: $\dfrac{8 - 5}{5 - 3} = \dfrac{3}{2}$ Slope of AD: $\dfrac{11 - 2}{7 - 1} = \dfrac{9}{6}$, or $\dfrac{3}{2}$

The fact that these slopes are equal suggests that the slope of any segment of the line is $\frac{3}{2}$. Then the slope of the line is $\frac{3}{2}$.

Constant slope property: The slopes of any two segments of a line are equal.

Three or more points are said to be collinear if they lie on the same straight line. The *constant-slope* property provides a simple test for collinear points.

Example 2.

Determine if the points $P(-3, 6)$, $Q(2, 2)$, and $R(6, -1)$ are collinear.

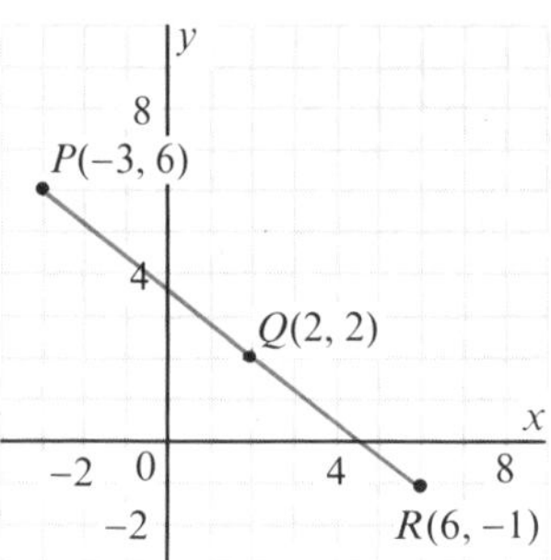

Solution.

Slope of PQ: $\dfrac{2-6}{2-(-3)} = -\dfrac{4}{5}$

Slope of QR: $\dfrac{-1-2}{6-2} = -\dfrac{3}{4}$

Since the slopes of segments PQ and QR are not equal, the points P, Q, and R are not collinear.

Example 2 shows that points that appear to be collinear may not, in fact, be so.

Slopes of Parallel and Perpendicular Lines

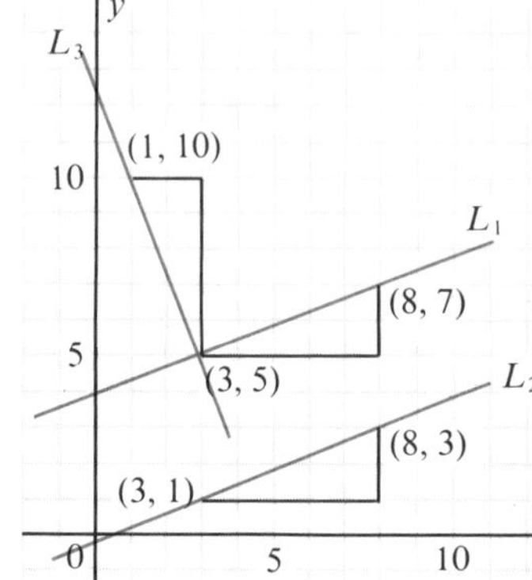

In the diagram, lines L_1 and L_2 are parallel.

Slope of L_1: $\dfrac{7-5}{8-3} = \dfrac{2}{5}$ Slope of L_2: $\dfrac{3-1}{8-3} = \dfrac{2}{5}$

This suggests that the slopes of parallel lines are equal.
L_3 is perpendicular to L_1.

Slope of L_1: $\dfrac{2}{5}$ Slope of L_3: $\dfrac{10-5}{1-3} = -\dfrac{5}{2}$

This suggests that the slopes of perpendicular lines are negative reciprocals.

The slopes of parallel lines are equal.
The slopes of perpendicular lines are negative reciprocals.

Example 3.

A quadrilateral has vertices $A(0, -4)$, $B(5, -2)$, $C(1, 8)$, $D(-4, 6)$. Determine whether or not it is a rectangle.

Solution.

Graph the quadrilateral and find the slope of each side.

Slope of AB: $\dfrac{-2-(-4)}{5-0} = \dfrac{2}{5}$

Slope of DC: $\dfrac{8-6}{1-(-4)} = \dfrac{2}{5}$

Since the slopes are equal, $AB \| DC$.

Slope of AD: $\dfrac{6-(-4)}{-4-0} = -\dfrac{5}{2}$

Slope of BC: $\dfrac{8-(-2)}{1-5} = -\dfrac{5}{2}$

Since the slopes are equal, $AD \| BC$.

Since the slopes of adjacent sides are negative reciprocals, the sides are perpendicular and $ABCD$ is a rectangle.

EXERCISES 6-3

Ⓐ

1. Find the slope of the line segment with endpoints:
   a) (2, 3), (9, 12); b) (−3, 1), (5, −7);
   c) (15, 8), (−4, 8); d) (−2, −6), (2, 10);
   e) (−5, 9), (−5, −6); f) (−7, 10), (8, −2).
2. Determine if the three points are collinear:
   a) (8, 5), (3, 2), (−3, −1) b) (−3, 3), (2, 1), (12, −3)
3. Which pairs of numbers are slopes of perpendicular lines?
   a) $\frac{9}{4}, -\frac{4}{9}$ b) $-\frac{5}{2}, \frac{5}{2}$ c) $-\frac{2}{7}, \frac{7}{5}$
   d) 1.2, −0.8 e) $2\frac{1}{3}, -\frac{3}{7}$ f) −5, 0.2
4. What is the slope of a line: i) parallel to, ii) perpendicular to, a line with slope:
   a) $\frac{2}{5}$? b) $-\frac{4}{3}$? c) −2? d) $\frac{3}{7}$? e) −1? f) 0.6?
5. Find the slopes of the sides of a triangle with vertices:
   a) (2, 6), (0, 3), (6, −1); b) (−2, −1), (5, −3), (3, 1).
6. In Exercise 5, which triangle is a right triangle?
7. On a grid, draw a line through:
   a) (3, 1) with slope $\frac{2}{3}$; b) (−2, 3) with slope $-\frac{1}{4}$;
   c) (−4, 5) with slope $-\frac{5}{2}$; d) (6, 7) with slope 0;
   e) (1, −3) with slope $\frac{1}{3}$; f) (7, −4) with slope undefined.

Ⓑ

8. From the coordinates of the vertices given, determine if the quadrilateral is a rectangle.
   a) (−4, 3), (−2, −7), (8, −3), (6, 1)
   b) (−6, −2), (3, −5), (5, 1), (−4, 4)
   c) (−2, 6), (−5, −1), (2, −4), (5, 3)
9. A wheelchair ramp rises 38 cm in a horizontal distance of 3.60 m.
   a) What is the slope of the ramp?
   b) How long is the ramp?
   c) If the maximum permissible slope is 0.125, how high could the ramp rise over the same distance?
10. Guy wires supporting a broadcasting tower are fastened to the ground 20 m from its base. The first set of wires is attached to the top of the tower and has a slope of 2.4. The second set is attached part way up and has a length of 29 m.
    a) Find the height of the tower.
    b) Find the slope of the second set of wires.
11. The coordinates of three vertices of a parallelogram are given. Find all possible coordinates of the fourth vertex.
    a) (1, −1), (6, −2), (3, 3)
    b) (−2, −4), (4, −3), (−3, −1)
    c) (−1, 5), (−3, 1), (0, 3)
    d) (2, 4), (4, −2), (6, 8)
12. The coordinates of adjacent vertices of a square are given. Find the possible coordinates of the other two vertices.
    a) (0, 4), (3, 0)
    b) (2, 2), (5, 4)
    c) (−2, 1), (5, −2)
    d) (2, −8), (8, −9)
13. The upper diagram shows a 5 by 13 rectangle divided into five parts. The lower diagram shows the same rectangle with the parts rearranged. Explain why there is an empty space in the second rectangle.

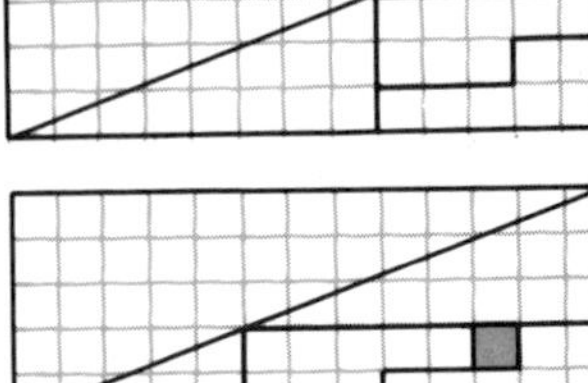

Ⓒ

14. The coordinates of two vertices of a square are given. Find the possible coordinates of the other two vertices.
    a) (0, 2), (4, 6)
    b) (0, 4), (2, 0)
15. Right $\triangle ABC$ has vertices $A(1, 4)$, $B(9, 3)$, and C on the x-axis. If side AB is the hypotenuse, find the coordinates of C.
16. Two vertices of a right triangle are (3, 2) and (11, 6). If the third vertex is on the x-axis, find its possible coordinates.

6-4 THE EQUATION OF A LINE

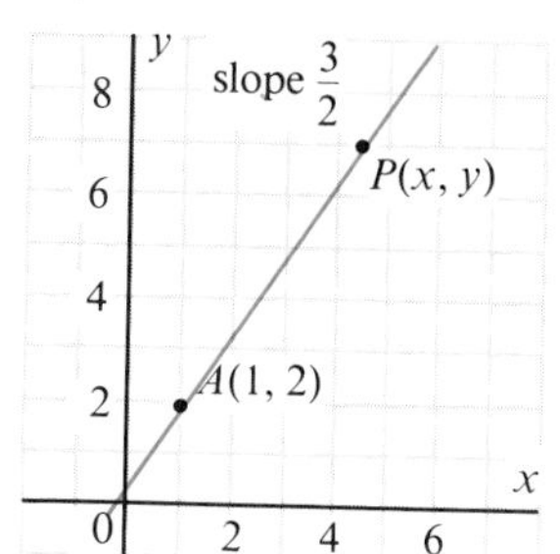

We can use the constant-slope property of a line to find an equation which is satisfied by all points $P(x, y)$ on the line and only those points. This is called the **equation of the line.**

Example 1.

Find the equation of the line through $A(1, 2)$ with slope $\frac{3}{2}$.

Solution.

Let $P(x, y)$ be any point on the line.

Slope of AP: $\frac{y-2}{x-1}$ Slope of the line: $\frac{3}{2}$

Since these slopes are equal: $\frac{y-2}{x-1} = \frac{3}{2}$

$$3x - 3 = 2y - 4$$
$$3x - 2y + 1 = 0$$

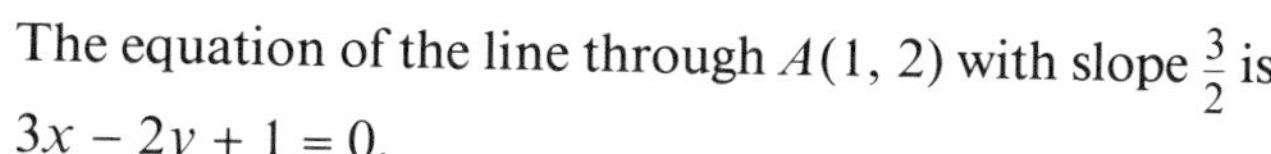

The equation of the line through $A(1, 2)$ with slope $\frac{3}{2}$ is $3x - 2y + 1 = 0$.

The equation of the line with slope m which passes through the point (x_1, y_1) is:

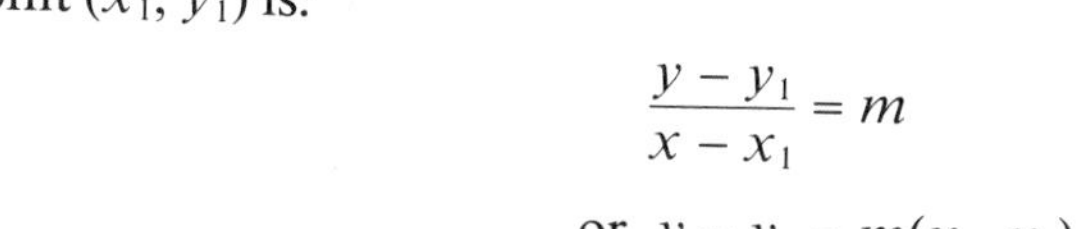

$$\frac{y - y_1}{x - x_1} = m$$

$$\text{or, } y - y_1 = m(x - x_1)$$

This is called the **slope-point** form of the equation of a line. This formula can be used to find the equation of a line through two points.

Example 2.

Find the equation of the line through $A(1, 3)$ and $B(4, 5)$.

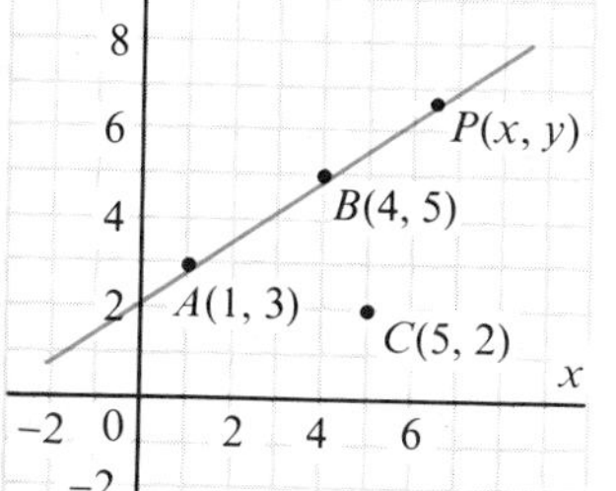

Solution.

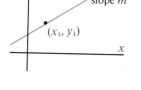

Slope of AB: $\frac{5-3}{4-1} = \frac{2}{3}$

The line passes through $B(4, 5)$ with slope $\frac{2}{3}$.

Point $A(1, 3)$ could also be used.

Substituting these values in $y - y_1 = m(x - x_1)$:

$$y - 5 = \frac{2}{3}(x - 4)$$

$$3y - 15 = 2x - 8$$
$$2x - 3y + 7 = 0$$

The equation of the line through A and B is $2x - 3y + 7 = 0$.

In *Example 2*, point $A(1, 3)$ is on the line and point $C(5, 2)$ is not on the line. If the coordinates of these points are substituted into the equation of the line, we obtain:

For point A:

L.S. $= 2(1) - 3(3) + 7$
$\quad = 0$ R.S.$= 0$

For point C:

L.S. $= 2(5) - 3(2) + 7$
$\quad = 11$ R.S.$= 0$

The coordinates of A satisfy the equation because A is on the line. The coordinates of C do not satisfy the equation because C is not on the line.

This suggests that the equation of a line has these properties:

- The coordinates of points on the line *satisfy* the equation of the line.
- The coordinates of points not on the line *do not satisfy* its equation.

If the slope and a point on a line are not given, they must be found before the equation of the line can be determined.

Example 3.

Find the equation of the perpendicular bisector of the line segment with endpoints $A(-2, 3)$ and $B(8, -1)$.

Solution.

The coordinates of M, the midpoint of segment AB, are:

$\left(\frac{-2+8}{2}, \frac{3-1}{2}\right)$, or $(3, 1)$.

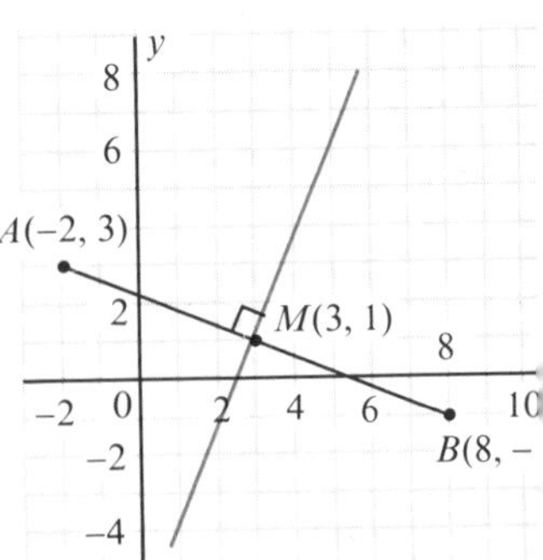

Slope of AB: $\frac{-1-3}{8-(-2)} = -\frac{2}{5}$

Slope of the perpendicular bisector of AB: $\frac{5}{2}$

The equation of the perpendicular bisector is:

$$y - 1 = \frac{5}{2}(x - 3)$$

$$2y - 2 = 5x - 15$$

$$5x - 2y - 13 = 0$$

The equation of the perpendicular bisector of line segment AB is: $5x - 2y - 13 = 0$.

EXERCISES 6-4

A

1. Given the slope and a point on a line, find its equation:

a) $2, (5, 1)$ b) $4, (3, -2)$ c) $-1, (-2, 3)$

d) $-3, (2, 0)$ e) $\frac{1}{2}, (-4, -1)$ f) $0, (5, 2)$

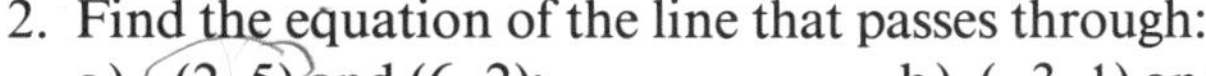

2. Find the equation of the line that passes through:
   a) (2, 5) and (6, 2); b) (−3, 1) and (5, 3);
   c) (5, 0) and (−3, 12); d) (1, 3) and (3, 9);
   e) (−6, 2) and (2, 2); f) (4, 1) and (4, −3).
3. Which of the following points lie on $3x + 2y - 12 = 0$?
   a) (2, 3) b) (6, −3) c) (−1, 7) d) (0, 6)
4. Which of the following lines pass through (−3, 2)?
   a) $2x - y + 8 = 0$ b) $x + 3y - 6 = 0$
   c) $5x - 4y + 20 = 0$ d) $4x + 7y - 2 = 0$
5. The equation of a line is $y = -2x + b$. Find the value of b if the line passes through:
   a) (1, 3); b) (−3, 2); c) (0, −6); d) (−3, 6).

(B)

6. Find the equation of a line given its slope and a point through which it passes:
   a) $\frac{1}{3}$, (−1, −5) b) $-\frac{5}{2}$, (−3, 4) c) $\frac{2}{9}$, (−4, −10)
   d) $-\frac{7}{3}$, (6, −8) e) $\frac{2}{7}$, (0, 3) f) $-\frac{1}{2}$, (−2, 0)
7. A triangle has vertices (4, 6), (−8, −3), (8, −1). Find the equations of its sides.
8. a) Find the equation of the line with slope $-\frac{2}{3}$ through:
      i) (5, 9); ii) (5, 6); iii) (5, 3);
      iv) (5, 0); v) (5, −3); vi) (5, −6).
   b) Graph the equations of (a) on the same axes.
   c) Describe how the graph of the equation of the line with slope $-\frac{2}{3}$ through (5, k) changes as k changes.
9. a) Find the equation of the line through (5, −2) with slope:
      i) 4; ii) 3; iii) 2; iv) 1;
      v) 0; vi) −1; vii) −2; viii) −3.
   b) Graph the equations of (a) on the same axes.
   c) Describe how the graph of the equation of the line through (5, −2) with slope m changes as m changes.
10. Line segment AB has endpoints $A(-1, 3)$ and $B(5, -1)$.
    a) Graph segment AB and find the equation of its perpendicular bisector.
    b) Show that the perpendicular bisector passes through $P(6, 7)$.
    c) Calculate the lengths of PA and PB.

11. Determine if the given point lies on the line:
   a) $(3, 1)$ b) $(4, 3)$ c) $(8, -3)$

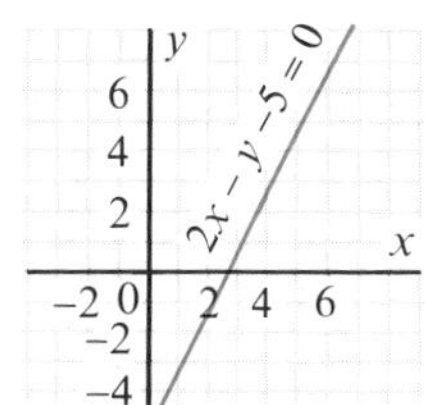

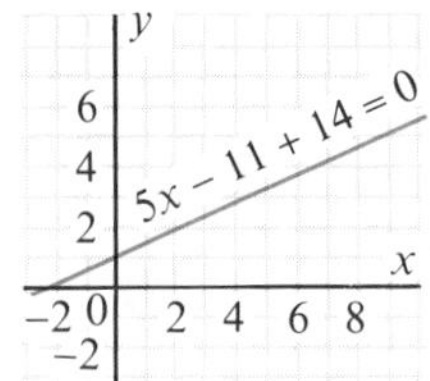

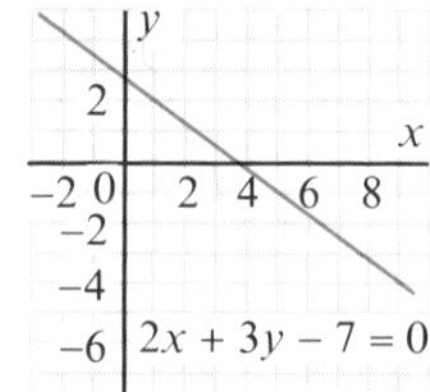

12. For what value of t does the given point lie on the given line?
   a) $(3, 7)$, $5x - 2y + t = 0$
   b) $(4, -3)$, $tx + 5y + t = 0$
   c) $(2, 5)$, $3x + ty - 6 = 0$
   d) $(3, -1)$, $(t + 2)x + (t + 1)y + t = 0$

Ⓒ

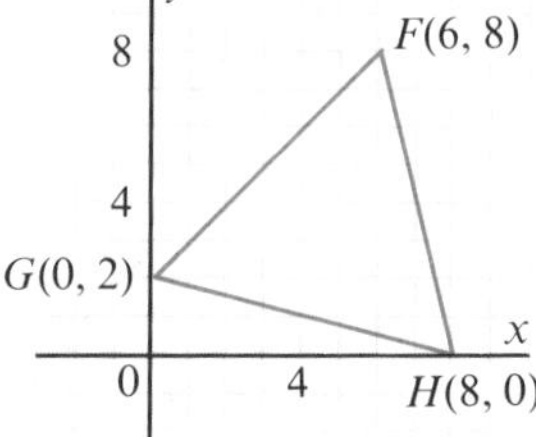

13. From the graph of $\triangle FGH$, find the equation of:
   a) the median from H to FG;
   b) the altitude from F to GH;
   c) the line through F parallel to GH.
14. A triangle has vertices $(-5, 2)$, $(9, 6)$, $(1, -4)$. Find the equations of the three medians.
15. A line passes through $(-2, 6)$ and $(14, -2)$. Find the length of the segment between the two axes.
16. The line $2x - 5y + 10 = 0$ bisects the line segment joining $(10, 0)$ and $(0, b)$. Find the value of b.

MATHEMATICS AROUND US

The Spiral Tunnels

When British Columbia entered into the Canadian Confederation on July 20, 1871, the federal government agreed to build a railway to link the province with the rest of Canada. The railway was completed in 1885. The track through the mountains was kept to a maximum gradient of 2.2% (a rise of 2.2 m in 100 m of track) with one exception—the section of track between Hector, B.C. and Field, B.C. There, a rise of 297 m in only 6.6 km was necessary. This section became known as Big Hill. Taking trains up and down this hill required additional locomotives, and on the downhill run there was always the danger of runaway trains.

The only way to reduce the gradient of Big Hill to 2.2% was to lengthen the track between the two towns. This was done in 1907–1909 when a pair of spiral tunnels was built into the mountains. These tunnels are the only ones of their kind in North America. One of them can be seen by travellers from the Trans-Canada Highway in Yoho National Park. As many as 15 trains a day pass through the tunnels in each direction. The long freight trains can be seen coming out of a tunnel before they have finished going in.

QUESTIONS

1. What was the gradient of the track on Big Hill?
2. By how much did the track have to be lengthened to reduce the gradient to 2.2%?
3. The train in the photograph is passing through Lower Tunnel, which is about 880 m long and curves through 288°. Each car in the train is about 12.2 m long.
   a) How many cars are in the train?
   b) What is the difference in height between the two sections of track shown in the photograph?
   c) If the speed of the train is 40.5 km/h, how long does it take to pass completely through the tunnel?
4. What is the radius of the spiral?

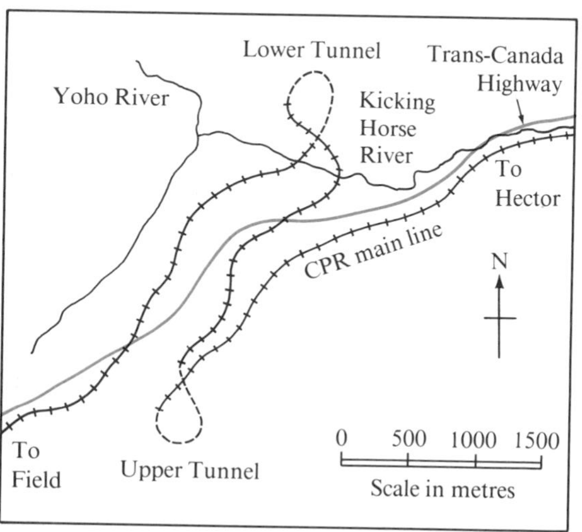

6-5 GRAPHING THE EQUATION OF A LINE

In *Section 6-4* we found that the equation of a line of slope m which passes through the point (x_1, y_1) is:

$$y - y_1 = m(x - x_1).$$

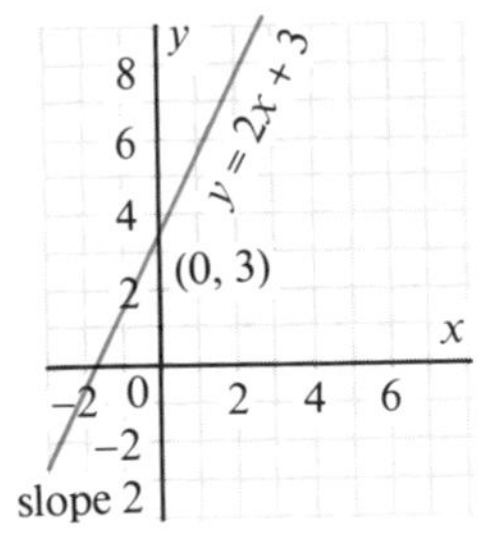

If the given point is on the y- axis, the above equation reduces to a simpler form. For example, if a line of slope 2 passes through (0, 3), its equation is:

$$y - 3 = 2(x - 0)$$
$$y - 3 = 2x$$
$$y = 2x + 3$$

slope y-intercept

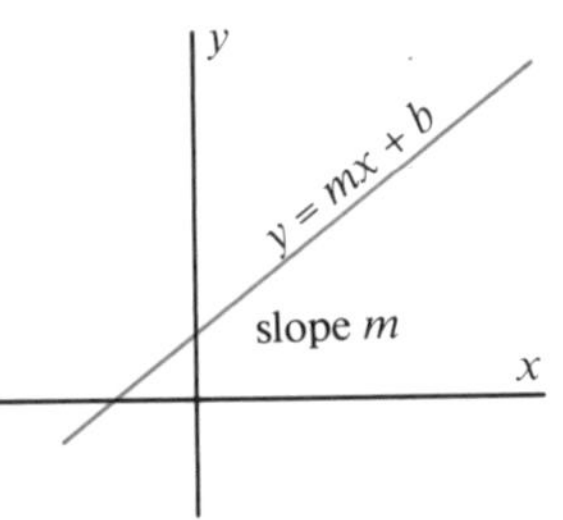

In general, the equation of the line of slope m through $(0, b)$ is:

$$y - b = m(x - 0)$$

or, $\quad y = mx + b$

This is called the **slope y-intercept** form of the equation of a line. The y-intercept is the value of y when $x = 0$.

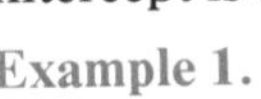
Example 1.

Find the equation of the line from the graph:

a)

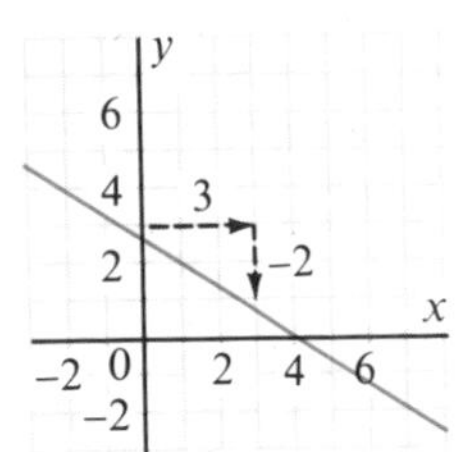

b)

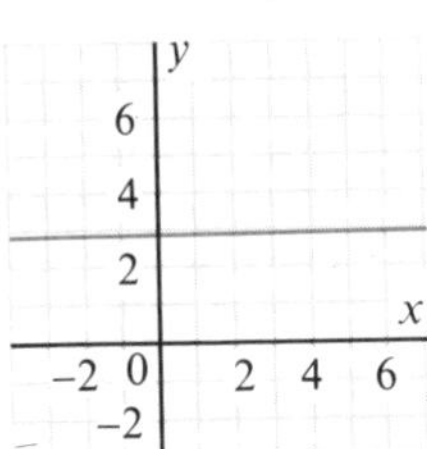

c)

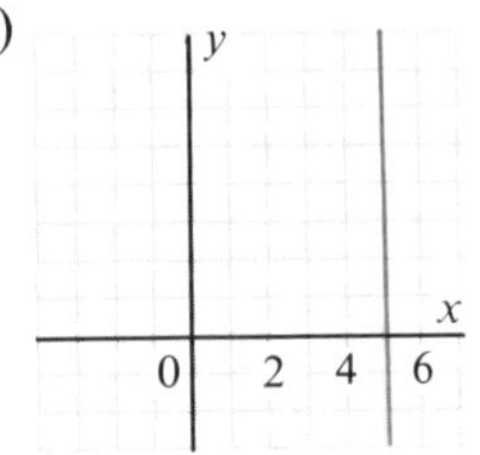

Solution.

a) The y-intercept is 3. The slope is $-\frac{2}{3}$.

Substituting these values in $y = mx + b$:

The equation of the line is $y = -\frac{2}{3}x + 3$

or, $\quad 2x + 3y - 9 = 0$

b) The y-intercept is 3. The slope is 0.
The equation of the line is $y = 0x + 3$

$$y = 3$$

c) Since there is no y-intercept and the slope is undefined, the equation of the line cannot be written in the form $y = mx + b$. However, since the line is parallel to the y-axis, the points (x, y) which satisfy its equation have first coordinate 5. That is, the equation of the line is: $x = 5$.

From *Example 1b* and *1c*, we conclude the following:

- The equation $y = k$ represents a horizontal line.
- The equation $x = k$ represents a vertical line.

Example 2.

Given: $x - 2y + 6 = 0.$

Find the slope and the y-intercept, and graph the line.

Solution.

Solve $x - 2y + 6 = 0$ for y:

$$2y = x + 6$$

$$y = \frac{1}{2}x + 3$$

The slope of the line is $\frac{1}{2}$ and the y-intercept is 3. This information is used to draw the graph.

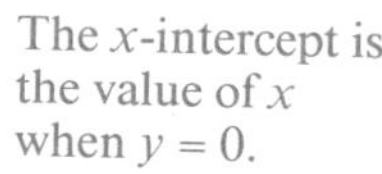

The x-intercept is the value of x when $y = 0$.

It is customary to express equations of lines in the form $Ax + By + C = 0$, where A, B, and C are constants. This is called the **standard form** of the equation of a line. The slope and the x- and y-intercepts can still be found when the equation is in this form, and the information used to graph the line.

Example 3.

Given: $2x + 3y - 12 = 0.$

Find the x- and y-intercepts, and graph the line.

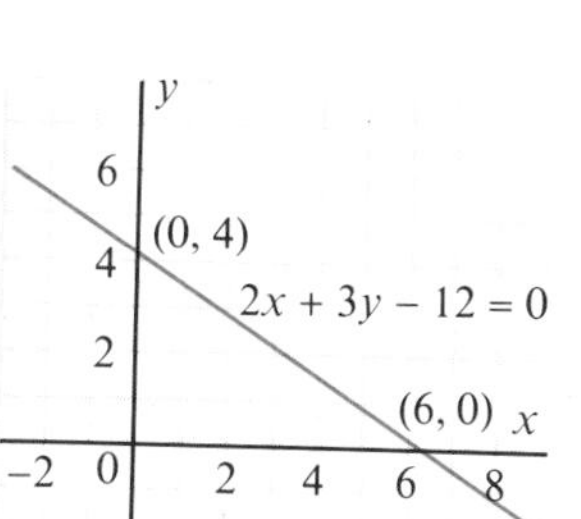

Solution.

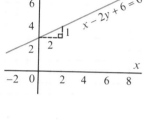

To find the x-intercept, let $y = 0$.

$$2x + 3(0) - 12 = 0$$

$$x = 6$$

To find the y-intercept, let $x = 0$

$$2(0) + 3y - 12 = 0$$

$$y = 4$$

The x-intercept is 6 and the y-intercept is 4.

The graph shows the line drawn through (6, 0) and (0, 4).

Example 4.

Find the equation of the line that passes through (2, −3) and is perpendicular to $x + 2y - 10 = 0$.

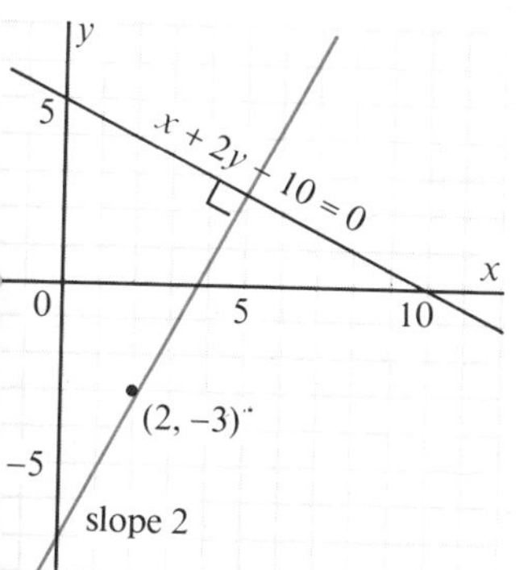

Solution.

Solve $x + 2y - 10 = 0$ for y:

$$2y = -x + 10$$

$$y = -\frac{1}{2}x + 5$$

Slope of the line: $-\frac{1}{2}$

Slope of a perpendicular line: 2

The equation of the line with slope 2 through (2, −3):

$$\begin{aligned} y - (-3) &= 2(x - 2) \\ y + 3 &= 2x - 4 \\ 2x - y - 7 &= 0 \end{aligned}$$

The equation of the required line is: $2x - y - 7 = 0$.

EXERCISES 6-5

Ⓐ

1. Find the equation of the line with:
   a) slope 5, y-intercept 8;
   b) slope −4, y-intercept 3;
   c) slope $\frac{2}{5}$, y-intercept −1;
   d) slope −1, y-intercept −6;
   e) slope $-\frac{4}{3}$, y-intercept $\frac{1}{3}$;
   f) slope $-\frac{5}{8}$, y-intercept $-\frac{1}{2}$.

2. Find the equations represented by the graphs:

a)

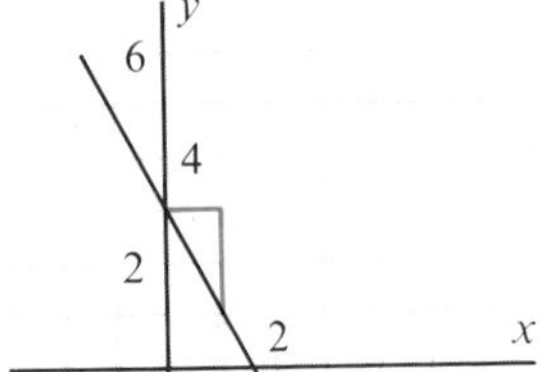

b)

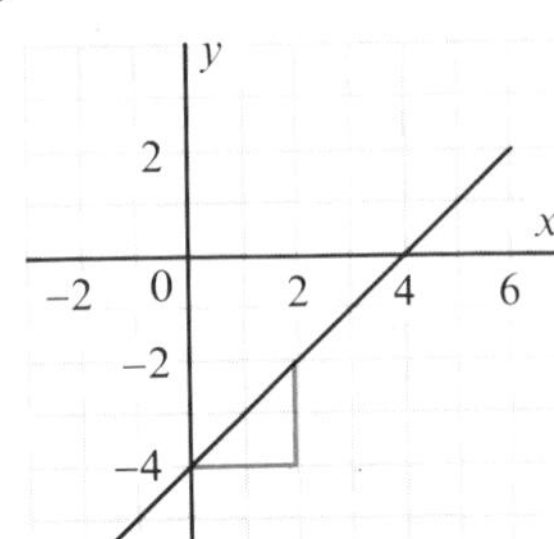

c)

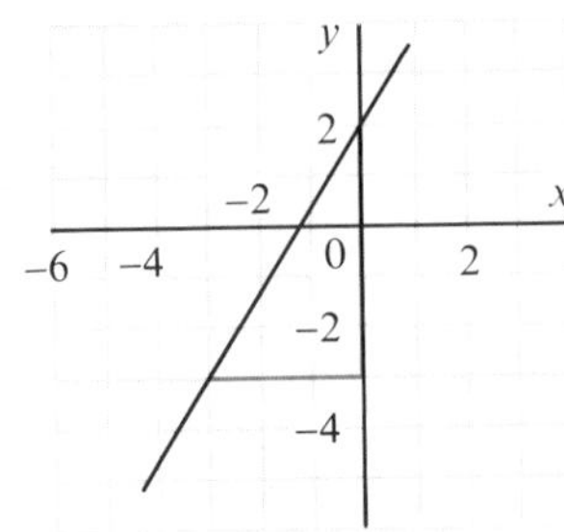

d)

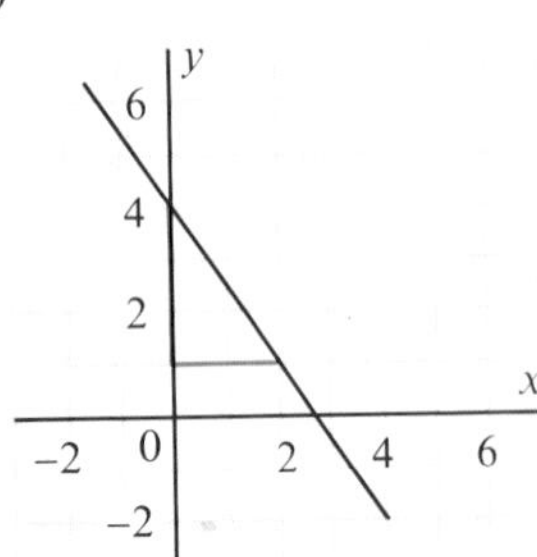

e)

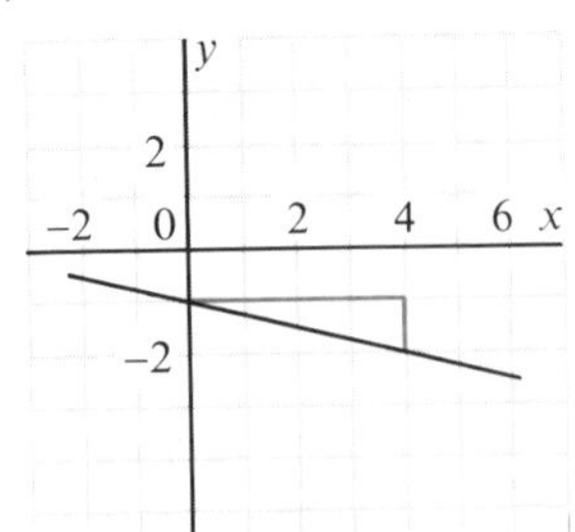

f)

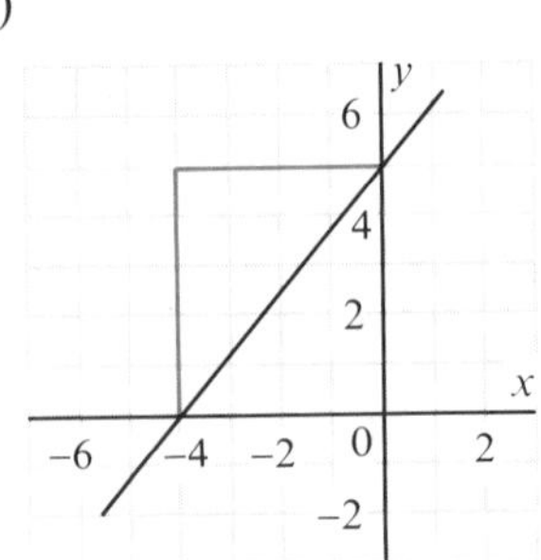

3. Find the equation of the horizontal line that passes through:
a) (2, −2); b) (−1, 3); c) (0, 5); d) (−4, 0).
4. Find the equation of the vertical line that passes through:
a) (4, 1); b) (−3, −5); c) (2, 0); d) (0, −3).
5. Find the x- and y-intercepts and graph the line:
a) $x - 2y + 6 = 0$ b) $3x + 4y - 24 = 0$
c) $5x - y - 7 = 0$ d) $2x + 9y + 15 = 0$
6. Find the slope and y-intercept and then graph the line:
a) $x - y - 4 = 0$ b) $2x + 3y - 18 = 0$
c) $5x + 4y + 20 = 0$ d) $x - 7y + 14 = 0$
7. Does every line have two intercepts? Explain.
8. Graph $4x + 3y - 24 = 0$ and find the length of the segment between the x- and y- axes.

(B)

9. a) Graph the following on one pair of axes:
$$y = \frac{3}{2}x - 4, \quad y = \frac{3}{2}x - 1, \quad y = \frac{3}{2}x + 1,$$
$$y = \frac{3}{2}x + 2, \quad y = \frac{3}{2}x + 4.$$
b) Graph the following on one pair of axes:
$$y = \frac{1}{2}x + 2, \quad y = 2x + 2, \quad y = -4x + 2,$$
$$y = -\frac{3}{2}x + 2, \quad y = -\frac{1}{3}x + 2.$$
c) Describe how the graph of $y = mx + b$ changes as:
i) b changes while m remains constant;
ii) m changes while b remains constant.
10. Which lines are parallel to the line $5x + 2y - 10 = 0$?
a) $5x + 2y - 20 = 0$ b) $5x - 2y + 20 = 0$
c) $4x - 10y - 15 = 0$ d) $15x + 6y + 10 = 0$
11. Find the equation of the line through (9, −2) that is parallel to the line $y = -3x + 6$.
12. Which lines are perpendicular to the line $3x + 6y - 5 = 0$?
a) $3x - 6y + 14 = 0$ b) $2x - y + 3 = 0$
c) $x + 2y = 0$ d) $8x - 4y - 7 = 0$
e) $6x - 3y + 20 = 0$ f) $4x + 2y + 9 = 0$
13. Find the equation of the line through (5, 2) that is perpendicular to the line $2x - 3y + 18 = 0$.

14. Which lines have the same y-intercept as $5x - 6y + 9 = 0$?
    a) $2x - 3y + 2 = 0$
    b) $3x + 4y - 6 = 0$
    c) $x + 8y + 12 = 0$
    d) $8x - 10y + 15 = 0$
15. Find the equation of the line that is parallel to $5x - y + 3 = 0$ and has the same y-intercept as $3x + 2y + 6 = 0$.
16. The equation of a line is $3x - 5y + C = 0$. Find the value of C if the line passes through:
    a) (0, 0);
    b) (1, 1);
    c) (4, 2);
    d) (3, −1);
    e) (0, 5);
    f) (−6, −3).
17. Find the equation of the line through (−1, 6) that has equal x- and y-intercepts.

Ⓒ

18. A line through (6, 2) forms a triangle with the positive arms of the axes. If the area of the triangle is 27 units², find the equation of the line.
19. a) $P_1(x_1, y_1)$ and $P_2(x_2, y_2)$ are two points with coordinates that satisfy the equation $y = mx + b$. Show that $y = mx + b$ represents a straight line by showing that the slope of P_1P_2 is constant.
    b) Show that $Ax + By + C = 0$, where A, B, and C are constants, represents a straight line.

LEADERS IN MATHEMATICS

James Sylvester

James Sylvester was born in London and attended private schools until age 14. At the age of 17 he entered Cambridge University. He finished his studies with honors, but not being a member of the Church of England, he could neither receive his degree nor continue with graduate work. It wasn't until 1872, when Cambridge rescinded its religious requirements, that he was awarded his long overdue degree.

James Joseph Sylvester (1814-1897)

He taught at the University of London and Trinity College in Dublin before accepting a professorship at Johns Hopkins University in Baltimore, Maryland.

While at Johns Hopkins, he founded the American Journal of Mathematics and is credited by most scholars with initiating mathematical research in North America. He collaborated with Arthur Cayley in ground-breaking research in matrices and linear transformations. Students who study matrices in depth will encounter Sylvester's Law of Nullity.

He finished his academic and mathematical career at Oxford University, continuing his research, despite failing heath, until his death in 1897.

6-6 THE EQUATION OF A CIRCLE WITH CENTRE (0, 0)

A circle is a set of points in the plane which are the same distance from a point called the **centre**. This distance is called the **radius**. An equation that is satisfied by all points $P(x, y)$ on a circle, and only those points, is called the **equation of the circle**.

Example 1.

The sun is the centre of our solar system. Of all the planets orbiting the sun, the orbit of Venus is closest to being circular. Find the equation of the path of Venus around the sun if the radius of its path is 108 Gm (gigametres, where 1 Gm = 1×10^9 m).

Solution.

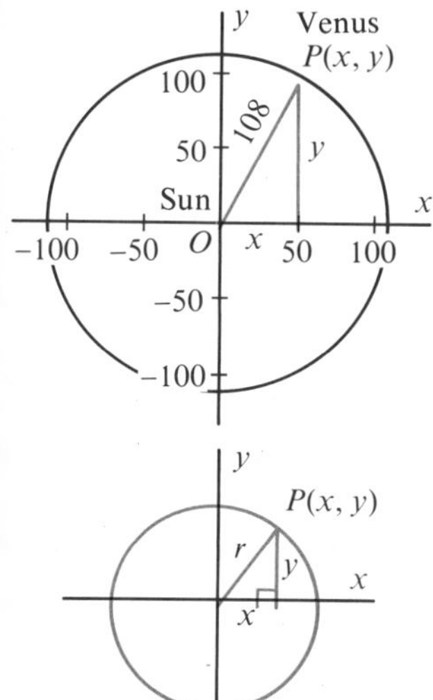

Let $O(0, 0)$ represent the position of the sun. At any point $P(x, y)$ in its orbit, Venus is 108 Gm from O. That is, $OP = 108$.
By the Pythagorean theorem: $x^2 + y^2 = 108^2$
The equation of the path of Venus around the sun is:

$$x^2 + y^2 = 11\ 664$$

Using the method of *Example 1*, we can find the equation of any circle with centre $O(0, 0)$ and radius r. If $P(x, y)$ is any point on the circle, $OP = r$ and $x^2 + y^2 = r^2$. The coordinates of any point not on the circle do not satisfy this equation.

> The equation of a circle with centre (0, 0) and radius r is $x^2 + y^2 = r^2$.

Example 2.

Given: circle $x^2 + y^2 = 16$

a) State:
   i) the coordinates of the centre;
   ii) the radius;
   iii) the diameter;
   iv) the x-intercepts;
   v) the y-intercepts.

b) Graph the circle.

Solution.

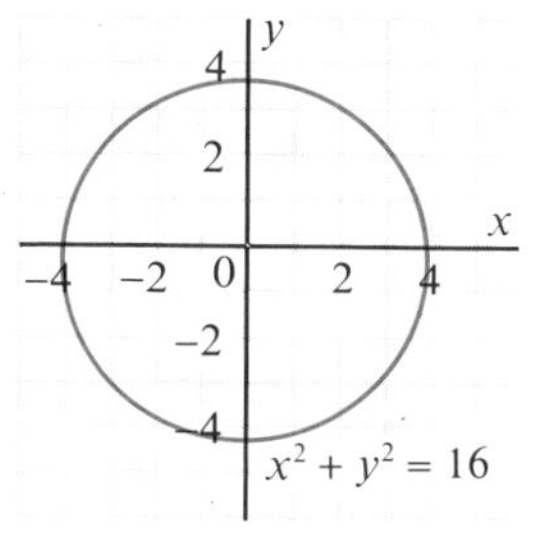

a) i) The coordinates of the centre are (0, 0).
   ii) $r^2 = 16$. Since $r > 0$, $r = 4$.
   The radius of the circle is 4.
   iii) The diameter of the circle is 8.
   iv) The x-intercepts are 4 and −4.
   v) The y-intercepts are 4 and −4.

b) The circle is graphed using the information in (a).

EXERCISES 6-6

(A)

1. Write the equation of the circle with centre (0, 0) and radius:
   a) 5; b) 12; c) 16; d) $6\frac{1}{4}$; e) 0.3; f) 23.

2. Given: circle $x^2 + y^2 = 25$.
   a) State:
      i) the coordinates of the centre;
      ii) the radius;
      iii) the diameter;
      iv) the x-intercepts;
      v) the y-intercepts.
   b) Draw the graph.

3. a) What is the radius of the circle?
      i) $x^2 + y^2 = 81$ ii) $x^2 + y^2 = 121$
      iii) $x^2 + y^2 = 64$ iv) $x^2 + y^2 = \frac{49}{4}$
      v) $x^2 + y^2 = 36$ vi) $x^2 + y^2 = 2.25$
   b) Graph each circle in (a).

4. (3, −4) is an endpoint of a diameter of the circle $x^2 + y^2 = r^2$.
   a) What is the radius of the circle?
   b) What are the coordinates of the other endpoint of the diameter?

(B)

5. Find the equation of the circle with centre (0, 0) which passes through the point:
   a) (3, 0); b) (0, −4); c) (5, 2); d) (−1, 3).

6. Find the value of r if point (3, −7) lies on $x^2 + y^2 = r^2$.

7. The following points lie on $x^2 + y^2 = 32$. Find the value of k.
   a) $(4, k)$ b) $(k, 5)$ c) $(k, 2\sqrt{7})$ d) $(2\sqrt{5}, k)$

8. a) Graph the circle $x^2 + y^2 = 100$.
   b) On the same graph as in (a), plot the points (6, 8), (−10, 1), and (−7, −7).
   c) Determine whether the points are on the circle, inside the circle, or outside the circle.

9. Determine whether the point is on, inside, or outside, the circle $x^2 + y^2 = 64$:
   a) (5, 6) b) (8, 1) c) (−4, 7)

10. Which of the following points are inside the circle $x^2 + y^2 = 20$?
    (1, −2) (4, 2) (−3, 3) (0, 4) (5, −1)

11. a) A line segment has endpoints $A(6, 2)$ and $B(2, -6)$. Show that AB is a chord of the circle $x^2 + y^2 = 40$.
    b) Find the equation of the perpendicular bisector of chord AB.
    c) Show that the perpendicular bisector is a diameter of the circle.
12. a) A line segment has endpoints $M(8, 6)$ and $N(-6, 8)$. Show that MN is a chord of the circle $x^2 + y^2 = 100$.
    b) Find the equation of the line that passes through the centre of the circle and the midpoint of chord MN.
    c) Show that the line in (b) is perpendicular to chord MN.
13. a) A line segment has endpoints $P(2, 5)$ and $Q(5, -2)$. Show that PQ is a chord of the circle $x^2 + y^2 = 29$.
    b) Find the equation of the line perpendicular to chord PQ that passes through the centre of the circle.
    c) Show that the line in (b) passes through the midpoint of chord PQ.

Ⓒ

14. Describe the graphs of the equations:

    a) $x^2 + y^2 = 0$ b) $x^2 + y^2 = -9$

    c) $y = \sqrt{25 - x^2}$ d) $x = \sqrt{25 - y^2}$
15. Four circles, each with radius 5, touch the x- and y-axes and a smaller circle with centre (0, 0), as shown. Find the equation of the smaller circle.

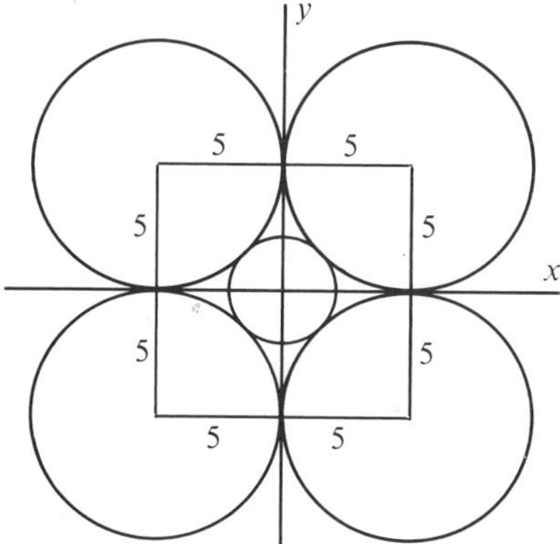

INVESTIGATE

'he equation $x^2 + y^2 = r^2$ epresents a circle with centre), 0) and radius r. What do iese equations represent?

$x^2 - y^2 = 9$

$x^2 + 4y^2 = 4$

$x^4 + y^4 = 16$

$\sqrt{x} + \sqrt{y} = 4$

ivestigate other equations ke these and write a report of our findings.

6-7 THE EQUATION OF A CIRCLE WITH CENTRE (h, k)

To find the equation of a straight line we require two pieces of information, the slope and a point on the line. The two pieces of information needed to obtain the equation of a circle are the centre and radius.

Example 1.

Find the equation of the circle with centre $C(-3, 7)$ and radius 4.

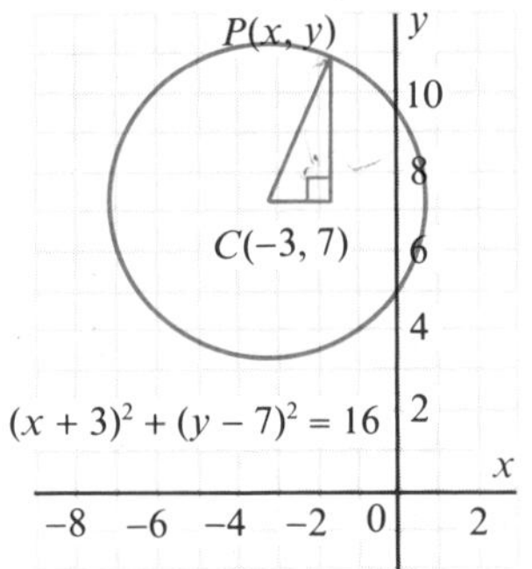

Solution.

Let $P(x, y)$ be any point on the circle.
Since CP is a radius, $CP = 4$.
By the Pythagorean theorem: $\sqrt{(x + 3)^2 + (y - 7)^2} = 4$
Square both sides to eliminate the radical:

$$(x + 3)^2 + (y - 7)^2 = 16$$

This is the equation of the circle.

In *Example 1*, the left side of the equation could be expanded and the equation written as $x^2 + y^2 + 6x - 14y + 42 = 0$. One disadvantage of this form of the equation is that the coordinates of the centre and the radius cannot be as easily seen.

We can find the equation of any circle with centre $C(h, k)$ and radius r. If $P(x, y)$ is any point on the circle, then

$$CP = r$$

$$\sqrt{(x - h)^2 + (y - k)^2} = r$$

Square both sides: $(x - h)^2 + (y - k)^2 = r^2$

The equation of the circle with centre (h, k) and radius r is:

$$(x - h)^2 + (y - k)^2 = r^2$$

Example 2.

a) Graph the circle $(x - 3)^2 + (y + 5)^2 = 100$.
b) Determine if points $R(10, 2)$, $S(9, -13)$, and $T(-6, 0)$ lie on the circle.

Solution.

a) From the equation, the circle has centre $(3, -5)$ and radius 10.
b) The points R, S, T are plotted on the graph. Since it is difficult to see if they lie on the circle or just close to it, their distances from the centre must be calculated.

$CR = \sqrt{(10 - 3)^2 + (2 + 5)^2} = \sqrt{98}$
$CS = \sqrt{(9 - 3)^2 + (-13 + 5)^2} = \sqrt{100}$, or 10
$CT = \sqrt{(-6 - 3)^2 + (0 + 5)^2} = \sqrt{106}$
Since only $CS = 10$, then only point S is on the circle.

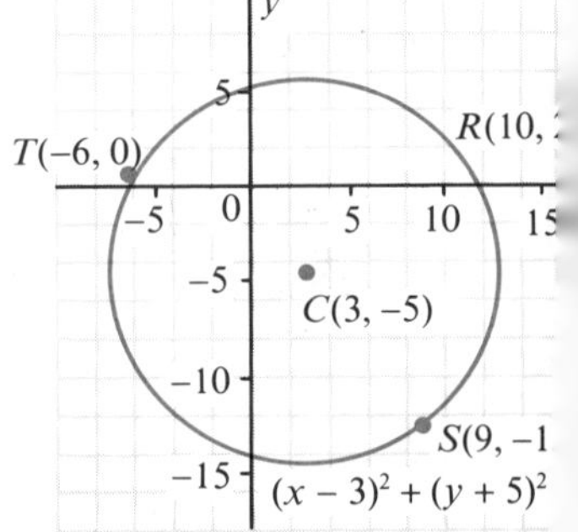

Example 3.

A circle has radius $\sqrt{13}$ and passes through point $A(3, 1)$. Find its equation if its centre lies on the y-axis.

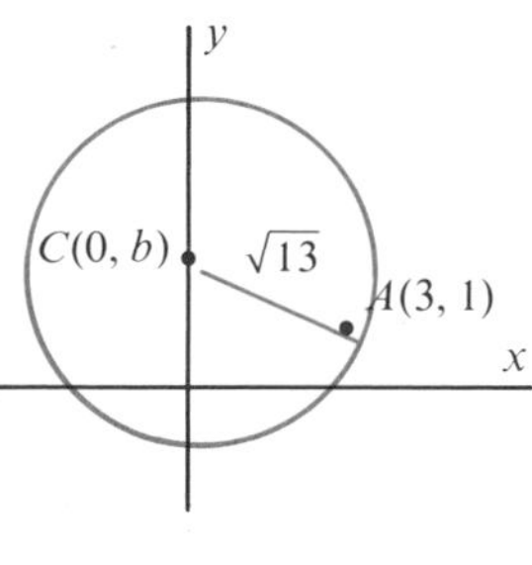

Solution.

Let $C(0, b)$ be the centre of the circle.

Then, since AC is a radius, $AC = \sqrt{13}$.

$$\sqrt{(0-3)^2 + (b-1)^2} = \sqrt{13}$$

Square both sides to eliminate the radical:

$$9 + b^2 - 2b + 1 = 13$$
$$b^2 - 2b - 3 = 0$$
$$(b-3)(b+1) = 0$$

Either $b = 3$ or $b = -1$.

Since there are two values of b, there are two circles that satisfy the given conditions.

When $b = 3$, the centre is $(0, 3)$ and the equation of the circle is: $x^2 + (y-3)^2 = 13$

When $b = -1$, the centre is $(0, -1)$ and the equation of the circle is: $x^2 + (y+1)^2 = 13$

EXERCISES 6-7

Ⓐ

1. State the centre and the radius of each circle:
   a) $(x-4)^2 + (y-1)^2 = 36$ b) $(x-2)^2 + (y+5)^2 = 9$
   c) $(x+7)^2 + (y+3)^2 = 16$ d) $(x+2)^2 + (y-2)^2 = 5$
   e) $x^2 + (y-8)^2 = 25$ f) $(x+3)^2 + y^2 = 13$

2. Draw the graphs of the circles in Exercise 1.

3. Write the equation of the circle with the given centre and radius:
   a) $(6, 2)$, 3 b) $(-4, 5)$, 7 c) $(-1, -3)$, 5
   d) $(-8, -2)$, 2 e) $(3, 0)$, 1 f) $(0, -4)$, 6

4. Write the equations of these circles:

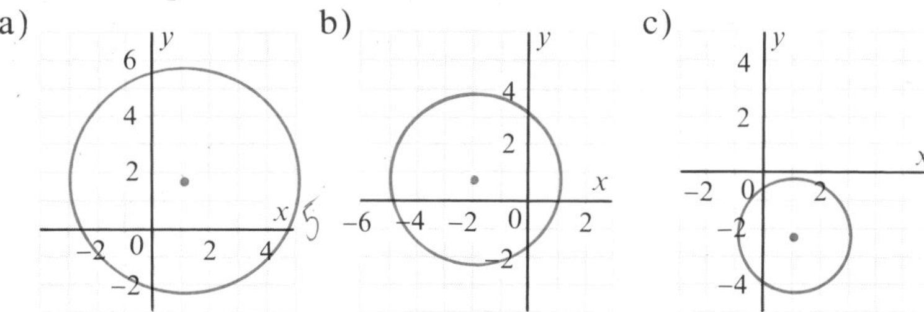

5. a) Graph the circle $(x-5)^2 + (y+3)^2 = 49$.
   b) Determine if points $A(10, 2)$, $B(-1, -6)$, and $C(5, -10)$ lie on the circle.

6. A circle has centre (3, 0) and radius 5.
   a) Find the equation of the circle.
   b) Find the coordinates of the points of intersection of the circle and the x-axis.

(B)

7. Which of the given circles have:
   a) a radius less than 5?
   b) their centres on the x-axis?
   c) their centres on the line $y = x$?
      i) $(x - 3)^2 + (y - 3)^2 = 1$ ii) $(x + 2)^2 + (y - 4)^2 = 9$
      iii) $x^2 + (y + 7)^2 = 13$ iv) $(x - 5)^2 + y^2 = 20$
      v) $(x + 1)^2 + (y + 1)^2 = 25$ vi) $x^2 + y^2 = 32$
8. Given: circle $(x - 6)^2 + (y + 2)^2 = 85$. State:
   a) the coordinates of the centre; b) the radius;
   c) the diameter; d) the x-intercepts; e) the y-intercepts.
9. Find the equation of the circle that has:
   a) the line segment with endpoints (–2, 0), (6, –6) as a diameter;
   b) centre (–4, 2) and passes through (1, –6)
   c) centre (5, 4) and just touches the x-axis.
10. The diameter of a circle has endpoints (4, 0) and (0, 4).
    a) Find the equation of the circle.
    b) Show that the circle passes through the origin.
11. The centre of a circle lies on the x-axis, 3 units from the origin. If the circle passes through (6, –4), find the possible equations of the circle.
12. A circle of radius $3\sqrt{5}$ passes through (–1, 3). Find its equation if its centre lies on the x-axis.
13. a) Graph $(x + 3)^2 + (y - 1)^2 = 25$ and $(x - 4)^2 + (y - 5)^2 = 9$.
    b) Do the circles in (a) intersect?
14. a) Graph the circle $(x - 1)^2 + (y - 2)^2 = 64$
    b) On the same axes as (a), graph:
       i) $(x + 2)^2 + (y - 1)^2 = 16$ ii) $(x + 7)^2 + (y - 8)^2 = 25$
       iii) $(x - 5)^2 + (y - 5)^2 = 9$ iv) $(x - 12)^2 + (y - 1)^2 = 9$
       v) $(x - 8)^2 + (y + 5)^2 = 4$ vi) $(x - 3)^2 + (y - 1)^2 = 121$
    c) Which of the circles in (b) intersect the circle in (a) in
       i) 2 points? ii) 1 point? iii) 0 points?
15. Two chords of the circle $(x + 1)^2 + (y - 4)^2 = 65$ are formed by segments of the two axes. Find the ratio in which the origin divides each chord.

(C)

16. A circle has centre (0, 9) and radius 9. A second circle, with radius 4, touches the first circle and the x-axis.
    a) If the second circle lies in the first quadrant, find its equation.
    b) Find the possible equations for the second circle if it does not lie in the first quadrant.

17. A circle passes through (0, 7) and (4, 3). If its centre lies on the line $y = 2x$, find the equation of the circle.

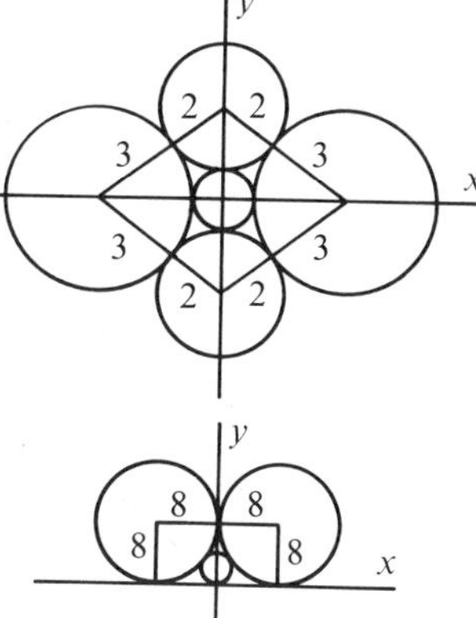

18. a) Graph the circle $(x + 4)^2 + (y - 2)^2 = 20$.
    b) If the circle $(x - 2)^2 + (y - 5)^2 = r^2$ just touches the circle in (a), find the value of r.

19. Four circles, two with radius 3 and two with radius 2, surround and touch the circle $x^2 + y^2 = r^2$, as shown.
    a) Find the value of r.
    b) Find the equations of the four circles.

20. Two circles, each with radius 8, touch the x- and y- axes and a small circle with centre on the y-axis, as shown. Find the equation of the small circle.

Forms of Circle Equations

1. By expanding the left side, the equation of the circle $(x + 3)^2 + (y - 7)^2 = 16$ can be written in the form $x^2 + y^2 + 6x - 14y + 42 = 0$. Determine how the coordinates of the centre and the radius can be found from this second equation.

2. Find the coordinates of the centre and the radius of the circle:
    a) $x^2 + y^2 - 6x - 10y + 18 = 0$;
    b) $x^2 + y^2 + 2x - 12y + 12 = 0$;
    c) $x^2 + y^2 + 8x + 14y - 16 = 0$.

3. There are two standard forms for the equation of a circle:

$$(x - h)^2 + (y - k)^2 = r^2 \quad \ldots .(i)$$

$$x^2 + y^2 + 2gx + 2fy + c = 0 \quad \ldots .(ii)$$

    a) Find expressions for the coordinates of the centre and the radius of the circle represented by equation (ii).
    b) Suggest why the coefficients of x and y in equation (ii) contain the factor 2.
    c) For what values of r does equation (i) represent a circle?
    d) If equation (ii) represents a circle, what condition must $g, f,$ and c satisfy?

6-8 TANGENTS TO A CIRCLE

For any straight line and any circle, one of the following occurs:

There are two points of intersection.

There is one point of intersection.

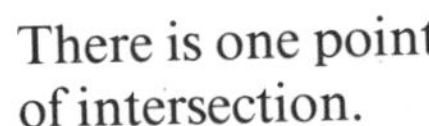

There is no point of intersection.

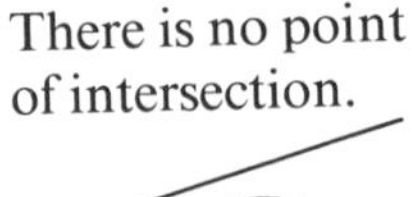

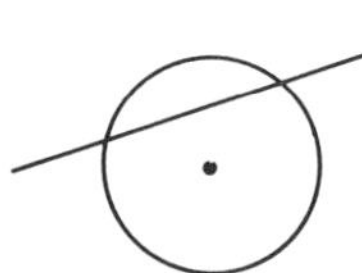

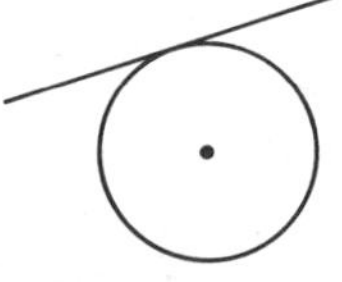

The line is called a **secant**.

The line is called a **tangent**.

A wheel standing on level ground illustrates a tangent to a circle. The centre of the wheel is directly above the point where the wheel touches the ground. That is, the angle formed by the radius to this point and the ground is 90°.

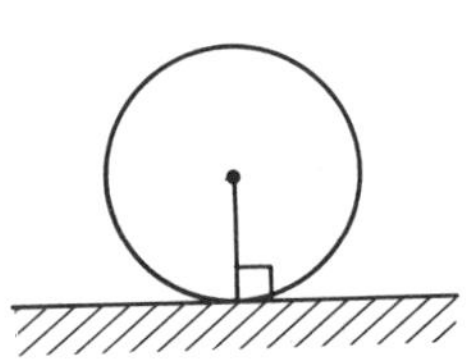

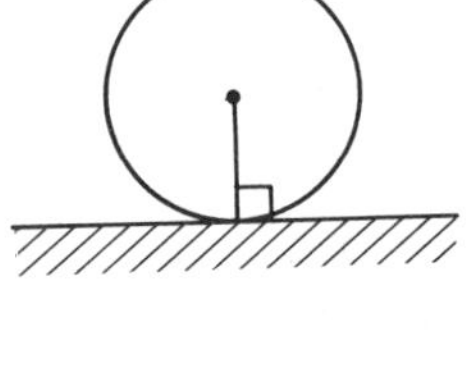

Tangent property of a circle: The angle between the tangent to a circle and the radius it touches is 90°.

Length of a Tangent

The tangent property can be used to calculate the length of the tangent to a circle from any point outside it.

Example 1.

Find the length of the tangent from point $P(5, 7)$ to the circle $x^2 + y^2 = 10$.

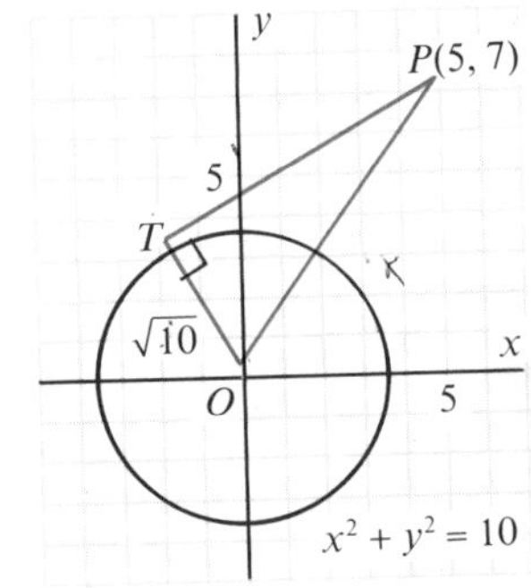

Solution

Let the tangent from P intersect the circle at T. Since $PT \perp OT$, by the Pythagorean theorem:

$$OP^2 = OT^2 + PT^2$$

$OP = \sqrt{5^2 + 7^2}$, or $\sqrt{74}$, and $OT = \sqrt{10}$

Therefore,
$$74 = 10 + PT^2$$
$$PT^2 = 64$$
$$PT = 8$$

The tangent from $P(5, 7)$ to the circle is 8 units long.

Note that in the above example it was not necessary to find the coordinates of the point of tangency in order to find the length of the tangent.

Equation of a Tangent

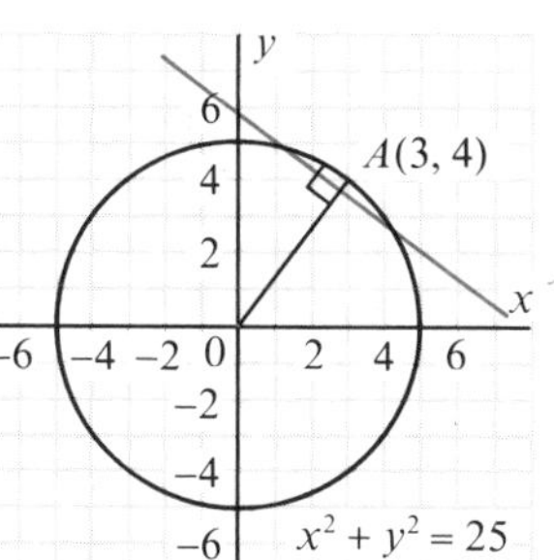

The tangent property can also be used to find the equation of the tangent of any point on a given circle.

Example 2.
$A(3, 4)$ is a point on the circle $x^2 + y^2 = 25$. Find the equation of the tangent through A.

Solution.

Slope of radius OA: $\dfrac{4-0}{3-0} = \dfrac{4}{3}$

Since the tangent is perpendicular to OA, the slope of the tangent is $-\frac{3}{4}$.

Since the tangent passes through (3, 4), its equation is:

$$y - 4 = -\frac{3}{4}(x - 3)$$

$$4y - 16 = -3x + 9$$

$$3x + 4y - 25 = 0$$

EXERCISES 6-8

(A)

1. Find the length of tangent PQ:

a)

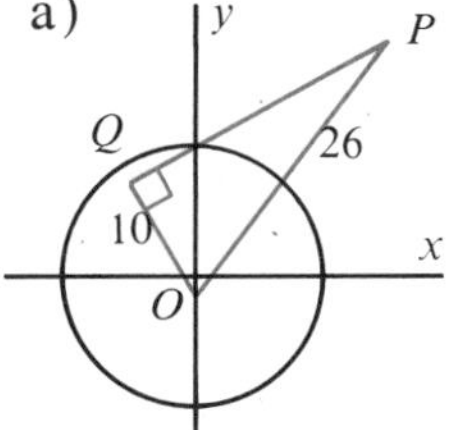

b)

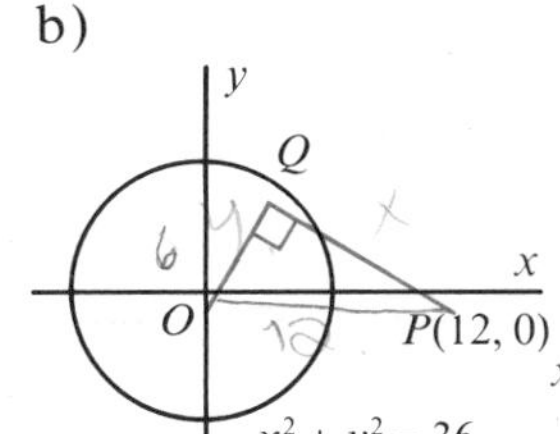

c)

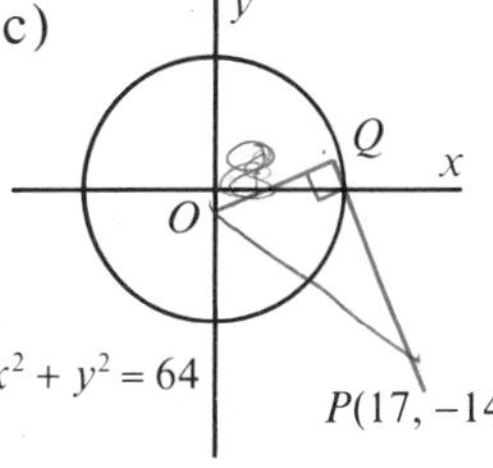

2. a) Graph the circle $x^2 + y^2 = 25$
   b) Find the lengths of the tangents to the circle from:
   i) (11, −2); ii) (8, 6); iii) (3, 8).
3. Find the lengths of the tangents from (8, 3) to the circle:
   a) $x^2 + y^2 = 9$; b) $x^2 + y^2 = 36$; c) $x^2 + y^2 = 65$.
4. The equation of a circle and a point on it are given. Find the equation of the tangent at that point.
   a) $x^2 + y^2 = 25$, (4, 3) b) $x^2 + y^2 = 100$, (6, −8)
   c) $x^2 + y^2 = 5$, (1, 2) d) $x^2 + y^2 = 13$, (−3, −2)

(B)

5. a) Graph the circle $(x - 2)^2 + (y - 3)^2 = 25$.
   b) Find the lengths of the tangents to the circle from:
   i) (5, −3); ii) (−1, −6); iii) (−6, 2).

6. Find the length of the tangent to the circle from the given point:
   a) $(x - 4)^2 + (y + 3)^2 = 25,\quad (7, 4)$
   b) $(x + 4)^2 + (y - 1)^2 = 36,\quad (6, 3)$
   c) $(x - 3)^2 + (y + 5)^2 = 12,\quad (-4, 1)$
   d) $(x + 5)^2 + (y + 2)^2 = 48,\quad (-3, 8)$

7. If the tangent from $(8, -1)$ to the circle $x^2 + y^2 = r^2$ has length 4, find the value of r.

8. P is a point on the line $x = 4$ such that the tangent from P to the circle $x^2 + y^2 = 4$ has length 6. Find the possible coordinates of P, and illustrate graphically.

9. The equation of a circle and a point on it are given. Find the equation of the tangent at that point.
   a) $x^2 + y^2 = 10,\quad (-1, 3)$
   b) $x^2 + y^2 = 16,\quad (0, -4)$
   c) $x^2 + y^2 = 4,\quad (\sqrt{2}, \sqrt{2})$
   d) $x^2 + y^2 = 11,\quad (3, -\sqrt{2})$

10. The three lines given pass through $(2, -3)$ on the circle $x^2 + y^2 = 13$. Which line is the tangent at $(2, -3)$?
    $3x + 2y = 0,\qquad 3x - 2y - 12 = 0,\qquad 2x - 3y - 13 = 0$

11. A diameter of the circle $x^2 + y^2 = 29$ has one endpoint $(5, 2)$. Find the equations of the tangents at both endpoints.

12. In the diagram, $A(-5, 0)$ and $B(4, 3)$ are points on the circle $x^2 + y^2 = 25$.
    a) Show that point $P(7, 4)$ lies on line AB.
    b) Find the length of tangent PT.
    c) Show that $PT^2 = PA \times PB$.

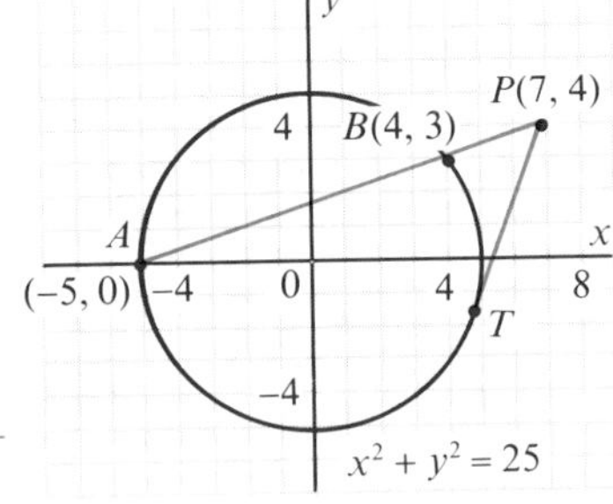

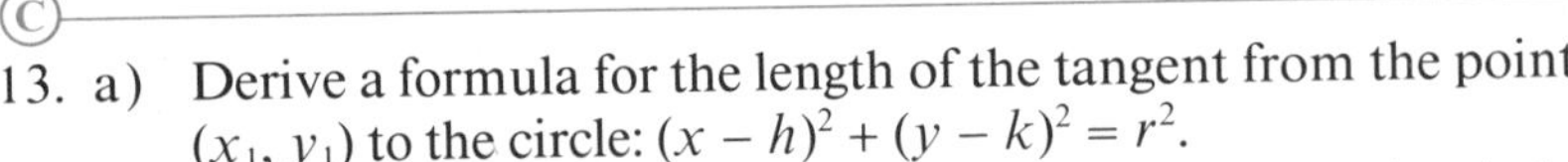

13. a) Derive a formula for the length of the tangent from the point (x_1, y_1) to the circle: $(x - h)^2 + (y - k)^2 = r^2$.
    b) Use the formula to find the length of the tangent to the circle $(x - 3)^2 + (y - 2)^2 = 25$ from the point:
       i) $(8, 9)$; ii) $(-4, 2)$; iii) $(0, 6)$; iv) $(0, 0)$.
    c) What is the geometric significance of the last two answers in part (b)?

14. Find the equation of the tangent at the point (x_1, y_1) on the circle $x^2 + y^2 = r^2$.

15. P is any point on $x^2 + y^2 = 29$. Find the length of the tangent from P to the circle $x^2 + y^2 = 13$.

16. One of the world's longest straight stretches of railway track runs 140 km between Regina and Stoughton, Saskatchewan. As the diagram shows, the track is not perfectly straight because of the curvature of Earth. If the track were perfectly straight, its end at Stoughton would be a certain distance, h, above the town. Estimate the value of h assuming that the radius of Earth is approximately 6370 km.

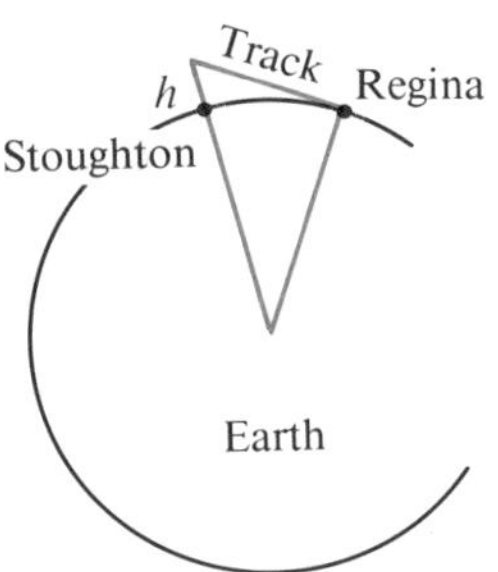

MATHEMATICS AROUND US

How Far Is the Horizon?

Have you ever wondered how far you can see from the top of a tall building or from an airplane? The answer, of course, depends on how high you are above the ground.

If d is the distance to the horizon from height x, and R is the radius of Earth, then:

$$\begin{aligned} d^2 &= (R + x)^2 - R^2 \\ &= R^2 + 2Rx + x^2 - R^2 \\ &= 2Rx + x^2 \end{aligned}$$

$$d = \sqrt{2Rx + x^2}$$

Since the radius of Earth is about 6370 km,

$$d \doteq \sqrt{12\,740\, x + x^2}$$

x^2 is usually very small compared with $12\,740\, x$ and may be omitted. And since it is more convenient to measure heights in metres than in kilometres, we can write $\frac{h}{1000}$ for x. So that the formula becomes:

$$d \doteq \sqrt{12\,740 \times \frac{h}{1000}}$$

$d \doteq 3.57\sqrt{h}$, where d is in kilometres and h is in metres.

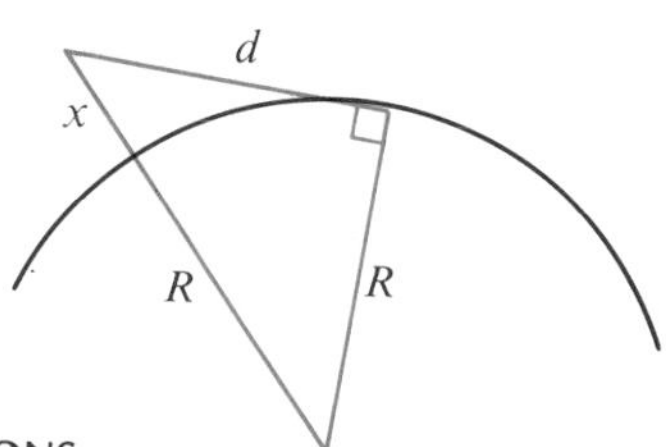

QUESTIONS

1. To the nearest kilometre, how far is the horizon viewed from:
   a) a beach, eye level being 1.5 m above the ground?
   b) the top of Mount Royal, 234 m?
   c) an aircraft cruising at 12 000 m?
   d) the space shuttle in orbit at 200 km?
2. From what height would the distance to the horizon be:
   a) 36 km? b) 72 km? c) 250 km?
3. The Cabot Strait between Newfoundland and Cape Breton Island is about 105 km wide at its narrowest point. How high above a point on the shore would you have to be to see the opposite shore?
4. Graph the relation between d and h for reasonable values of the variables.
5. What assumptions are you making in answering questions 1-3?
6. Investigate how the value of $\sqrt{12\,740\, x + x^2}$ compares with that of $\sqrt{12\,740\, x}$ for various values of x. How large does x have to be before the difference is:
   a) 1 km? b) 1% of $\sqrt{12\,740\, x + x^2}$?
7. Obtain formulas for the distance to the horizon on the following heavenly bodies:

Moon	1 738 km radius
Mars	3 380 km radius
Jupiter	69 000 km radius

6-9 COORDINATE PROOFS IN GEOMETRY

The seventeenth century French mathematician, René Descartes, after whom the Cartesian coordinate system is named, is credited with being the first to apply arithmetic and algebraic thinking to geometric concepts. This is the essence of analytic geometry. We can use algebra to prove geometric theorems. The following example illustrates the method of doing this. Note the steps involved.

Example.

Prove that the line segment joining the midpoints of two sides of a triangle is parallel to the third side and half its length.

Proof.

Step 1. Draw a diagram.
Draw $\triangle ABC$. Let D and E be the midpoints of sides AB and AC respectively.

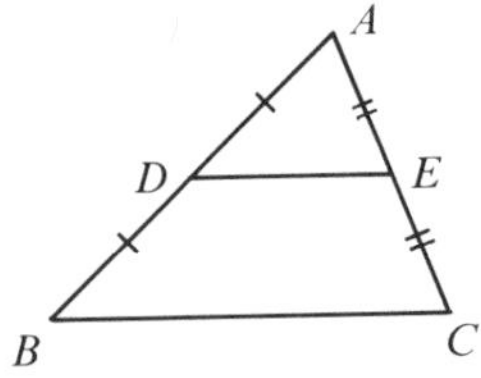

Step 2. State what is to be proved.

Prove: a) $DE \parallel BC$ b) $DE = \frac{1}{2}BC$

Step 3. Draw axes on the diagram in convenient locations.
Let B be the origin. Draw the x-axis along side BC.
Draw the y-axis through B perpendicular to BC.

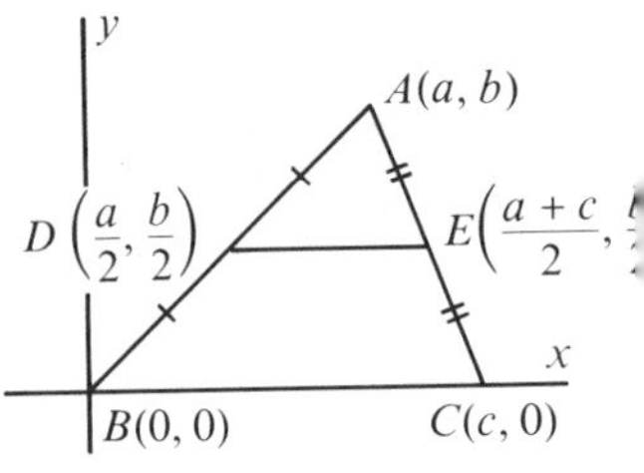

Step 4. Write coordinates for the points of the figure.
Let the coordinates of the vertices of $\triangle ABC$ be $A(a, b)$, $B(0, 0)$, $C(c, 0)$.
The coordinates of D, the midpoint of AB, are $\left(\frac{a}{2}, \frac{b}{2}\right)$

The coordinates of E, the midpoint of AC, are $\left(\frac{a+c}{2}, \frac{b}{2}\right)$

Step 5. Use the coordinates to establish the proof.

a) Since D and E have the same y-coordinate, segment DE is parallel to the x-axis. That is, $DE \parallel BC$.

b) $DE = \sqrt{\left(\frac{a+c}{2} - \frac{a}{2}\right)^2 + \left(\frac{b}{2} - \frac{b}{2}\right)^2} = \sqrt{\left(\frac{c}{2}\right)^2}$, or $\frac{c}{2}$ (since $c > 0$)

Since $c = BC$, $DE = \frac{1}{2}BC$.

When placing a system of coordinates on a figure, we are free to choose:

- any convenient point to be the origin;
- any line through this point to be the x-axis (or y-axis).

A good choice of axes and coordinates is important in order to simplify the algebra. The following are some examples:

Diagram	Good choice of axes and coordinates
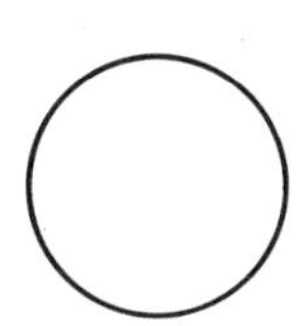 Any circle	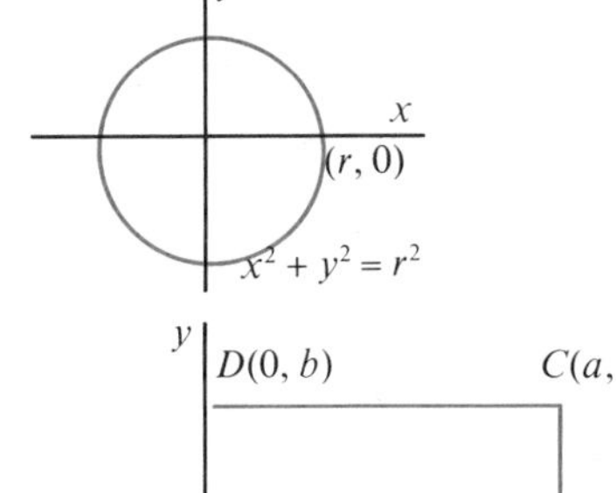
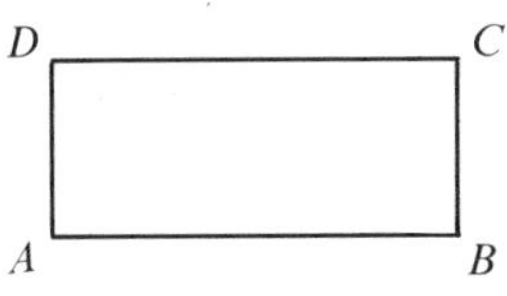 Any rectangle	
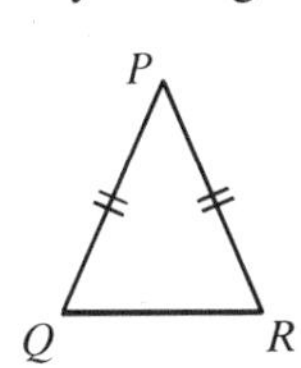 Any isosceles triangle	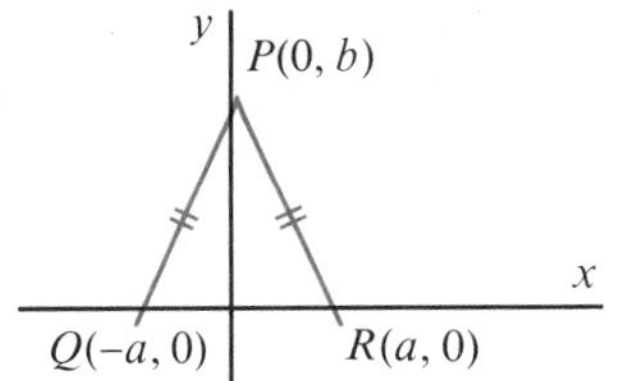

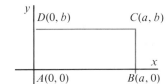

EXERCISES 6-9

(A)

1. Which of the two choices of axes is the better?

a) i) ii)

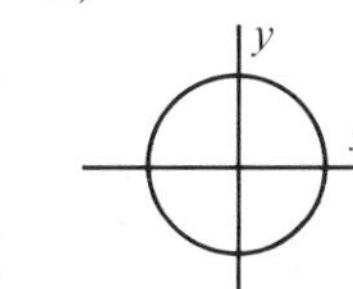

b) i) ii)

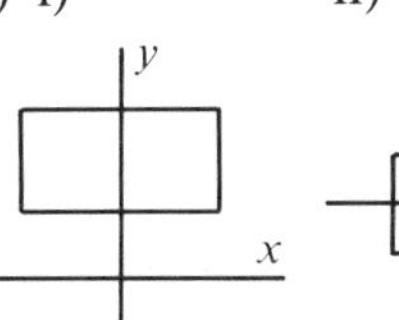

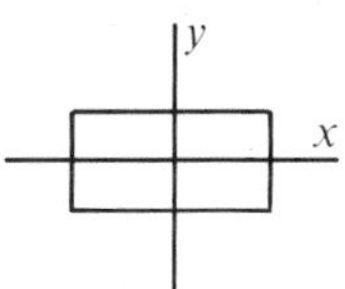

c) i) ii)

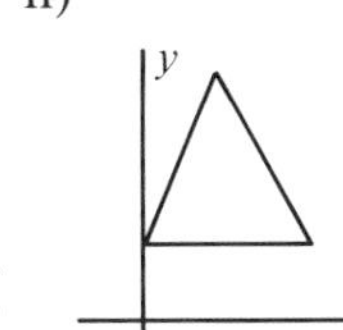

d) i) ii)

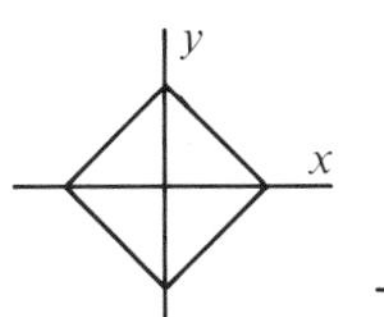

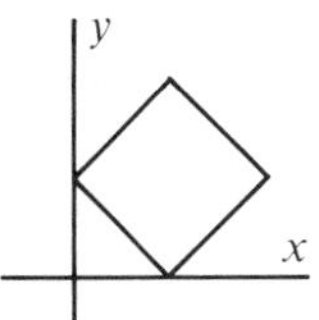

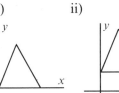

2. Use the diagram to prove that the diagonals of a square are perpendicular to each other.

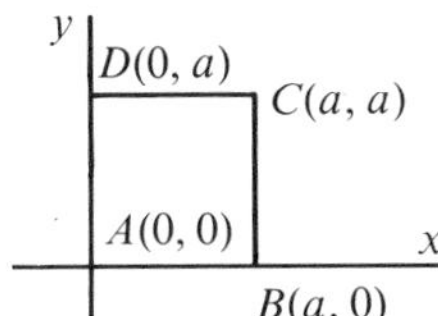

3. Use the diagram to prove that the midpoint of the hypotenuse of a right triangle is equidistant from the three vertices.

Ⓑ

4. Prove that the diagonals of a rectangle are equal.
5. a) Which of the diagrams below is the better one to use to prove that the line segments joining the midpoints of adjacent sides of a rectangle form a rhombus?

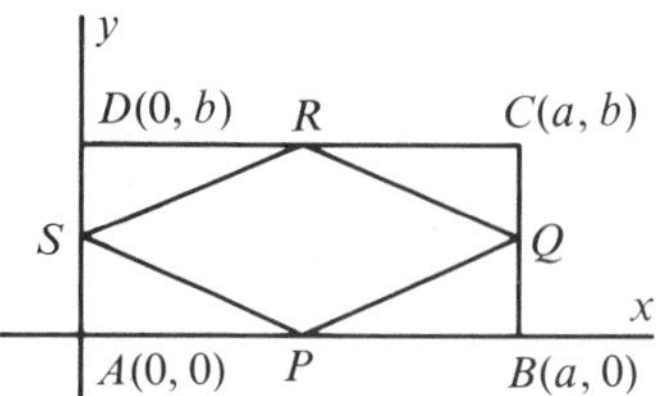

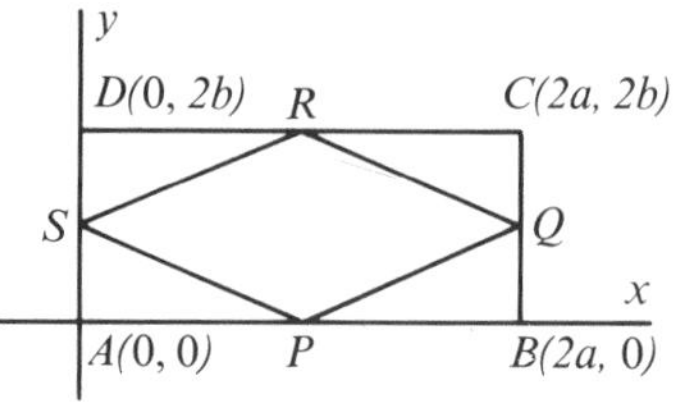

   b) Prove the theorem in (a) using the diagram chosen.
6. In $\triangle ABC$, D is the midpoint of AB and E is a point on AC such that $DE \parallel BC$. Prove that E is the midpoint of BC.
7. In $\triangle PQR$, $PQ = PR$. If M and N are the midpoints of PQ and PR respectively, prove that $MR = NQ$.
8. Use the diagram to prove that the diagonals of a parallelogram bisect each other.

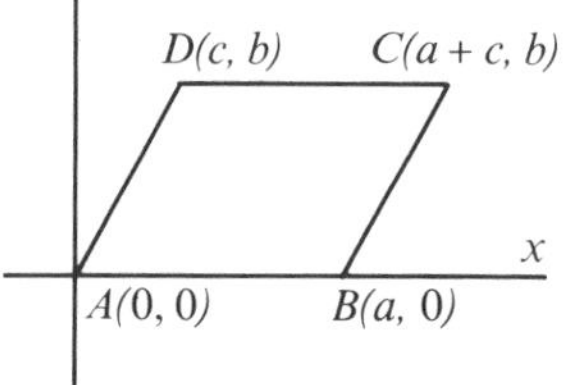

9. In any triangle ABC, if AD is the median from A to BC, prove that: $AB^2 + AC^2 = 2BD^2 + 2AD^2$.
10. If $ABCD$ is any rectangle and P is any point, prove that: $PA^2 + PC^2 = PB^2 + PD^2$.

Ⓒ

11. Prove that the line segments joining the midpoints of adjacent sides of a quadrilateral form a parallelogram.
12. AD, BE, and CF are the medians of any triangle ABC.
    a) Use a convenient system of coordinates to determine the coordinates of the points which divide the medians in the ratio 2 : 1.
    b) What have you just proved about the medians of a triangle?
13. In $\triangle ABC$, $\angle B = 90°$ and P is the centre of the square on AC. Prove that PB bisects $\angle B$.

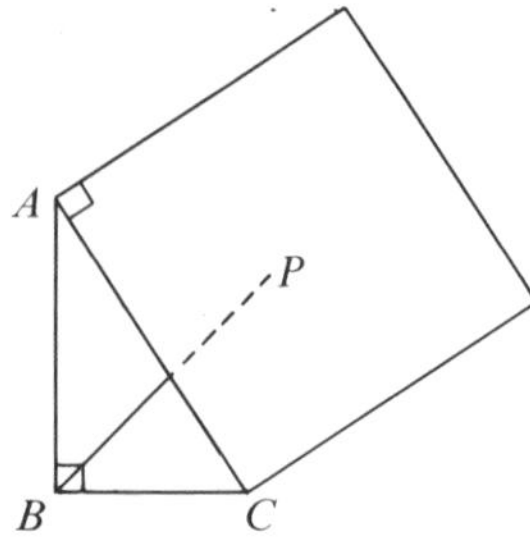

6-10 PROPERTIES OF CIRCLES

We can use coordinate geometry to prove an important theorem about the chords of a circle.

Theorem:

The perpendicular bisector of a chord of a circle passes through the centre of the circle.

Proof.

Step 1. Draw any circle with centre C and draw any chord AB.
Step 2. Let LM be the perpendicular bisector of AB. We are required to prove that LM passes through C.
Step 3. Using coordinates, let C be the origin, and choose the x-axis to be parallel to AB.
Step 4. Let the coordinates of A be (a, b).
Step 5. Since LM is the perpendicular bisector of AB, the coordinates of B are $(-a, b)$. The coordinates of M are $\left(\frac{a+(-a)}{2}, \frac{2b}{2}\right)$, or $(0, b)$; and LM must be the y-axis which passes through C.

Corollary 1. The line containing the centre of a circle and the midpoint of a chord is perpendicular to the chord.

Corollary 2. The perpendicular from the centre of a circle to a chord bisects the chord.

The following examples show how this theorem and its corollaries can be used to solve problems.

Example 1.

Calculate the value of x correct to two decimal places.

a)

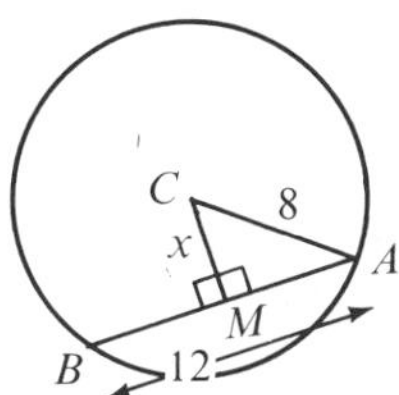

b)

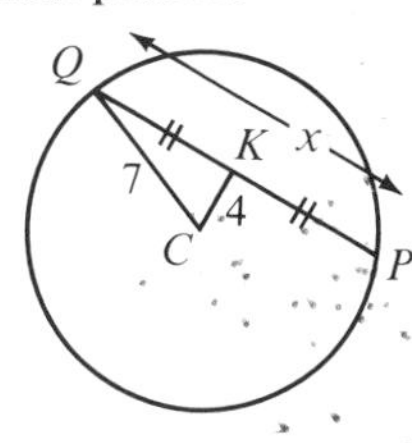

Solution

a) Since $CM \perp AB$, $AM = \frac{1}{2}AB$. That is, $AM = \frac{1}{2}(12)$, or 6

By the Pythagorean theorem:

$$x = \sqrt{8^2 - 6^2}$$
$$= \sqrt{64 - 36}$$
$$= \sqrt{28}, \text{ or about } 5.2915$$

To two decimal places, $x \doteq 5.29$.

b) Since $PK = KQ$, $CK \perp PQ$ and $\angle CKQ = 90°$.
By the Pythagorean theorem:

$$KQ = \sqrt{7^2 - 4^2}$$
$$= \sqrt{49 - 16}, \text{ or } \sqrt{33}$$

Therefore, $x = 2\sqrt{33}$, or about 11.4891

To two decimal places, $x \doteq 11.49$.

Example 2.

The arch of a highway tunnel is an arc of a circle. If the arch has a maximum height of 10 m and a width of 32 m, what is its radius?

Solution.

Let the road be the x-axis and let the y- axis pass through the centre of the highway. Then the coordinates of the points of the tunnel are as shown in the diagram. The centre, C, is on the y-axis. Let its coordinates be $(0, c)$. Draw CB.

$$CB = CD \quad \ldots\text{radii of the same circle}$$

$$\sqrt{(16-0)^2 + (0-c)^2} = \sqrt{(0-0)^2 + (10-c)^2}$$

Square both sides:

$$256 + c^2 = 100 - 20c + c^2$$
$$156 = -20c$$
$$c = -7.8$$

The centre of the circle is 7.8 m below the highway.
The radius of the arch is 10 + 7.8, or 17.8 m.

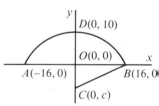

y
D(0, 10)
O(0, 0)
x
A(−16, 0)
B(16, 0)
C(0, c)

EXERCISES 6-10

(A)

1. Calculate the value of x:

a)
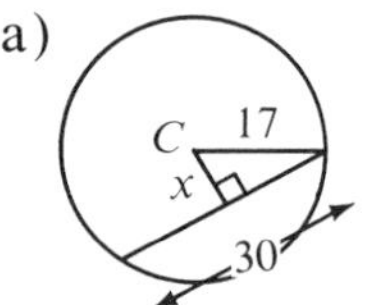

b)
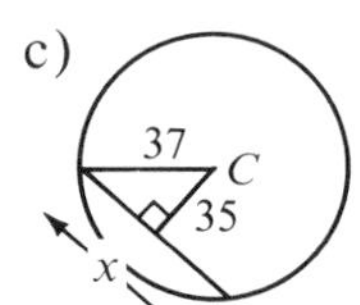

c)
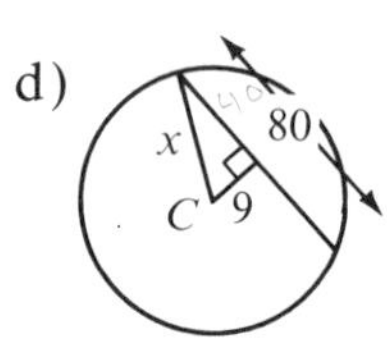

d)
x
80
C
9

2. A chord of a circle with radius 16 cm is 10 cm long. How far is the chord from the centre of the circle?

3. A chord of a circle is 4 cm long. Calculate the radius of the circle if the chord is 6 cm from the centre.

(B)

4. Calculate the value of x:

a)
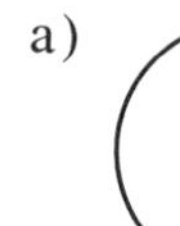

b)

c)
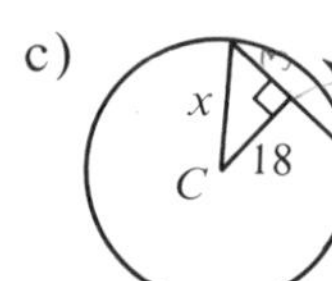

5. What is the length of a chord of a circle with diameter 10 cm when the distance of the chord from the centre is:
   a) 1 cm? b) 2 cm? c) 3 cm? d) 4 cm?

6. Prove that the line containing the centre of a circle (below, left) and the midpoint of a chord is perpendicular to the chord.

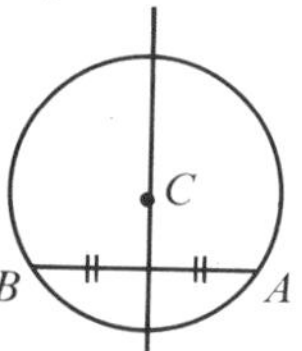

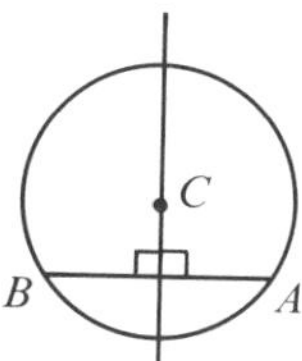

7. Prove that the perpendicular from the centre of a circle to a chord (above, right) bisects the chord.

8. A highway overpass is supported by an arch 7.2 m high. If the highway is 28 m wide and the arch is an arc of a circle, find the radius of the circle.

9. Near St. Jacobs, Ontario, a circular tunnel beneath Highway 86 allows horse-and-buggy traffic to cross the highway safely. If the diameter of the tunnel is 4.1 m and the road through it is 3.1 m wide, what is its height?

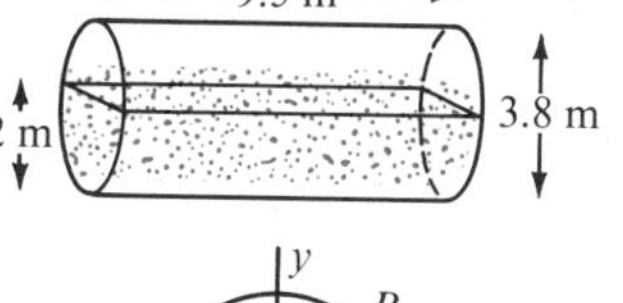

10. A cylindrical fuel tank 9.5 m long and 3.8 m in diameter contains fuel to a depth of 2.2 m. What is the surface area of the fuel exposed to the air inside the tank?

Ⓒ

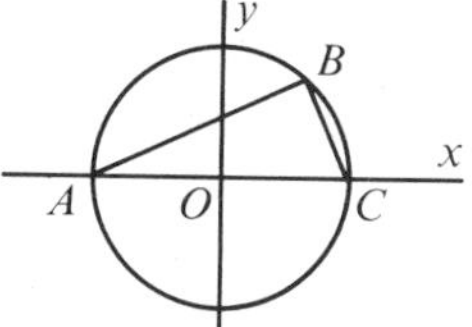

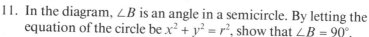

11. In the diagram, $\angle B$ is an angle in a semicircle. By letting the equation of the circle be $x^2 + y^2 = r^2$, show that $\angle B = 90°$.

12. The Long Sault Dam in Ontario is part of the St. Lawrence Power Project. It is an arc of a circle with radius 518 m, and spans a width of 792 m across the river. Calculate, to the nearest metre, the distance, h, shown on the diagram.

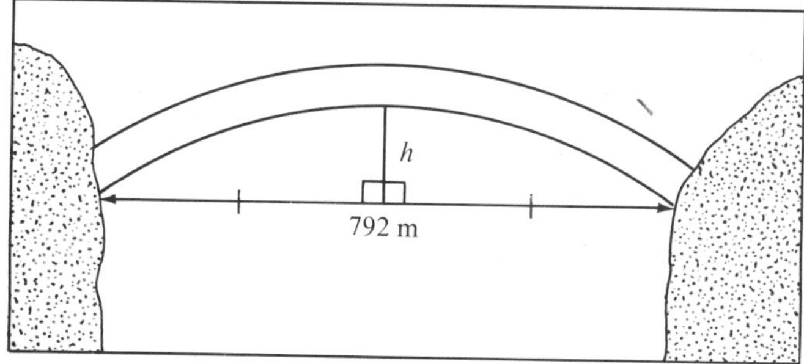

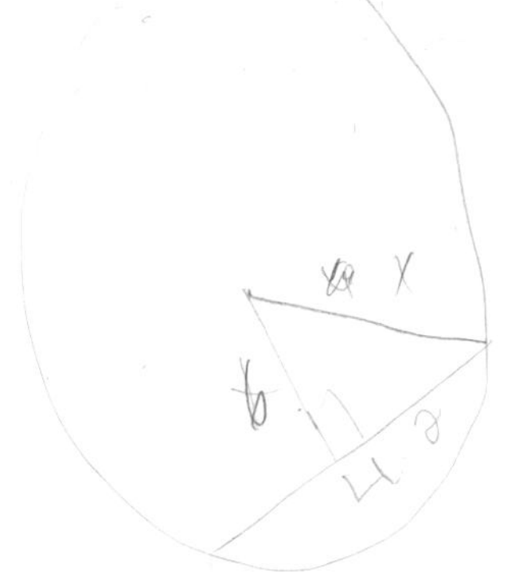

MATHEMATICS AROUND US

The Line of Best Fit—Athletics

Although the mile is not a metric distance, the one-mile race has always been an important track event. The four-minute mile, once considered impossible to achieve, was accomplished in 1954 by two runners in the same race. Since then, the record for the mile has dropped steadily.

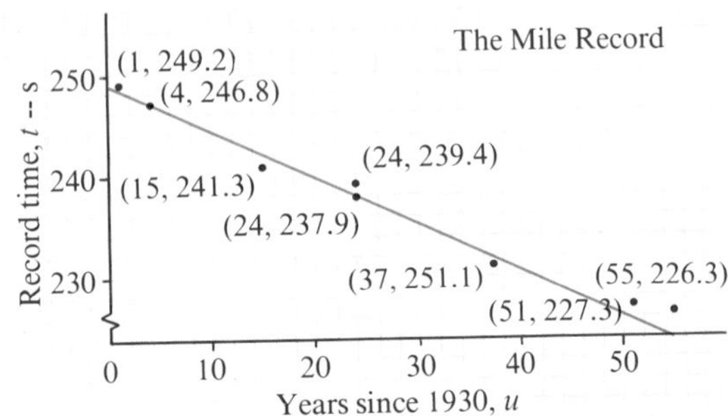

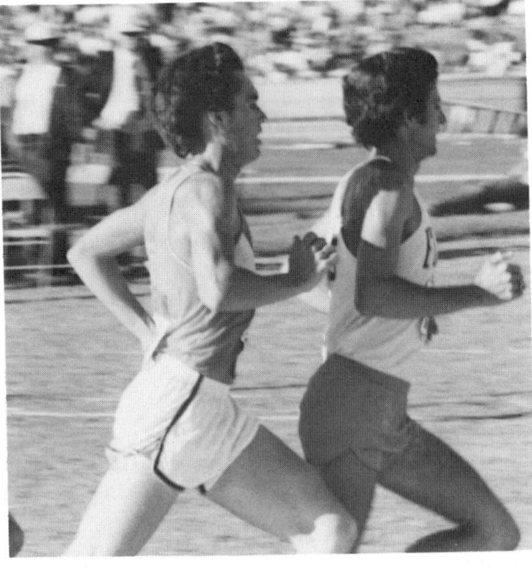

Record Holder	Year	Record Time min : s
Jules Ladoumègue	1931	4:09.2
Glenn Cunningham	1934	4:06.8
Gunder Hagg	1945	4:01.3
Roger Bannister	1954	3:59.4
John Landy	1954	3:57.9
Jim Ryun	1967	3:51.1
Sebastian Coe	1981	3:47.3
Steve Cram	1985	3:46.3

A plot of the data suggests that the record times have decreased at a fairly constant rate. An approximate relationship between the time, t, and the number of years since 1930, u, can be found by drawing a *line of best fit* which passes near the plotted points.

A more accurate line can be drawn by using a scientific calculator with the capability of determining the slope and vertical intercept of the line when the coordinates of the known data are entered. For the above data, such a calculator gives:

slope: -0.4397 vertical intercept: 248.8

The equation of the line of best fit is therefore:

$$t = -0.4397u + 248.8$$

QUESTION

Assuming that the trend indicated by the graph continues, use the equation of the line of best fit to predict:

a) what the record might be in the year 2000;

b) when the record might be as low as 3:30. It has been suggested that, for physiological reasons, the record may never become much lower.

Review Exercises

1. Find the length of the line segment with endpoints:
   a) (0, 0), (−3, 4);
   b) (−3, −7), (9, −2);
   c) (4, 2), (5, −3);
   d) (−6, −4), (−2, 7).
2. Find the coordinates of the midpoint of each line segment in Exercise 1.
3. Determine if the following points are collinear:
   a) (−4, 1), (0, 2), (8, 4)
   b) (−5, 2), (2, −1), (5, −2)
   c) (−6, −3), (2, 0), (7, 2)
   d) (−7, −4), (3, 3.5), (5, 5)
4. If the three points are collinear, what is the value of k?
   a) (−5, 6), (k, 0), (4, 3)
   b) (−4, −2), (1, 0), (k, 2)
   c) (−4, 6), (−3, 1), (−1, k)
   d) (10, 6), (6, 3), (−4, k)
5. A line segment has endpoints (−3, −1) and (12, 9). In what ratio is it divided by: a) (0, 1)? b) (6, 5)?
6. A is a point on the x-axis and B is a point on the y-axis. If point (2, 3) divides line segment AB in the ratio 3 : 1, find the coordinates of A and B.
7. A line segment with endpoints (12, 2) and (0, 5) is intersected by the line $y = mx$. Find the value of m for the point of intersection to divide the segment in the ratio: a) $\frac{2}{1}$; b) $\frac{1}{2}$.
8. Do the graphs of the equations form a right triangle?
   a) $x - 2y + 4 = 0$, $8x - y + 32 = 0$, $4x + 7y - 44 = 0$
   b) $2x + 3y - 6 = 0$, $3x - 2y + 18 = 0$, $x - 3y + 15 = 0$
   c) $x - y + 1 = 0$, $x - 5 = 0$, $x + y + 3 = 0$
9. Show that (3, 2) is the point of intersection of the altitudes of the triangle with vertices (−4, −4), (8, −1), (2, 6).
10. Find the equations of the altitudes of the triangle in Exercise 9.
11. Find the equation of the line:
    a) 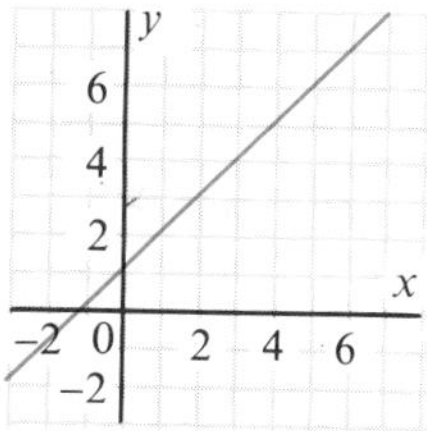
    b) 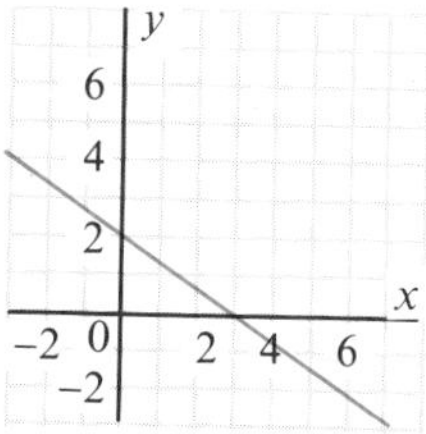
    c) 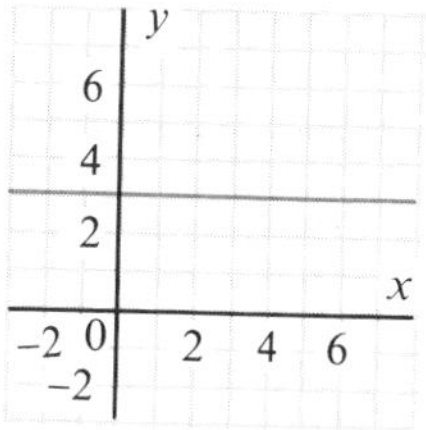
12. Find the equation of the line through:
    a) (0, 0) and (6, −2);
    b) (−3, −4) and (8, 6);
    c) (1, 4) and (6, 9);
    d) (−7, 1) and (3, −4).
13. Which lines are parallel to the line $3x - 4y + 6 = 0$?
    a) $6x + 8y - 3 = 0$
    b) $9x - 12y + 6 = 0$
    c) $x - \frac{4}{3}y - 7 = 0$
    d) $12x - 8y + 12 = 0$

14. Which lines are perpendicular to $4x + 8y + 3 = 0$?
    a) $8x + 4y + 3 = 0$ b) $6x - 3y + 2 = 0$
    c) $-2x + 4y + 6 = 0$ d) $2x - y - 1 = 0$
15. Find the equation of the line:
    a) with slope $-\frac{5}{4}$ that passes through $(-1, 5)$;
    b) with y-intercept $-\frac{3}{2}$ that passes through $(4, 3)$;
    c) with x-intercept -2 that passes through $(3, 5)$;
    d) through $(7, -3)$ parallel to $4x + 3y - 7 = 0$.
16. Find the equation of the circle, centre $(0, 0)$, which passes through:
    a) $(0, -2.5)$; b) $(7, 3)$; c) $(5, -5)$; d) $(-1, -7)$.
17. Which of the following points are inside the circle $x^2 + y^2 = 50$?
    $(0, 7)$ $(7, -3)$ $(1, 8)$ $(-4, 6)$ $(6, 3.5)$
18. a) Show that the line segment with endpoints $A(5, 3)$ and $B(3, -5)$ is a chord of the circle $x^2 + y^2 = 34$.
    b) Find the equation of the line through $(0, 0)$ and the midpoint of chord AB.
    c) Show that the line in (b) is perpendicular to chord AB.
19. Find the equation of the circle
    a) with centre $(-3, -5)$ which passes through $(5, -1)$;
    b) with centre $(2, -4)$ and a y-intercept 1;
    c) with $(-2, -8)$ and $(16, -2)$ as endpoints of a diameter.
20. A circle with centre $(5, 4)$ intersects the x-axis 3 units from the origin. Find the possible equations of the circle.
21. A circle of radius $2\sqrt{10}$ units passes through $(2, -5)$. If its centre lies on the y-axis, find its equation.
22. If the tangent from $(-4, 12)$ to the circle $x^2 + y^2 = r^2$ is 12 units long, find the value of r.
23. P is a point on the line $y = x$ such that the tangent from P to the circle $x^2 + y^2 = 1225$ has length 5. Find the possible coordinates of P and illustrate by a graph.
24. Prove that the medians to the equal sides of an isosceles triangle are equal.
25. Prove that if the midpoints of adjacent sides of a rectangle are joined, the quadrilateral formed is a rhombus.
26. A device for finding the diameters of large wheels consists of a rod with a fixed leg at each end. A centre leg can be adjusted until all three legs are in contact with the rim of the wheel, and then the difference in leg length is read off. For one wheel, this difference is 8 cm. What is its diameter if the length of the rod is 1.2 m?

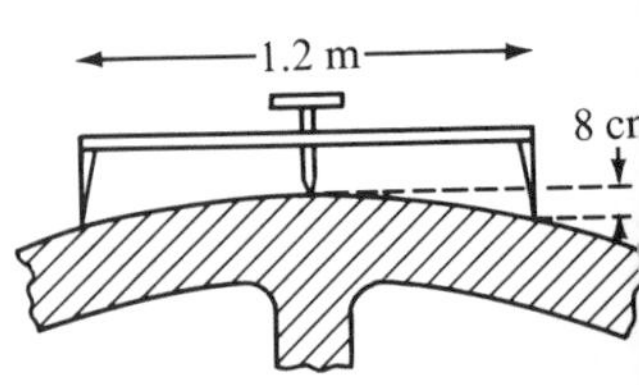

7 Analytic Geometry: Systems of Equations

A skydiver jumped from an airplane and fell freely for several seconds before releasing her parachute. If the equations giving her height above the ground before and after opening her parachute are known, how may her height at the time of releasing the parachute be determined? (See *Example 2* in Section 7-7.)

7-1 SOLVING SYSTEMS OF LINEAR EQUATIONS BY GRAPHING

Every so often, a new board game captures the public's imagination and it is in great demand. The sales of one such game, at the height of its popularity, topped 10 000 per week.

Suppose that it costs \$40 000 to develop a board game and \$5.00 to manufacture each one. If the games are sold at \$20.00 each, how many games must be sold to break even? This problem can be answered using graphs.

The cost of producing x games is: $y = 5x + 40\ 000$

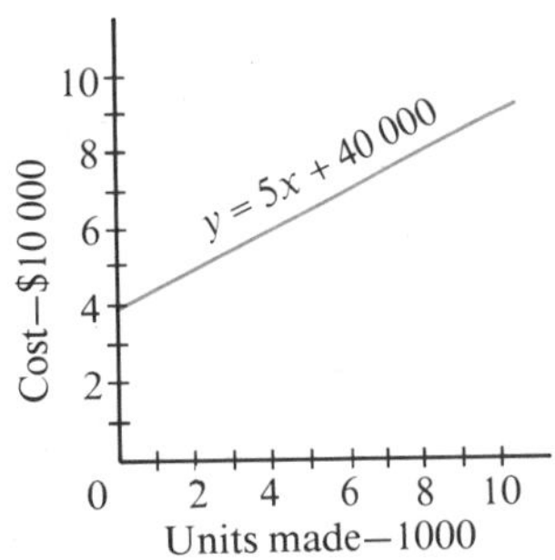

The income from the sale of x games is: $y = 20x$

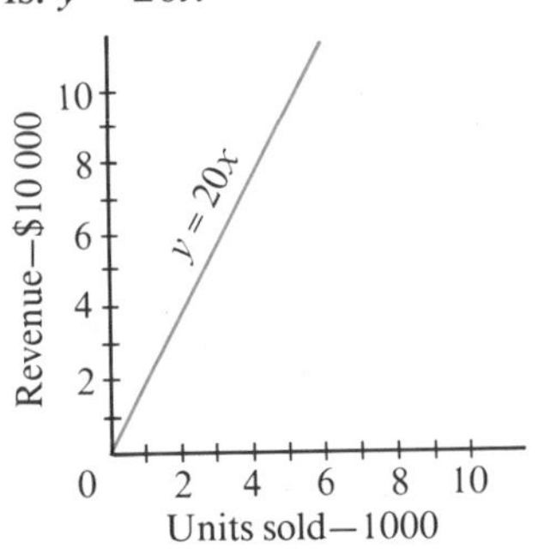

Draw the two graphs on the same axes:

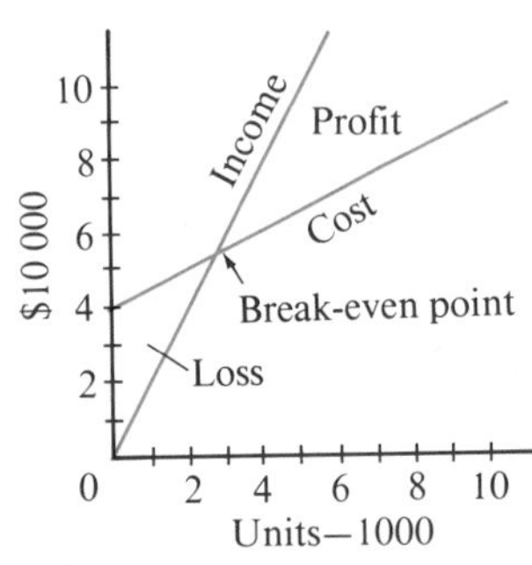

When the cost and income equations are graphed on the same axes, the point of intersection of the two lines indicates that the income from the sale of about 2700 games equals the cost of producing them. This is the break-even point. There will be a loss if fewer games are sold, and a profit if more are sold.

The equations $y = 5x + 40\ 000$ and $y = 20x$ are called **linear equations** because their graphs are straight lines. The general linear equation is $ax + by + c = 0$.

> An equation that can be written in the form $ax + by + c = 0$ is called a **linear equation**.

A pair of linear equations, considered together, is called a **linear system**. To solve a linear system in two variables such as x and y means to find all the ordered pairs (x, y), if any, that satisfy both equations. These may be found by graphing both equations on the same axes.

- If the lines intersect, one ordered pair satisfies both equations.
- If the lines are parallel, no ordered pairs satisfy both equations.
- If the lines coincide, infinitely many ordered pairs satisfy both equations.

Intersecting Lines	Parallel Lines	Coincident Lines
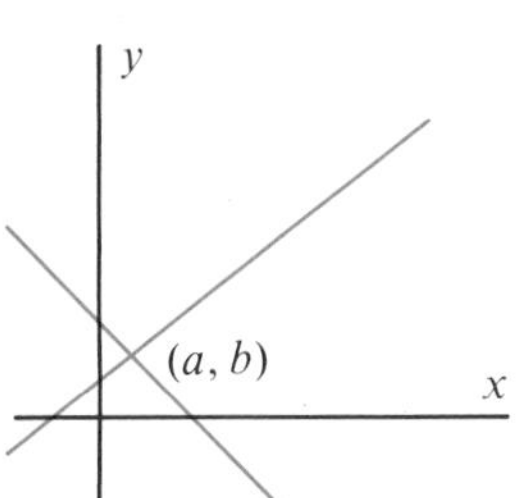	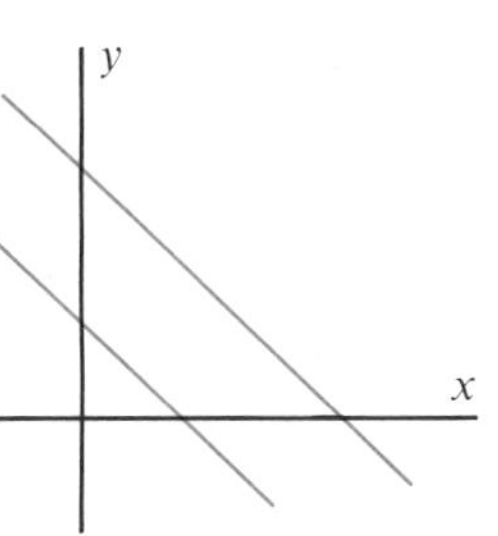	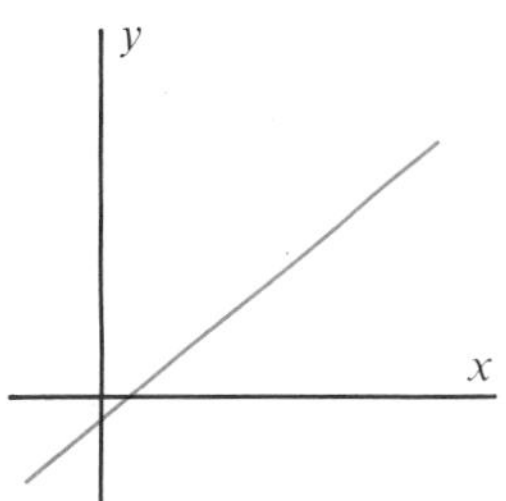
(a, b) is the only solution.	There is no solution.	There are infinitely many solutions.

Example.

Solve graphically:

a) $\begin{matrix} 3x + 2y = 4 \\ x - 3y = 5 \end{matrix}$ b) $\begin{matrix} 5x + 2y = 10 \\ 10x + 4y = 4 \end{matrix}$ c) $\begin{matrix} 2x - 6y = -12 \\ -3x + 9y = 18 \end{matrix}$

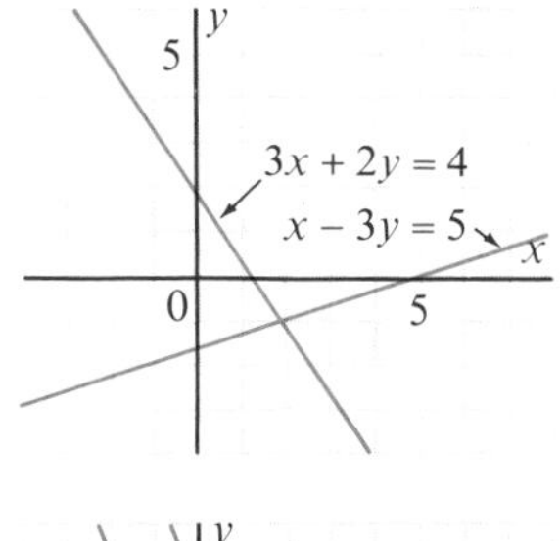

Solution.

a) The solution is $(2, -1)$. It is the only point common to both lines.

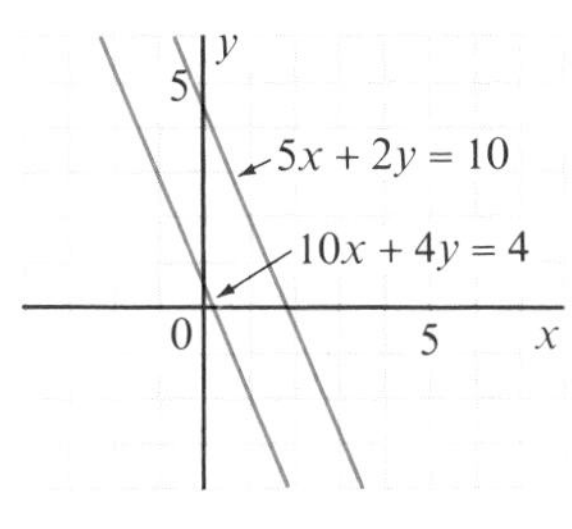

b) There is no solution. If both sides of the second equation are divided by 2, the system becomes: $\begin{matrix} 5x + 2y = 10 \\ 5x + 2y = 2 \end{matrix}$. Clearly, no ordered pair can satisfy both equations.

c) There are an infinite number of solutions. If both sides of the second equation are multiplied by $-\frac{2}{3}$, the system becomes:

$\begin{matrix} 2x - 6y = -12 \\ 2x - 6y = -12 \end{matrix}$. Clearly, every ordered pair (x, y) that satisfies one equation satisfies the other equation.

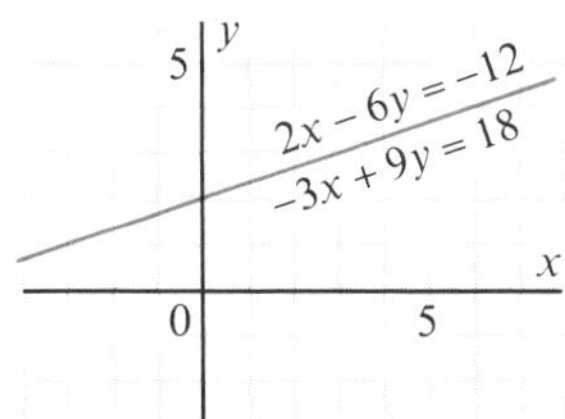

It is not always possible to obtain the exact coordinates of the point of intersection of two lines by graphing.

EXERCISES 7-1

(A)

1. Solve graphically:

a) $\begin{matrix} y = x + 1 \\ y = -x + 5 \end{matrix}$ b) $\begin{matrix} x - y = 2 \\ y = 2x - 4 \end{matrix}$

c) $\begin{matrix} x - y = 4 \\ 2x + y + 4 = 0 \end{matrix}$ d) $\begin{matrix} x + y - 3 = 0 \\ x - 2y - 6 = 0 \end{matrix}$

e) $\begin{matrix} 8x - 3y = 24 \\ 4x - 6y = 12 \end{matrix}$ f) $\begin{matrix} 3x + y - 12 = 0 \\ x + y - 8 = 0 \end{matrix}$

2. Solve graphically:

a) $\begin{aligned} 2x + 3y &= 12 \\ 2x - y &= 4 \end{aligned}$

b) $\begin{aligned} x - y - 5 &= 0 \\ 3x + 4y + 6 &= 0 \end{aligned}$

c) $\begin{aligned} 3x + 4y + 12 &= 0 \\ 6x + y - 18 &= 0 \end{aligned}$

d) $\begin{aligned} 5x - 2y &= 15 \\ 2x + y &= 6 \end{aligned}$

e) $\begin{aligned} 5x - 10y - 25 &= 0 \\ 2x + 3y - 3 &= 0 \end{aligned}$

f) $\begin{aligned} 2x + 3y &= 9 \\ 5x - 3y &= 12 \end{aligned}$

3. Solve graphically:

a) $\begin{aligned} x + y &= 4 \\ x - y &= 1 \end{aligned}$

b) $\begin{aligned} 2x + 3y - 12 &= 0 \\ 3x - 2y - 5 &= 0 \end{aligned}$

c) $\begin{aligned} 3x - 6y &= 21 \\ 2x - 4y &= 14 \end{aligned}$

d) $\begin{aligned} 6x + 10y &= 18 \\ 9x + 15y &= 45 \end{aligned}$

e) $\begin{aligned} 5x - 3y + 20 &= 0 \\ 10x - 6y - 20 &= 0 \end{aligned}$

f) $\begin{aligned} 2x + 3y &= 2 \\ 4x - 3y &= 1 \end{aligned}$

4. Under what conditions does a pair of equations have:
   a) one solution?
   b) no solutions?
   c) infinitely many solutions?

(B)

5. For which system is (−3, 5): i) a solution?
   ii) the only solution?

a) $\begin{aligned} 2x + y + 1 &= 0 \\ x + 2y - 7 &= 0 \end{aligned}$

b) $\begin{aligned} 5x - 3y &= 12 \\ 2x + 3y &= 18 \end{aligned}$

c) $\begin{aligned} 4x - 3y &= -27 \\ 2x + 4y &= 14 \end{aligned}$

d) $\begin{aligned} 3x + 2y &= 1 \\ 6x + 4y &= 2 \end{aligned}$

6. How many solutions does each system have?

a) $\begin{aligned} 3x + 2y &= 8 \\ 9x + 6y &= 24 \end{aligned}$

b) $\begin{aligned} 5x - 2y &= 15 \\ 3x + 4y &= -4 \end{aligned}$

c) $\begin{aligned} 6x - 4y &= 18 \\ -15x + 10y &= 30 \end{aligned}$

d) $\begin{aligned} 7x + 4y &= 6 \\ 5x - 2y &= 14 \end{aligned}$

7. How many solutions does each system have?

a) $\begin{aligned} 3x + y &= 7 \\ x - 2y &= -1 \end{aligned}$

b) $\begin{aligned} x - 4y - 6 &= 0 \\ -4x + 16y + 24 &= 0 \end{aligned}$

c) $\begin{aligned} 5x - 2y &= 3 \\ 15x - 6y &= 10 \end{aligned}$

d) $\begin{aligned} 2x - 3y &= 5 \\ -12x + 18y &= 30 \end{aligned}$

8. Given: line L_1: $2x - y - 6 = 0$. Determine the equation of any line L_2 such that:
   a) L_1 and L_2 are parallel;
   b) L_1 and L_2 coincide;
   c) L_1 and L_2 form a system with (4, 2) the only solution.

There are three possible arrangements when two lines are drawn on the same grid. How many possible arrangements are there for three lines?

9. Determine if the graphs of the three equations form a triangle:

a) $2x + y = 8$
$4x + 2y = -16$
$x - y = 3$

b) $3x + y = 15$
$4x + 7y = 20$
$2x - 5y = -24$

c) $2x - 3y = 10$
$-6x + 9y = -30$
$x + 2y = 20$

d) $6x - 5y = 7$
$2x + 7y = 11$
$x - 2y = -3$

7-2 EQUIVALENT LINEAR SYSTEMS

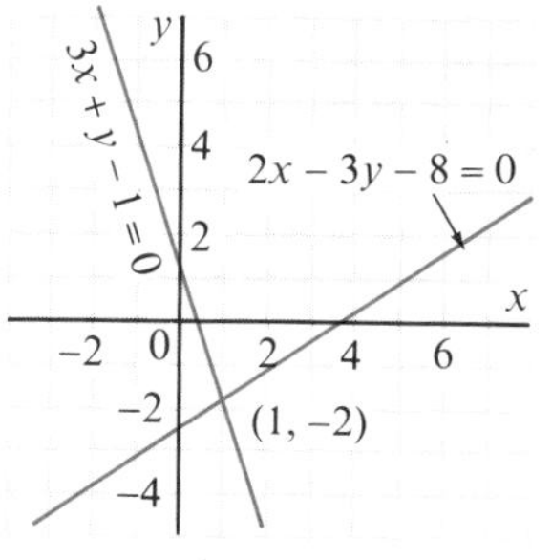

The equations formed by adding or subtracting the equations, or their multiples, of a given system have a special property.

When we solve this system graphically:
$3x + y - 1 = 0$ ...①
$2x - 3y - 8 = 0$ ...②
the solution is found to be (1, −2).

Consider what happens if we add ① and ②.

$3x + y - 1 = 0$
$2x - 3y - 8 = 0$

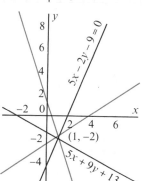

Add: $5x - 2y - 9 = 0$ ...③

If this equation is graphed on the same axes as ① and ②, the line is seen to pass through the same point, (1, −2).

Consider what happens if we multiply ① by 3 and ② by 2 and subtract the results:

① × 3: $9x + 3y - 3 = 0$
② × 2: $4x - 6y - 16 = 0$
Subtract: $5x + 9y + 13 = 0$ ...④

If this equation is graphed on the same axes as ① and ②, this line also passes through (1, −2).

This example illustrates the following general result:

> When multiples of the equations in a linear system are added or subtracted, the solution of the system satisfies the new equation.

This result shows that we can combine the equations of a linear system without changing the solution.

Example 1.

Given: $3x + 4y = 24$
$x - 2y = -2$

a) Solve the system graphically.
b) Give an example of another system which has the same solution.
c) Verify the answer to (b) using the solution for (a).

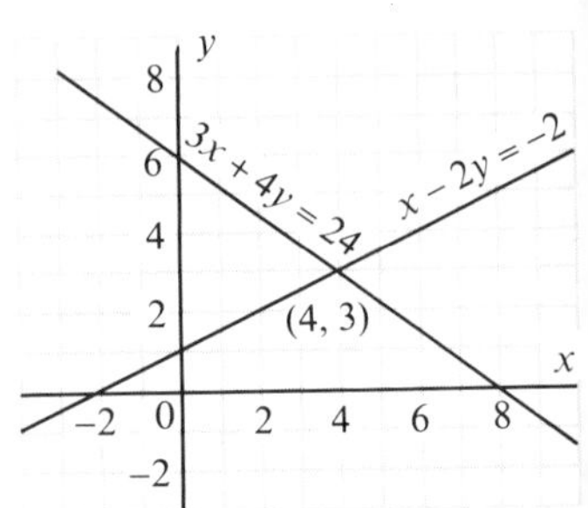

Solution.

a) The graph shows that the solution is (4, 3).
b) Write the equations in standard form:

$$3x + 4y - 24 = 0 \quad \ldots① $$
$$x - 2y + 2 = 0 \quad \ldots② $$

Add any multiple of ① to any multiple of ②:

$$2(3x + 4y - 24) + 3(x - 2y + 2) = 0$$
$$9x + 2y - 42 = 0 \quad \ldots③ $$

Therefore, a system which has the same solution as the given system is:

$$3x + 4y - 24 = 0 \quad \ldots① $$
$$9x + 2y - 42 = 0 \quad \ldots③ $$

c) Substitute 4 for x and 3 for y in ③:

L.S.: $9x + 2y - 42 = 9(4) + 2(3) - 42$, or 0
R.S.: 0

In *Example 1*, the system formed by ① and ③ has the same solution as the system formed by ① and ②. Two linear systems that have the same solution are called **equivalent systems**.

Example 2.

The graphs of four equations are shown. Name:
a) three equivalent systems;
b) two systems that are not equivalent.

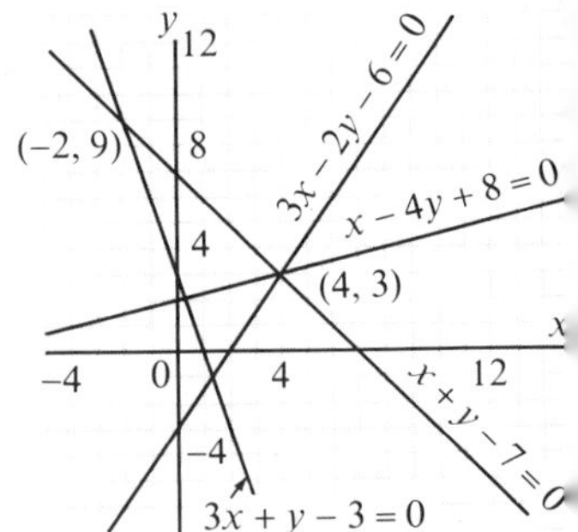

Solution.

a) Three lines intersect at (4, 3). The equations of these lines taken in pairs form equivalent systems:

$$3x - 2y - 6 = 0 \qquad x - 4y + 8 = 0$$
$$x + y - 7 = 0 \qquad x + y - 7 = 0$$

and

$$3x - 2y - 6 = 0$$
$$x - 4y + 8 = 0$$

b) The following two systems are not equivalent because they have different solutions, (4, 3) and (−2, 9).

$$3x - 2y - 6 = 0 \qquad 3x + y - 3 = 0$$
$$x + y - 7 = 0 \quad \text{and} \quad x + y - 7 = 0$$

EXERCISES 7-2

Ⓐ

1. Which of the four linear systems are equivalent?

a)

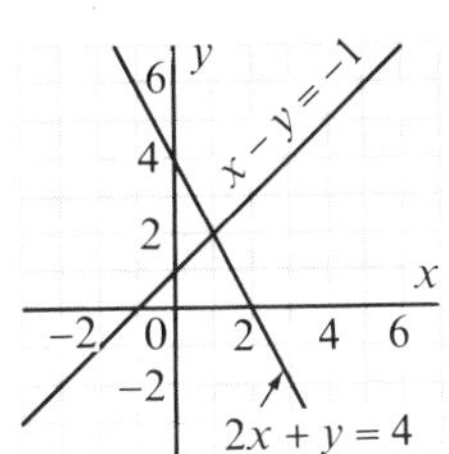

b)

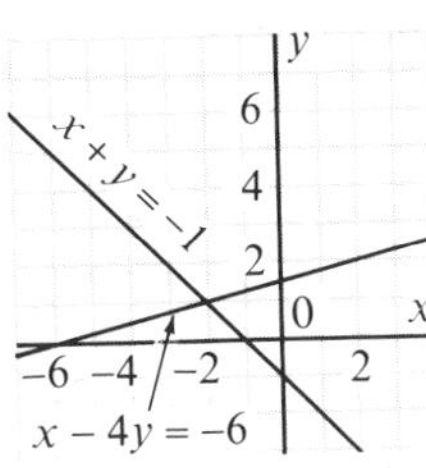

c)

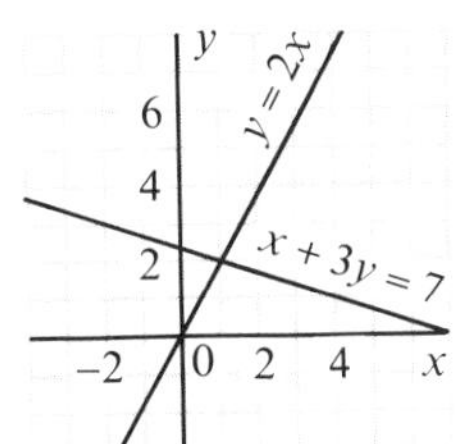

d)

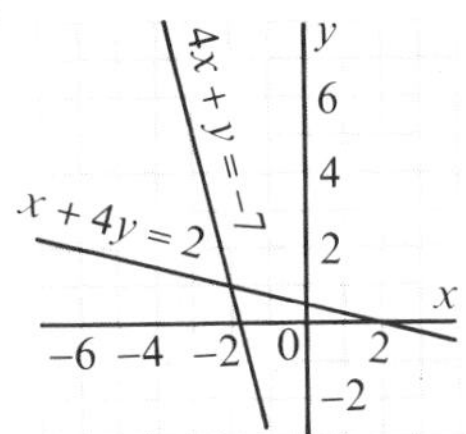

2. The graphs of four equations are shown. Name:
   a) three equivalent systems;
   b) three systems that are not equivalent.

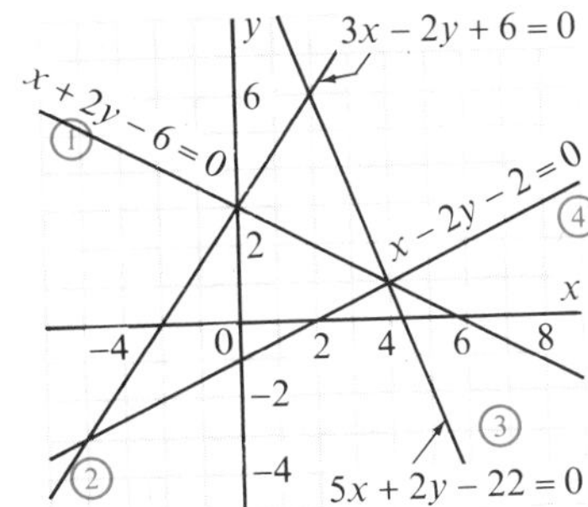

3. Given: $2x + y - 6 = 0$
   $x + 4y - 10 = 0$
   a) Solve the system graphically.
   b) Give another system that has the same solution.
   c) Verify your answer to (b) using the solution for (a).

4. Give three linear systems equivalent to the one shown:

a)

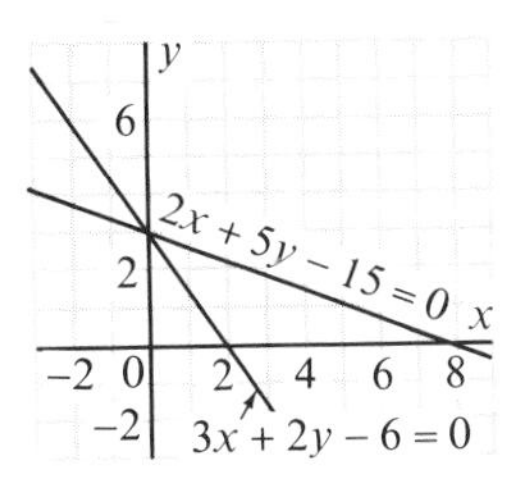

b)

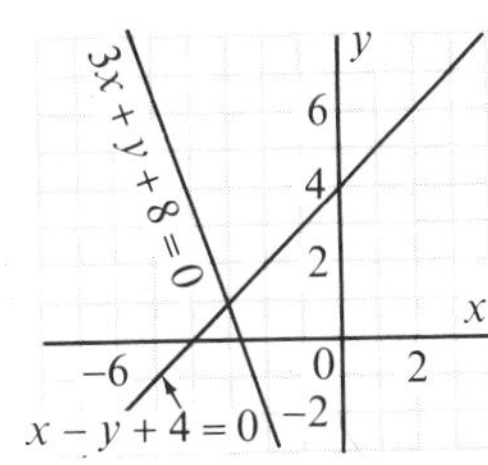

Ⓑ

5. Which of the four linear systems given are equivalent?

a) $\begin{aligned} x - 3y &= 4 \\ 2x + 3y &= -1 \end{aligned}$ b) $\begin{aligned} 5x - 2y &= 16 \\ x + 3y &= 10 \end{aligned}$

c) $\begin{aligned} 4x + y - 18 &= 0 \\ 7x - 6y - 16 &= 0 \end{aligned}$ d) $\begin{aligned} 8x - 9y - 17 &= 0 \\ -x + 5y + 6 &= 0 \end{aligned}$

6. Give two systems that are equivalent to $\begin{aligned} 3x - 2y + 12 &= 0 \\ 5x + 2y + 4 &= 0 \end{aligned}$, and verify your answer graphically.

7. Given: lines L_1: $x + y + 2 = 0$, L_2: $x - 3y + 6 = 0$.

   a) Form equations represented by:

      i) $L_1 + L_2$; ii) $2L_i + L_2$; iii) $L_1 + 2L_2$;
      iv) $2L_1 - L_2$; v) $L_1 - 2L_2$; vi) $2L_1 + 3L_2$.

   b) Graph L_1, L_2, and the other six equations on the same axes.

8. Given: lines L_1: $4x + 3y - 24 = 0$, L_2: $4x + 3y + 12 = 0$.

   a) Graph L_1, L_2, and the equations represented by:

      i) $L_1 + L_2$; ii) $L_1 - L_2$; iii) $2L_1 + L_2$;
      iv) $3L_1 - 2L_2$; v) $3L_1 + 2L_2$ vi) $2L_1 - 5L_2$.

   b) State a conclusion.

Ⓒ

9. Simplify each equation and find values of w and t that make the coefficient of: i) x equal to zero;
   ii) y equal to zero.

   a) $w(x - y + 4) + t(x + 3y) = 0$
   b) $w(2x - y + 3) + t(2x + 5y - 15) = 0$
   c) $w(3x + y - 8) + t(x + 4y - 10) = 0$

10. a) Solve by graphing: $\begin{aligned} 2x - y - 4 &= 0 \\ x + 3y - 9 &= 0 \end{aligned}$

   b) Verify that $5x + 8y - 31 = 0$ passes through the point of intersection of the lines in (a).

   c) Find values of w and t such that $5x + 8y - 31 = 0$ can be written in the form: $w(2x - y - 4) + t(x + 3y - 9) = 0$.

INVESTIGATE

Given: the lines
L_1: $2x - 3y + 8 = 0$
L_2: $3x + y - 10 = 0$
Investigate how the graphs of the equations represented by $L_1 + kL_2$ vary as k varies.

7-3 SOLVING LINEAR SYSTEMS ALGEBRAICALLY

To solve a linear system such as $\begin{aligned} 5x + 3y &= 14 \\ 2x - y &= 10 \end{aligned}$ means to find all the ordered pairs (x, y), if any, that satisfy both equations. A pair of equations can be solved algebraically by reducing to an equivalent system of the form $\begin{aligned} x &= a \\ y &= b \end{aligned}$. The solution of the original system is therefore (a, b). This can be done in different ways.

Solving by Addition or Subtraction

One way to reduce a given pair of equations to the form $\begin{aligned} x &= a \\ y &= b \end{aligned}$ is to eliminate either x or y by adding or subtracting multiples of the given equations.

Example 1.

Solve: $5x + 3y = 14$ ...①

$2x - y = 10$ ...②

Solution.

Multiply ① by 2: $10x + 6y = 28$
Multiply ② by 5: $10x - 5y = 50$
Subtract: $11y = -22$
$y = -2$

f the value of the first variable found is not an integer, it may be easier o find the value of the econd variable by elimination than by substitution.

Substitute -2 for y in ②: $2x - (-2) = 10$
$2x + 2 = 10$
$x = 4$

The solution of the system is $(4, -2)$.

Check.

When $x = 4$ and $y = -2$,

$5x + 3y = 5(4) + 3(-2) = 20 - 6 = 14$

$2x - y = 2(4) - (-2) = 8 + 2 = 10$

The solution is correct.

The procedure in *Example 1* may be better seen graphically.

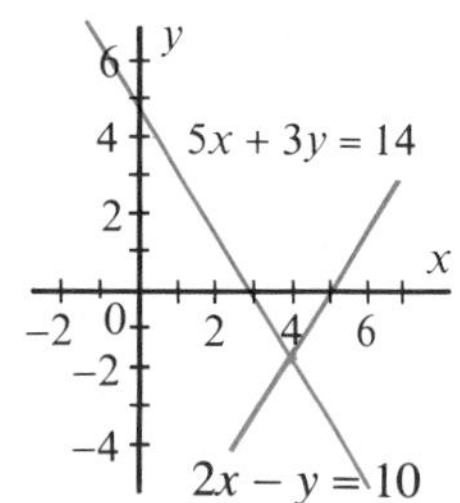

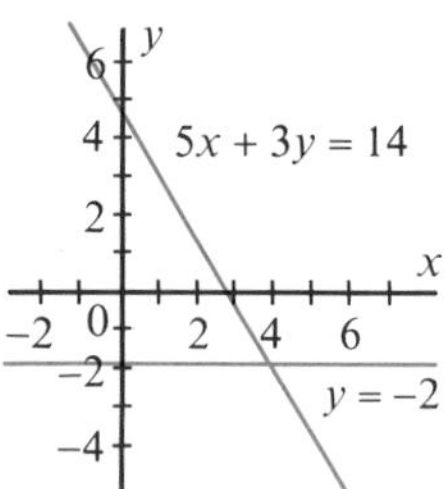

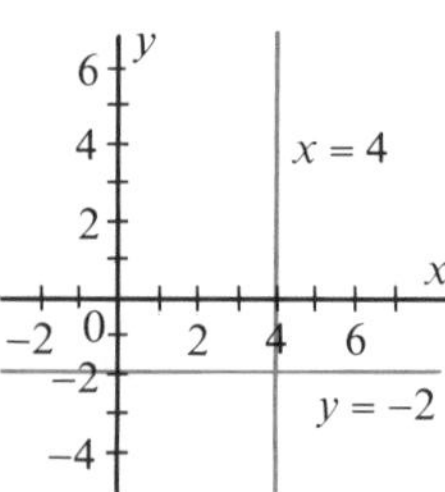

The given linear system:

$$\begin{aligned} 5x + 3y &= 14 \\ 2x - y &= 10 \end{aligned}$$

Substituting -2 for y in $2x - y = 10$ gives the equivalent system:

$$\begin{aligned} y &= -2 \\ 5x + 3y &= 14 \end{aligned}$$

The final equivalent system:

$$\begin{aligned} x &= 4 \\ y &= -2 \end{aligned}$$

Solving by Substitution

A second way to solve a linear system algebraically is to substitute the expression for one of the variables obtained from one of the equations in the other equation. This method is particularly appropriate if one of the equations has a variable with a coefficient of 1 or -1.

Example 2.

Solve: $\begin{aligned} 3x + y &= 3 & \ldots① \\ 7x - 2y &= 20 & \ldots② \end{aligned}$

Solution.

Express y in terms of x in ①: $3x + y = 3$

$$y = 3 - 3x \quad \ldots③$$

Substitute this expression for y in ② and solve for x:

$$\begin{aligned} 7x - 2(3 - 3x) &= 20 \\ 7x - 6 + 6x &= 20 \\ 13x &= 26 \\ x &= 2 \end{aligned}$$

Substitute 2 for x in ③ and solve for y:

$$\begin{aligned} y &= 3 - 3(2) \\ &= -3 \end{aligned}$$

The solution of the system is $(2, -3)$.

The procedure in *Example 2* may be better seen graphically:

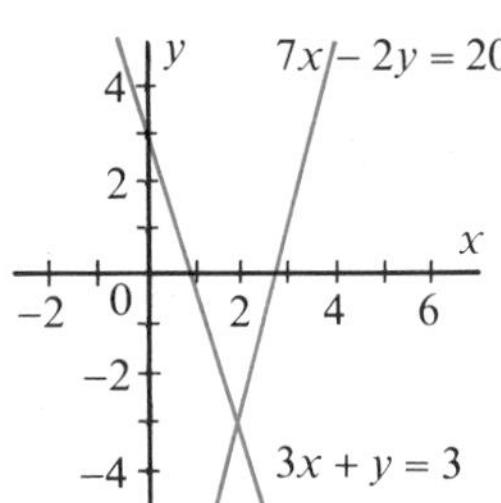

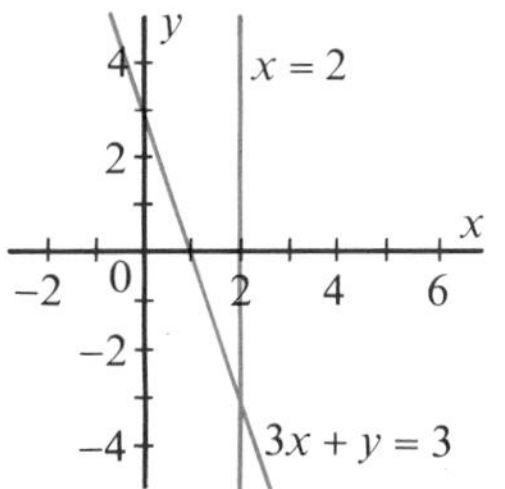

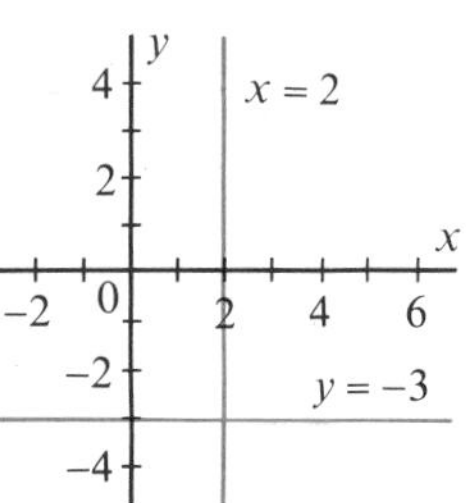

The given linear system:

$$\begin{aligned} 3x + \quad y &= 3 \\ 7x - 2y &= 20 \end{aligned}$$

Substituting 2 for x in $y = 3 - 3x$ gives the equivalent system:

$$\begin{aligned} x &= 2 \\ y &= 3 - 3x \end{aligned}$$

The final equivalent system:

$$\begin{aligned} x &= 2 \\ y &= -3 \end{aligned}$$

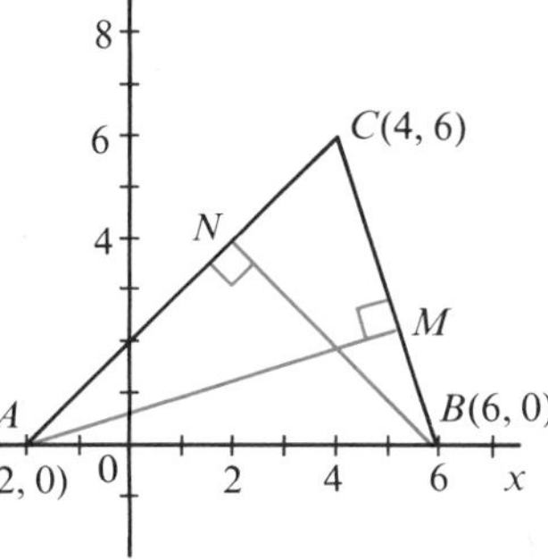

Sometimes the equations of lines have to be determined before their point of intersection can be found.

Example 3.

$\triangle ABC$ has vertices $A(-2, 0)$, $B(6, 0)$, $C(4, 6)$. Find the point of intersection of the altitudes from A and B.

Solution.

Let AM and BN be the two altitudes.

Slope of BC: $\frac{6}{-2}$, or -3. Slope of AM: $\frac{1}{3}$

The equation of AM is: $\frac{y - 0}{x - (-2)} = \frac{1}{3}$

$$x - 3y = -2 \quad \ldots①$$

Slope of AC: $\frac{6}{6}$, or 1. Slope of BN: -1

The equation of BN is: $\frac{y - 0}{x - 6} = -1$

$$x + y = 6 \quad \ldots②$$

The point of intersection of AM and BN is the solution of

$$\begin{aligned} x - 3y &= -2 \\ x + \quad y &= 6 \end{aligned}.$$

Subtract ① from ②: $4y = 8$

$$y = 2$$

Substitute 2 for y in ②: $x + 2 = 6$

$$x = 4$$

In $\triangle ABC$, the altitudes from A and B intersect at (4, 2).

EXERCISES 7-3

(A)

1. Solve by addition or subtraction:

a) $\begin{aligned} 2x + 3y &= 7 \\ x - y &= 1 \end{aligned}$ b) $\begin{aligned} 5x + 3y &= 9 \\ x - 4y &= 34 \end{aligned}$ c) $\begin{aligned} 4x - y &= -5 \\ 3x - 5y &= 9 \end{aligned}$

d) $\begin{aligned} 3x + 10y &= -4 \\ 4x + 2y &= 6 \end{aligned}$ e) $\begin{aligned} 2x - 5y + 18 &= 0 \\ 8x + 3y + 26 &= 0 \end{aligned}$ f) $\begin{aligned} 6x - 5y + 2 &= 0 \\ 2x - 3y + 6 &= 0 \end{aligned}$

2. Solve by addition or subtraction:

a) $\begin{aligned} 8x + 5y &= 2 \\ 5x + 2y &= 8 \end{aligned}$ b) $\begin{aligned} 3x + 4y &= 29 \\ 2x - 5y &= -19 \end{aligned}$ c) $\begin{aligned} 2x + 3y &= 12 \\ 3x - 4y &= 1 \end{aligned}$

d) $\begin{aligned} 3x - 4y + 6 &= 0 \\ 2x - 3y + 5 &= 0 \end{aligned}$ e) $\begin{aligned} 9x + 5y - 7 &= 0 \\ 6x + 7y + 10 &= 0 \end{aligned}$ f) $\begin{aligned} 5x + 8y + 2 &= 0 \\ 4x + 6y &= -2 \end{aligned}$

3. Solve by substitution:

a) $\begin{aligned} 2x - y &= 13 \\ 3x + 4y &= -8 \end{aligned}$ b) $\begin{aligned} 3x - y &= 5 \\ 5x - 2y &= 8 \end{aligned}$ c) $\begin{aligned} 3x + y &= 5 \\ 4x + 3y &= 10 \end{aligned}$

d) $\begin{aligned} 5x + 3y &= 5 \\ 2x + y &= 8 \end{aligned}$ e) $\begin{aligned} 4s - 3t &= 9 \\ 5s - t &= 14 \end{aligned}$ f) $\begin{aligned} 2x - 3y &= -14 \\ x - 5y &= 0 \end{aligned}$

4. Solve:

a) $\begin{aligned} 7x + 2y &= 23 \\ 5x - 4y &= 49 \end{aligned}$ b) $\begin{aligned} 2x + 5y &= 11 \\ 7x + 3y &= 24 \end{aligned}$ c) $\begin{aligned} 2x - 3y &= 5 \\ 5x + 7y &= -31 \end{aligned}$

d) $\begin{aligned} 4x - 5y &= 12 \\ 7x + 2y - 21 &= 0 \end{aligned}$ e) $\begin{aligned} 6x - 3y &= -3 \\ 2x &= 5y \end{aligned}$ f) $\begin{aligned} 9x + 6y &= 4 \\ x &= -3y - 5 \end{aligned}$

(B)

5. Solve, correct to two decimal places:

a) $\begin{aligned} 12x + 8y &= 11 \\ 2x - y &= 3 \end{aligned}$ b) $\begin{aligned} 12x - 18y &= 17 \\ 3x + 4y &= 0 \end{aligned}$

c) $\begin{aligned} 6x - 2y &= 21 \\ 3y + 4x &= 1 \end{aligned}$ d) $\begin{aligned} 6x + 2y - 27 &= 0 \\ 3x + 6y - 31 &= 0 \end{aligned}$

e) $\begin{aligned} 3x + 2y &= 7 \\ y &= 5x - 11 \end{aligned}$ f) $\begin{aligned} y &= -3x + 7 \\ 5x - 2y - 9 &= 0 \end{aligned}$

6. Solve:

a) $\begin{aligned} 12 &= x - 3y \\ 7x + 2y + 3 &= 18 \end{aligned}$ b) $\begin{aligned} (x - 1)(y - 2) - (y - 3)(x + 1) &= 17 \\ (x - 3)(y - 5) - (x - 5)(y - 3) &= -22 \end{aligned}$

c) $\begin{aligned} \frac{3x + 1}{4} &= \frac{y - 1}{2} \\ \frac{2x + 4}{3} + \frac{1}{2} &= \frac{2y - 1}{2} \end{aligned}$ d) $\begin{aligned} 5(x + 2y) - (3x + 11y) &= 14 \\ 7x - 9y - 3(x - 4y) &= 38 \end{aligned}$

e) $\begin{aligned} 3x + 2 - \frac{y + 7}{11} &= 10 \\ 2y + \frac{x + 11}{7} &= 10 \end{aligned}$ f) $\begin{aligned} 1 - \frac{x + 3}{3} + \frac{3y - 1}{5} &= 0 \\ \frac{2 - 3x}{4} - \frac{y + 3}{6} &= 5 \end{aligned}$

7. Find the values of m and n for $(-3, 7)$ to be a solution for each pair of equations:

a) $mx + y = 7$
$nx - y = -16$

b) $mx + ny = 5$
$mx - ny = -23$

c) $mx - ny = 9$
$2mx - ny = -3$

d) $3mx + 2ny = -38$
$5mx + 3ny = -54$

8. Find the equation of the line that passes through $(-7, -3)$ and the point of intersection of $4x - y = 3$ and $2x + y = 9$.

9. The lines $2x - y - 8 = 0$ and $x + 2y - 14 = 0$ intersect at A and the lines $2x - y + 6 = 0$ and $x + 2y + 8 = 0$ intersect at B.

a) Find the equation of the line through A and B.

b) Illustrate the results in (a) by a graph.

10. The lines $5x - y = 1$ and $3x - 2y = 11$ intersect at C, and the lines $7x + 2y = -2$ and $4x + 3y = 10$ intersect at D. Find the equation of the line through C and D.

11. Find the equation of the line through the point of intersection of $4x + 7y = 2$ and $3x - 5y = -19$ that is:

a) parallel to $4x + 5y - 20 = 0$;

b) perpendicular to $4x + 5y - 20 = 0$.

12. Find the coordinates of the vertices of the triangle formed by the three lines:

a) $2x - y - 7 = 0$
$3x + 4y - 16 = 0$
$x - 6y + 24 = 0$

b) $x - 2y + 10 = 0$
$3x + y - 19 = 0$
$2x + 3y - 8 = 0$

13. Determine if the triangle formed by the three lines is right, isosceles, or both:

a) $2x - 5y = -23$
$7x - 3y = 21$
$5x + 2y = 15$

b) $2x + 3y = 19$
$4x - 11y = 21$
$8x - 5y = -9$

14. A triangle has vertices $(-2, 2)$, $(7, -1)$, $(4, 8)$. It is intersected by the line $2x + 3y - 18 = 0$ at J and K.

a) Find the coordinates of J and K.

b) Find the length of JK correct to two decimal places.

15. A triangle has vertices $A(5, 10)$, $B(-3, 4)$, $C(7, 0)$.

a) Find the equations of the medians from A and B.

b) Find the point of intersection, G, of the medians in (a).

c) Show that G lies on the median from C.

16. In what ratio is the line segment with endpoints:

 a) (3, 0) and (0, 6) divided by the line $y = 4x$?

 b) (8, 1) and (2, 7) divided by the line $y = \frac{1}{2}x$?

 c) (−1, 11) and (7, −1) divided by the line $y = 2x - 8$?

(C)

17. In what ratio is the line segment with endpoints $(a, 0)$ and $(0, b)$ divided by the line $y = mx$?

18. A square has sides 6 cm in length. Four semicircles are drawn internally on the sides of the square, as shown. Find the areas of the regions marked x and y.

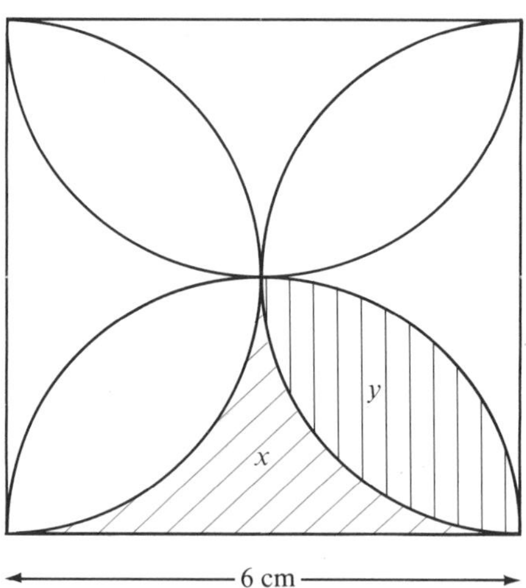

19. Solve:

 a) $\frac{5}{x} + \frac{3}{y} = 2$
 $\frac{9}{x} - \frac{3}{y} = 5$

 b) $\frac{2}{x} + \frac{9}{y} = 9$
 $\frac{1}{x} - \frac{2}{y} = 1$

 c) $2x^2 + y^2 = 19$
 $3x^2 - 2y^2 = 25$

 d) $5x^2 - 2y^2 = -30$
 $9x^2 + 3y^2 = 111$

Determine if it is possible to solve a linear system by eliminating the constant term.

7-4 SOLVING PROBLEMS USING LINEAR SYSTEMS

Many problems involve two unknown quantities. The quantities can be found if two equations relating them can be formed.

Example 1.

In a play-off football game at B.C. Place Stadium, the Winnipeg Blue Bombers and the B.C. Lions drew 59 420 fans. Depending on seat location, the ticket prices were \$19, \$16, and \$10. The total revenue from the \$10 and \$16 tickets was \$654 000. If 48 000 of these tickets were purchased, how many \$10 and \$16 tickets were sold?

Solution.

Let t be the number of \$10 tickets
and w be the number of \$16 tickets sold.

Then, $10t + 16w = 654\,000$ ...①

$t + w = 48\,000$ ...②

Multiply ② by 10: $10t + 10w = 480\,000$ ...③

Subtract ③ from ①: $6w = 174\,000$

$w = 29\,000$

Substitute 29 000 for w in ② : $t + 29\,000 = 48\,000$

$t = 19\,000$

There were 19 000 \$10 tickets and 29 000 \$16 tickets sold.

Check.

Revenue from \$10 tickets: 19 000 × \$10 = \$190 000
Revenue from \$16 tickets: 29 000 × \$16 = \$464 000
Total revenue from \$10 and \$16 tickets: \$654 000
The solution is correct.

Example 2.

A pulp-and-paper company owns two factories that produce both medium- and high-grade paper. The daily production capabilities of each factory are given in the table. A publishing firm places an order for 16 t of medium-grade and 20 t of high-grade paper. If each factory operates at full capacity on this order, about how many days must each operate to fill it?

Grade	Production Capability	
	Factory *A* t/day	Factory *B* t/day
Medium	8	2
High	2	7

Solution.

Let x and y represent the number of days that factories A and B, respectively, must operate to fill the order. Since 16 t of medium-grade paper are required:

$$8x + 2y = 16 \quad \ldots①$$

and since 20 t of high-grade paper are required:

$$2x + 7y = 20 \quad \ldots②$$

Multiply② by 4: $8x + 28y = 80 \quad \ldots③$

Subtract① from③ : $26y = 64$

$y \doteq 2.5$

Multiply① by 7: $56x + 14y = 112 \quad \ldots④$

Multiply② by 2: $4x + 14y = 40 \quad \ldots⑤$

Subtract⑤ from④ : $52x = 72$

$x \doteq 1.4$

It takes factory A about 1.4 days and factory B about 2.5 days to fill the order.

EXERCISES 7-4

Ⓐ

1. If Jerry bought two shirts and one sweater for \$60 and Doug paid \$104 for three shirts and two sweaters, find the prices of shirts and sweaters.
2. At a sale, all records are one price and all tapes another. Sandra bought three records and 2 tapes for \$24.50. David bought 1 record and 3 tapes for \$21.00. What are the prices of records and tapes?
3. Divide 200 into two parts such that the larger part is 20 more than four times the smaller part.

Ⓑ

4. Elva invested \$2100 in the stock market. She purchased shares in World Oil at \$7.50/share, and in Zinco Mines at \$3.25/share. If the total number of shares was 450, how many of each stock did she buy?
5. Tickets to a school play cost \$4.00/adult and \$2.50/student. If 900 tickets were sold for \$2820, how many of each kind were sold?
6. A firm hires 7 technicians and 3 apprentices for total daily wages of \$820. If one of the apprentices is promoted to a technician, the total daily wages become \$880. What are the daily wages for a technician and an apprentice?

7. A football stadium has 20 000 seats between the goal lines and 5000 in the end zones. An end-zone seat is \$5 cheaper than one between the goal lines. If the revenue when all seats are sold is \$350 000, what are the costs of the seats?
8. Determine the angles of an isosceles triangle if double the sum of the two equal angles is equal to three times the third angle.
9. Determine the angles of an isosceles triangle if the difference between the two sizes of angle is 30°.
10. A car's rate of fuel consumption averages 9.0 L/100 km in city driving and 5.5 L/100 km on the highway. After 450 km it has used 35.6 L of fuel. How far was the car driven in the city and on the highway?
11. A patrol plane can carry fuel for 8 h flying time, and can fly at 300 km/h in still air. If its outbound patrol is against a 30 km/h headwind and it returns with a 30 km/h tailwind, how far can it fly against the headwind and return safely?
12. An aircraft travels 5432 km from Montreal to Paris in 7 h and returns in 8 h. If the wind speed is constant, find the wind speed and the speed of the aircraft in still air.
13. Two cyclists, 25 km apart, set out at the same time and meet in 50 min. Had they been cycling in the same direction, the faster would have overtaken the slower in 5 h. Find their cycling speeds.
14. In a provincial mathematics examination, the average mark of those who passed was 64%, and of those who failed 43%. If the average mark of the 840 students who participated was 58%, how many passed?
15. 5 kg of tea and 8 kg of coffee cost \$58. If the price of tea increases 15% and that of coffee 10%, the new total is \$65.30. What are the new prices for 1 kg of tea and 1 kg of coffee?

(C)

16. A school play ran for two nights to audiences totalling 1390 adults and students who paid \$4285 for admission. Adult tickets cost \$4.00 and student tickets cost \$2.50. If the ratio of adults to students was 3 : 5 on the first night and 2 : 3 on the second, how many students attended each night?
17. When each of three numbers is added to twice the sum of the other two, the results are 64, 62, and 59. Find the numbers.

MATHEMATICS AROUND US

The Law of Supply and Demand

Many different crops are grown in Canada, and Canadian factories produce a wide variety of goods. Whatever is grown or made is produced in a certain quantity and sold at a certain price. These are determined by the supply of and demand for the product.

Supply

Suppose that the quantity of grapes, s, in kilograms, that growers are willing to harvest is given by the formula:

$$s = 5000p - 5000$$

where p is the price of grapes in dollars per kilogram. The table and graph show the relation between s and p.

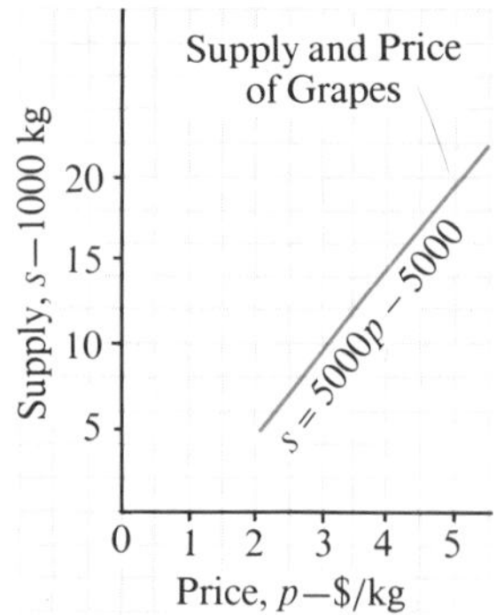

Grapes	
Price, p $/kg	Supply, s 1000 kg
2	5
3	10
4	15
5	20

Can you give reasons why the supply increases as the price increases?

Demand

Suppose that the quantity of grapes, d, in kilograms, that shoppers are willing to buy is given by the formula:

$$d = -4000p + 26\ 000$$

where p is the price of grapes in dollars per kilogram. The table and graph show the relation between d and p.

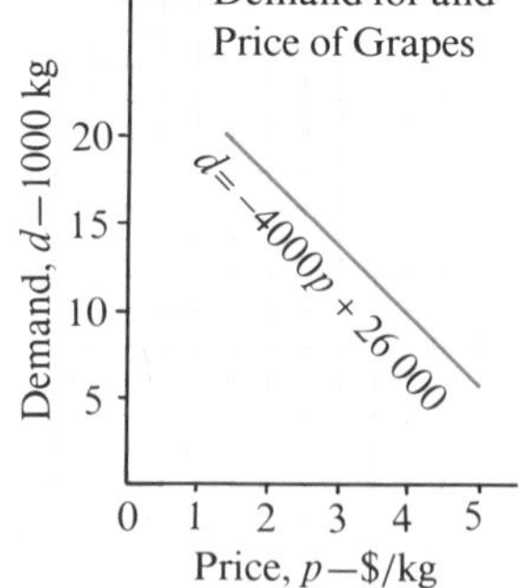

Grapes	
Price, p $/kg	Demand, d 1000 kg
2	18
3	14
4	10
5	6

Can you give reasons why the demand decreases as the price increases?

The two graphs are shown on the same axes. The point of intersection indicates that at about \$3.50/kg, the quantity of grapes that people are willing to buy is equal to the quantity that growers are willing to harvest. This is the best selling price for grapes.

Since the supply equals the demand at this price, we can find the exact price by solving the equation:

$$\begin{aligned} 5000p - 5000 &= -4000p + 26\,000 \\ 9000p &= 31\,000 \\ p &= \frac{31}{9} \\ &\doteq 3.44 \end{aligned}$$

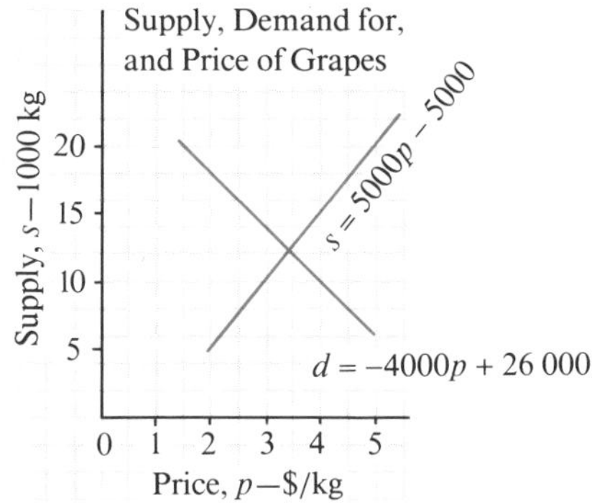

At a price of \$3.44/kg, the supply of grapes equals the demand. What happens when the price is not \$3.44/kg?

At \$2.50/kg, from the graph $s = 7500$ and $d = 16\,000$. That is, the demand exceeds the supply. Many people would be willing to pay a higher price. The price would rise.

At \$4.50/kg, from the graph $s = 17\,500$ and $d = 8000$. That is, the supply exceeds the demand. Sellers would have to lower the price to get rid of the surplus. The price would fall.

Law of Supply and Demand

If demand exceeds supply, the price should rise.
If supply exceeds demand, the price should fall.

QUESTIONS

s, d, and p represent supply, demand, and price respectively.

1. Assume that $s = 4000p - 2000$.
   a) Find the supply if the price is i) 3; ii) 4; iii) 5.
   b) Find the price if the supply is i) 12 000; ii) 17 000; iii) 22 800.
   c) What is the lowest price at which the product will be supplied?
2. Assume that $d = -3000p + 7500$.
   a) Find the demand if the price is i) 1; ii) 1.5; iii) 2.
   b) Find the price if the demand is i) 5100; ii) 3750; iii) 900.
   c) What is the highest price anyone will pay for the product?
   d) What is the demand if the product is free?
3. Assume that, for brand A,
   $s = 8000p - 2000$ and
   $d = -2000p + 6000$
   a) What is the best selling price?
   b) What amount should be produced at this price?

7-5 SOLVING SYSTEMS IN THREE VARIABLES

The methods developed for solving two-equation linear systems in two variables can be extended to solve systems of three equations in three variables.

Example 1.

Solve and check:

$$\begin{aligned} 2x - 3y + z &= 14 \quad \ldots① \\ 4x + 2y - 5z &= -3 \quad \ldots② \\ x + y + 2z &= 1 \quad \ldots③ \end{aligned}$$

Solution

Eliminate y from ① and ③:

$$2x - 3y + z = 14$$

Multiply ③ by 3: $3x + 3y + 6z = 3$

Add: $5x + 7z = 17$

Eliminate y from ② and ③:

$$4x + 2y - 5z = -3$$

Multiply ③ by 2: $2x + 2y + 4z = 2$

Subtract: $2x - 9z = -5$

The system has now been reduced to two equations in two variables:

$$\begin{aligned} 5x + 7z &= 17 \quad \ldots④ \\ 2x - 9z &= -5 \quad \ldots⑤ \end{aligned}$$

Multiply ④ by 2: $10x + 14z = 34$

Multiply ⑤ by 5: $10x - 45z = -25$

Subtract: $59z = 59$

$$z = 1$$

Substitute 1 for z in ④: $5x + 7(1) = 17$

$$5x = 10$$
$$x = 2$$

Substitute 1 for z and 2 for x in ③ : $2 + y + 2(1) = 1$

$$y + 4 = 1$$
$$y = -3$$

The solution of the system is $x = 2$, $y = -3$, $z = 1$.

Check.

Substitute in ① : $2x - 3y + z = 2(2) - 3(-3) + 1$
$= 4 + 9 + 1$, or 14

Substitute in ② : $4x + 2y - 5z = 4(2) + 2(-3) - 5(1)$
$= 8 - 6 - 5$, or -3

Substitute in ③ : $x + y + 2z = 2 - 3 + 2(1)$
$= 1$

The solution is correct.

In *Example 1*, the system of three equations in three variables was reduced to a system of two equations in two variables by eliminating the same variable from two pairs of the three equations. The two-equation system was then solved in the usual way.

The solution of a system of three equations in three variables is an ordered triple, written (x, y, z), which satisfies all three equations.

Example 2.

A concert hall has 900 main-floor seats, 500 mezzanine seats, and 200 balcony seats. If tickets for the main-floor seats are \$4 and \$8 more than those for the mezzanine and balcony seats respectively, what are the ticket prices if the revenue from a full house is \$31 600?

Solution.

Let the cost of the main-floor seats be x dollars, the cost of the mezzanine seats be y dollars, and the cost of the balcony seats be z dollars.

$$900x + 500y + 200z = 31600 \quad \ldots ①$$
$$x = y + 4 \quad \ldots ②$$
$$x = z + 8 \quad \ldots ③$$

Divide ① by 100: $9x + 5y + 2z = 316 \quad \ldots ④$

From ②: $y = x - 4 \ldots ⑤$

From ③: $z = x - 8 \ldots ⑥$

Substitute these expressions for y and z in ④:

$$9x + 5(x - 4) + 2(x - 8) = 316$$
$$16x - 36 = 316$$
$$16x = 352$$
$$x = 22$$

Substitute 22 for x in ⑤ and ⑥: $y = 18$, $z = 14$

Tickets for main-floor, mezzanine, and balcony seats are \$22, \$18, and \$14 respectively.

EXERCISES 7-5

Ⓐ

1. Solve:

a) $x + y - z = 3$
$x - y - z = -7$
$x + y + z = 1$

b) $x + y + z = 6$
$x + y - z = 2$
$x - y + z = 8$

c) $2x + y + 3z = -1$
$3x + y - 5z = 16$
$5x - y - 2z = 6$

d) $2x + y - z = 12$
$x - 3y + z = -2$
$3x - 2y - z = 13$

2. Solve:

a) $\begin{aligned} 3x - 4y + 2z &= -2 \\ 5x - y + 3z &= 1 \\ x + y - z &= -5 \end{aligned}$

b) $\begin{aligned} x - 3y + 2z &= -10 \\ 2x + y - 3z &= 1 \\ 5x - y - 2z &= -4 \end{aligned}$

c) $\begin{aligned} 2x - y + 3z &= 7 \\ 3x + y - 4z &= 7 \\ 6x - y + 5z &= 21 \end{aligned}$

d) $\begin{aligned} x - 2y + z &= 10 \\ 3x + 5y - 2z &= -6 \\ 4x + y - z &= 6 \end{aligned}$

3. Solve:

a) $\begin{aligned} x - 3y + z &= 10 \\ 4x + y + 5z &= 29 \\ 5x + 6y - 8z &= 3 \end{aligned}$

b) $\begin{aligned} x + 3y + 4z &= 14 \\ x + 2y - z &= 5 \\ 2x + y + 2z &= 2 \end{aligned}$

c) $\begin{aligned} 2x - 7y + 4z &= -11 \\ x + 3y - 2z &= -1 \\ 3x - y + 5z &= 24 \end{aligned}$

d) $\begin{aligned} 5x + 2y + 10z &= 5 \\ 3x - y + 5z &= -6 \\ 2x - 3y - 7z &= 5 \end{aligned}$

(B)

4. Solve:

a) $\begin{aligned} 9x + 3y + z &= 6 \\ 4x + 2y + z &= 3 \\ x + y + z &= 1 \end{aligned}$

b) $\begin{aligned} x + 2y + 3z &= 16 \\ x + 3y + 4z &= 24 \\ x + 4y + 10z &= 41 \end{aligned}$

c) $\begin{aligned} 3x + 4y + 8z &= 5 \\ 9x - 5y + 6z &= 2 \\ 15x + 2y - 4z &= 5 \end{aligned}$

d) $\begin{aligned} 6x + 2y - 5z &= 1 \\ 3x + 3y - 2z &= 1 \\ 7x + 5y - 3z &= 2 \end{aligned}$

5. Solve:

a) $\begin{aligned} 2x + y &= 2 \\ x + 3y + z &= 8 \\ 4y - z &= 19 \end{aligned}$

b) $\begin{aligned} x + y &= -3 \\ y + z &= -7 \\ x + z &= 8 \end{aligned}$

c) $\begin{aligned} x - 4y &= 2 \\ 7y - z &= 2 \\ x - 3y + z &= 0 \end{aligned}$

d) $\begin{aligned} 5x + 2y - z &= 22 \\ 4x + 7z &= -37 \\ x - 3y + z &= -4 \end{aligned}$

6. If $a + b = 38$, $b + c = 32$, $c + d = 25$, find the value of $a + d$.

7. The sum of three numbers is 9. The sum of the first, twice the second, and three times the third is 22. The sum of the first, four times the second, and nine times the third is 58. What are the numbers?

8. When three numbers are combined in pairs, their sums are 33, 39, and 42. What are the numbers?

9. Divide 120 into three parts so that three-quarters of the greatest exceeds the middle number by 5, and three-quarters of the middle number exceeds the least by 10.

10. The sum of the digits of a three-digit number is 12. If the units and tens digits are interchanged the number is increased by 36, and if the units and hundreds digits are interchanged, it is increased by 198. Find the number.

11. Divide 36 into three parts such that if the first is increased by 1, the second decreased by 1, and the third divided by 2, the resulting numbers are the same.

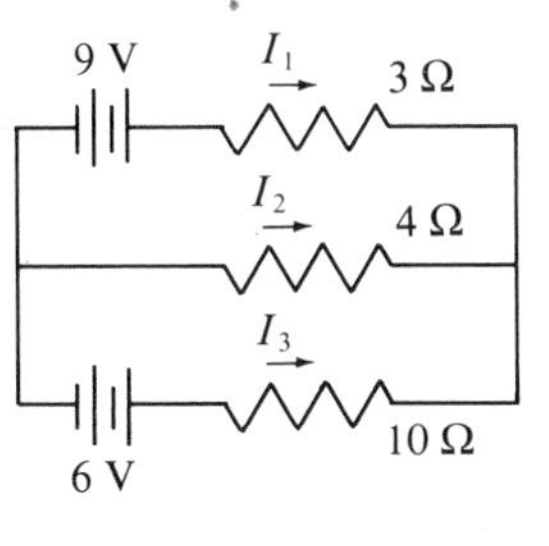

12. For the electrical circuit shown, the laws of physics show that the three currents, I_1, I_2, I_3, in amperes, are given by the system:

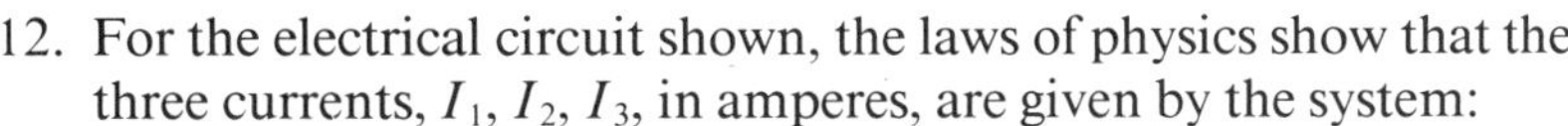

$$\begin{aligned} I_1 + I_2 + I_3 &= 0 \\ 3I_1 - 4I_2 &= 9 \\ -4I_2 + 10I_3 &= 6 \end{aligned}$$

Solve the system to determine the three currents.

13. The composition of three alloys is given in the table. In what ratio should they be mixed so that the resulting alloy is 50% copper, 15% tin, and 35% nickel?

Alloy	Copper	Tin	Nickel
A	60%	10%	30%
B	50%	30%	20%
C	40%	—	60%

14. Solve:

a) $$\begin{aligned} \frac{2}{x} + \frac{1}{y} + \frac{3}{z} &= 13 \\ \frac{1}{x} + \frac{3}{y} - \frac{1}{z} &= 4 \\ \frac{3}{x} - \frac{1}{y} + \frac{2}{z} &= 7 \end{aligned}$$

b) $$\begin{aligned} \frac{3}{x} - \frac{2}{y} + \frac{5}{z} &= 37 \\ \frac{5}{x} + \frac{3}{y} - \frac{4}{z} &= -19 \\ \frac{1}{x} + \frac{1}{y} + \frac{1}{z} &= 4 \end{aligned}$$

c) $$\begin{aligned} x^2 + y^2 - z^2 &= 21 \\ x^2 - y^2 + z^2 &= 11 \\ x^2 - y^2 - z^2 &= 3 \end{aligned}$$

d) $$\begin{aligned} 3x^2 + y^2 - z^2 &= 28 \\ 2x^2 - y^2 + 4z^2 &= 19 \\ 6x^2 - 2y^2 + 3z^2 &= 1 \end{aligned}$$

15. Divide 20 into four parts such that if the first part is increased by 1, the second decreased by 2, the third multiplied by 3, and the fourth divided by 4, the resulting numbers are the same.

7-6 SOLVING LINEAR-QUADRATIC SYSTEMS BY GRAPHING

$$\begin{aligned} 3x - 4y + 15 &= 0 \\ x^2 + y^2 &= 25 \end{aligned}$$

In the system of equations shown, the first equation is linear in x and y. The second equation contains squared terms, and is an example of a quadratic equation in x and y. Taken together, the pair of equations is called a **linear-quadratic** system.

A linear-quadratic system can be solved by graphing both equations on the same axes.

Example 1.

Solve graphically: a) $\begin{aligned} 3x - 4y + 15 &= 0 \\ x^2 + y^2 &= 25 \end{aligned}$

b) $\begin{aligned} 3x - 4y + 25 &= 0 \\ x^2 + y^2 &= 25 \end{aligned}$ c) $\begin{aligned} 3x - 4y + 35 &= 0 \\ x^2 + y^2 &= 25 \end{aligned}$

Solution.

a) Since the line intersects the circle in two points, there are two solutions. One solution is $(-5, 0)$. The other, estimated from the graph, is about $(1.5, 4.7)$.

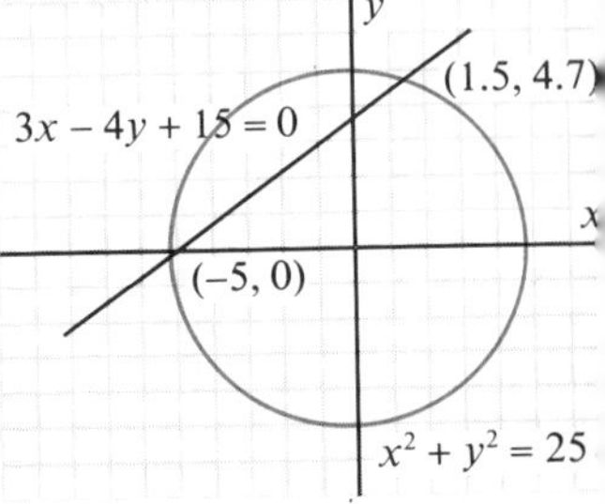

b) The line appears to touch the circle in only one point, $(-3, 4)$.

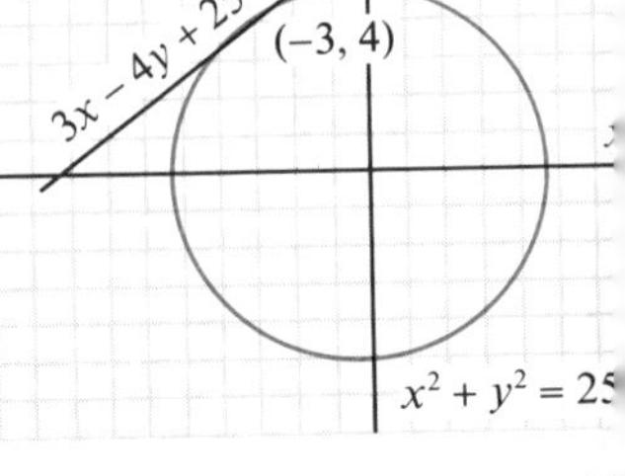

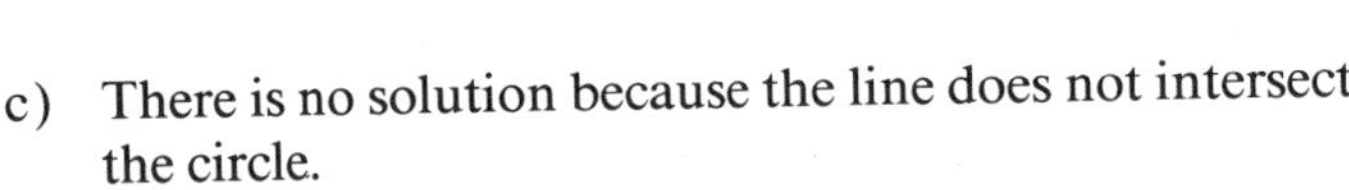
c) There is no solution because the line does not intersect the circle.

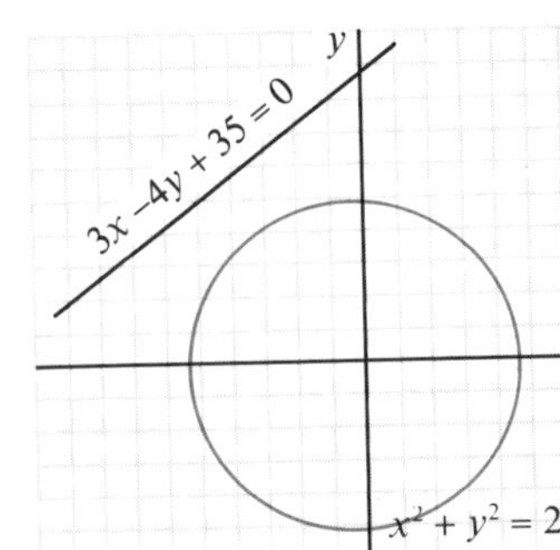

Example 1 illustrates that the exact coordinates of a point of intersection cannot always be read from a graph. In (b), it is not certain that the line intersects the curve at one point. It may intersect the curve at two points which are close together, or it may not intersect the curve at all.

Example 2.

Solve graphically:

a) $\begin{aligned} 2x - y - 5 &= 0 \\ y &= x^2 - 4x \end{aligned}$ b) $\begin{aligned} x + 3y - 12 &= 0 \\ xy &= 12 \end{aligned}$

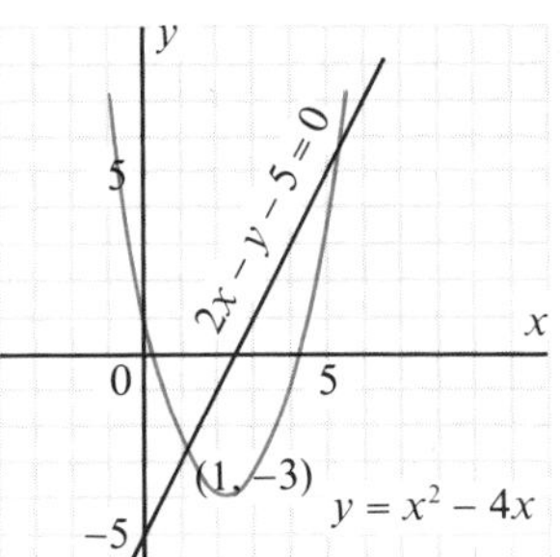

Solution.

a) The line $2x - y - 5 = 0$
has slope 2 and y-intercept −5.
The following is a table of values for $y = x^2 - 4x$:

x	−1	0	1	2	3	4	5
y	5	0	−3	−4	−3	0	5

This curve, a **parabola**, is intersected by the line in two points. The system has two solutions, (5, 5) and (1, −3).

b) The line $x + 3y - 12 = 0$
has x-intercept 12 and y-intercept 4.
The following is a table of values for $xy = 12$:

x	6	4	3	2	−2	−3	−4	−6
y	2	3	4	6	−6	−4	−3	−2

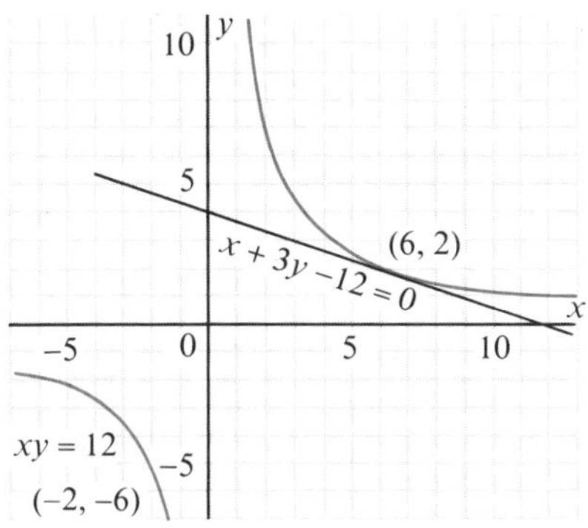

This curve, a **hyperbola**, is intersected by the line in one point. The system has one solution, (6, 2).

EXERCISES 7-6

(A)

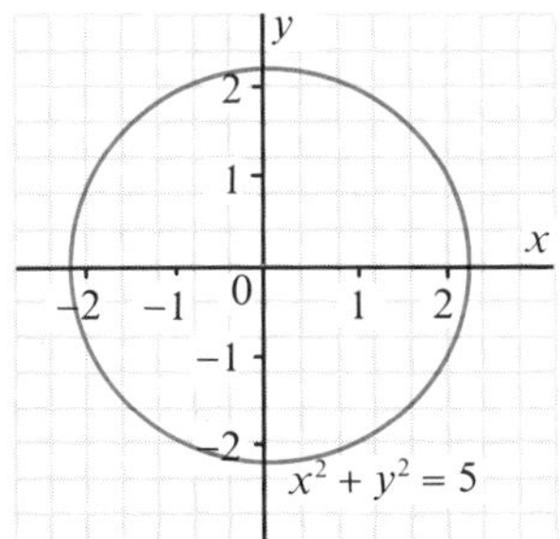

1. The graph of $x^2 + y^2 = 5$ is shown. Which of the following lines intersect it in two points? one point? no points?

   a) $y = x + 1$ b) $y = x + 5$
   c) $y = 2x$ d) $y = 2x + 5$

2. Solve graphically:

   a) $y = x - 2$, $x^2 + y^2 = 100$
   b) $x + 3y = 12$, $x^2 + y^2 = 9$
   c) $x^2 + y^2 = 25$, $y = 2x + 2$
   d) $x^2 + y^2 = 36$, $y = -6$

3. Solve graphically:

a) $y = x^2$
$y = 2x + 3$

b) $xy = -12$
$3x + 2y - 6 = 0$

c) $y = x^2 - 2x$
$x + y = 2$

d) $y = x^2 + 4x$
$4x - 3y - 12 = 0$

(B)

4. The graph of the parabola $y = x^2 - 4x + 2$ is shown. Which of the following lines intersect it in two points? one point? no points?

a) $y = \frac{1}{2}x + 3$

b) $y = \frac{1}{2}x - 4$

c) $y = -2x$

d) $x - 3 = 0$

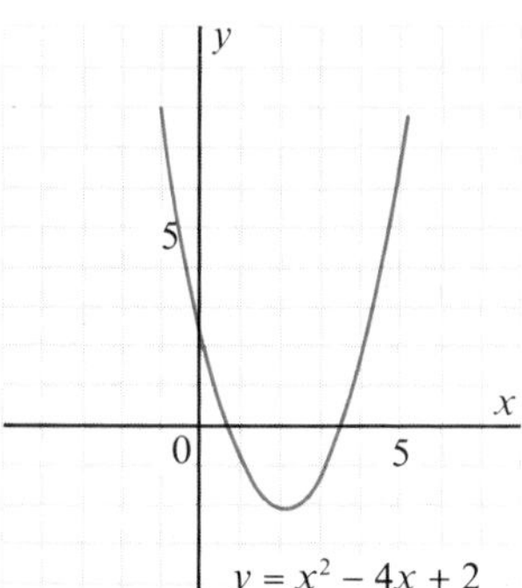

5. Solve graphically:

a) $x^2 + y^2 = 10$
$y = 3x$

b) $x^2 + y^2 = 10$
$y = 3x + 10$

c) $x^2 + y^2 = 32$
$x - 2y + 4 = 0$

d) $x^2 + y^2 = 65$
$x + 2y = 10$

6. Solve graphically:

a) $2x - y = 9$
$y = x^2 - 4x$

b) $y = x^2 - 4x + 7$
$3x - y = 3$

c) $y = 5 - 2x - x^2$
$2x + 3y = 0$

d) $xy = 6$
$x - 2y + 1 = 0$

7. Find the coordinates of the points of intersection of the circle $x^2 + y^2 = 25$ with the line:

a) $4x - 3y = 0$;

b) $4x - 3y + 25 = 0$;

c) $4x - 3y + 50 = 0$.

8. Find the coordinates of the points of intersection of the circle $(x - 4)^2 + y^2 = 9$ with the line:

a) $y = -x + 2$;

b) $y = \frac{1}{3}x + 2$;

c) $y = x - 2$.

9. Does the system have a solution?

a) $x^2 + y^2 = 29$
$2x - 3y + 12 = 0$

b) $y = x^2 + 4x + 3$
$x + 3y = -5$

c) $x^2 + y^2 = 50$
$6x + 5y = 60$

d) $xy = 18$
$5x + 3y = 15$

e) $y = x^2 - 4x + 7$
$2x + y = 6$

f) $(x - 2)^2 + (y + 5)^2 = 10$
$x + 3y + 5 = 0$

10. Given: circle C: $x^2 + y^2 = 20$. Write the equation of any line, L, such that:

a) C and L form a system with two different solutions;

b) C and L form a system with no solutions.

INVESTIGATE

There are three possible arrangements when a line and a circle are drawn. How many possible arrangements are there for two circles?

11. Solve graphically:

a) $(x + 3)^2 + (y - 1)^2 = 20$
$x - 2y + 5 = 0$

b) $(x + 2)^2 + (y + 3)^2 = 25$
$3x + 2y + 6 = 0$

c) $(x - 5)^2 + y^2 = 45$
$y = 2x + 5$

d) $(x - 4)^2 + (y - 1)^2 = 13$
$4x - y = 5$

Ⓒ

12. Solve the following quadratic-quadratic systems graphically:

a) $x^2 + y^2 = 9$
$(x - 3)^2 + (y - 3)^2 = 9$

b) $x^2 + y^2 = 13$
$y = x^2 - 7$

7-7 SOLVING LINEAR-QUADRATIC SYSTEMS ALGEBRAICALLY

A linear-quadratic system is solved algebraically by a method we used for solving linear systems. The linear equation is solved for either variable, and the expression obtained substituted in the quadratic equation.

Example 1.

Find the coordinates of the points of intersection of the circle $x^2 + y^2 = 10$ and the line $3x + y = 6$.

Solution.

$$x^2 + y^2 = 10 \quad \ldots ①$$
$$3x + y = 6 \quad \ldots ②$$

Solve ② for y: $y = 6 - 3x \ldots ③$

Substitute this expression for y in ① and solve for x:

$$x^2 + (6 - 3x)^2 = 10$$
$$x^2 + 36 - 36x + 9x^2 = 10$$
$$10x^2 - 36x + 26 = 0$$
$$5x^2 - 18x + 13 = 0$$
$$(x - 1)(5x - 13) = 0$$

Either $x - 1 = 0$ or $5x - 13 = 0$

$x = 1$ or $x = \frac{13}{5}$, or 2.6

Substitute in the linear equation ③ to find y for each value of x:

When $x = 1$, $y = 6 - 3(1)$
$= 3$

When $x = 2.6$, $y = 6 - 3(2.6)$
$= -1.8$

The system has two solutions, (1, 3) and (2.6, −1.8). These are the coordinates of the points of intersection.

Check.

When $x = 1$ and $y = 3$:

$$x^2 + y^2 = 1^2 + 3^2 = 10 \qquad 3x + y = 3(1) + 3 = 6$$

When $x = \frac{13}{5}$, or 2.6, and $y = -\frac{9}{5}$, or -1.8:

$$\begin{aligned} x^2 + y^2 &= (2.6)^2 + (-1.8)^2 \\ &= 6.76 + 3.24 \\ &= 10.00 \end{aligned} \qquad \begin{aligned} 3x + y &= 3(2.6) - 1.8 \\ &= 7.8 - 1.8 \\ &= 6.0 \end{aligned}$$

The solutions are correct.

The procedure in *Example 1* may be better seen graphically.

The given linear-quadratic system: $\begin{aligned} x^2 + y^2 &= 10 \\ 3x + y &= 6 \end{aligned}$

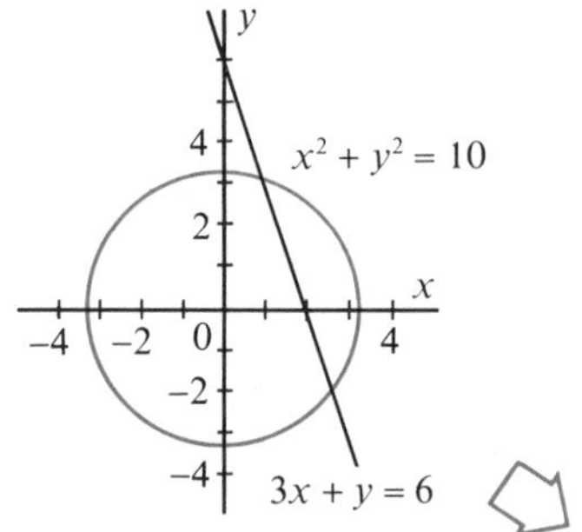

Substituting $6 - 3x$ for y in $x^2 + y^2 = 10$ gives $x = 1$ and $x = 2.6$.

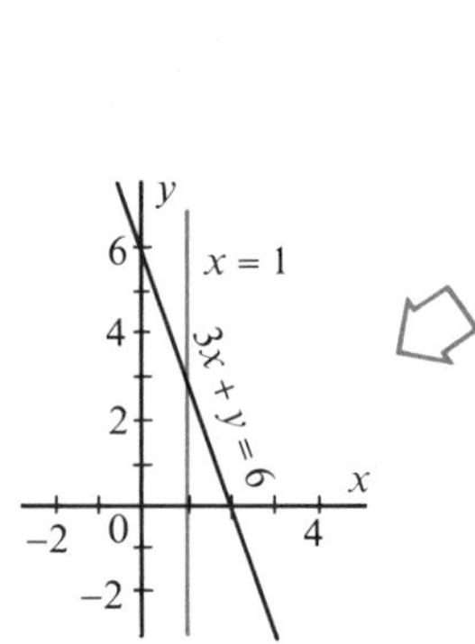

Substituting 1 for x in $y = 6 - 3x$ gives the related system

$x = 1$
$y = 6 - 3x$

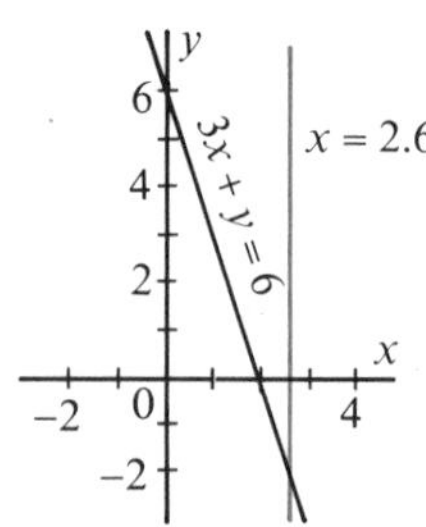

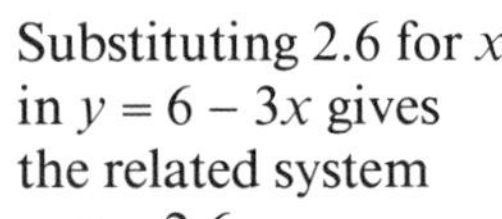

Substituting 2.6 for x in $y = 6 - 3x$ gives the related system

$x = 2.6$
$y = 6 - 3x$

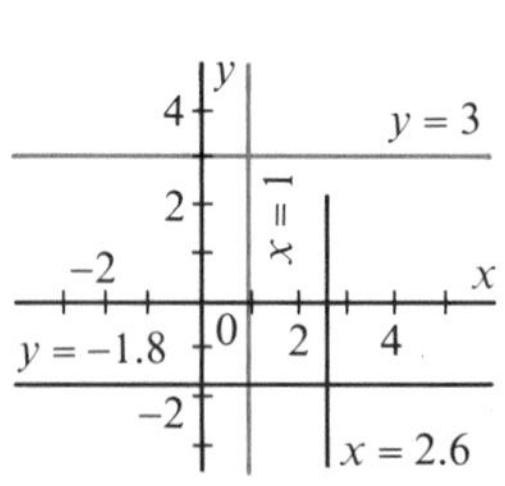

The final equivalent systems:

$\begin{aligned} x &= 1 \\ y &= 3 \end{aligned}$ and $\begin{aligned} x &= 2.6 \\ y &= -1.8 \end{aligned}$

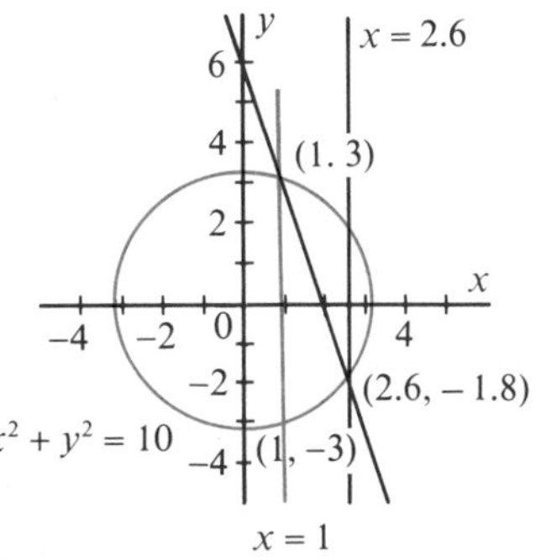

The reason why the values found for x must be substituted in the linear equation and not in the quadratic equation may be seen from this graph.

If, for example, $x = 1$ were substituted in the equation of the circle, two values of y would result, 3 and −3. One might think that (1, 3) and (1, −3) are both solutions of the linear-quadratic system. But, as the graph shows, (1, −3) is not on the given line, and therefore (1, −3) is not a solution of the system.

Example 2.

A sky diver jumped from an airplane and fell freely for several seconds before releasing her parachute. Her height, h, in metres, above the ground at any time is given by:
$h = -4.9t^2 + 5000$ before she released her parachute, and
$h = -4t + 4000$ after she released the parachute.
How long after jumping did she release her parachute?
How high was she above the ground at that time?

Solution.

At the moment of releasing her parachute, both equations apply. Therefore, we solve the system:

$$h = -4.9t^2 + 5000 \quad \ldots ①$$

and $$h = -4t + 4000 \quad \ldots ②$$

Substituting $-4t + 4000$ for h in ① :

$$-4t + 4000 = -4.9t^2 + 5000$$
$$4.9t - 4t - 1000 = 0$$

Using the quadratic formula, $t = \dfrac{-b \pm \sqrt{b^2 - 4ac}}{2a}$

$$t = \frac{4 \pm \sqrt{(-4)^2 - 4(4.9)(-1000)}}{2(4.9)} \qquad \begin{aligned} a &= 4.9 \\ b &= -4 \\ c &= -1000 \end{aligned}$$
$$= \frac{4 \pm \sqrt{19\,616}}{9.8}$$
$$= \frac{4 \pm 140.1}{9.8}$$
$$\doteq 14.7 \text{ or } -13.9$$

Since the time is positive, the negative root is rejected. She opened her parachute after about 14.7 s.

To find her height at this point, substitute 14.7 for t in ② :

$$h = -4(14.7) + 4000$$
$$= 3941.2$$

She opened her parachute when she was about 3940 m above the ground.

EXERCISES 7-7

(A)

1. Find the coordinates of the points of intersection of the line and the circle:

a) $y = 2x$
$x^2 + y^2 = 5$

b) $y = 2x - 5$
$x^2 + y^2 = 5$

c) $y = 2x - 5$
$x^2 + y^2 = 10$

d) $x - y = 8$
$x^2 + y^2 = 25$

2. Solve:

a) $x^2 + y^2 = 25$
$y = 3x - 5$

b) $y = x^2$
$x - y = -2$

c) $x^2 + y^2 = 20$
$y = 2x - 10$

d) $xy = 12$
$y = 2x - 2$

3. The sum of two numbers is 10 and the sum of their squares is 58. Find the numbers.

4. The perimeter of a rectangle is 13 cm and its area is 10 cm^2. Find its length and width.

5. A movie stunt man jumped from the CN Tower and fell freely for several seconds before releasing his parachute. His height, h, in metres, t seconds after jumping is given by:
$h = -4.9t^2 + t + 350$ before he released his parachute, and
$h = -4t + 141$ after he released his parachute.

a) How long after jumping did he release his parachute?

b) How high was he when he released his parachute?

(B)

6. Solve:

a) $x^2 + y^2 = 13$
$2x + 3y = 5$

b) $x^2 + y^2 = 13$
$2x + 3y = 13$

c) $y = x^2 + 6x + 5$
$x + 3y + 15 = 0$

d) $x^2 - y^2 = 4$
$x + 2y = 0$

e) $(x - 4)^2 + (y + 2)^2 = 10$
$2x - y = 2$

f) $xy = -4$
$3x - 2y + 10 = 0$

7. Point P is on the line $3x + y = 26$ and is 10 units from the origin. Find the coordinates of P, and illustrate by a graph.

8. From a lighthouse, the range of visibility on a clear day is 40 km. On a coordinate system, where (0, 0) represents the lighthouse, a ship is travelling on a course represented by $y = 2x + 80$. Between what two points on the course can the ship be seen from the lighthouse?

9. Show that the graphs of $2x + 5y = 11$ and $x^2 + y^2 = 4$ do not intersect.

Is it possible for a linear-quadratic system to have infinitely many solutions?

10. What two numbers differ by 4 and have squares that differ by 80?

11. What two numbers differ by 4 and have squares with a sum of 136?

12. A rectangular field has a perimeter of 500 m and an area of 14 400 m^2. Find the lengths of its sides.

13. A right triangle has a hypotenuse 10 cm long. If the perimeter is 22 cm, find the lengths of the other two sides.

14. A line through (6, 2) forms a triangle with the positive arms of the coordinate axes. If the area of the triangle is 27 $units^2$, find the equation of the line.

15. $A(-3, 4)$ and $B(5, 3)$ are two points.
   a) Find the coordinates of a point P on $y = x + 4$ such that $\angle APB = 90°$, and illustrate by a graph.
   b) Show that there is no point P on $y = x - 4$ such that $\angle APB = 90°$.

16. a) Solve graphically:
   i) $5x + 4y - 32 = 0$
   $x^2 + y^2 = 25$
   ii) $y = x + 9$
   $x^2 + y^2 = 40$
   b) Check the results of (a) by solving algebraically.

17. $A(-3, 4)$, $B(3, 4)$, and $C(4, 3)$ are points on $x^2 + y^2 = 25$. $P(5, 10)$ is a point outside the circle (below, left).
   a) Show that line AP intersects the circle in only one point.
   b) Lines PB and PC intersect the circle again at D and E respectively. Find the coordinates of D and E.
   c) Show that $PA^2 = PB \times PD = PC \times PE$.

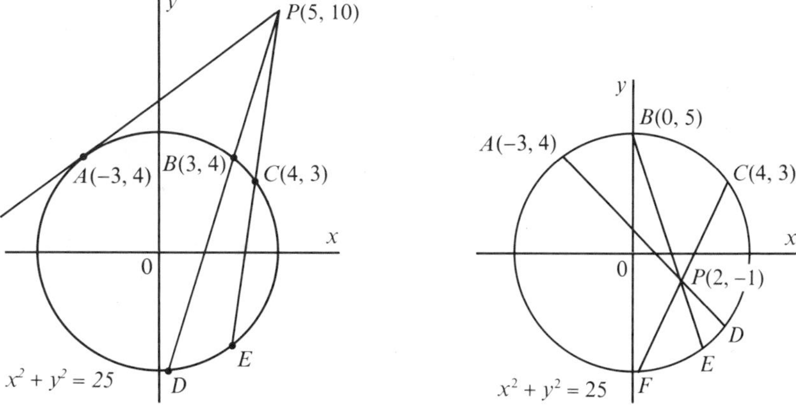

18. Chords AD, BE, and CF of the circle $x^2 + y^2 = 25$ (above, right) intersect at point $P(2, -1)$.
   a) If A, B, and C have the coordinates shown, find the coordinates of D, E, and F.
   b) Show that $PA \times PD = PB \times PE = PC \times PF$.

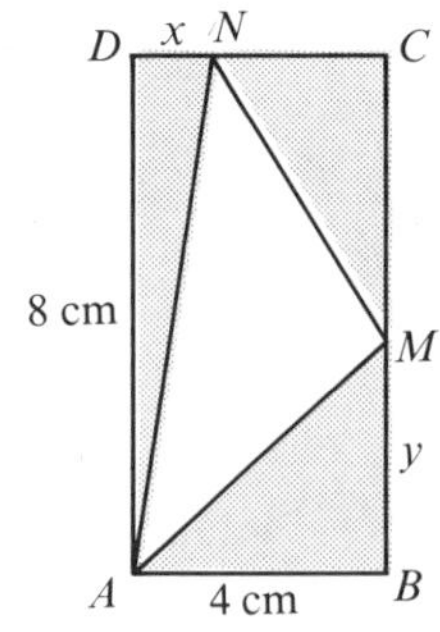

19. Rectangle $ABCD$ has the dimensions shown.
    a) Find the values of x and y such that the three shaded triangles all have the same area.
    b) If the shaded triangles all have the same area, show that M divides BC in the same ratio as N divides DC.

20. A rectangle has area A and perimeter P.
    a) Find an expression in terms of A and P for:
       i) the length; ii) the width.
    b) Show that, for any rectangle, $P^2 \geqslant 16A$.
    c) Use the expressions found in (a) to calculate the perimeter and area, and simplify the results.

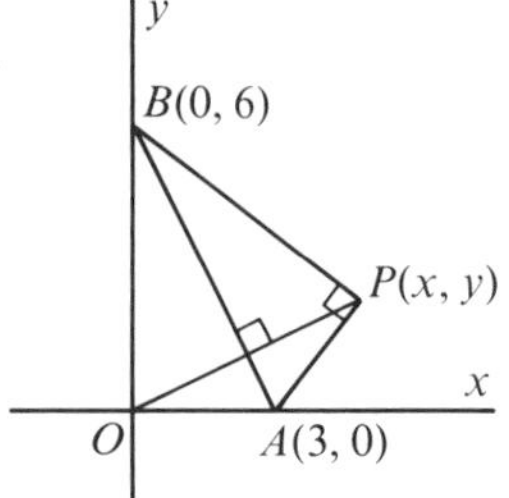

21. $A(3, 0)$ and $B(0, 6)$ are opposite vertices of quadrilateral $OAPB$. Diagonals AB and OP are perpendicular, and $\angle APB = 90°$.
    a) Find the coordinates of P.
    b) Compare the lengths of: i) OA and AP;
       ii) OB and BP.

22. a) Solve the system:
$$\begin{aligned} y &= mx + b \\ x^2 - y^2 &= 0 \end{aligned}$$
    b) Show that the system in (a) always has at least one solution regardless of the values of m and b.
    c) Give a graphical interpretation of the solution.

Ⓒ

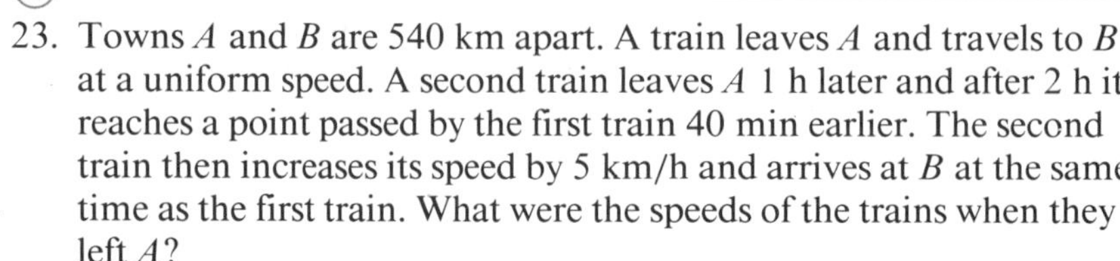

23. Towns A and B are 540 km apart. A train leaves A and travels to B at a uniform speed. A second train leaves A 1 h later and after 2 h it reaches a point passed by the first train 40 min earlier. The second train then increases its speed by 5 km/h and arrives at B at the same time as the first train. What were the speeds of the trains when they left A?

24. Karen catches an earlier train than planned and arrives at her home station 36 min before her father is due to meet her on the later train. She promptly sets out to jog home at 7.5 km/h knowing she will meet her father coming for her. They meet when he has driven 32 km from their home. She arrives home 8 min earlier than if she had caught the later train. How far is Karen's home from the station? What was the average speed of the car?

7-8 EQUATIONS OF TANGENTS

When the equations of a line and a circle are given, the coordinates of their point(s) of intersection, if any, are found by solving a linear-quadratic system. To determine if the line intersects the circle, it is not necessary to solve the system completely. The quadratic equation which occurs in the solution of the system gives this information.

Example 1.

Determine if the line intersects the circle $x^2 + y^2 = 5$:

a) $y = x + 1$ b) $y = 2x + 6$ c) $y = 2x - 5$

Solution.

a) Consider the system: $x^2 + y^2 = 5$ ..①
$y = x + 1$ ..②

Substitute② into①: $x^2 + (x + 1)^2 = 5$
$$x^2 + x^2 + 2x + 1 = 5$$
$$2x^2 + 2x - 4 = 0$$
$$x^2 + x - 2 = 0 \quad ..③$$

If the line intersects the circle, equation③ has two real roots. This is the case when its discriminant is zero or positive.

$$b^2 - 4ac = (1)^2 - 4(1)(-2)$$
$$= 9$$

Since the discriminant is positive, the line $y = x + 1$ intersects the circle in two different points.

b) Consider the system: $x^2 + y^2 = 5$ ..①
$y = 2x + 6$ ..④

Substitute④ into① : $x^2 + (2x + 6)^2 = 5$
$$x^2 + 4x^2 + 24x + 36 = 5$$
$$5x^2 + 24x + 29 = 0 \quad ..⑤$$

Calculate the discriminant: $b^2 - 4ac = 24^2 - 4(5)(29)$
$$= -4$$

Since the discriminant is negative, equation⑤ has no real roots. The line $y = 2x + 6$ does not intersect the circle.

c) Consider the system: $x^2 + y^2 = 5$ ..①
$y = 2x - 5$ ..⑥

Substitute⑥ into① : $x^2 + (2x - 5)^2 = 5$
$$x^2 + 4x^2 - 20x + 25 = 5$$
$$5x^2 - 20x + 20 = 0$$
$$x^2 - 4x + 4 = 0 \quad ..⑦$$

Calculate the discriminant: $b^2 - 4ac = (-4)^2 - 4(1)(4)$
$$= 0$$

Since the discriminant is zero, equation⑦ has two equal roots. That is, the line $y = 2x - 5$ intersects the circle in only one point. It is a **tangent** to the circle.

As we see in *Example 1c*, when the discriminant of the quadratic equation which occurs in the solution of a linear-quadratic system is equal to zero, the line is a tangent to the curve. This property can be used to find the equations of tangents.

Example 2.

A tangent to the circle $x^2 + y^2 = 9$ has y-intercept 5. Find its equation.

Solution.

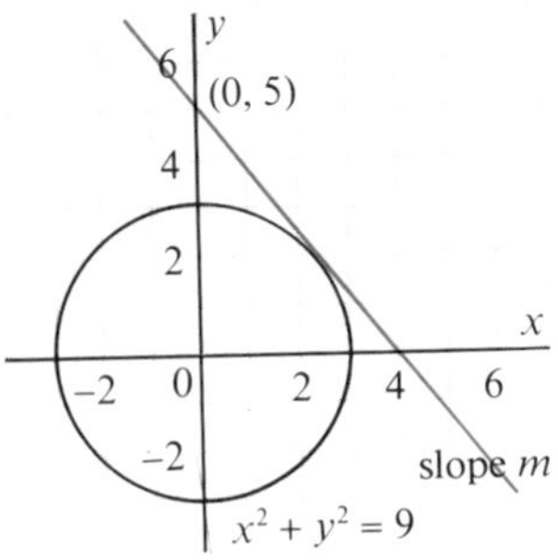

Step 1. Write a general equation for the tangent. Let the slope of the tangent be m. Then the equation of the tangent is $y = mx + 5$.

Step 2. Substitute for y in the equation of the circle and write the resulting equation as a quadratic in x.
Substitute $mx + 5$ for y in $x^2 + y^2 = 9$:

$$x^2 + (mx + 5)^2 = 9$$
$$x^2 + m^2x^2 + 10mx + 25 = 9$$
$$(1 + m^2)x^2 + 10mx + 16 = 0$$

Step 3. Impose the condition for equal roots: $b^2 - 4ac = 0$.
Substitute $1 + m^2$ for a, $10m$ for b, and 16 for c:

$$(10m)^2 - 4(1 + m^2)(16) = 0$$

Step 4. Solve the resulting equation.

$$100m^2 - 64 - 64m^2 = 0$$
$$36m^2 = 64$$
$$m^2 = \frac{16}{9}$$
$$m = \pm\frac{4}{3}$$

Step 5. Write the equation(s) of the tangents.
Since there are two values of m, there are two tangents.

The equations are: $y = \frac{4}{3}x + 5$, or $4x - 3y + 15 = 0$

and $y = -\frac{4}{3}x + 5$, or $4x + 3y - 15 = 0$

The above method can also be used to find equations of tangents to certain other curves, such as parabolas.

Example 3.

A tangent to the parabola $y = x^2 - 2x$ has slope 2. Find its equation.

Solution.

Step 1. Let the y-intercept of the tangent be b. Then the equation of the tangent is $y = 2x + b$.

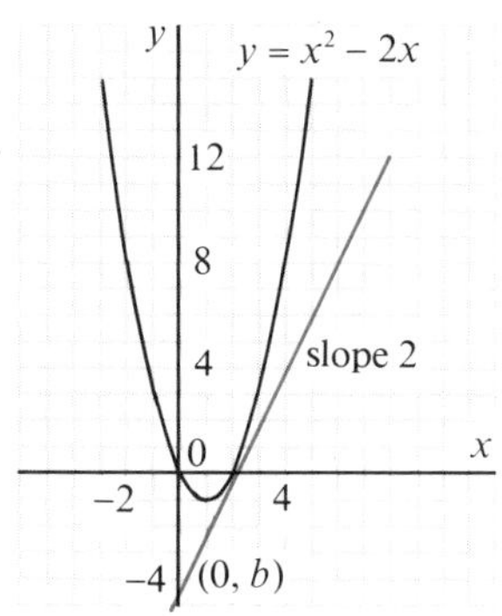

Step 2. Substitute $2x + b$ for y in $y = x^2 - 2x$:

$$2x + b = x^2 - 2x$$
$$x^2 - 4x - b = 0$$

Step 3. For a tangent, the discriminant of this equation equals 0: and 4.

$$(-4)^2 - 4(1)(-b) = 0$$
$$16 + 4b = 0$$
$$b = -4$$

Step 5. The y-intercept to the tangent is −4. Since the slope is 2, the equation of the tangent is $y = 2x - 4$.

EXERCISES 7-8

1. Determine if the given line intersects the circle $x^2 + y^2 = 25$
   a) $y = x - 8$ b) $y = 5 - x$ c) $4x + 3y = 25$
2. Find the equations of the tangents with y-intercept 5 to the circle $x^2 + y^2 = 5$.
3. The graph shows the parabola $y = x^2$ and a tangent to it with y-intercept −1.
   a) What is the equation of the tangent?
   b) What is the equation of the tangent with negative slope that has the same y-intercept?
4. Find the equations of the tangents with y-intercept −4 to the parabola $y = x^2$.
5. Find the equation of the tangent to the parabola $y = x^2 + 2x$ with slope −3.

(B)

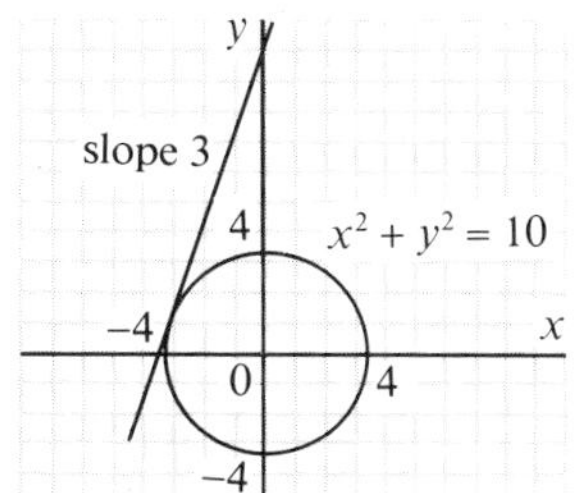

6. The graph of $x^2 + y^2 = 10$ and a tangent with slope 3 is shown.
   a) What is the equation of the tangent?
   b) What is the equation of another tangent with slope 3?
7. Find the equations of the tangents with slope 2 to the circle $x^2 + y^2 = 25$.
8. Find the equations of the tangents with y-intercept −3 to the parabola $y = x^2 + 4x + 1$.
9. Find the equations of the tangents to $(x - 5)^2 + y^2 = 5$ with y-intercept 5.
10. Find the equation of the tangent to $y = \frac{1}{16}x^2$ at (−8, 4).
11. a) Show that no tangent to $y = x^2$ has a positive y-intercept.
    b) Show that no tangent to the hyperbola $xy = 12$ has a positive slope.

Ⓒ

12. Find the equations of the tangents from (1, 3) to the circle $x^2 + y^2 = 5$.
13. Find the equations of the tangents to $y = x^2$ which pass through (1, −3).
14. The line $3x + y = 6$ is tangent to a circle with centre (0, 0). Find the radius of the circle correct to two decimal places.
15. Find the equations of the tangents with slope $\frac{1}{2}$ to the circle $(x - 4)^2 + (y - 5)^2 = 20$.

MATHEMATICS AROUND US

The Line of Best Fit—Biology

Skeletal remains of the now extinct Irish elk suggest that its antlers reached a spread of 4 m. Stephen Gould, of Harvard University, wondered if the antlers grew in the same proportion as the rest of the animal. He compared measures of antler-size and skull-length of dozens of specimens. Some results are shown in the table and the graph.

Skull-length cm	46.0	47.1	48.1	49.0	50.1
Antler-size cm	31.5	34.1	36.2	39.1	41.4

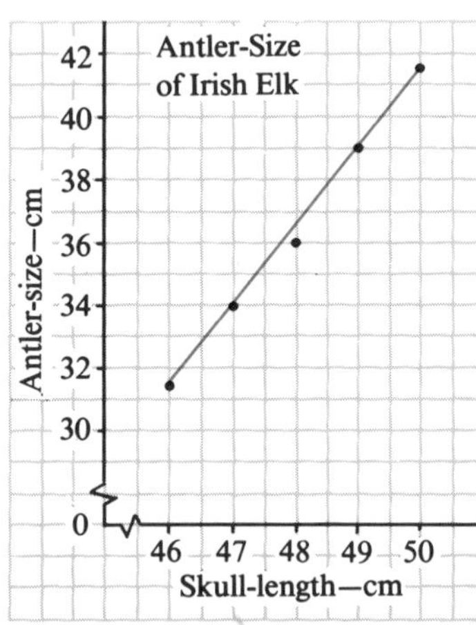

Stephen Gould concluded that the animal's antlers grew about $2\frac{1}{2}$ times the rate of the animal itself. Investigations of other species of deer have yielded similar results.

QUESTIONS

1. What is the equation of the line of best fit?
2. Use the equation to find:
   a) the approximate antler-size for a skull-length of 47.5 cm;
   b) the skull-length for an antler-size of 40 cm.
3. How did Stephen Gould reach his conclusion about the comparative rates of growth of the antlers and the rest of the animal from the equation of the line of best fit?

Review Exercises

1. Solve graphically:

   a) $\begin{aligned}2x - y &= 3\\ 3x - 5y &= 15\end{aligned}$ b) $\begin{aligned}-2x + y &= 3\\ x + y &= 6\end{aligned}$

   c) $\begin{aligned}3x - y &= -4\\ x - y &= -8\end{aligned}$ d) $\begin{aligned}2y - 5x &= 15\\ 3y - 4x &= 12\end{aligned}$

2. Solve graphically:

   a) $\begin{aligned}x + 3y &= 2\\ 3x + 9y &= 8\end{aligned}$ b) $\begin{aligned}3x + 7y &= 27\\ 5x + 2y &= 16\end{aligned}$

   c) $\begin{aligned}4x - 6y &= -10\\ -6x + 9y &= 15\end{aligned}$ d) $\begin{aligned}4x - 3y &= 0\\ 5x - 6y &= -18\end{aligned}$

3. Given: lines L_1: $5x + 2y + 10 = 0$, L_2: $x + 3y - 11 = 0$. On the same grid, graph L_1 and L_2, and the equations represented by:
   a) $L_1 + L_2$; b) $L_1 - L_2$; c) $3L_1 - 2L_2$; d) $L_1 + 3L_2$.

4. Solve algebraically:

   a) $\begin{aligned}2x + y &= 3\\ 4x - y &= -6\end{aligned}$ b) $\begin{aligned}y &= 3x - 7\\ y &= 5 - x\end{aligned}$

   c) $\begin{aligned}5x - 7y &= 0\\ 7x + 5y &= 74\end{aligned}$ d) $\begin{aligned}3x + y &= 6\\ 2x - 3y - 9 &= 0\end{aligned}$

5. Find the solution correct to two decimal places:

   a) $\begin{aligned}5x - 3y &= 9\\ 2x + 5y &= 8\end{aligned}$ b) $\begin{aligned}10x - 3y &= 1\\ y &= -2x + 7\end{aligned}$

   c) $\begin{aligned}8x + 7y &= 3\\ 2x - 6y - 1 &= 0\end{aligned}$ d) $\begin{aligned}3x + 8y + 2 &= 0\\ 2x - y + 1 &= 0\end{aligned}$

6. The lines $2x + y = 10$ and $7x + 8y = 53$ intersect at A, and the lines $2x - y = 12$ and $x + 3y = 27$ intersect at B. Find the equation of the line through A and B.

7. A triangle has vertices $(-1, 3)$, $(4, -2)$, $(8, 6)$. It is intersected by the line $3x - y - 10 = 0$ at P and Q. Find:
   a) the coordinates of P and Q; b) the length of PQ.

8. An office is equipped with two card-sorting machines, A and B. If A is operated for 2 min and B for 5 min, 20 500 cards can be sorted. If A is operated for 5 min and B for 2 min, 25 000 can be sorted. What are the sorting rates of the machines?

9. A motorist travels 400 km partly at 100 km/h and partly at 80 km/h. If he had travelled at 80 km/h instead of 100 km/h and 100 km/h instead of 80 km/h, the journey would have taken 0.5 h longer. Find his time for the trip.

10. Solve graphically:

    a) $\begin{aligned}x^2 + y^2 &= 17\\ y &= 4x\end{aligned}$ b) $\begin{aligned}x^2 + y^2 &= 18\\ y &= 2x + 3\end{aligned}$

    c) $\begin{aligned}y &= x^2\\ x - y + 6 &= 0\end{aligned}$ d) $\begin{aligned}y &= x^2 - 3x + 5\\ x + y &= 8\end{aligned}$

11. Find, graphically, the coordinates of the points of intersection of the circle $(x-2)^2+(y-3)^2=16$ with the line:
    a) $x-y=3$; b) $x+y=9$; c) $x=6$.
12. Solve.
    a) $x+y=2$, $y=x^2$
    b) $2x+y=6$, $x^2+y^2=20$
    c) $3x+2y=16$, $xy=10$
    d) $3x^2-y^2=47$, $3x-y=11$
13. A father is four times as old as his daughter. The sum of the squares of their ages is 1088. Find their ages.
14. The hypotenuse of a right triangle is 168 mm long and the perimeter is 398 mm. Find the lengths of the two shorter sides.
15. Two rectangles have the same area, 480 m^2. If the difference in their lengths is 10 m and the difference in their widths is 4 m, find the lengths of their sides.
16. a) Find two numbers with sum 10 and product 20.
    b) Show that it is impossible for two real numbers to have a sum 10 and product 30.
    c) Two numbers have a sum 10. What is the greatest possible product they can have?
17. Find the equations of the tangents with slope -2 to $x^2+y^2=36$.
18. Find the equations of the tangents with y-intercept -4 to the parabola $y=x^2-x-1$.
19. Find the equation of the tangent to the parabola $y=x^2$ at (2, 4).
20. Find the equations of the tangents with slope -3 to the hyperbola $xy=12$.

Cumulative Review (Chapters 5–7)

1. Find the unknown term:
   a) $\frac{9}{15}=\frac{x}{25}$ b) $\frac{4}{18}=\frac{14}{a}$ c) $\frac{3+b}{5+b}=\frac{11}{21}$
2. The ratio of brain mass to body mass for an elephant is 1 : 600. The largest known elephant had a body mass of 9790 kg. What was its brain mass?
3. Find the missing numbers:
   a) m varies directly as c^2.

m	2	8	12		
c	5			15	22

   b) y varies inversely as $\sqrt{t}$.

t	9	16			400
y		18	12	10	

4. The free end of a diving board dips a distance which varies directly with the mass of a person standing on it. The board dips 15 cm under Ben's mass of 67 kg. How far will it dip under Phil's 74 kg?

5. The number of years required for an investment to double varies inversely as the interest rate. At 6% compound interest, an investment doubles in about 12 years.
   a) How many years will it take for an investment to double at 9%? at 16%?
   b) At what rate of interest will the investment double in 3 years?

6. Solve for a and b: a) $10:a:b = 7:4:3$ b) $a:12:9 = 5:7:b$

7. A punch recipe calls for lemonade, orange juice, and ginger ale in the ratio 3:5:12. If 5 L of ginger ale are used, what quantities of the other ingredients will the punch contain?

8. Find the values of x and y:

a)

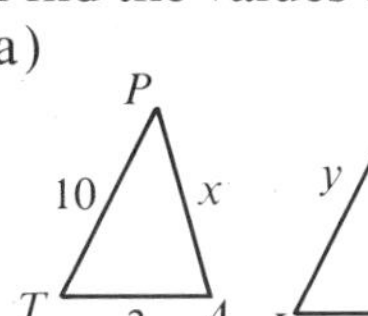

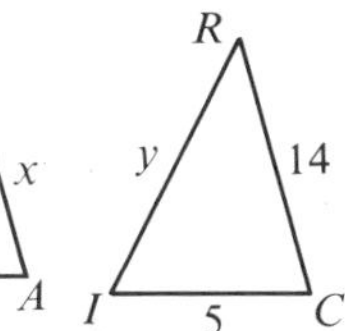

b)

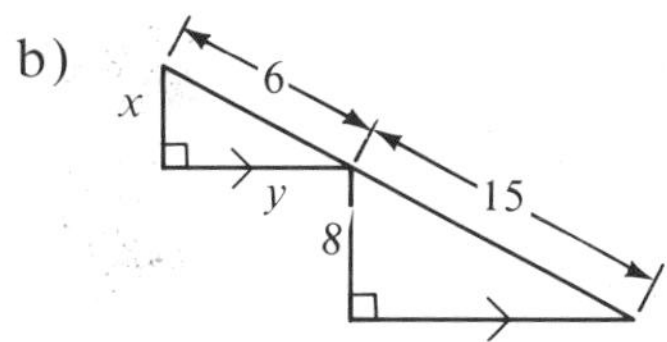

9. A vertical metre stick casts a shadow 1.25 m long. A fir tree casts a shadow 15 m long. How tall is the tree?

10. A line segment has endpoints:
    a) (6, 3), (4, 1); b) (5, 2), (−1, −3); c) (−7, −8), (−5, −2).
    Find: i) its length; ii) the coordinates of its midpoint.

11. A triangle has vertices $T(-2, -3)$, $R(6, -3)$, and $Y(2, 5)$. Show that the length of the line segment joining the midpoints of sides TY and RY is half the length of TR.

12. A line segment has endpoints (8, 4) and (−4, 1). In what ratio is it divided by the point (0, 2)?

13. A line segment has endpoints (−3, 0) and (−1, −2). Find the coordinates of the point that divides it in the ratio 2:1.

14. Does the line pass through (−1, 4)?
    a) $2x - 2y + 10 = 0$ b) $-x + 3y - 13 = 0$ c) $4x - y = 8$

15. State the slope and x- and y-intercepts:
    a) $3x + 4y + 12 = 0$ b) $-x - 3y = 5 = 0$
    c) $y - 3 = 0$ d) $x + 2 = 0$

16. Find the equation of the line:
    a) through (−1, −6) with slope 3; b) through (4, 6) and (7, 4);
    c) with the same y-intercept as $3x - 2y + 8 = 0$ and slope $-\frac{2}{5}$;
    d) parallel to $4x - y + 6 = 0$ with the same x-intercept as $2x - 3y - 12 = 0$.

17. Graph the circle and give its centre and radius:
    a) $(x - 4)^2 + (y - 2)^2 = 25$ b) $(x + 3)^2 + (y + 5)^2 = 16$
18. The centre and radius of a circle are given. Write its equation.
    a) (0, 0), 10 b) (3, 7), 7 c) (−2, 5), 11
19. The diameter of a circle has endpoints (−8, 0) and (0, −8).
    a) Find the equation of the circle.
    b) Is the point (−4, 5) on, inside, or outside the circle?
20. Find the length of the tangent from (10, 12) to $x^2 + y^2 = 100$.
21. Find the equation of the tangent to $x^2 + y^2 = 20$ at (−4, 2).
22. Prove that the diagonals of a rhombus bisect each other at right angles.
23. Find the value of x:
    a) 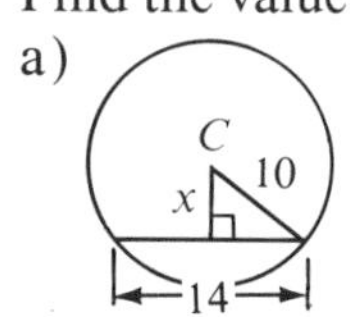

    b) 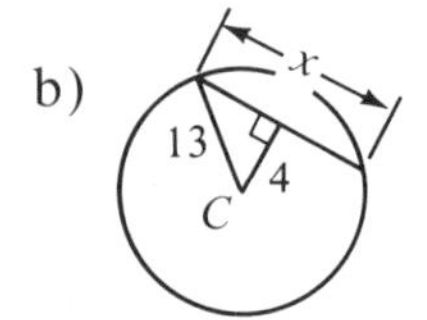

    c) 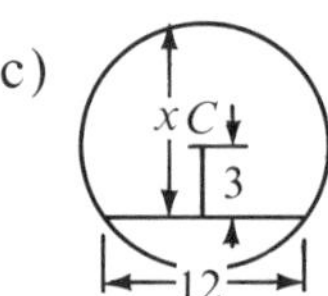

24. Solve graphically: a) $2x + 3y = 4$, $7x + 6y = 5$ b) $2x - y = 3$, $4x - 2y + 6 = 0$
25. Give two systems equivalent to: $3x - 2y = 3$, $4x + 3y = -30$
26. Solve algebraically:
    a) $3x = 5y - 21$, $2y = -4x - 28$
    b) $x + 6y = 17$, $3x - 7y - 1 = 0$
    c) $3(x - 1) - 4(y + 2) = -5$, $4(x + 5) - (y - 1) = 16$
    d) $4a - b + 3c = -11$, $8a - 2b + 5c = -19$, $6a - 3b - 2c = -3$
27. Cheerleaders raised money for new uniforms by washing cars and trucks. Charging \$3 for a car and \$5 for a truck, they washed 49 vehicles and earned \$181. How many of each kind of vehicle did they wash?
28. In an archery competition, a bull's-eye scores 5 points and an inner scores 4. Each of Victor's 10 shots hit the target for a score of 46. How many were bull's-eyes?
29. Solve graphically: a) $x^2 + y^2 = 20$, $y - 2x = 0$ b) $x + y = 2$, $y - x^2 + 4 = 0$
30. Solve algebraically: a) $y - x - 3 = 0$, $x^2 + y^2 = 29$ b) $y = x^2 - x - 6$, $3x - 4y + 12 = 0$
31. What two numbers differ by 10 and have squares that add to 148?
32. Find the equations of the tangents with y-intercept −2 to:
    a) $y = x^2 - 6x + 2$; b) $x^2 + y^2 = 1$.
33. Find the equations of the tangents with slope 3 to:
    a) $y = x^2 + 4x + 8$; b) $x^2 + y^2 = 10$

8 Functions: Linear and Quadratic

Supermarket cashiers try to memorize current sale prices while they work. If the percent they memorize is a known function of time, what is the greatest percent they can memorize and how long does it take them? (See *Example 2* in Section 8-11.)

8-1 RELATIONS

In everyday language we frequently speak of two people or things which are related in some way.

These two are related; they are sisters.

The number of people using the pool is related to the temperature.

The value of a car is related to its age. The age and value of the cars in a parking lot are displayed in the table and the graph below.

Car	Age years	Value $
A	1	7000
B	2	5000
C	2	4500
D	4	2500
E	4	3500
F	5	3500
G	7	1200

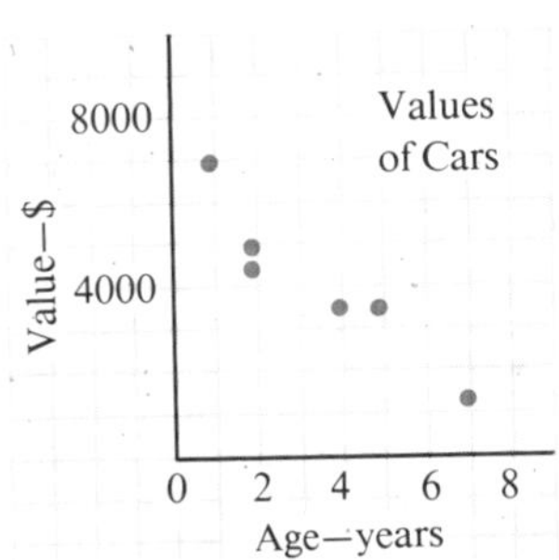

Each point on the graph corresponds to an ordered pair. The first coordinate is the age of the car, and the second is its value. The set of all these ordered pairs, R, is an example of a **relation**.

$$R = \{(1, 7000), (2, 5000), (2, 4500), (4, 2500), (4, 3500), (5, 3500), (7, 1200)\}$$

The set of first coordinates of R is $\{1, 2, 4, 5, 7\}$. This is the set of possible ages of the cars, and is called the **domain** of R. The set of second coordinates of R is $\{1200, 2500, 3500, 4500, 5000, 7000\}$. This is the set of possible values of the cars, and is called the **range** of R.

- A **relation**, R, is a set of ordered pairs.
- The **domain** of R is the set of *first* coordinates of the ordered pairs.
- The **range** of R is the set of *second* coordinates of the ordered pairs.

A relation can be represented in many different ways:

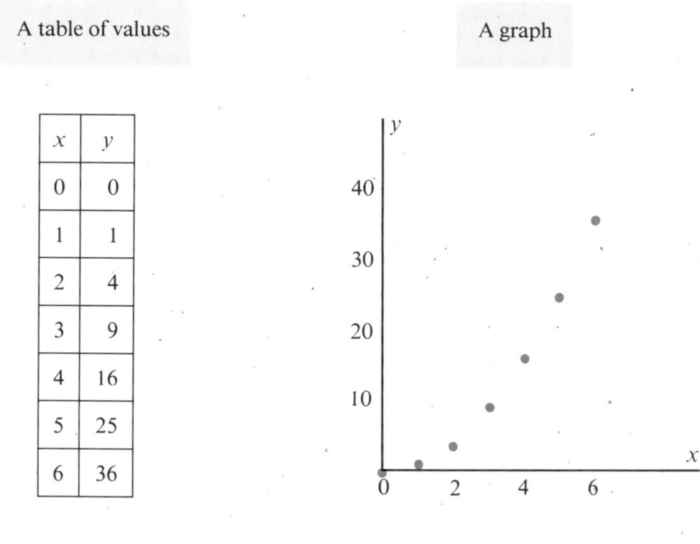

x	y
0	0
1	1
2	4
3	9
4	16
5	25
6	36

A set of ordered pairs

{(0, 0), (1, 1), (2, 4), (3, 9),
(4, 16), (5, 25), (6, 36)}

An equation

$$y = x^2$$
where $x \in I, 0 \le x \le 6$

In the above relation:
the domain is {0, 1, 2, 3, 4, 5, 6};
the range is {0, 1, 4, 9, 16, 25, 36}.

Example 1.

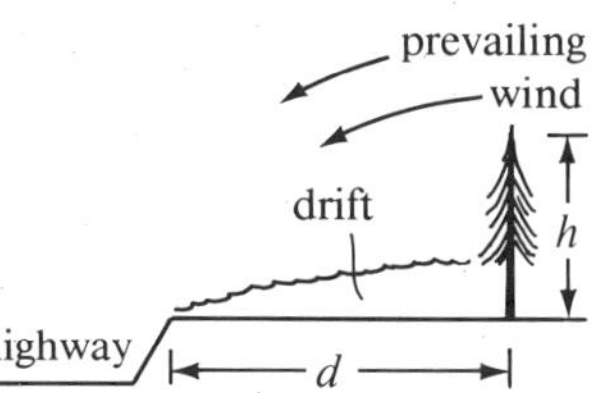

A row of trees is planted on the windward side of a section of highway to prevent snow from drifting onto it. The trees cause the snow to settle into a drift before it reaches the highway. The distance, d, in metres, that the trees need to be from the highway is related to their height, h, in metres, by the formula:

$$d = 12 + 5h.$$

The formula is valid for tree heights from 2 m to 10 m. Graph the relation, and state its domain and range.

Solution.

Construct a table using values of h between 2 and 10.

h	d
2	22
4	32
6	42
8	52
10	62

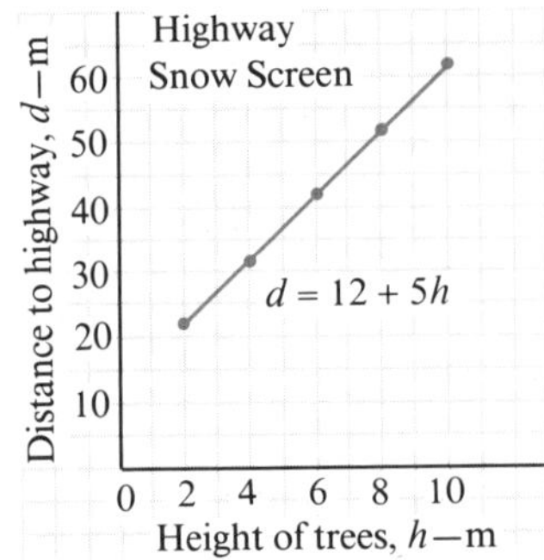

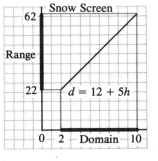

The table shows only the ordered pairs that were used to draw the graph. Joining the points shows that the relation includes more ordered pairs than those used.

The domain, the set of possible first coordinates of the ordered pairs represented by the graph, is the set of tree heights between 2 and 10 inclusive.

The range, the set of possible second coordinates, is the set of distances from the trees to the road between 22 and 62 inclusive.

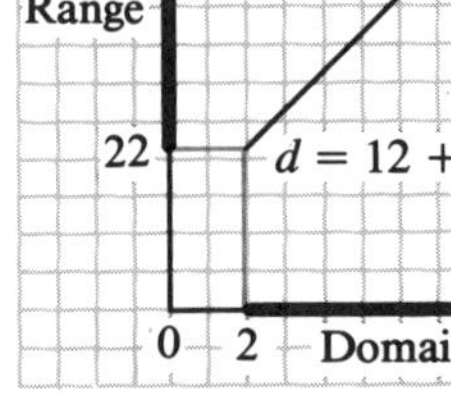

Given the *graph* of a relation:

The **domain** is the set of x values represented by the graph.

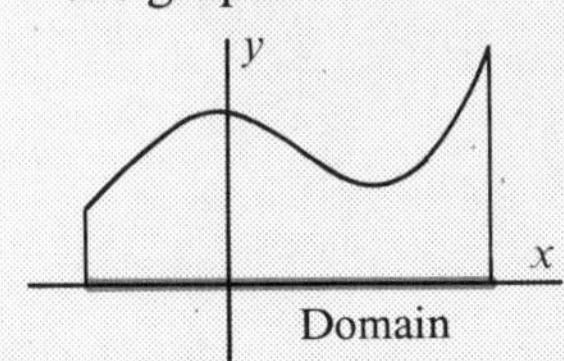

The **range** is the set of y values represented by the graph.

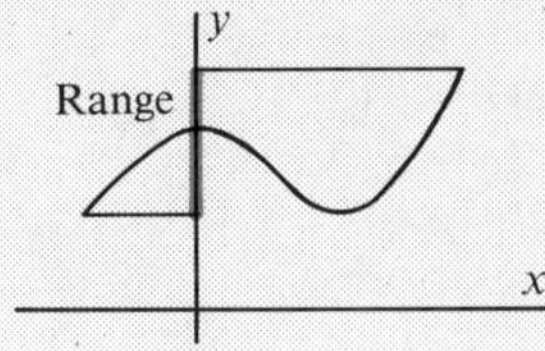

Example 2.

The graph shows the oxygen consumption of the body during and after 5 min of strenuous activity.

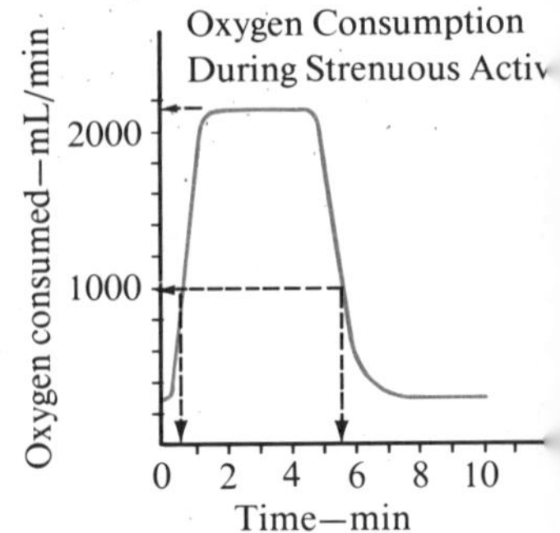

a) What was the greatest rate of oxygen consumption?
b) When was the oxygen consumption 1000 mL/min?
c) What are the domain and range of the relation?

Solution.

a) The greatest rate of consumption was about 2100 mL/min.
b) The rate of consumption was 1000 mL/min after about 0.5 min and 5.5 min.

c) The domain is the set of times represented by the graph. This is the set of positive real numbers up to 10.
The range is the set of consumption rates represented by the graph. This is the set of real numbers between 300 and 2100.

Given the *equation* of a relation:

The **domain** is the set of all values of x for which the equation is defined.	The **range** is the set of all values of y which are defined for the values of x in the domain.

For $y = x^2$:

Domain: all real numbers	Range: all non-negative real numbers

Example 3.

Find the domain and range of the relation $y = \sqrt{x - 1}$.

Solution.

Since square roots of negative numbers are not real numbers:

$$\text{Then, } x - 1 \geq 0$$
$$x \geq 1$$

The domain is the set of all real numbers greater than or equal to 1.
Since the radical sign indicates a positive square root, the expression $\sqrt{x - 1}$ is never negative. That is, $y \geq 0$.

The range is the set of all non-negative real numbers.

Ordered pairs need not involve numbers.

Example 4.

The four children in the Hayes family are Pat, Sandra, Bill, and Kathy, who were born in that order.

a) Express the relation "is a younger sister of" as a set of ordered pairs.

b) What are the domain and range of the relation?

Solution.

a) The relation is: {(Sandra, Pat),
(Kathy, Pat),
(Kathy, Sandra),
(Kathy, Bill)}

Read: "Kathy is a younger sister of Pat."

b) The domain is the set of children who are younger sisters: {Sandra, Kathy}. The range is the set of children who have a younger sister, {Pat, Sandra, Bill}.

EXERCISES 8-1

(A)

1. On six consecutive weekends, a hotel made a survey to find out how the temperature affected the number of people using the outdoor pool. The table shows the results.
   a) List the ordered pairs of the relation.
   b) State the domain and range.

Temperature °C	Number using pool
15	2
20	10
18	15
23	30
20	25
28	40

2. The graph displays the relation between the term and final marks of several mathematics students.
   a) List the ordered pairs of the relation.
   b) State the domain and range.

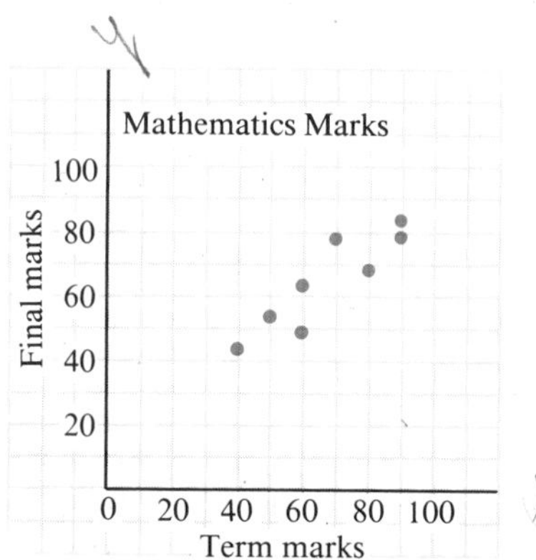

3. The Thurs have two sons, Craig and Colin, and a daughter, Gayle.
   a) Express the relation "is a brother of" as a set of ordered pairs.
   b) What are the domain and range of the relation?
4. The world track records, to the nearest second, for races up to 1500 m are given in the table.
   a) Graph the relation between time and distance:
      i) for men;
      ii) for women.
   b) State the domain and range for each relation in (a).

Distance	World Record	
m	Men s	Women s
100	10	11
200	20	22
400	44	48
800	102	113
1500	211	232

5. The recommended mass corresponding to height for women is given in the table.

Height cm	145	150	155	160	165	170	175	180	185
Mass kg	46	48	50	53	56	60	63	67	71

   a) Graph the relation.
   b) State the domain and range.

6. State the domain and range:

a) 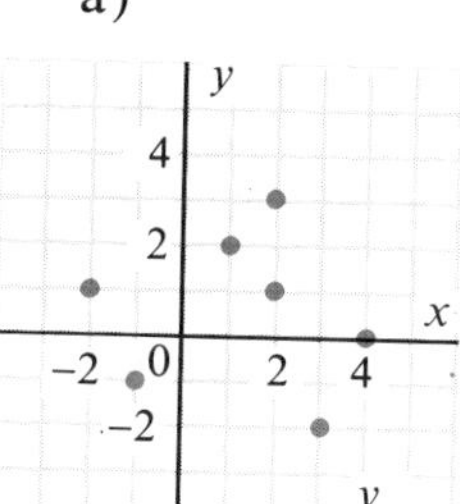

b) 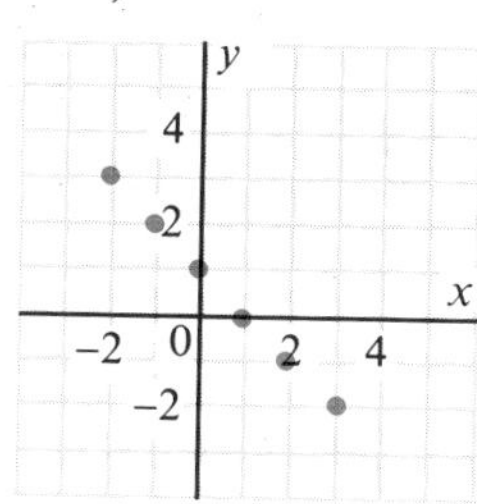

c) 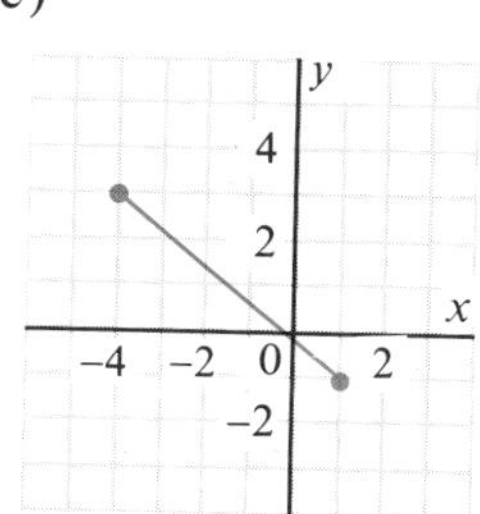

d) 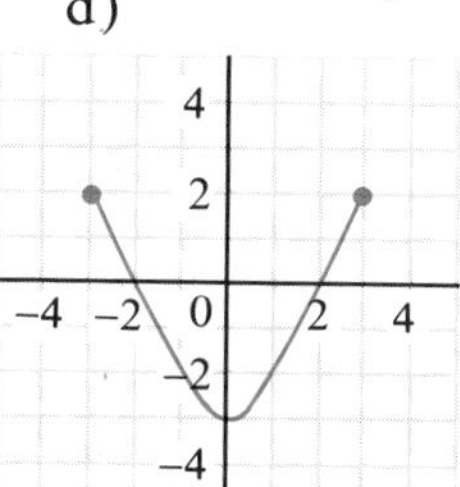

e) 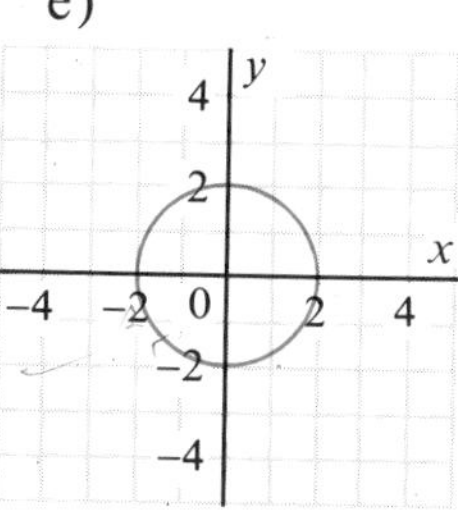

f) 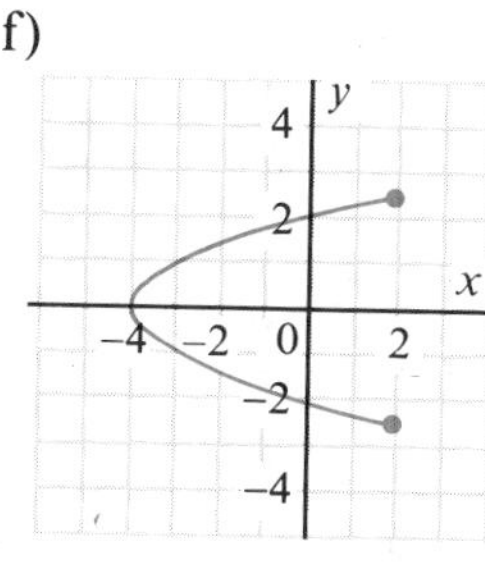

Ⓑ

Model	Fuel Consumption L/100 km	
	City	Highway
Rabbit	6.1	4.2
Civic	8.1	5.3
Omni	10.3	5.5
Corolla	9.7	7.5
Skylark	12.2	7.6
Audi	14.0	9.1
Camaro	18.1	12.7

7. The fuel consumption in the city and on the highway for seven different models of cars is given in the table.
   a) Graph the relation between the highway and city fuel consumption.
   b) What are the domain and range of the relation?

8. a) Using only the single digit numbers, list the ordered pairs of the relation "is a factor of".
   Example: (2, 6) indicates that 2 is a factor of 6.
   b) State the domain and range of the relation.

9. The five children of the Lalonde family, in order of birth, are: Tobie, Lise, Suzette, Urbain, and Claire.
   a) List the ordered pairs of the relation "is older than".
   b) State the domain and range of the relation.

10. State the domain and range:
   a) $y = \sqrt{x}$
   b) $y = \sqrt{x + 1}$
   c) $y = 2x - 3$
   d) $y = \frac{1}{x}$
   e) $y = \frac{1}{x - 2}$
   f) $y = (x + 4)^2$

11. State the domain and range:

a)

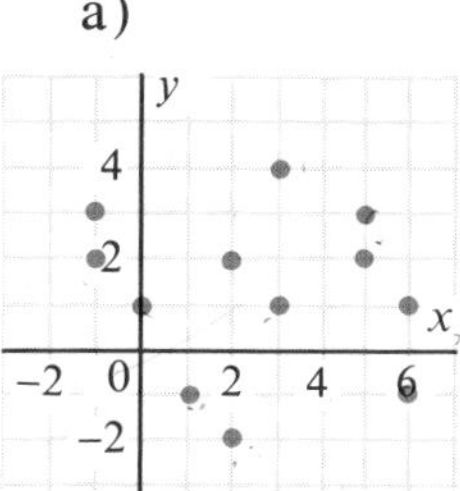

b)

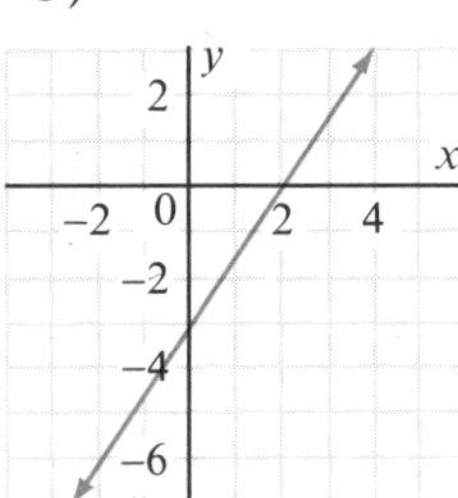

c)

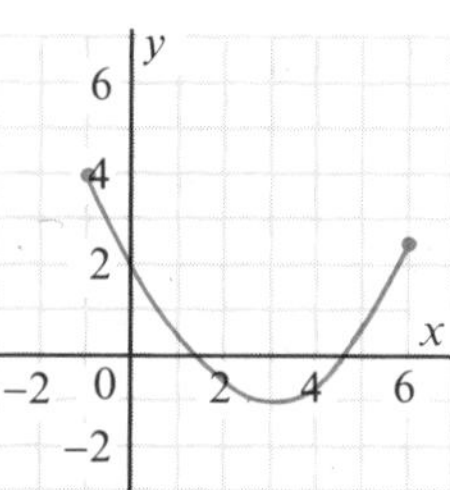

d)

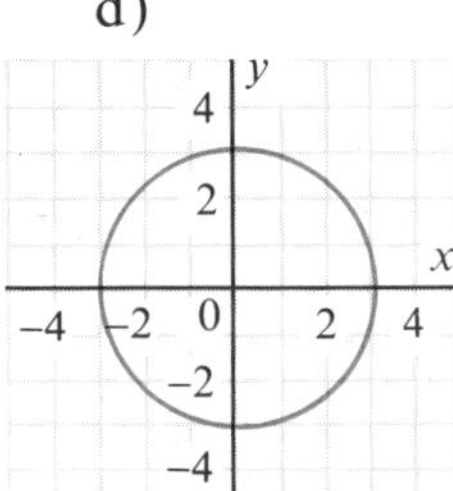

e)

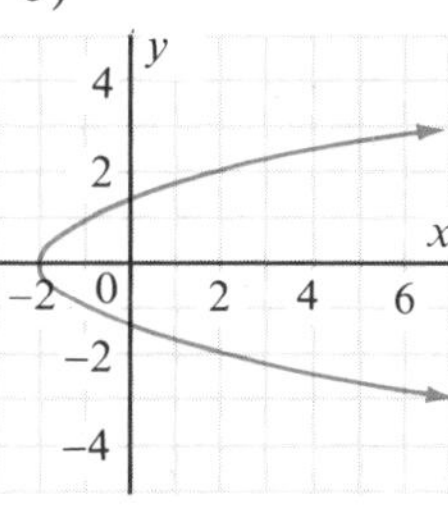

f)

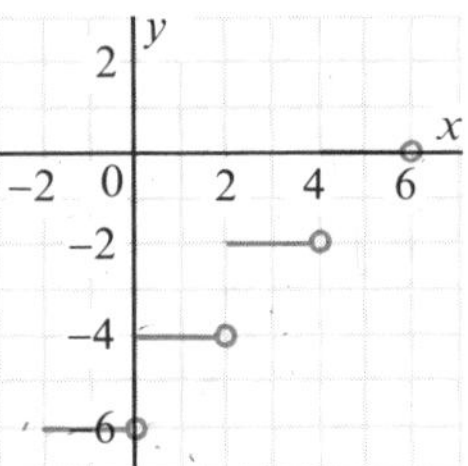

12. Graph these relations and state the domain and range:
    a) $y = 3x + 5$
    b) $y = 2 - x$
    c) $x + 2y - 6 = 0$
    d) $y = x^2$
    e) $x^2 + y^2 = 25$
    f) $x^2 + y^2 = 1$
13. Long distance track records for men are given in the table.

Distance	km	5	10	20	25	30
Record Time	min : s	13:08	27:23	57:24	74:17	91:30

    a) Graph the relation between time and distance.
    b) State the domain and range.
14. The velocity, v, in metres per second, of a freely falling object after it has fallen through a distance of h m from the point of release is given by the formula: $v \doteq 4.4\sqrt{h}$.
    a) Graph the relation.
    b) State the domain and range.
    c) Find v when $h = 6.5$ m.

Ⓒ

15. Dominic fills a kettle, boils the water, makes a cup of coffee, and allows it to cool before drinking it.
    a) Sketch a graph showing how the temperature of the water is related to the time since the kettle was filled.
    b) State the domain and range of the relation.

8-2 FUNCTIONS

In mathematics, the word "function" is used to express the idea that one quantity depends on another. For each illustration below, try to express the accompanying statement without using "function".

The distance to the horizon is a function of the observer's height above the ground.

Stopping distance is a function of speed.

The length of a tree's shadow is a function of the time of day. Donna measured the length of the shadow of a tree at 2 h intervals on a summer day. The results are shown in the table and the graph.

Time of day	Shadow length m
08:00	12.0
10:00	7.7
12:00	5.7
14:00	6.0
16:00	7.7
18:00	10.3
20:00	14.2

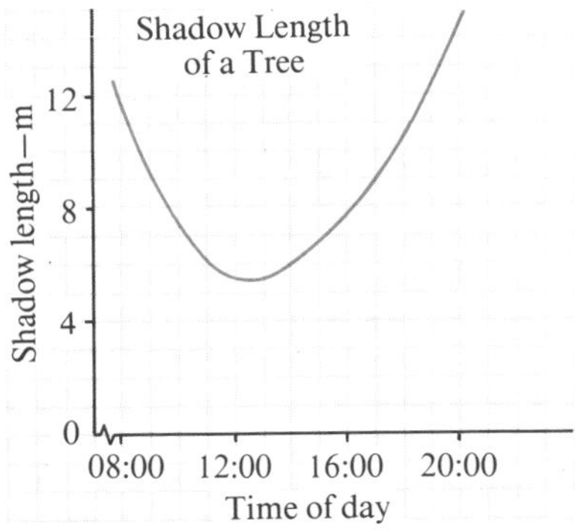

The relation between time of day and shadow length can be expressed as a set of ordered pairs.

$$R = \{(8, 12.0), (10, 7.7), (12, 5.7), (14, 6.0), (16, 7.7), (18, 10.3), (20, 14.2)\}$$

Since the tree's shadow cannot have two different lengths at the same time, this relation has a special property. No two ordered pairs have the same first coordinate. For this reason, this relation is called a **function**.

> A **function** is a relation in which no two ordered pairs have the same first coordinate.

Example 1.

Is the relation a function?

a) {(2,1), (3,5), (3,6), (4,–2), (5,–1)}
b) {(3,–2), (4,1), (5,1), (6,0), (7,–2)}

Solution.

a) Two ordered pairs, (3,5) and (3,6), have the same first coordinate. Therefore, the relation is not a function.
b) Since every ordered pair has a different first coordinate, the relation is a function.

From the graphs of the relations in *Example 1*, we can find a simple way to determine if a relation is a function.

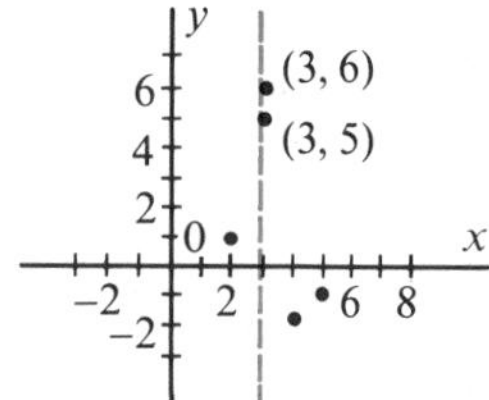

Since the points (3,5) and (3,6) have the same first coordinate, they can be joined by a vertical line. The relation is not a function.

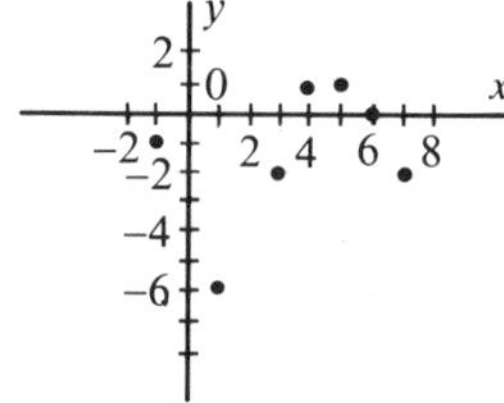

No two points can be joined by a vertical line. The relation is a function.

Vertical line test for a function. If no two points on a graph can be joined by a vertical line, the graph represents a function.

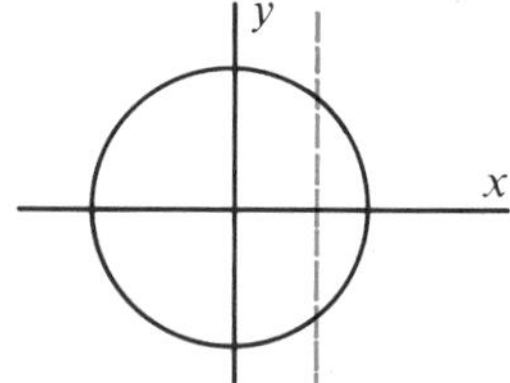

Since there is a vertical line which intersects the graph more than once, the relation is *not* a function.

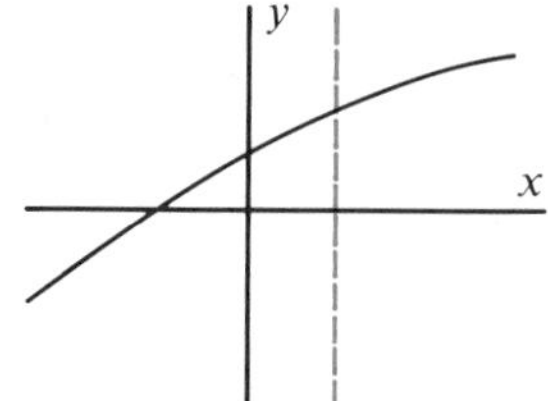

Since there is no vertical line which intersects the graph more than once, the relation *is* a function.

Example 2.

Given: the relation $y = x^2 - 5$.

a) Graph the relation and determine if it is a function.
b) State its domain and range.

Solution.

a)

x	y
−4	11
−3	4
−2	−1
−1	−4
0	−5

x	y
1	−4
2	−1
3	4
4	11

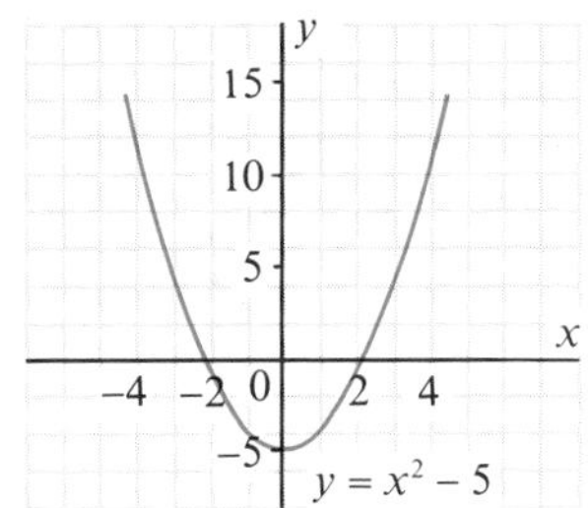

Domain
$y = x^2 - 5$
(0, −5)

The vertical line test shows that the relation is a function.

b) The domain is the set of x-values represented by the graph. Since the graph extends beyond the last points plotted, the domain is the set of all real numbers.
The range is the set of y values represented by the graph. This is the set of all real numbers greater than or equal to −5.

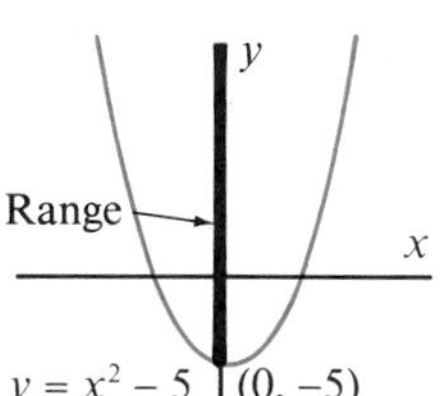

It is not necessary to graph a relation to tell if it is a function. This can be determined from the equation of the relation.

Equation test for a function. If a value of x can be found which produces more than one value of y when substituted in the equation, the equation *does not* represent a function. If there is no such value of x, the equation *does* represent a function.

Example 3.

Is the relation a function?

a) $x^2 + y^2 = 25$ b) $y = \sqrt{x}$ c) $y = \dfrac{1}{x - 2}$

Solution.

a) Is there any value of x which produces more than one value of y when substituted into $x^2 + y^2 = 25$?
If $x = 0$, $y^2 = 25$
$y = \pm 5$
When $x = 0$, there are two values of y.
The relation is not a function.

b) The relation $y = \sqrt{x}$ is only defined when $x \geq 0$. For any value of $x \geq 0$ there is only one value of y. Therefore, the relation is a function.

c) The relation $y = \dfrac{1}{x - 2}$ is undefined when $x = 2$. For any other value of x, there is only one value of y. Therefore, the relation is a function.

Example 4.

To deliver parcels in a metropolitan area, Rapidsend Courier Service charges \$5 for the first kilogram plus \$2 for each additional kilogram or part thereof.

a) Draw a graph showing how the delivery charge depends on the mass of the parcel.

b) For the relation in (a), state the domain and the range.

c) Is the relation a function? Why?

Solution.

a) Let the delivery charge for a parcel of mass m kg be \$$C$.

Mass, m kg	Delivery charge, C \$
$0 < m \leq 1$	5
$1 < m \leq 2$	7
$2 < m \leq 3$	9
$3 < m \leq 4$	11
$4 < m \leq 5$	13
$5 < m \leq 6$	15

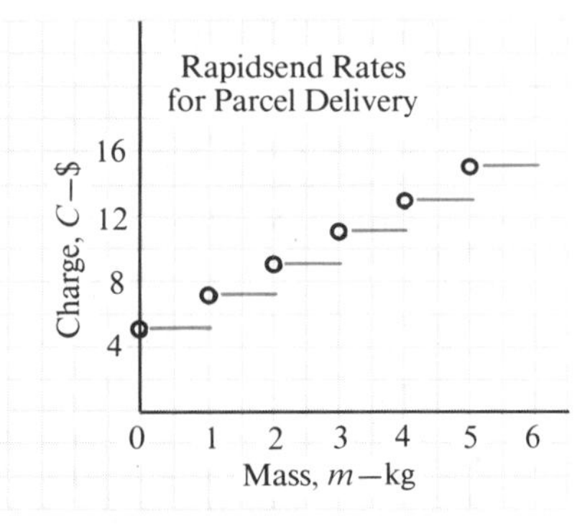

The small circles on the graph indicate points that are not part of the graph. For example, the delivery charge for a 1 kg parcel is \$5, and \$7 for one only slightly heavier. This is shown on the graph by the circle at (1,7).

b) The domain of the relation is the set of all possible masses of parcels. If the heaviest parcel accepted is 6 kg, the domain would be the set of all positive numbers less than or equal to 6. For this domain, the range is the set of delivery charges {5, 7, 9,. . ., 15}.

c) The vertical line test shows that the relation is a function.

Example 4 shows that a function can consist of two or more distinct parts, and these parts need not be connected on the graph.

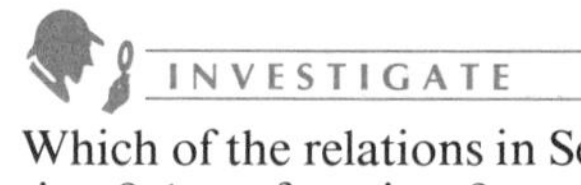

Which of the relations in Section 8-1 are functions?

EXERCISES 8-2

(A)

1. Does the graph represent a function?

a)

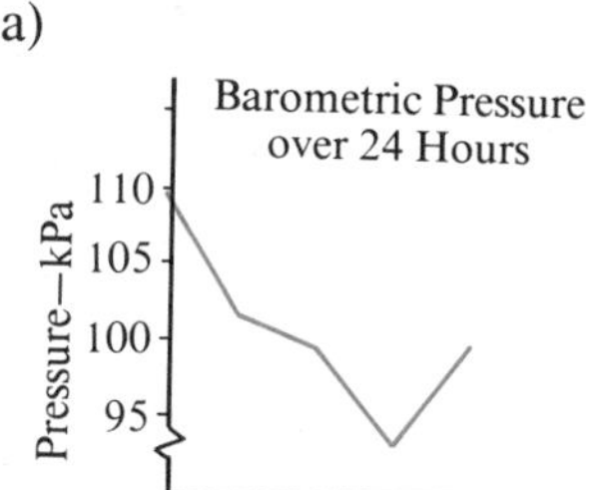

b)

Goals Scored
by Hockey Players
Number of goals scored
Number of shots on goal
0 5 10

c)

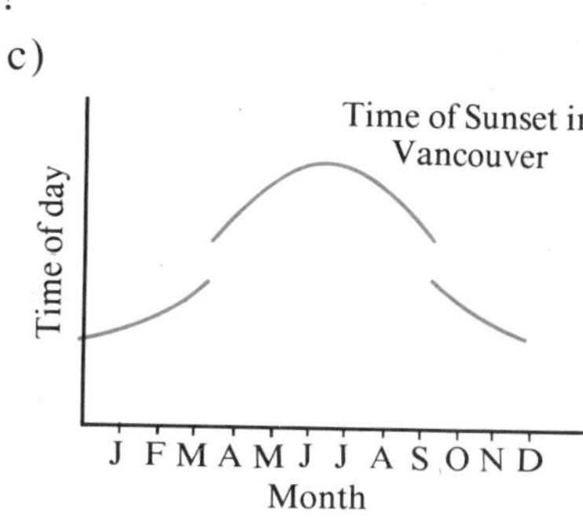

2. If the graph represents a function, state the domain and range:

a)

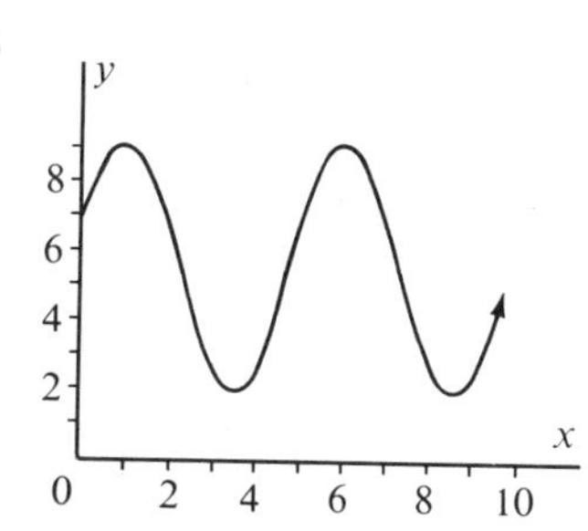

b)

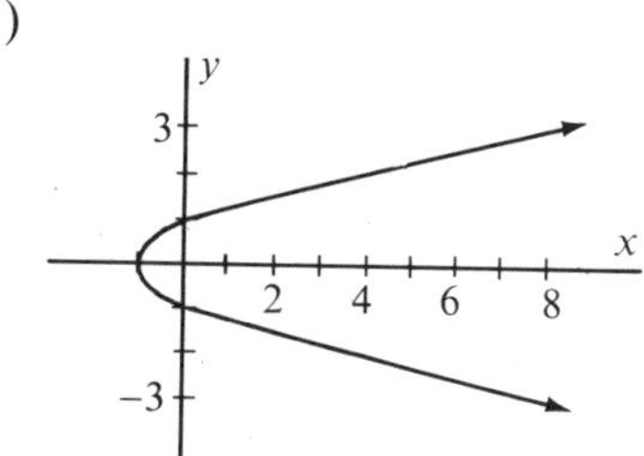

c)

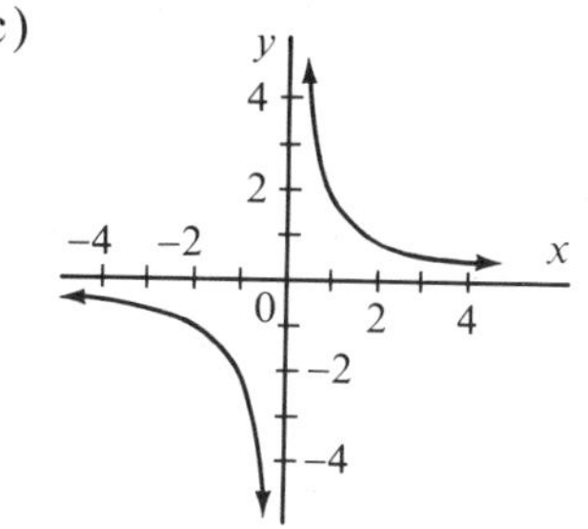

3. Does the set of ordered pairs represent a function?
   a) $\{(2,5), (3,10), (5,26), (7,50)\}$
   b) $\{(9,2), (6,5), (3,1), (6,8), (7,11)\}$
   c) $\{(0,4), (1,5), (2,8), (3,13), (-1,5), (-2,8), (-3,13)\}$
4. Determine if the relation is a function:
   a) $y = 3x - 7$
   b) $y = 1 - \frac{1}{2}x$
   c) $y = x^2 + 1$
   d) $x^2 + y^2 = 16$
   e) $x = y^2$
   f) $y = \frac{1}{x}$
   g) $x - y^2 = 4$
   h) $x^2 - y^2 = 9$
   i) $y = \sqrt{2x}$

(B)

5. Graph, and state the domain and range. Is the relation a function?
   a) $y = 3x - 1$
   b) $y = x^2 - 1$
   c) $x = y^2 + 1$
6. A ball bounces to a height h when dropped from a height x, where h is given by the formula: $h = \frac{3}{4}x$.
   a) Graph the relation. Is it a function?
   b) State the domain and range.
   c) If the ball bounces to a height 3.6 m, from what height was it dropped?

7. If the perimeter of a rectangle is 24 cm and its length is x cm, express the following as a function of x.
   a) the width b) the area c) the length of a diagonal
8. If the area of a rectangle is 24 cm^2 and its length is x cm, express the following as a function of x.
   a) the width b) the perimeter c) the length of a diagonal
9. Graph, and state the domain and range:
   a) $y = 2^x$ b) $y = \sqrt{x}$ c) $y = \sqrt{x^2}$
10. Long distance telephone charges between two cities are $3 for the first 3 min plus 50¢ for each additional minute or part of a minute.
    a) Draw a graph showing how the charge for a call depends on the length of the call.
    b) State the domain and range.
    c) Is the relation a function? Why?
11. A taxi company charges $2.50 for distances up to 1 km plus $1 for each additional half-kilometre or part thereof.
    a) Graph this relation. Is it a function?
    b) State the domain and range.
12. State the domain and range:
    a) $y = \sqrt{x-3}$ b) $y = 5x$ c) $x + y = 6$
    d) $y = \dfrac{1}{x+2}$ e) $y = x^2 + 1$ f) $y = 3^x$

Ⓒ

13. a) Express as a function of x:
       i) The number of litres of water that must be added to 5 L of antifreeze to make a solution that is x% antifreeze.
       ii) The number of litres of antifreeze that must be added to 5 L of water to make a solution that is x% antifreeze.
    b) What are the domain and range of each function in (a)?
    c) Graph the functions in (a), and compare them. Account for the similarities and differences.
14. Some geography textbooks contain a graph like the one shown which illustrates how the temperature of the atmosphere varies with increasing altitude.
    a) Is the relation a function? That is, is altitude a function of temperature?
    b) Is temperature a function of altitude? How might the graph be drawn to show this? Give reasons why the graph is not drawn this way in geography textbooks.

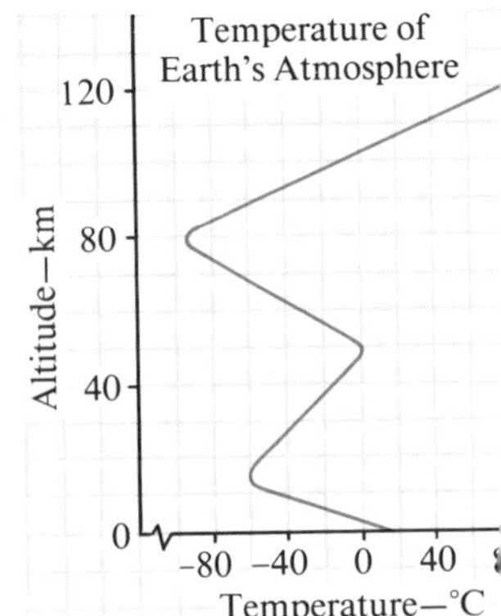

MATHEMATICS AROUND US

Recording Instruments

Doctors use electrocardiograms to study the electrical activity of the heart. The data is displayed as a graph on a computer screen or on a roll of graph paper.

Similar instruments are used to record other kinds of data in medicine, industry, geography, seismography (the scientific study of earthquakes), meteorology, and so on.

The graphs shown are:

- an electrocardiogram—measuring heart activity
- a barograph—measuring air pressure
- a recording thermometer—showing temperature over a week
- an electroencephalogram—recording the electrical activity of the brain

QUESTIONS

1. Can you identify each graph?
2. Explain how the graphs illustrate the concept of a function.

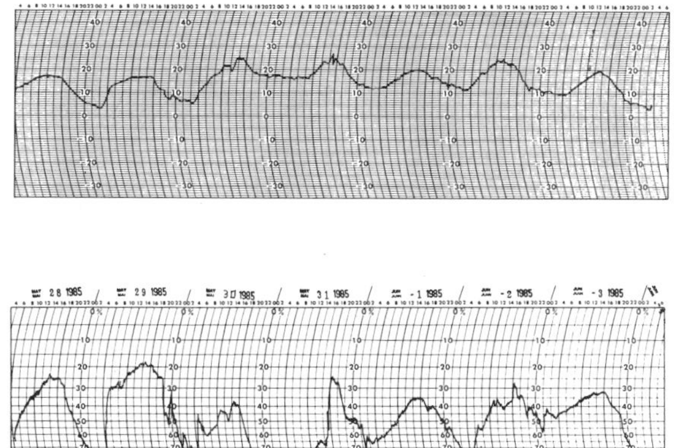

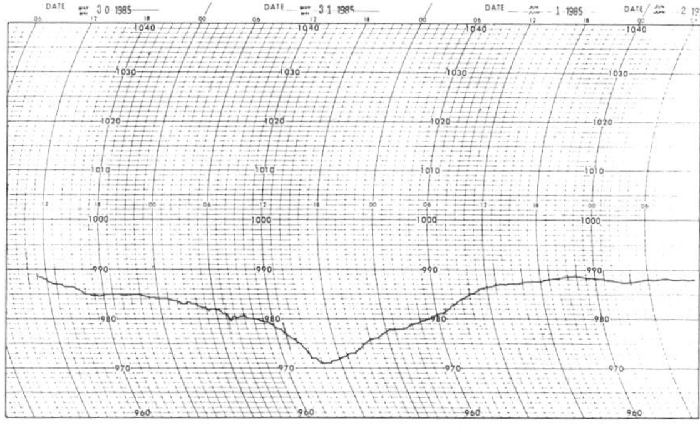

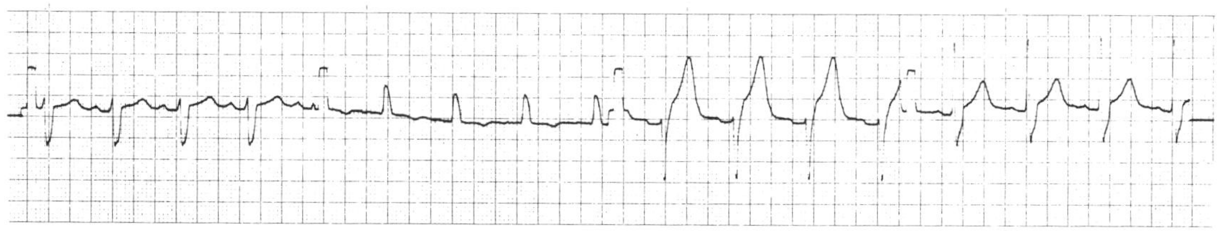

8-3 FUNCTION NOTATION

In algebra, symbols such as x and y are used to represent numbers. To represent functions, we often use symbols such as $f(x)$ and $g(x)$. For example, we may write:

$$f(x) = x^2 - 3x - 4.$$

The symbol, $f(x)$, is read "f of x", and simply means that the expression which follows contains x as a variable. This notation is useful because it simplifies recording the values of the function for several values of x. For example, $f(6)$ means to substitute 6 for x everywhere x occurs in the expression.

$$f(x) = x^2 - 3x - 4$$
$$\downarrow \quad \downarrow \quad \downarrow$$
$$f(6) = 6^2 - 3(6) - 4$$
$$= 36 - 18 - 4, \text{ or } 14$$

Example 1.

If $f(x) = 3x^2 - x - 6$, find:

a) $f(2)$; b) $f(-1)$; c) $f(0.5)$.

Solution.

a) Substitute 2 for x in $f(x) = 3x^2 - x - 6$

$$f(2) = 3(2)^2 - 2 - 6$$
$$= 12 - 2 - 6, \text{ or } 4$$

b) Substitute -1 for x: $f(-1) = 3(-1)^2 - (-1) - 6$

$$= 3 + 1 - 6, \text{ or } -2$$

c) Substitute 0.5 for x: $f(0.5) = 3(0.5)^2 - (0.5) - 6$

$$= 0.75 - 0.5 - 6$$
$$= -5.75$$

Example 2.

Given: the function $g(x) = \sqrt{x + 2}$

a) Graph the function.
b) State the domain and range.

Solution.

a)

x	$g(x)$
-2	0.00
-1	1.00
0	1.41
1	1.73
2	2.00

x	$g(x)$
3	2.24
4	2.45
5	2.65
6	2.83
7	3.00

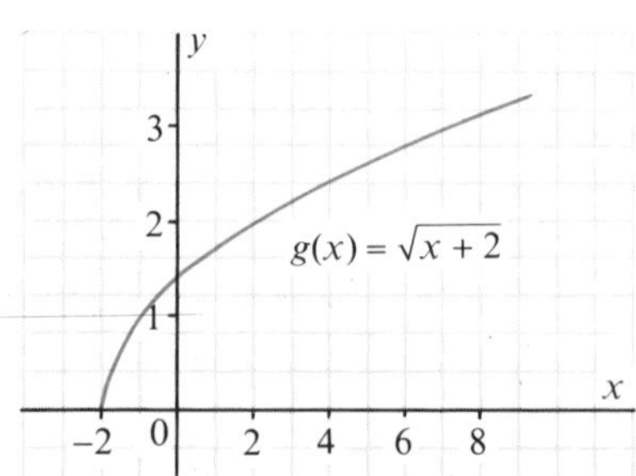

b) Since only non-negative numbers have real square roots, the function $g(x)$ is defined only when $x + 2 \geqslant 0$, or $x \geqslant -2$. The domain is the set of all real numbers greater than or equal to -2. The range is the set of non-negative real numbers.

Function notation can be used even when there is no known equation relating the variables.

Example 3.

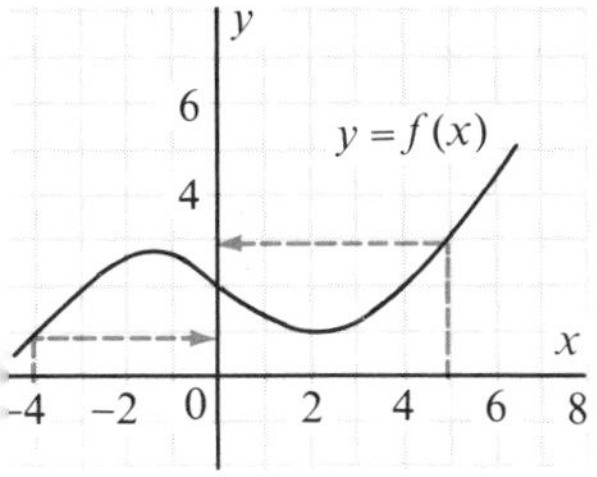

From the graph of $y = f(x)$ shown, find:

a) $f(5)$; b) $f(0)$; c) $f(-4)$.

y
6
y = f(x)
4
x
-4 -2 0 2 4 6 8

Solution.

a) When $x = 5$, $y = 3$. that is, $f(5) = 3$.

b) $f(0) = 2$

c) $f(-4) = 1$

Other algebraic expressions may be substituted for the variable in the equation of a function.

Example 4.

Given: $f(x) = 3x - 1$. Find:

a) $f(c)$; b) $f(2x)$; c) $f\left(\frac{1}{x}\right)$, $x \neq 0$; d) $f(x - 2)$.

Solution.

a) Substitute c for x:

$$f(x) = 3x - 1$$

$$f(c) = 3c - 1$$

b) Substitute $2x$ for x:

$$f(x) = 3x - 1$$

$$f(2x) = 3(2x) - 1$$
$$= 6x - 1$$

c) Substitute $\frac{1}{x}$ for x:

$$f(x) = 3x - 1$$

$$f\left(\frac{1}{x}\right) = 3\left(\frac{1}{x}\right) - 1$$
$$= \frac{3}{x} - 1$$
$$= \frac{3 - x}{x} \quad (x \neq 0)$$

d) Substitute $x - 2$ for x:

$$f(x) = 3x - 1$$

$$f(x - 2) = 3(x - 2) - 1$$
$$= 3x - 6 - 1$$
$$= 3x - 7$$

EXERCISES 8-3

(A)

1. If $f(x) = 1 - x^2$, evaluate:

a) $f(2)$; b) $f(3)$; c) $f(0.5)$.

2. If $g(x) = 3x - 1$, evaluate:

   a) $g(1)$; b) $g(5)$; c) $g\left(\frac{1}{2}\right)$.

3. Find $f(-1)$, $f(2)$, and $f(0.5)$ for:

   a) $f(x) = 3x^2 - 2x + 1$; b) $f(x) = 2x^3 + 5x^2 + 3x - 4$.

4. a) Graph: i) $f(x) = \frac{1}{2}x - 1$

   ii) $f(x) = \sqrt{x - 1}$

   b) State the domain and range of the functions in (a).

5. For each graph of $y = f(x)$, find $f(-2)$, $f(1)$, $f(3)$:

   a) b) c)

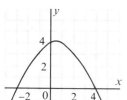

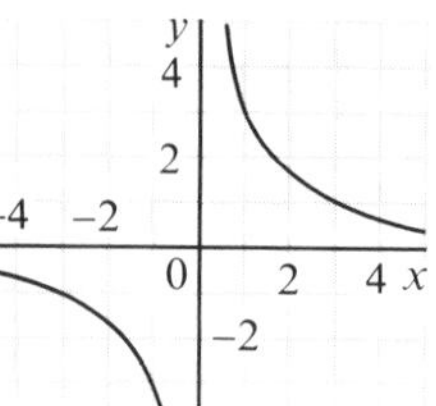

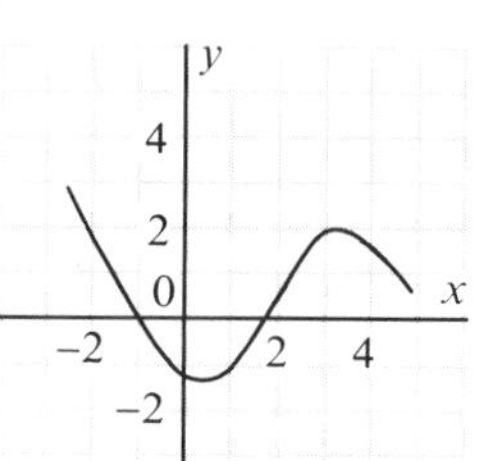

6. If $f(x) = 3x - 5$, find:

   a) $f(m)$; b) $f(4x)$; c) $2f(x)$; d) $f\left(\frac{2}{x}\right)$; e) $f(2x + 1)$.

7. If $g(x) = 5x + 1$, find:

   a) $g(k)$; b) $g(x - 1)$; c) $g(2x + 1)$; d) $g(4 - 3x)$.

8. For each definition of $f(x)$, find $f(2)$, $f(-5)$, $f(0.5)$:

   a) $f(x) = 4x - 7$ b) $f(x) = 8x^2 + x - 9$

   c) $f(x) = \sqrt{6x - 1}$ d) $f(x) = x^2 + \frac{1}{x}$

   e) $f(x) = x^3 - x^2$ f) $f(x) = \frac{4x}{2x + 1}$

(B)

9. Graph, and state the domain and range:

   a) $f(x) = \frac{1}{2}x + 3$ b) $f(x) = x^2 + 1$ c) $f(x) = x(x - 3)$

10. Graph each function for $-3 \leq x \leq 3$:

   a) $f(x) = x^3$ b) $f(x) = x^3 - 4x$

   c) $f(x) = 2^x$ d) $f(x) = \frac{6}{x^2 + 1}$

11. State the domain and range:

    a) $f(x) = \sqrt{x+5}$ b) $f(x) = \dfrac{5}{x+2}$ c) $g(x) = 2x + 1$

    d) $g(x) = x^2 + 3$ e) $f(x) = x^3$ f) $g(x) = 1 + \sqrt{x}$

12. If $f(x) = 2x^2 + 3x - 5$, find:

    a) $f(x + 1)$; b) $f(x + 2)$; c) $f(x + 3)$;

    d) $f(2x)$; e) $f(3x)$; f) $f(-x)$.

13. If $f(x) = 3x-2$ and $g(x) = 5x + 7$, find:

    a) $f(x) - g(x)$; b) $2f(x) + g(x)$; c) $f(x) \times g(x)$;

    d) $4f(x) - 2g(x)$; e) $f(2x) - g(2x)$; f) $3f(2x) + 2g(3x)$

14. The area, A of an equilateral triangle is a function of its side length, x, and is given by the formula: $A = \dfrac{\sqrt{3}}{4}x^2$.

    a) Graph the function and state the domain and range.
    b) If the side length is doubled, how is the area affected?
    c) If the length of each side is increased by 3 units, by how much does the area increase?
    d) If the length of each side is decreased by h units, by how much does the area decrease?

15. If $f(x) = 5 - 3x$ and $g(x) = 4x + 1$, find a value of x such that:

    a) $f(x) = g(x)$; b) $f(x + 2) = g(x - 1)$;

    c) $f(2 - 5x) = g(4x + 1)$; d) $f(2x + 2) = g(x^2)$.

16. Given: $g(x) = 2x + 3$. Find x when:

    a) $g(x) = 5$; b) $g(x) = -9$; c) $g(x) = 0$.

17. If $f(x) = x^2 + 3x - 10$, what values of x make:

    a) $f(x) = 0$? b) $f(x) = 8$? c) $f(x) = -6$?

Ⓒ

---

18. For $-5 \leq x \leq 5, x \neq 0$, graph: a) $f(x) = \dfrac{1}{x}$; b) $f(x) = \dfrac{1}{x^2}$.

19. Given: $f(x) = \dfrac{x}{1+x}$.

    a) Find: i) $f(2) + f\left(\dfrac{1}{2}\right)$; ii) $f(3) + f\left(\dfrac{1}{3}\right)$.

    b) Predict the value of $f(n) + f\left(\dfrac{1}{n}\right)$, and prove that your prediction is correct.

    c) For what values of n does the result in (b) hold?

20. Given: $g(x) = 3^x$.
    a) Show that: i) $g(2x) = [g(x)]^2$; ii) $g(3x) = [g(x)]^3$.
    b) What is $g(nx)$ equal to?

21. a) If $f(x) = 3x + 2$, show that $f(a + b) \neq f(a) + f(b)$.
    b) Give an example of a function $f(x)$ such that the identity $f(a + b) = f(a) + f(b)$ is true for all values of a and b.

22. Let n be a positive integer and let $f(n)$ represent the number of factors of n.
    a) Graph the function $f(n)$.
    b) Describe the numbers for which:
       i) $f(n) = 2$; ii) $f(n) = 3$;
       iii) $f(n) = 4$; iv) $f(n) = 5$.

8-4 LINEAR FUNCTIONS

Sales personnel at a computer store are paid a monthly salary of \$300 plus a 4% commission on monthly sales. The table and the graph show the income for monthly sales up to \$30 000.

Monthly Sales, s	Monthly Income, I
\$ 0	\$ 300
10 000	700
20 000	1100
30 000	1500

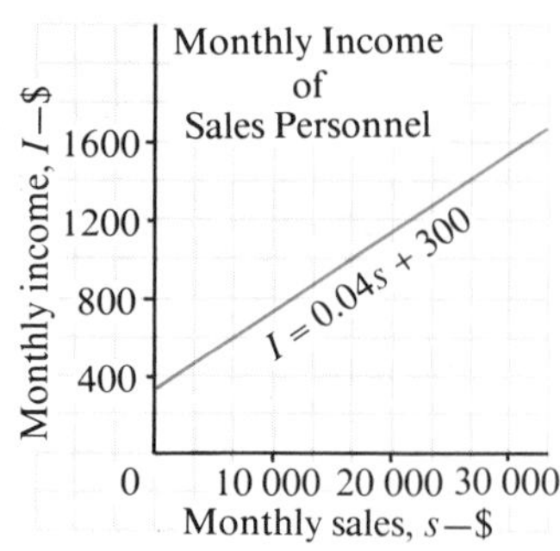

The equation for I in terms of s is: $I = 0.04s + 300$.

Since there is only one value of I for each value of s, the relation between s and I is a function. It is a **linear function** because its graph is a straight line and its equation has the same form as the equation of a line with slope m and y-intercept b. When x and y are not used, the y-intercept is called the **vertical intercept**.

$$\text{Compare } y = mx + b$$
$$\text{with } I = 0.04s + 300$$

The slope represents the rate of commission, 4%.

The vertical intercept represents the base salary, \$300.

A **linear function** has a defining equation which can be written in the form:

$$y = mx + b \quad \text{or} \quad f(x) = mx + b,$$

where m and b are constants. The graph of a linear function is a straight line with slope m and vertical intercept b.

We will use both forms, $y = mx + b$ and $f(x) = mx + b$, in subsequent work. The equation form is familiar from your work in analytic geometry. The function notation, of course, denotes a function.

These are linear functions because they can be expressed in either of the above forms.

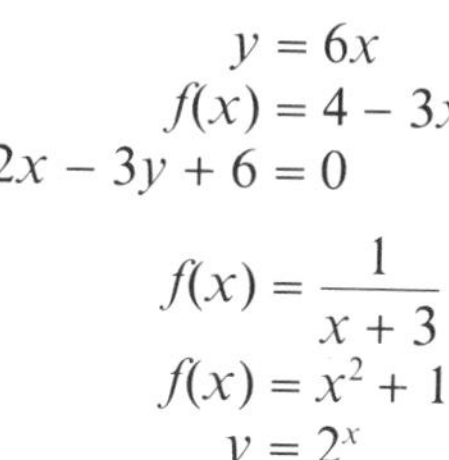

$$y = 6x$$
$$f(x) = 4 - 3x$$
$$2x - 3y + 6 = 0$$

These are not linear functions because they cannot be expressed in the above forms.

$$f(x) = \frac{1}{x + 3}$$
$$f(x) = x^2 + 1$$
$$y = 2^x$$

Example 1.

Graph: $f(x) = -\frac{1}{2}x + 3$

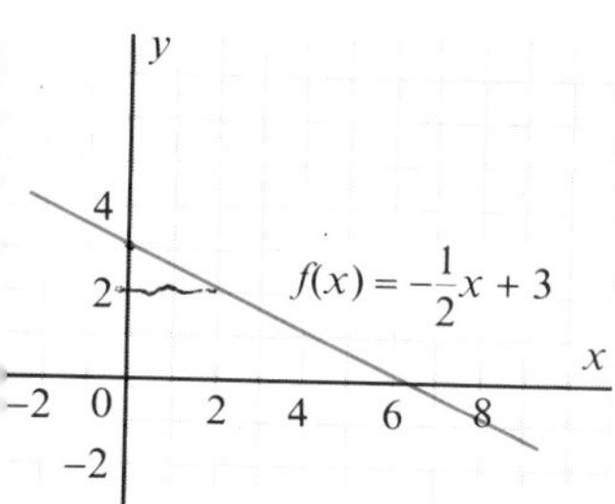

Solution.

The graph is the line $y = -\frac{1}{2}x + 3$ which has slope $-\frac{1}{2}$ and y-intercept 3.

Frequently, the defining equation of a linear function can only be approximated from a graph.

Example 2.

The boiling point of water is a function of altitude. The table shows the boiling points at various altitudes.

Location	Altitude, h m	Boiling Point of Water, t °C
Halifax, N.S.	0	100
Banff, Alberta	1383	95
Quito, Ecuador	2850	90
Mount Everest	8848	71

a) Graph the relation between altitude, h, and boiling point, t.

b) Find an equation which expresses the boiling point in terms of the altitude.

c) Use the equation to determine approximately:

i) the boiling point of water at Lhasa, Tibet, altitude 3680 m;

ii) the altitude where the boiling point is 75°C.

d) What are the domain and the range of the function in (a)?

Solution.

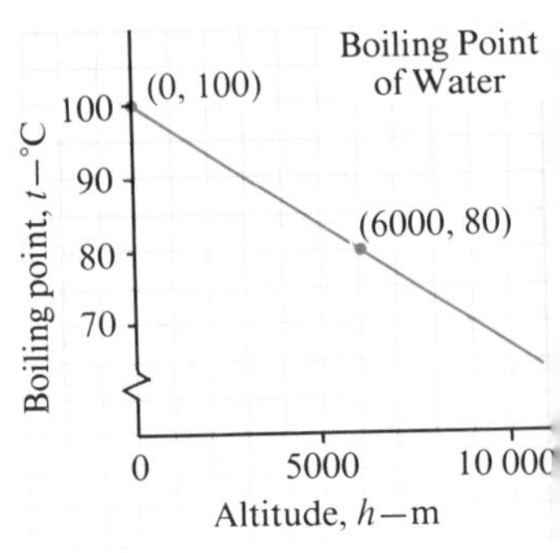

a) Plot the points and draw the best straight line through them.

b) Choose any two points which lie on the line (they need not be the plotted points), say (6000, 80) and (0, 100). The slope of the line through these points is $\frac{100 - 80}{0 - 6000}$, or about -0.0033. Since the vertical intercept is 100, the equation of the line is:

$t = -0.0033h + 100$

c) i) When $h = 3680$, $t = -0.0033(3680) + 100$, or 88. The boiling point of water at Lhasa, Tibet, is approximately 88°C.

ii) When $t = 75$, $75 = -0.0033h + 100$

$$0.0033h = 25$$
$$h \doteq 7500$$

The boiling point of water is 75°C at an altitude of 7500 m.

d) The domain is the set of all possible altitudes, h, where $h \leq 8848$. The range is the set of all possible boiling points, t, where $71 \leq t \leq 100$.

EXERCISES 8-4

(A)

1. Which functions are linear?

a) $f(x) = 4x$ b) $f(x) = 2 - x$ c) $y = x^2$

d) $f(x) = \frac{2x + 5}{10}$ e) $y = \frac{1}{x}$ f) $f(x) = (x - 2)(x + 1)$

2. Graph:

a) $f(x) = \frac{3}{4}x + 2$ b) $g(x) = 2x + 3$

c) $f(x) = 4 - x$ d) $g(x) = -\frac{3}{2}x$

3. An airplane at an altitude of 10 000 m begins to descend at 300 m/min.

a) Draw a graph showing the altitude of the airplane as a function of time for the first 10 min of descent.

b) Find the equation giving the altitude, h, as a function of time, t.

4. The temperature of Earth's crust, T, in degrees Celsius, is a function of the depth, d, in kilometres, below the surface:

$$T = 10d + 20$$

a) Graph the function for values of d up to 5 km.
b) The deepest mine is in South Africa, and reaches 3.8 km below the surface. Use the equation or the graph to find the approximate temperature at the bottom.

5. Sales personnel are offered three choices of salary payment:

Plan A: \$1000 per month + 5% of sales
Plan B: \$1000 per month + 10% of sales over \$20 000
Plan C: 30% of all sales over \$20 000

Which graph represents which plan?

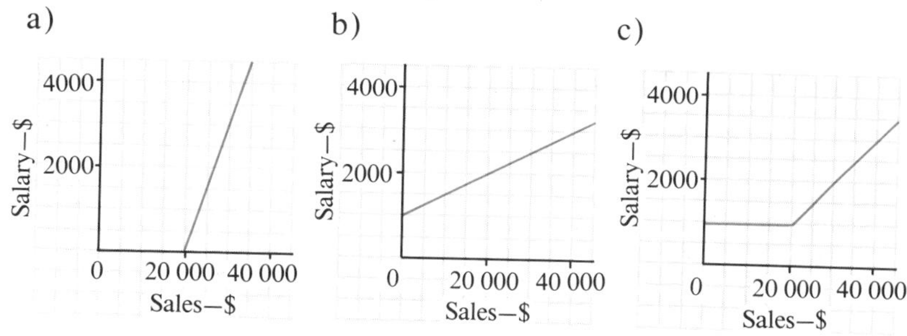

(B)

Altitude km	Temperature °C
0	15
2	2
4	−11
6	−24
8	−37
10	−50

6. The approximate temperature of Earth's atmosphere at different altitudes up to 10 km is given in the table.
a) Draw a graph showing temperature as a function of altitude.
b) Find the equation relating temperature and altitude.
c) Determine approximately
 i) the temperature at an altitude of 7 km;
 ii) the altitude at which the temperature is 0°C.
d) Above 11 km, the temperature remains fairly constant at −56°C. Show this on the graph for (a).

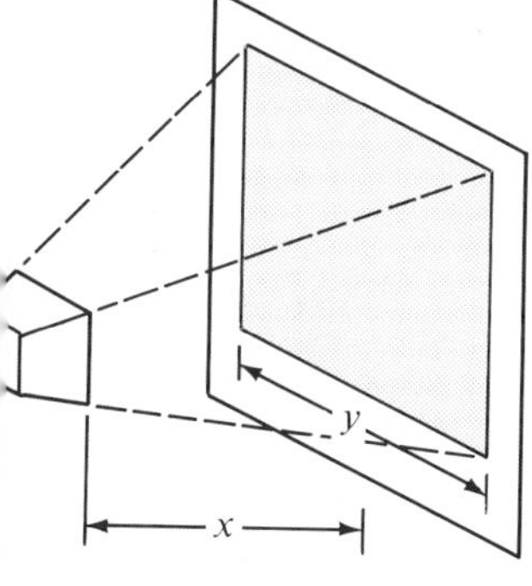

7. A projector throws an image on a screen. To determine how the width of the image is related to the distance of the screen from the projector, the following measurements were made.

Distance from screen to projector, x	m	1.4	2.7	3.9	5.0
Width of image, y	m	0.9	1.8	2.6	3.4

a) Graph the data and find the equation relating x and y.

b) Find the width of the image when the projector is 3.0 m from the screen.
c) Find the distance from the projector to the screen when the image is 3.0 m wide.
d) What is the domain of the relation?

8. A rectangle has a perimeter of 24 cm.
   a) Express its length as a function of its width.
   b) What is the domain of the function in (a)?

9. Express y as a function of x and state the domain:

a) 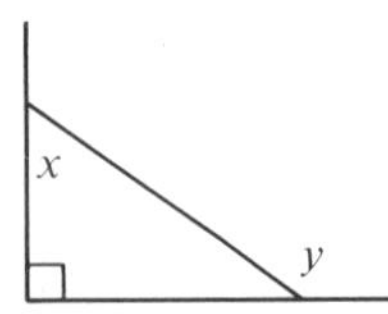

b) 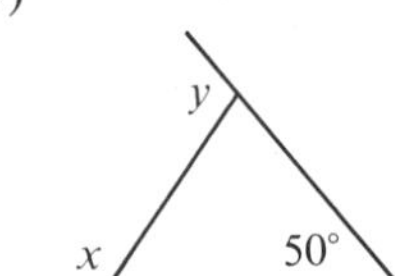

c) 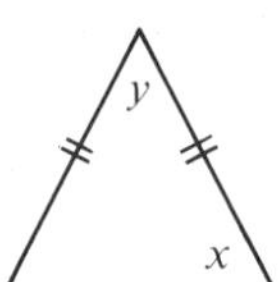

10. Michael works as a lifeguard and earns $4.50/h for a 32 h week. He is paid time-and-a-half for any additional hours. Draw a graph showing Michael's weekly earnings for up to 50 h work.

11. Using the rates given in the table, draw a graph showing the cost of water for consumptions up to 300 kL.

Municipal Water Rates	
First 100 kL	$0.55/kL
Next 100 kL	$0.35/kL
Additional	$0.15/kL

12. The graph shows how the volume of fuel in a car's fuel tank varies during a trip. The graph consists of six line segments.
    a) Describe what each line segment tells about the trip.
    b) Is the relation between the amount of fuel in the tank and the elapsed time a function? Explain.
    c) If the car was driven at an average speed of 100 km/h, find its rate of fuel consumption in litres per 100 km.

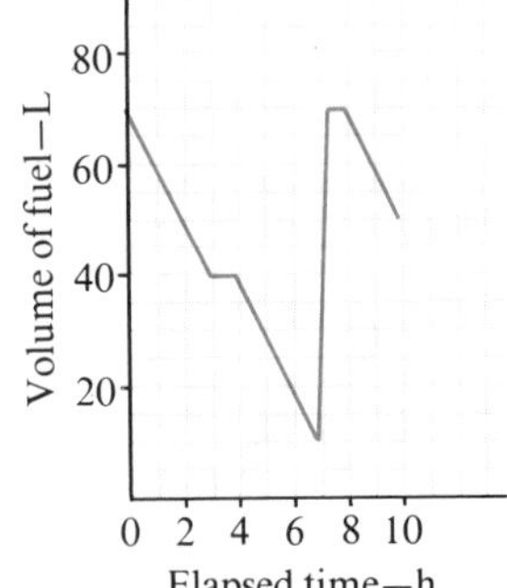

13. The number of litres of fuel, n, in a car's fuel tank is given by the formula $n = 72.5 - 0.082d$, where d is the distance the car has been driven, in kilometres, since the tank was filled.
    a) Graph the function for reasonable values of d.
    b) i) About how much fuel would be left after 175 km?
       ii) If 10 L of fuel are left, about how far was the car driven?
    c) i) What is the car's rate of fuel consumption in litres per 100 km?
       ii) How far can the car be driven on one tank of fuel?
    d) What are the domain and range of the function?

14. If $f(x) = mx + b$, find m and b if the graph of the function:

    a) has slope $\frac{2}{5}$ and y-intercept 7;

    b) has slope $-\frac{4}{3}$ and $f(6) = 2$;

    c) has y-intercept 4 and passes through $(-3, 10)$;

    d) passes through $(5, 9)$ and $(0, -6)$;

    e) has $f(-2) = 8$ and $f(3) = -12$;

    f) has $f(4) = 3$ and $f(-3) = 7$.

Ⓒ

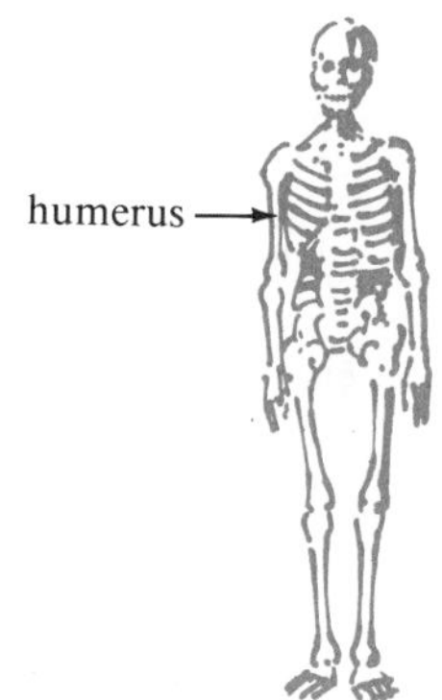

15. Archaeologists can estimate a person's height from the skeletal remains. One method uses the fact that height is a linear function of the length of the humerus, the bone of the upper arm. It is known that the humerus of a 160 cm adult is about 30 cm long, while that of a 190 cm adult is about 40 cm long.

    a) Express height, h, as a function of humerus length, l.

    b) What is the approximate height of an adult whose humerus measures 38.2 cm?

16. An arena manager asks for 25% of the gate receipts for a boxing match. The match promoter wants him to accept \$10 000 plus 50% of the gate receipts over \$150 000.

    a) Draw graphs to show how the arena manager's income depends on the gate receipts for each plan.

    b) For what gate receipts does the arena manager's plan provide the greater income?

17. $ABCD$ is a trapezoid with $AB = 10$ cm and $DC = 6$ cm. P is a point on AB such that $AP = x$ cm, and Q is a point on DC such that $DQ = y$ cm.

    a) If trapezoids $APQD$ and $PBCQ$ have equal areas, find the relation between x and y.

    b) For what positions of P on AB is it possible to find a point Q on DC such that the trapezoids $APQD$ and $PBCQ$ have equal areas?

18. If all the circles have a radius R, express the perimeter of each figure as a function of R.

    a)

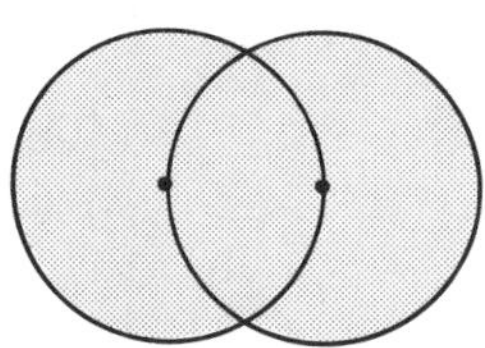

    b)

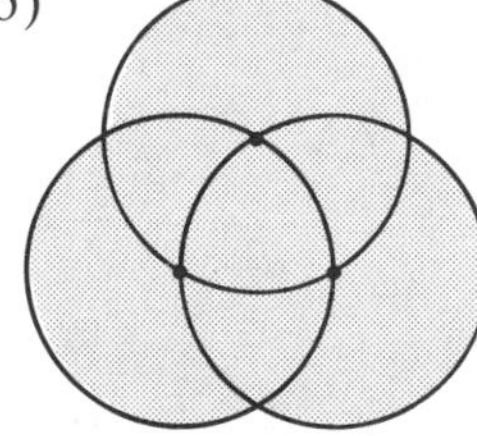

MATHEMATICS AROUND US

The Line of Best Fit—Geography

Geographers have studied sediments found near islands in the Atlantic Ocean and related the age of the sediment to the distance from the Mid-Atlantic Ridge. The table shows the results for a few islands.

Islands	Age of Sediment millions of years	Distance to Mid-Atlantic Ridge km
Azores	25	350
Bahamas	135	2800
Bermuda	95	1900
Faroes	20	250
St. Helena	35	700

In 1961, a Canadian, J. Tuzo Wilson theorized that this data provides evidence for the *continental drift*. He reasoned that volcanic activity at the Mid-Atlantic Ridge forms new parts of the earth's crust. These tend to push aside the older crust. Over millions of years, this spreading of the sea floor has caused the continents to move to their present positions.

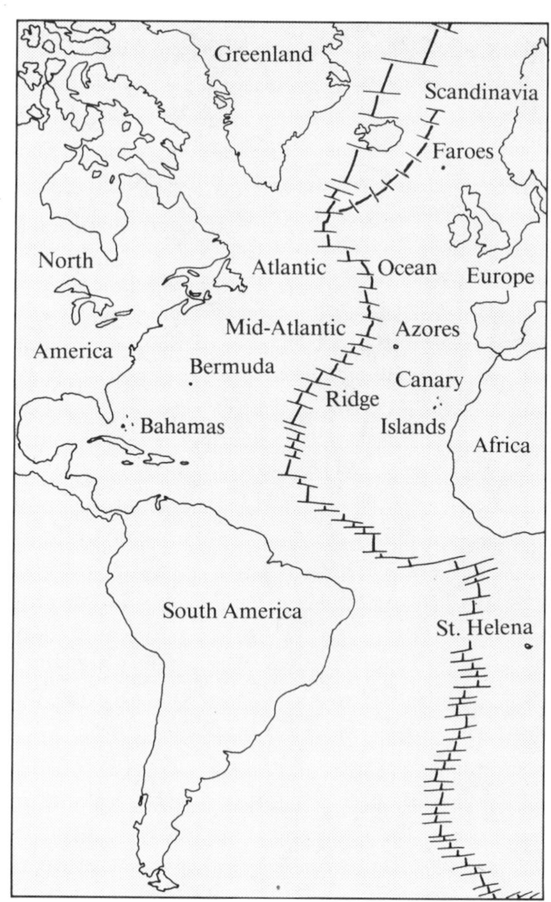

QUESTIONS

1. Find the equation of the line of best fit. What does the slope represent?
2. Use the equation of the line of best fit:
   a) to predict the age of sediment near the Canary Islands, which are about 1500 km from the Mid-Atlantic Ridge.
   b) to find the approximate yearly increase in distance between Europe and North America.

8-5 QUADRATIC FUNCTIONS

In case of a forced landing, private and military aircraft often carry a flare pistol which can be used to attract the attention of those looking for them. The height of the bullet, or flare, above the ground is a function of the elapsed time since firing. A typical expression for the height might be: $h = -5t^2 + 100t$.

The table of values and the graph show how h depends on t.

Time, t s	Height, h m
0	0
2	180
5	375
10	500
15	375
18	180
20	0

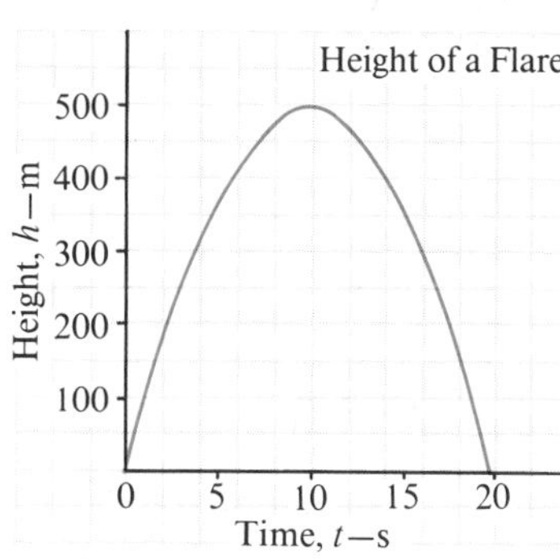

Since there is only one value of h for each value of t, the relation between h and t is a function. It is called a **quadratic function** because the equation contains a term, $-5t^2$, in which the variable is squared.

The graph of every quadratic function is a **parabola**. Parabolic curves arise in many areas of science, and they are used in art and architecture.

A **quadratic function** has a defining equation which can be written in the form:

$$y = ax^2 + bx + c \qquad \text{or} \qquad f(x) = ax^2 + bx + c$$

where a, b, c are constants and $a \neq 0$. The graph of a quadratic function is a parabola.

These are quadratic functions because they can be expressed in the form $f(x) = ax^2 + bx + c$.

$$f(x) = x^2 - 6$$
$$f(x) = 3x - 0.5x^2$$
$$f(t) = 2(t - 1)^2 + 5$$

These are not quadratic functions because they cannot be expressed in the form $f(x) = ax^2 + bx + c$.

$$f(x) = \frac{1}{x^2 - 4}$$
$$f(z) = \sqrt{z}$$

Example 1.

a) Graph the quadratic function: $y = 2x^2 - 4x - 11$

b) What are the domain and the range of the function?

Solution.

a)

x	y
−4	37
−3	19
−2	5
−1	−5
0	−11

x	y
1	−13
2	−11
3	− 5
4	5
5	19
6	37

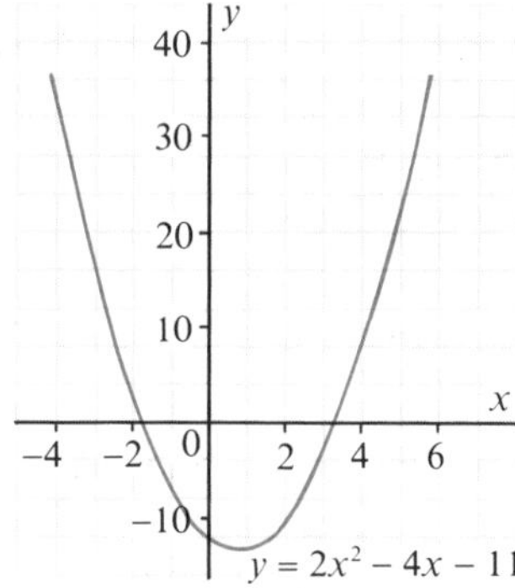

b) The domain of the function, the set of all possible values of x, is the set of all real numbers. The range is the set of all possible values of y. The table and graph suggest that this is the set of all numbers greater than or equal to −13.

In many applications of quadratic functions, the graph shows only that part of a parabola which is in the first quadrant. This happens when the variables are restricted to positive numbers.

Example 2.

In the open sea, the approximate height, h, in metres, of the waves is given by the formula: $h = 0.008v^2$, where v is the speed of the wind in knots.

a) Graph h as a function of v for $0 \leq v \leq 80$.

b) The highest wave ever measured at sea was 34 m. Use the graph to estimate the wind speed at the time.

Solution.

a)

Wind Speed knots	Wave Height m
0	0
20	3.2
40	12.8
60	28.8
80	51.2

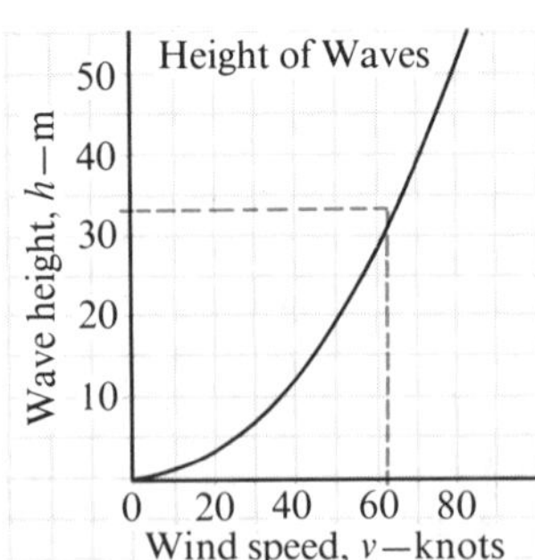

b) From the graph, a wave height of 34 m corresponds to a wind speed of about 65 knots.

EXERCISES 8-5

1. Is the function a quadratic?
   a) $y = 3x^2 + 7x - 2$
   b) $f(x) = x^2 + \sqrt{x}$
   c) $f(x) = 25 - 9x^2$
   d) $y = 7 - 5x^2$
   e) $y = 2x^2 + 11 - 4x$
   f) $f(x) = \dfrac{1}{4x^2 - 9x + 12}$

2. a) Graph the function: $y = 2x^2 + 5$.
   b) What are the domain and range of the function in (a)?

3. a) Graph the function: $y = x^2 - 6x + 2$.
   b) What are the domain and range of the function in (a)?

4. A pebble is dropped from a bridge into a river. Its height, h, in metres, above the river t s after the moment of release is given by:
   $$h = 82 - 4.9t^2.$$
   a) Graph the function for reasonable values of t.
   b) State the domain and range.
   c) How high is the pebble after 2.5 s?

(B)

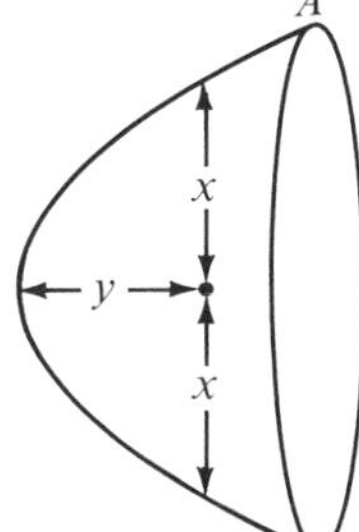

5. The shape of a parabolic mirror in a certain reflecting telescope is defined by the equation: $y = 0.1x^2 - 20$, where x and y are in centimetres.
   a) Graph the function for $0 \le x \le 25$.
   b) How deep is the mirror if the diameter AB is 50 cm?

6. Graph, and state the domain and range:
   a) $f(x) = 2x^2 - 6x + 5$
   b) $g(t) = 3 + 2t - 0.5t^2$

7. The Viking 1 spacecraft made a soft landing on Mars on July 20, 1976. Its speed, v, in metres per second, t s before touchdown was given by: $v = 1.2 + 3.2t$. Its height, h, in metres, t s before touchdown was given by: $h = 1.2t + 1.6t^2$.
   a) Draw graphs of the speed and height as functions of time.
   b) Determine the speed and height of the spacecraft 90 s before touchdown.

8. When a flare is fired vertically, its height, h, in metres, after t seconds is given by: $h = -4.9t^2 + 143.2t$.
   a) How high is the flare after 5 s?
   b) How long does it take the flare to reach a height of 1 km?

9. In *Example 2*, what is the effect on the height of the waves if the windspeed is:
   a) doubled?
   b) tripled?

10. A landscape architect plans a circular flowerbed with a bordering pathway. The total diameter of flowerbed and pathway is 20 m.
    a) If the width of the pathway is x m, express the area, A, of the flowerbed as a function of x.
    b) Graph the function in (a).
    c) What is the domain of the function?

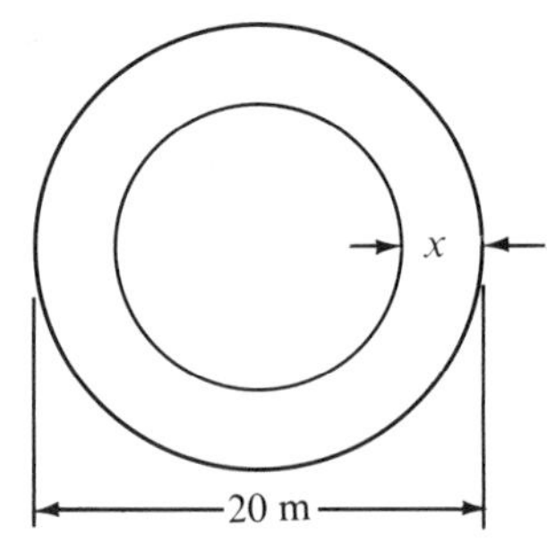

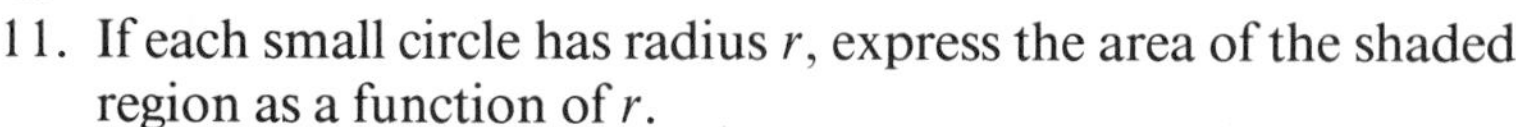

11. If each small circle has radius r, express the area of the shaded region as a function of r.
    a)

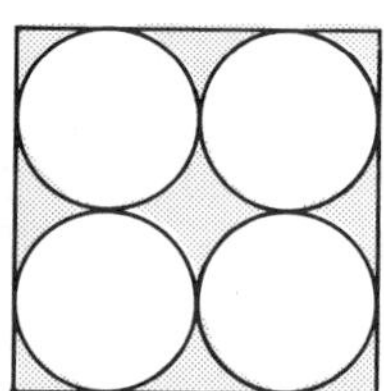

    b)

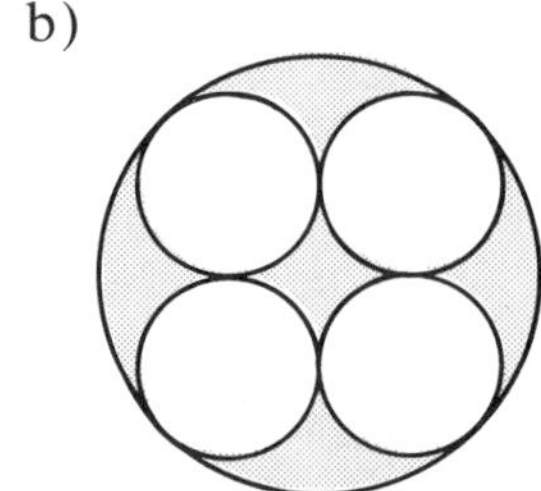

12. The velocity, v, in millimetres per second, of a particle falling through water is a function of its diameter, d, in millimetres. The formula is: $v = 655d^2$. How long will it take each of the particles listed to reach the seafloor where the ocean is 5000 m deep?

Particle	Diameter mm
Pebble	8.0
Coarse sand	0.5
Fine sand	0.1
Clay	0.004

13. The length, L, in metres, of an ocean wave is a quadratic function of the form $L = kT^2$, where T is the period in seconds and k is a constant.
    a) Find the value of k if a wave with length 25 m has a period of 4.0 s.
    b) What is the length of a wave if its period is 6.5 s?

8-6 COMPARING THE GRAPHS OF $y = x^2$ AND $y = x^2 + q$

In this and the following sections, we shall develop a technique for graphing quadratic functions without making a table of values. The first step is to investigate the effect on the graph of $y = x^2$ of adding some number q to get $y = x^2 + q$. We do this by substituting different values for q and graphing the resulting parabolas.

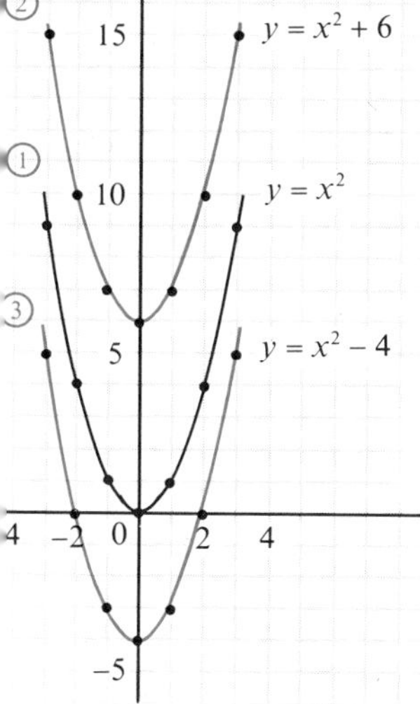

When $q = 0$, the equation becomes $y = x^2$. ...(1)

x	−3	−2	−1	0	1	2	3
y	9	4	1	0	1	4	9

When $q = 6$, the equation becomes $y = x^2 + 6$. ...(2)

x	−3	−2	−1	0	1	2	3
y	15	10	7	6	7	10	15

Since the y coordinates are all 6 greater than those of $y = x^2$, the curve is *translated*, or moved, 6 units up. The y-intercept is 6. The vertex is (0, 6) and the y-axis is still the axis of symmetry.

When $q = -4$, the equation becomes $y = x^2 - 4$. ...(3)

x	−3	−2	−1	0	1	2	3
y	5	0	−3	−4	−3	0	5

The curve is *translated* 4 units down. The y-intercept is −4, which is the minimum value of y. There are also two x-intercepts, 2 and −2.

Similar results will be found using other values of q.

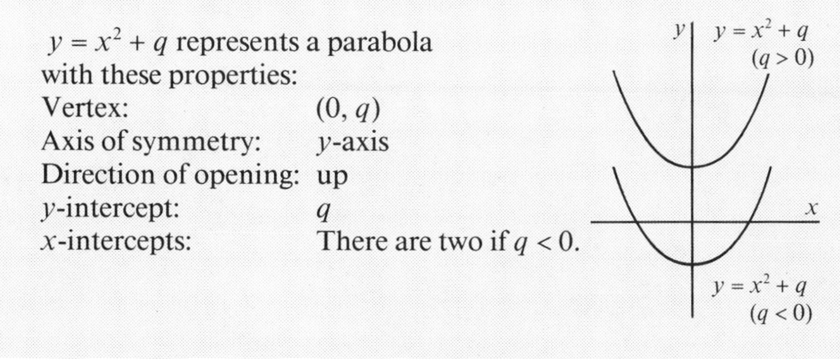

$y = x^2 + q$ represents a parabola with these properties:

Vertex:	$(0, q)$
Axis of symmetry:	y-axis
Direction of opening:	up
y-intercept:	q
x-intercepts:	There are two if $q < 0$.

Knowing that $y = x^2 + q$ represents a parabola with the above properties, we can sketch graphs of equations in this form without making tables of values.

Example.

Sketch the parabola $y = x^2 - 9$ for $-4 \le x \le 4$.

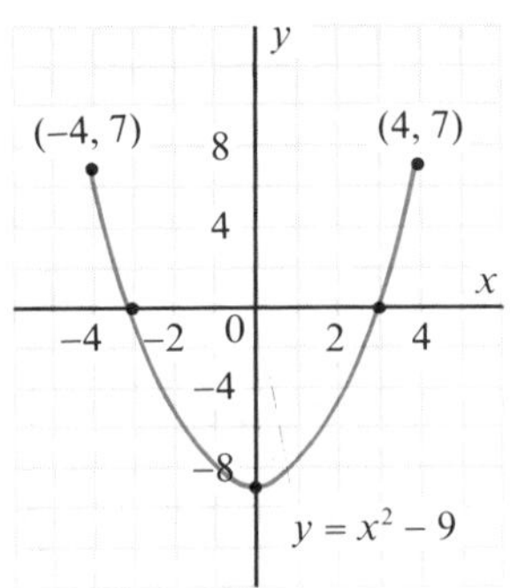

Solution.

The parabola $y = x^2 - 9$ has vertex (0, −9), opens up, and has the y-axis as the axis of symmetry. When $x = 4$, $y = 4^2 - 9$, or 7. (4, 7) is on the curve and so is (−4, 7). Knowing the vertex and these two points, we can now sketch the parabola.

When they exist and if they are integers, the x-intercepts are useful in sketching a parabola. In the example, the x-intercepts can be found by substituting 0 for y:

$$0 = x^2 - 9$$
$$x^2 = 9$$
$$x = \pm 3$$

(3, 0) and (−3, 0) are two additional points on the curve.

EXERCISES 8-6

1. a) Make a table of values and graph the following on the same axes for $-5 \le x \le 5$:
   $y = x^2$ $y = x^2 + 4$ $y = x^2 + 7$
   $y = x^2 - 2$ $y = x^2 - 5$ $y = x^2 + 1$
   b) Describe the effect of various values of q on the graph of $y = x^2 + q$.
2. Which graph best represents:
   a) $y = x^2 + 3$?   b) $y = x^2 - 4$?
   c) $y = x^2 - 1$?   d) $y = x^2 + 2$?

i)

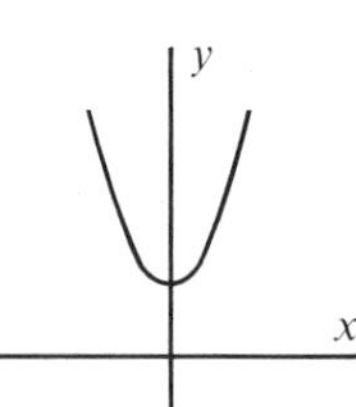

ii)

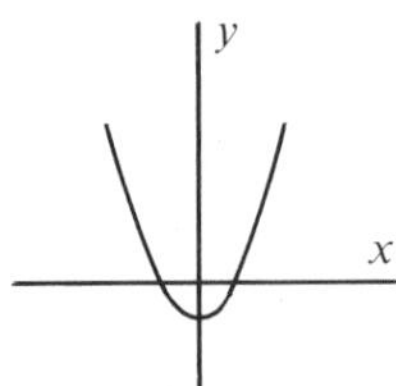

iii)

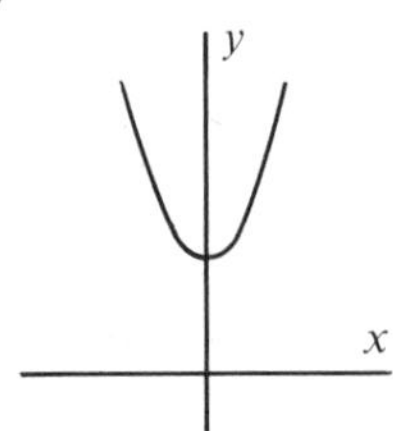

iv)

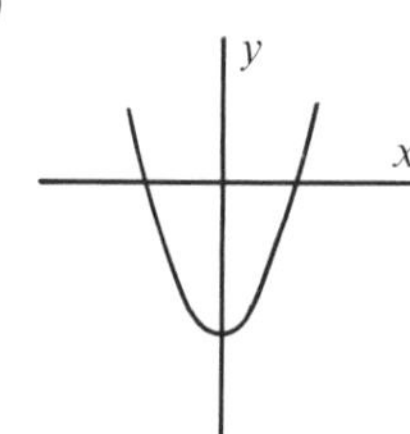

3. Write an equation that could correspond to each graph.

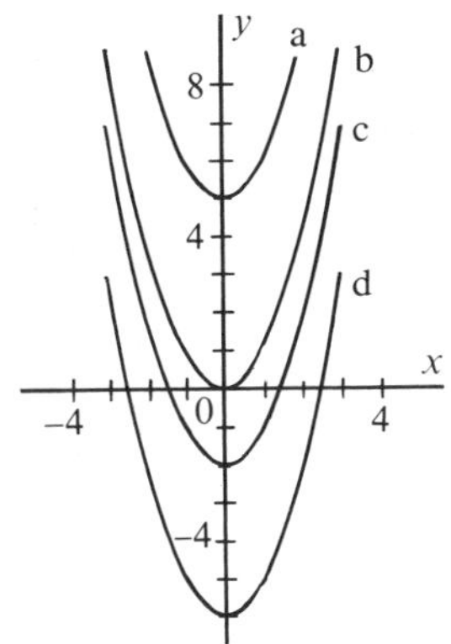

4. For each parabola state:
   i) direction of opening;
   ii) coordinates of the vertex;
   iii) y-intercept;
   iv) x-intercepts (if any).

a)

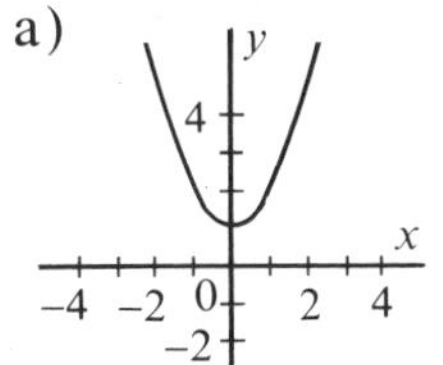

b)

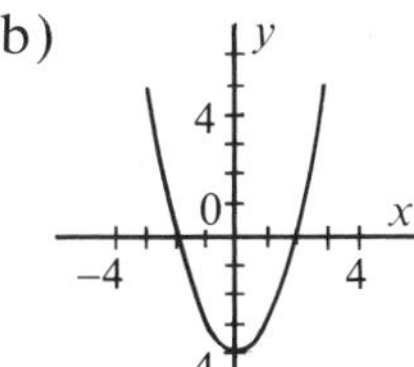

c)

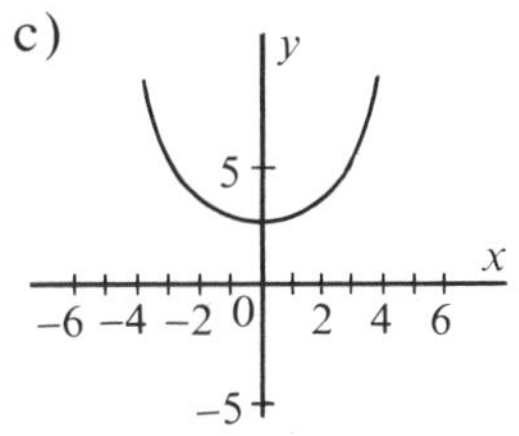

d)

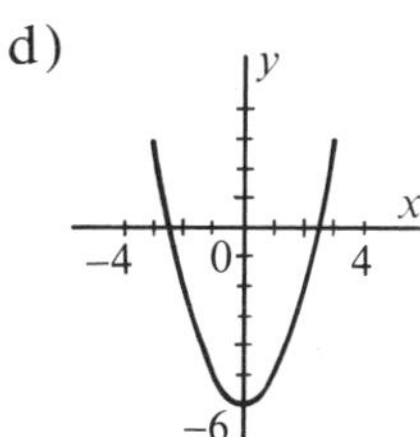

(B)

5. For each parabola state:
   i) direction of opening;
   ii) coordinates of the vertex;
   iii) y-intercept;
   iv) x-intercepts (if any).
   a) $y = x^2 + 5$
   b) $y = x^2 - 3$
   c) $y = x^2 + 2$
   d) $y = x^2 + 4$
6. Sketch on the same axes:
   a) $y = x^2 - 2, \quad y = x^2 + 1, \quad y = x^2 + 4$
   b) $y = x^2 - 1, \quad y = x^2 - 3, \quad y = x^2 + 2$
7. Find the equation of the parabola:
   a) with vertex (0, 2) through (−3, 11);
   b) with vertex (0, −9) and x-intercepts ±3;
   c) with vertex (0, 5) through (2, 9).

8-7 COMPARING THE GRAPHS OF $y = x^2$ AND $y = (x - p)^2$

In $y = x^2$, if x is replaced by $(x - p)$ we obtain $y = (x - p)^2$. To investigate the effect of this on the graph of the parabola $y = x^2$, we give different values to p and graph the resulting parabolas.
When $p = 0$, the equation becomes $y = x^2$. ...①

x	−3	−2	−1	0	1	2	3
y	9	4	1	0	1	4	9

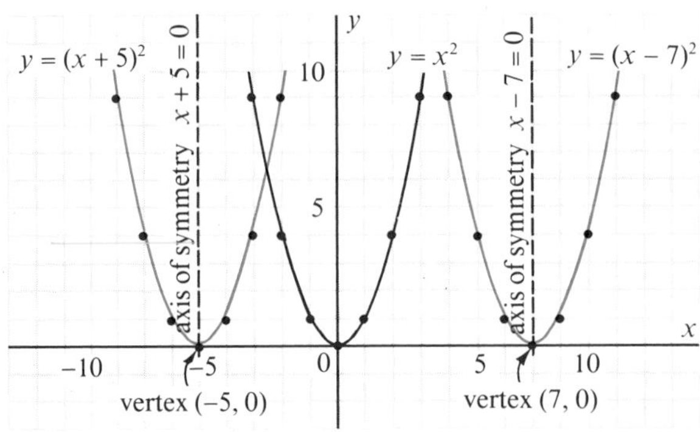

Negative values of p in $y = (x - p)^2$.

When $p = -5$, the equation becomes

$$y = (x + 5)^2$$

For convenience, we choose x-coordinates which give the same y-coordinates as those above. All are 5 *less* than the x-coordinates in ①

x	−8	−7	−6	−5	−4	−3	−2
y	9	4	1	0	1	4	9

The graph of $y = x^2$ is translated 5 units to the *left*. The vertex is $(-5, 0)$ and the line $x + 5 = 0$ is the axis of symmetry.

Positive values of p in $y = (x - p)^2$.

When $p = +7$, the equation becomes

$$y = (x - 7)^2$$

For convenience, we choose x-coordinates which give the same y-coordinates as those above. All are 7 *greater* than the x-coordinates in ①

x	4	5	6	7	8	9	10
y	9	4	1	0	1	4	9

The graph of $y = x^2$ is translated 7 units to the *right*. The vertex is $(7, 0)$ and the line $x - 7 = 0$ is the axis of symmetry.

Similar results will be found using other values of p.

$y = (x - p)^2$ represents a parabola with these properties:

Vertex:	$(p, 0)$
Axis of symmetry:	line $x - p = 0$
Direction of opening:	up

For any equation in the above form, the sign inside the brackets tells whether the parabola is moved to the left or the right of the y-axis.

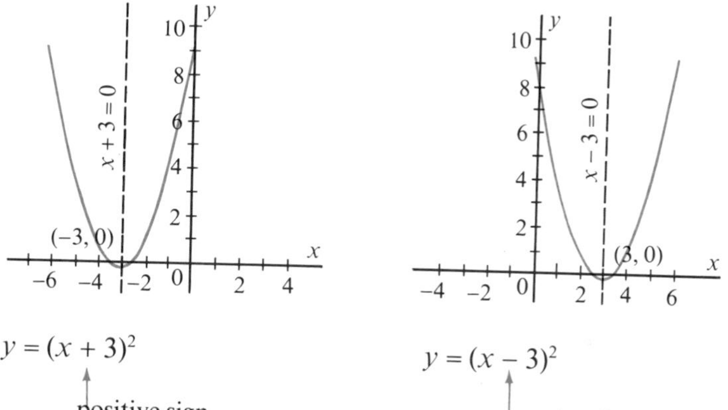

$y = (x + 3)^2$

positive sign, parabola moved left.

$y = (x - 3)^2$

negative sign, parabola moved right.

We can sketch graphs of equations in this form without using tables of values.

Example.

Graph on the same axes: a) $y = (x - 5)^2$ b) $y = (x + 7)^2$

Solution.

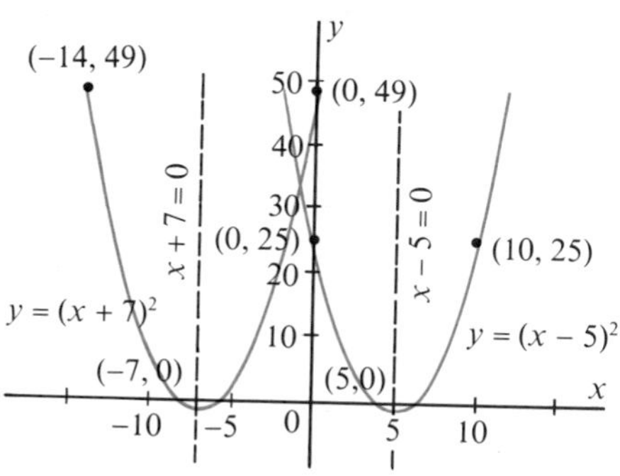

a) The parabola $y = (x - 5)^2$ has vertex (5, 0) and axis of symmetry $x - 5 = 0$. When $x = 0$, $y = 25$. Thus, one other point on the graph is (0, 25). Another point, (10, 25), is its reflection in the axis of symmetry.

b) The parabola $y = (x + 7)^2$ has vertex (−7, 0) and axis of symmetry $x + 7 = 0$. When $x = 0$, $y = 49$. Thus, two other points on the graph are (0, 49) and (−14, 49).

EXERCISES 8 - 7

(A)

1. On the same axes, sketch the graphs of:
   a) $y = x^2$, $y = (x - 2)^2$, $y = (x + 4)^2$;
   b) $y = x^2$, $y = (x + 3)^2$, $y = (x - 6)^2$;
   c) $y = x^2$, $y = (x - 4)^2$, $y = (x + 6)^2$.

2. Compare the graphs of $y = x^2$ and $y = (x - p)^2$ when:
   a) $p < 0$; b) $p > 0$.

3. Which graph best represents:
   a) $y = (x - 1)^2$? b) $y = (x + 2)^2$?
   c) $y = (x + 4)^2$? d) $y = (x - 4)^2$?

   i)

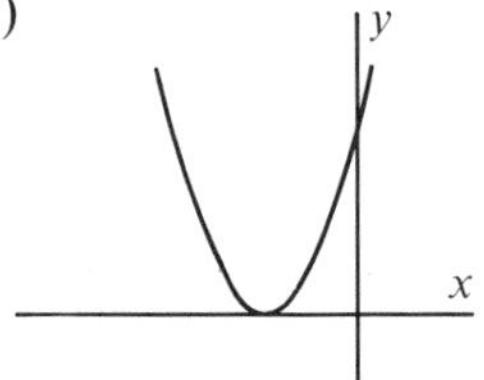

   ii)

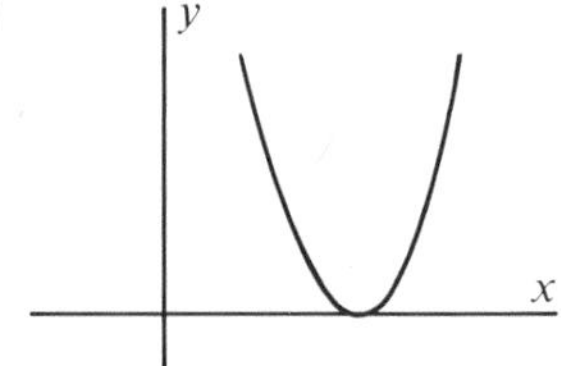

   iii)

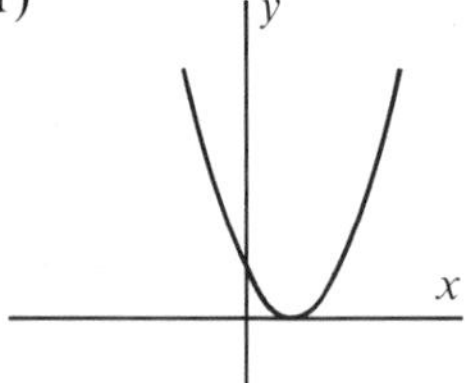

   iv)

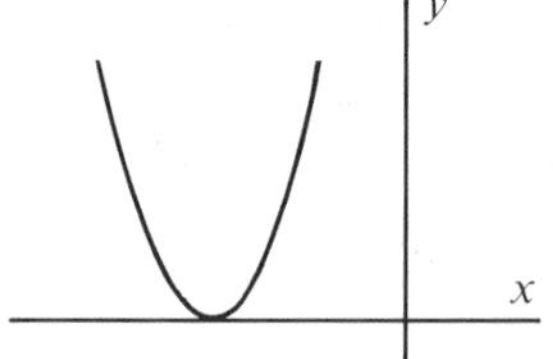

4. Write an equation that could correspond to each graph:

   a)

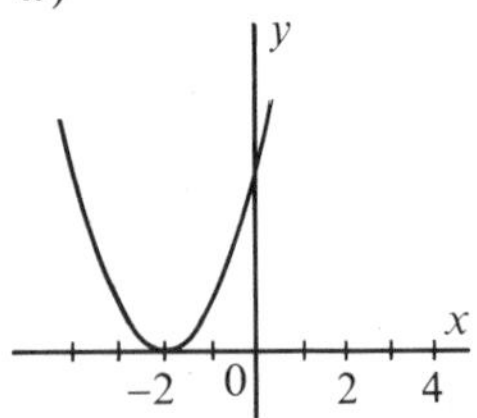

   b)

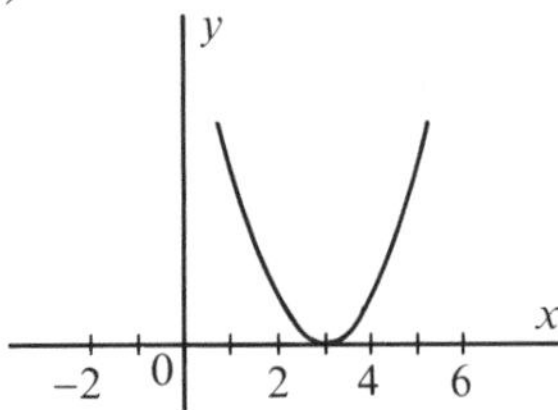

   c)

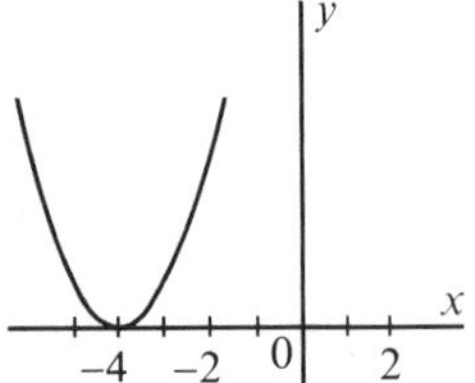

   d)

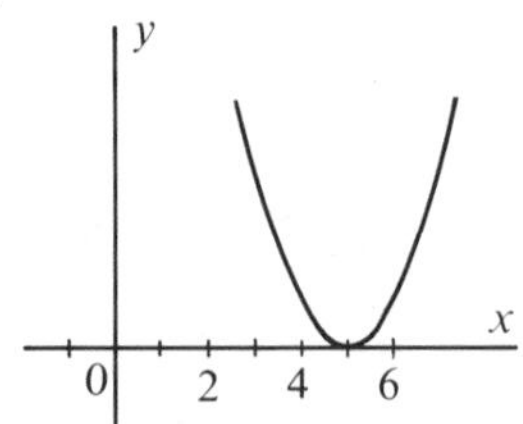

5. For each graph, state:
   i) coordinates of vertex; ii) axis of symmetry;
   iii) direction of opening; iv) y-intercept.

a)

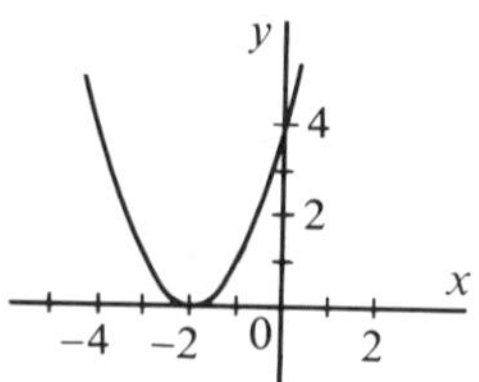

b)

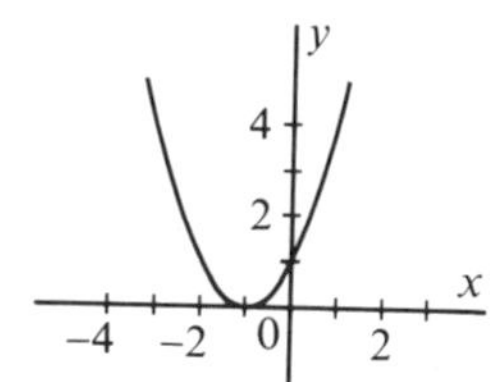

c)

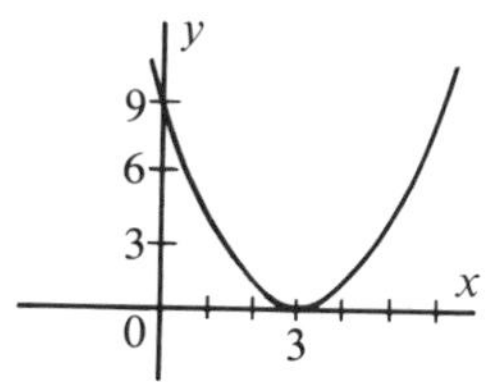

d)

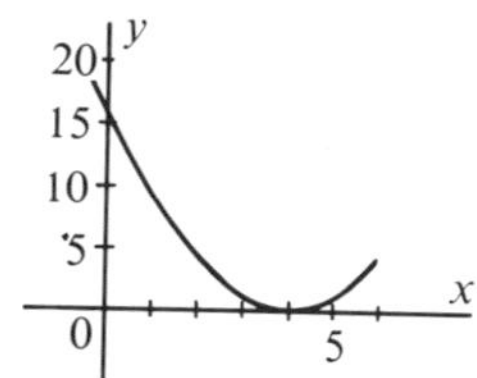

Ⓑ

6. State the equation of each parabola in Exercise 5.
7. For each parabola state:
   i) coordinates of vertex; ii) axis of symmetry;
   iii) direction of opening; iv) y-intercept.
   a) $y = (x + 3)^2$ b) $y = (x - 8)^2$
   c) $y = (x - 2)^2$ d) $y = (x + 4)^2$
8. Sketch the graphs of the parabolas in Exercise 7.
9. Sketch the graphs of:
   a) $y = (x - 2)^2$; b) $y = (x + 5)^2$;
   c) $y = (x - 6)^2$; d) $y = (x + 2)^2$.
10. Find the equation of the parabola:
    a) with vertex (4, 0), y-intercept 16;
    b) with vertex (−3, 0), y-intercept 9;
    c) with x-intercept 7, y-intercept 49, axis of symmetry $x - 7 = 0$.

Ⓒ

11. Sketch the graphs of:
    a) $y = (x + 4)^2 + 1$ and $y = (x + 4)^2 - 3$;
    b) $y = (x - 1)^2 + 2$ and $y = (x - 1)^2 - 2$;
    c) $y = x^2 + 6x + 9$ and $y = x^2 + 6x$;
    d) $y = (x - 10)^2$ and $y = (10 - x)^2$.

What conditions must be satisfied by a and c for the parabola $y = ax^2 + c$ to have x-intercepts?

COMPUTER POWER

Turtles Which Can Draw Parabolas

Some computer languages, such as LOGO, feature turtle graphics. The computer can be programmed so that a small shape on the screen, called a turtle, is moved around leaving a trail behind it. LOGO also permits a programmer to add new commands to the language to have the turtle carry out specialized tasks, such as drawing parabolas.

When this command is entered:

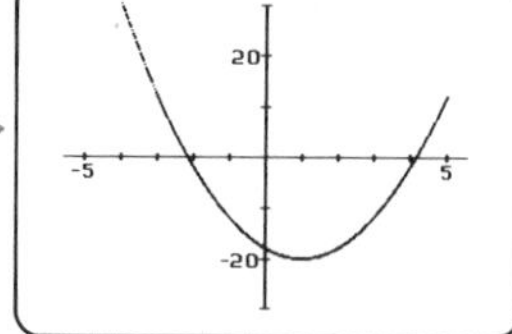

the turtle will draw this curve on the screen.

The turtle draws a parabola congruent to $y = 2x^2$, with vertex $(1, -20)$, that is, the parabola: $y = 2(x - 1)^2 - 20$.

1. Sketch the graph the turtle would draw on the command:
   a) PARABOLA 1 1 −10
   b) PARABOLA −2 1 −10
   c) PARABOLA 1 −1 0
   d) PARABOLA −3 −2 25
   e) PARABOLA 0.5 0 −15
   f) PARABOLA 0.01 0 10
2. Predict the command that would make the turtle draw:

a)

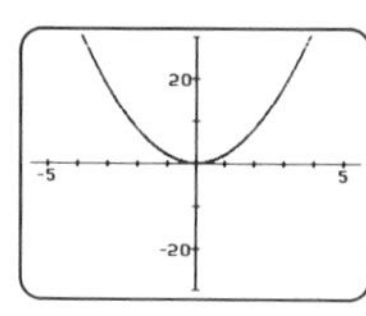

b)

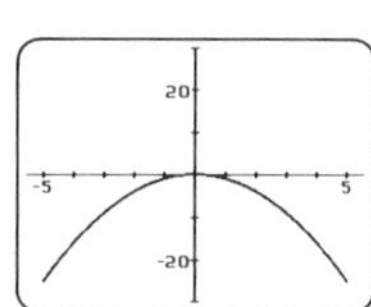

c)

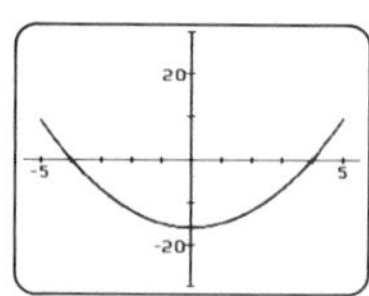

d)

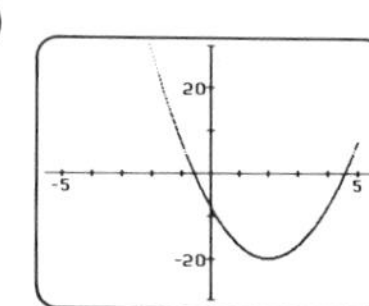

e)

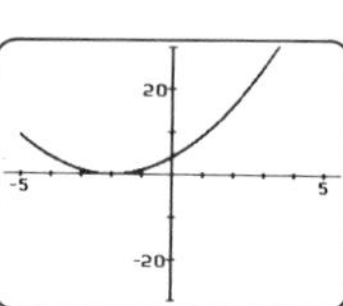

f)

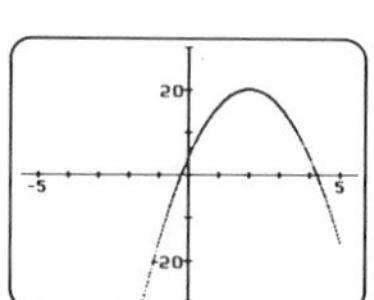

3. By giving more than one command, the turtle will draw several parabolas on the same axes.

   a) Sketch the screen for these commands:

PARABOLA	3	0	0
PARABOLA	1	0	0
PARABOLA	0.2	0	0
PARABOLA	−0.2	0	0
PARABOLA	−1	0	0
PARABOLA	−3	0	0

   b) What commands would you give the turtle for the screen to show:

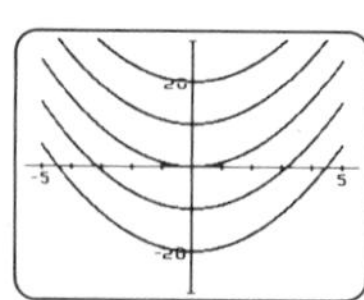

8-8 COMPARING THE GRAPHS OF $y = x^2$ AND $y = ax^2$

In this section, we investigate the effect on the graph of $y = x^2$ of multiplying x^2 by a constant a to get $y = ax^2$.

Positive values of *a*

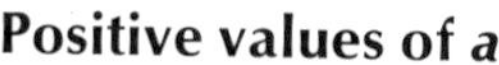

When $a = 1$, the equation becomes $y = x^2$. . . . ①

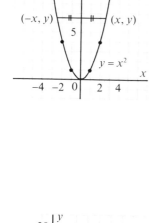

x	−3	−2	−1	0	1	2	3
y	9	4	1	0	1	4	9

The curve is a parabola with the following properties:

Axis of symmetry. The y-axis is the axis of symmetry of the curve. If (x, y) is any point on the curve, then $(-x, y)$ is also on the curve.

Vertex. The point where the axis of symmetry intersects the curve is called the vertex. For this curve the vertex is $(0, 0)$.

Direction of opening. The curve opens up.

Using the same x-coordinates as above, graph a curve of the form $y = ax^2$ for $a > 1$ and another for $a < 1$. Compare the tables of values and graphs with those for $y = x^2$.

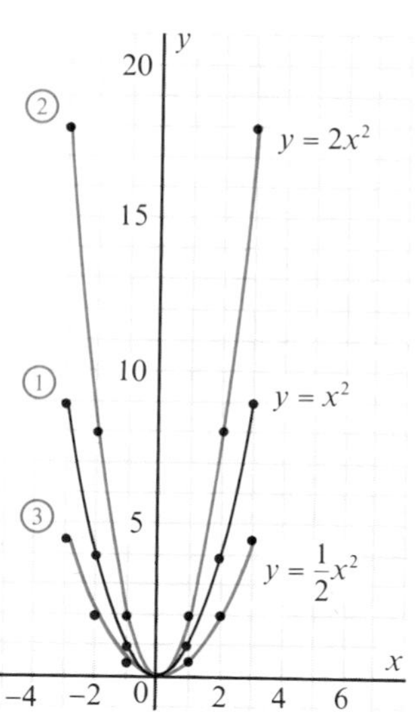

When $a = 2$, the equation becomes $y = 2x^2$. . . . ②

x	−3	−2	−1	0	1	2	3
y	18	8	2	0	2	8	18

Since the y-coordinates are all twice those of $y = x^2$, the curve is "stretched" vertically.

When $a = \frac{1}{2}$, the equation becomes $y = \frac{1}{2}x^2$. . . . ③

x	−3	−2	−1	0	1	2	3
y	4.5	2	0.5	0	0.5	2	4.5

Since the y-coordinates are half those of $y = x^2$, the curve is "compressed" vertically.

Negative values of *a*

Using the same x-coordinates as before, we graph curves of the form $y = ax^2$ for $a < 0$, and compare the tables of values and graphs with those for $y = x^2$.

When $a = -1$, the equation becomes $y = -x^2$. . . .④

x	−3	−2	−1	0	1	2	3
y	−9	−4	−1	0	−1	−4	−9

Since the y-coordinates are the opposites of those of $y = x^2$, the curve is reflected in the x-axis. It opens down.

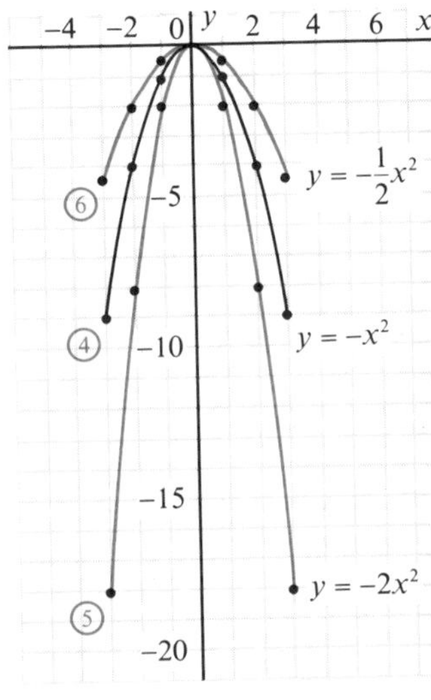

When $a = -2$, the equation becomes $y = -2x^2$. . . .⑤

x	−3	−2	−1	0	1	2	3
y	−18	−8	−2	0	−2	−8	−18

The curve $y = x^2$ is reflected in the x-axis and stretched vertically.

When $a = -\frac{1}{2}$, the equation becomes $y = -\frac{1}{2}x^2$. . . .⑥

x	−3	−2	−1	0	1	2	3
y	−4.5	−2	−0.5	0	−0.5	−2	−4.5

The curve $y = x^2$ is reflected in the x-axis and compressed vertically.

Similar results will be found using other values of a, $a \neq 0$.

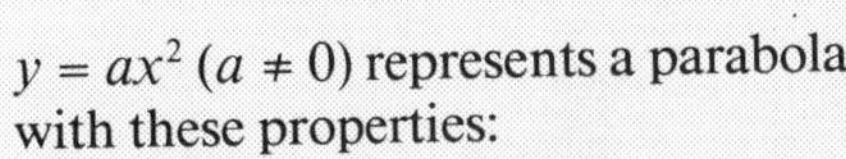

$y = ax^2$ ($a \neq 0$) represents a parabola with these properties:

Vertex: (0, 0)

Axis of symmetry: y-axis

Direction of opening: up if $a > 0$; down if $a < 0$

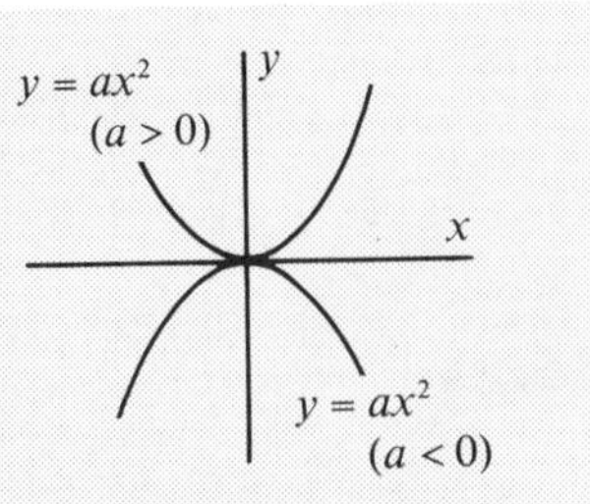

Knowing that $y = ax^2$ represents a parabola with the above properties, we can sketch graphs of equations in this form without making a table of values.

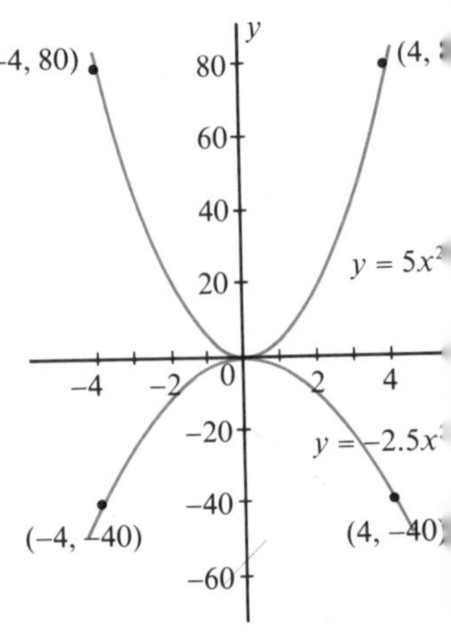

Example 1.

Graph these parabolas on the same axes:

a) $y = 5x^2$ b) $y = -2.5x^2$

Solution.

a) The parabola $y = 5x^2$ opens up. It has vertex (0, 0) and axis of symmetry the positive y-axis. A reasonable graph may be drawn by finding one other point on the curve. Substitute 4 for x in the equation: $y = 5(4)^2$, or 80. The point (4, 80) is on the curve, as is the point (−4, 80) since the y-axis is the axis of symmetry. The parabola with vertex (0, 0) and passing through (4, 80) and (−4, 80) can now be sketched.

b) The parabola $y = -2.5x^2$ opens down. It has vertex (0, 0) and axis of symmetry the negative y-axis. To find another point on the curve, substitute 4 for x in the equation: $y = -2.5(4)^2$, or -40. The parabola passes through (4, −40) and (−4, −40).

In *Example 1*, the scales on the axes were different. This is often necessary due to space requirements. While the choice of vertical scale affects the appearance of the curve, it does not change the vertex, axis of symmetry, or direction of opening.

Example 2.

Find the equation of the parabola through (6, 27) which has the y-axis as its axis of symmetry and (0, 0) as its vertex, and sketch the graph.

Solution.

Let the equation of the parabola be $y = ax^2$. Since (6, 27) lies on the curve, its coordinates satisfy the equation. That is,

$$27 = a(6)^2$$

$$a = \frac{27}{36}, \text{ or } \frac{3}{4}$$

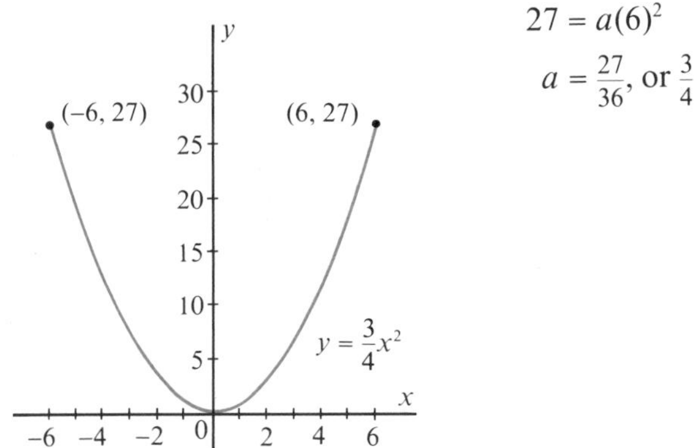

The equation of the parabola is $y = \frac{3}{4}x^2$. The parabola is sketched using the fact that it passes through (0, 0), (6, 27), and (−6, 27) since the y-axis is the axis of symmetry.

EXERCISES 8-8

Ⓐ

1. a) Make a table of values and graph the following equations on the same axes for $-5 \leq x \leq 5$:

$y = 3x^2$ $\quad y = \frac{1}{2}x^2$ $\quad y = -x^2$

$y = x^2$ $\quad y = -\frac{1}{3}x^2$ $\quad y = -4x^2$

b) Describe the effect on the graph of $y = ax^2$ as the value of a varies.

2. Which graph represents:

   a) $y = 5x^2$? b) $y = 0.2x^2$?

   c) $y = -1.5x^2$? d) $y = -3x^2$?

   i)

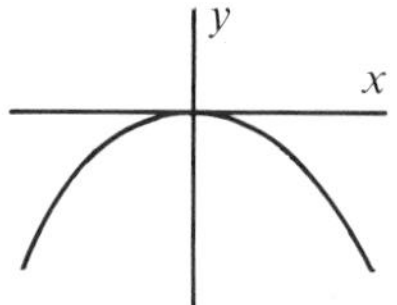

   ii)

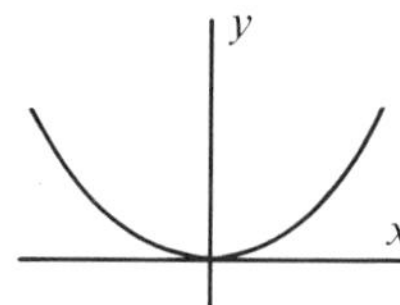

   iii)

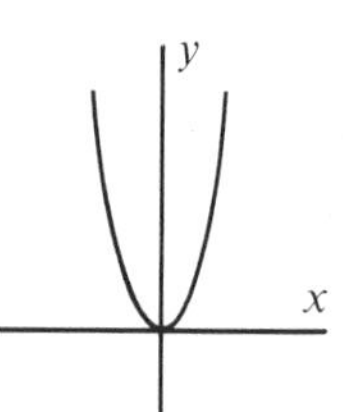

   iv)

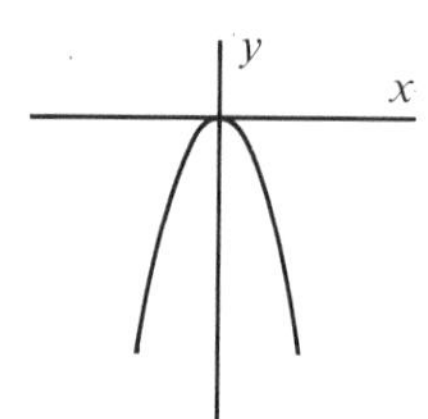

(B)

3. Sketch the parabolas on the same axes:

   a) $y = x^2$, $y = 3x^2$, $y = \frac{1}{2}x^2$

   b) $y = x^2$, $y = -x^2$, $y = 5x^2$, $y = -3x^2$

   c) $y = 2x^2$, $y = \frac{3}{4}x^2$, $y = -1.5x^2$, $y = -4x^2$

   d) $y = -2x^2$, $y = \frac{1}{4}x^2$, $y = 2.5x^2$, $y = -\frac{1}{2}x^2$

4. Find the equation of the parabola with vertex (0, 0) which passes through:

   a) (3, 18); b) (4, –16); c) (6, –9); d) (2, 24).

5. Find the equation of the parabola with vertex (0, 0) which passes through:

   a) (2, –10); b) (3, 5); c) $(\frac{3}{2}, \frac{1}{3})$; d) $(-\sqrt{2}, -6)$.

(C)

6. The line $3x - y - 3 = 0$ is tangent to a parabola which has vertex (0, 0) and axis of symmetry the y-axis. Find the equation of the parabola.

If the coordinates of any poin are given, is it always possibl to find the equation of a parabola through the point with vertex (0, 0) and axis of symmetry the y-axis?

8-9 GRAPHING $y = a(x - p)^2 + q$

In the last three sections we investigated the effect on the graph of $y = x^2$ of the constants a, p, and q in the equations: $y = ax^2$, $y = x^2 + q$, and $y = (x - p)^2$. We now investigate the effect on the graph when these three constants are combined in the same equation: $y = a(x - p)^2 + q$

y
$y = 2(x - 4)^2 + 3$
$y = (x - 4)^2 + 3$
axis of symmetry $x - 4 = 0$
vertex (4, 3)
x
20 15 10 5 0 2 4 6 8

Example 1.

Graph: a) $y = (x - 4)^2 + 3$; b) $y = 2(x - 4)^2 + 3$.

Solution.

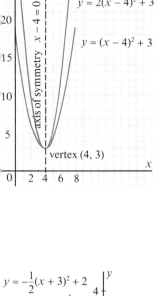

a) $y = (x - 4)^2 + 3$ represents a parabola congruent to $y = x^2$ which has been translated 4 units to the right and 3 units up from the position of $y = x^2$. The vertex is (4, 3) and the line $x - 4 = 0$ is the axis of symmetry.

b) $y = 2(x - 4)^2 + 3$ is similar to the equation in (a). The vertex is (4, 3) and the axis of symmetry is the line $x - 4 = 0$. The only difference is that this parabola is stretched vertically. It is congruent to $y = 2x^2$.

Example 2.

Sketch the graph of $y = -\frac{1}{2}(x + 3)^2 + 2$, and show on the graph the coordinates of the vertex, the equation of the axis of symmetry, and the coordinates of two points other than the vertex.

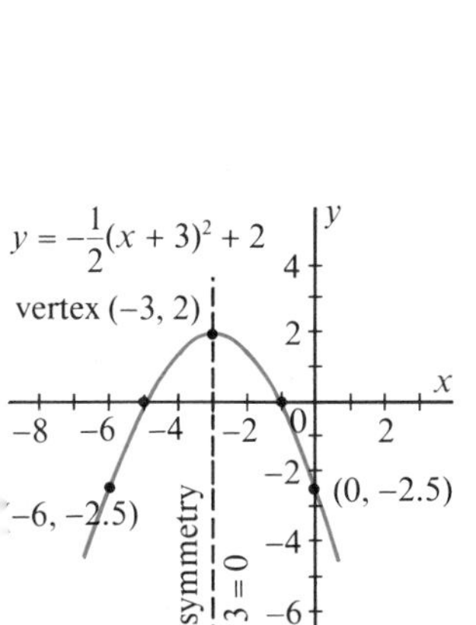

Solution.

The coordinates of the vertex are (−3, 2). The equation of the axis of symmetry is $x + 3 = 0$. The parabola opens down and is compressed vertically. It is congruent to $y = -\frac{1}{2}x^2$. When $x = 0$,

$y = -\frac{1}{2}(0 - 3)^2 + 2$, or −2.5. (0, −2.5) is a point on the graph. Since $x + 3 = 0$ is the axis of symmetry, (−6, −2.5) is also on the graph.

The above examples suggest that in the equation $y = a(x - p)^2 + q$, the constants a, p, and q have the following geometric meaning:

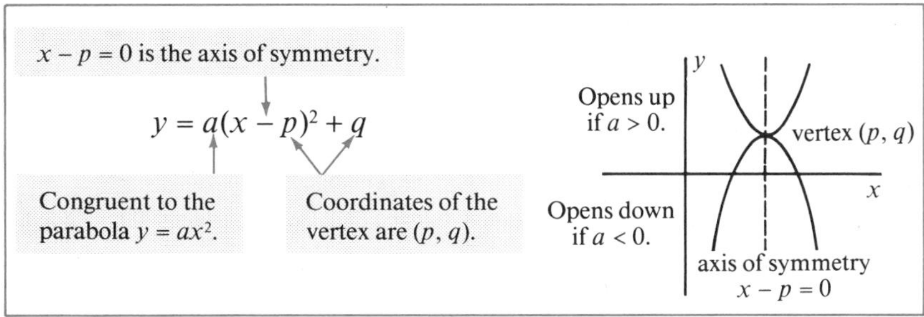

$x - p = 0$ is the axis of symmetry.
$y = a(x - p)^2 + q$
Congruent to the parabola $y = ax^2$.
Coordinates of the vertex are (p, q).
Opens up if $a > 0$.
Opens down if $a < 0$.
y
x
vertex (p, q)
axis of symmetry
$x - p = 0$

EXERCISES 8-9

(A)

1. Which graph best represents:

   a) $y = (x + 3)^2 + 1$?
   b) $y = -2(x + 4)^2 + 3$?
   c) $y = \frac{1}{2}(x - 2)^2 - 5$?
   d) $y = -(x - 3)^2 + 2$?

i)

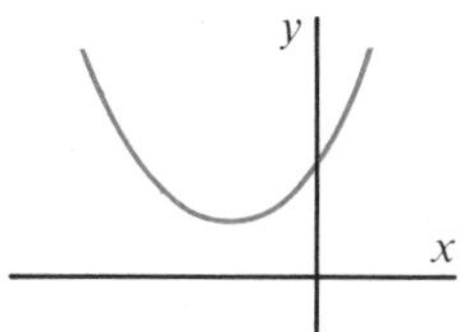

ii)

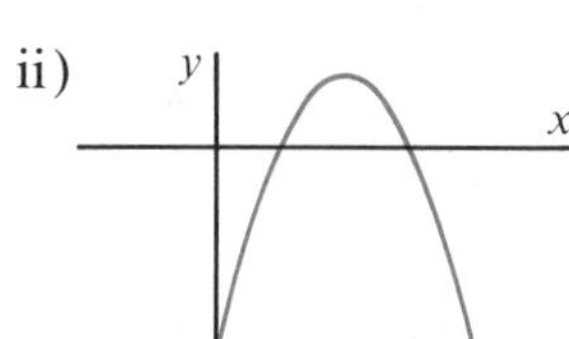

iii)

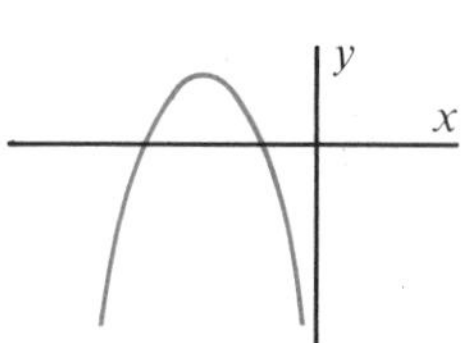

iv)

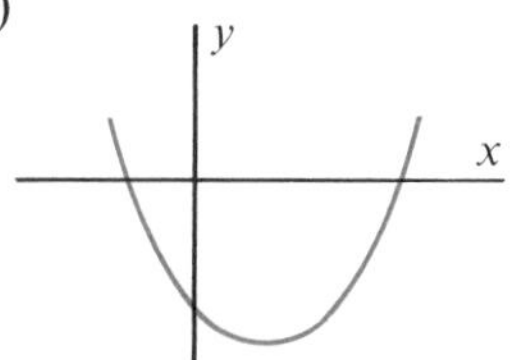

2. Sketch the graphs on the same axes:

   a) $y = (x - 5)^2 + 4$
   $y = (x - 5)^2 + 2$
   $y = (x - 5)^2$
   $y = (x - 5)^2 - 2$
   $y = (x - 5)^2 - 4$

   b) $y = (x - 5)^2 + 4$
   $y = (x - 3)^2 + 4$
   $y = (x - 1)^2 + 4$
   $y = (x + 1)^2 + 4$
   $y = (x + 3)^2 + 4$
   $y = (x + 5)^2 + 4$

   c) $y = (x - 5)^2 + 4$
   $y = 3(x - 5)^2 + 4$
   $y = \frac{1}{2}(x - 5)^2 + 4$
   $y = -\frac{1}{2}(x - 5)^2 + 4$
   $y = -(x - 5)^2 + 4$
   $y = -3(x - 5)^2 + 4$

3. For each graph state:

   i) coordinates of vertex;
   ii) axis of symmetry;
   iii) y-intercept;
   iv) x-intercepts, if any.

a)

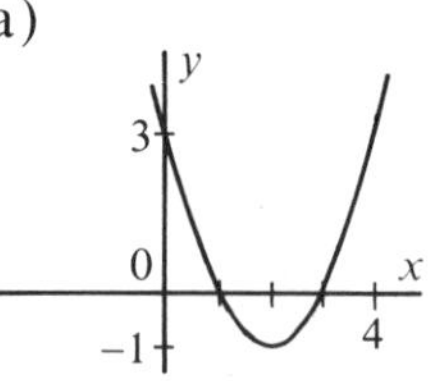

b)

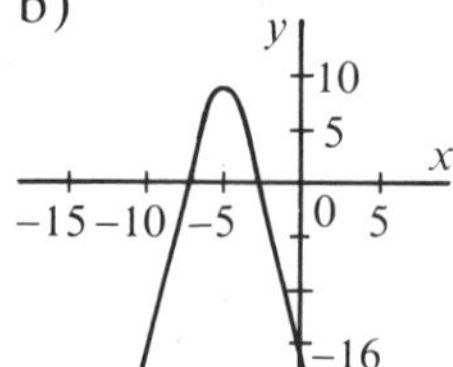

c)

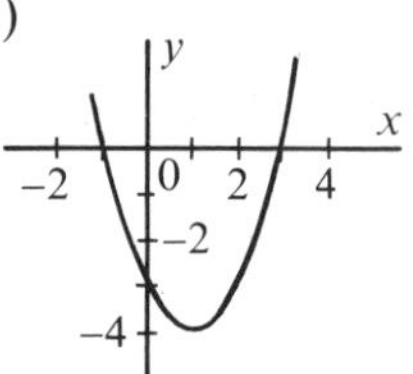

d)

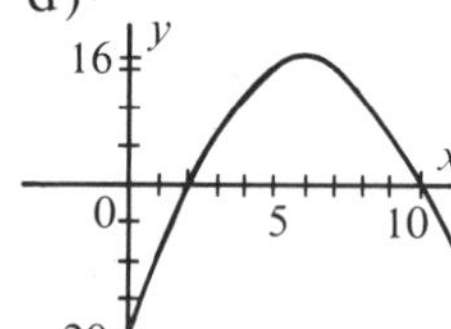

Ⓑ

4. Write the equations of the parabolas in Exercise 3.

5. For each parabola, state:

   i) coordinates of vertex; ii) axis of symmetry;
   iii) y-intercept; iv) x-intercepts, if any.

   a) $y = (x-5)^2 + 2$ b) $y = 2(x+3)^2 - 8$

   c) $y = -4(x+1)^2 + 4$ d) $y = \frac{1}{2}(x-2)^2 - 8$

6. Sketch the graphs of the functions in Exercise 5.

7. On a sketch of the graph of each parabola, show:

   i) coordinates of vertex; ii) equation of axis of symmetry;
   iii) coordinates of two points on the graph.

   a) $y = (x+2)^2 - 5$ b) $y = -(x-3)^2 + 2$

   c) $y = -\frac{1}{2}(x-4)^2 - 1$ d) $y = 2(x+1)^2 + 4$

   e) $y = -2(x-1)^2 + 3$ f) $y = 4(x-5)^2 - 10$

8. Sketch the graph of:

   a) $k = 2(l-3)^2 - 1$; b) $r = -2(t+3)^2 + 5$;

   c) $m = \frac{1}{2}(n-4)^2 - 3$; d) $p = 3(q-5)^2 + 1$;

   e) $f = -(g+2.5)^2 + 3$; f) $u = -0.2(v+2)^2 - 1.5$.

9. Write the equation of the parabola:

   a) with vertex (4, −1), that opens up, and is congruent to $y = 2x^2$;

   b) with vertex (−2, 3), that opens down, and is congruent to $y = \frac{1}{3}x^2$;

   c) with vertex (−3, 2), that opens down, and is congruent to $y = \frac{1}{2}x^2$;

   d) with vertex (3, −4), x–intercepts 1 and 5.

10. Write the equation of the parabola:

    a) with vertex (3, −1), x–intercepts 2 and 4;
    b) with vertex (−1, 4), y–intercept 2;
    c) with vertex (2, −27), y–intercept −15.

Ⓒ

11. Describe what happens to the graph of:

    a) $y = a(x-4)^2 + 3$ as a varies;
    b) $y = 2(x-p)^2 + 3$ as p varies;
    c) $y = 2(x-4)^2 + q$ as q varies.

12. Find the equation of the parabola, with axis of symmetry the y–axis, which passes through:

    a) (2, 9) and (3, 14); b) (−2, 1) and (4, −5).

MATHEMATICS PROJECT

Using Differences to Graph Parabolas

There is a pattern in the table of values for $y = x^2$ which is useful when graphing parabolas.

x	y	Differences
0	0	
1	1	1
2	4	3
3	9	5
4	16	7

The differences in the y–coordinates are consecutive odd numbers.

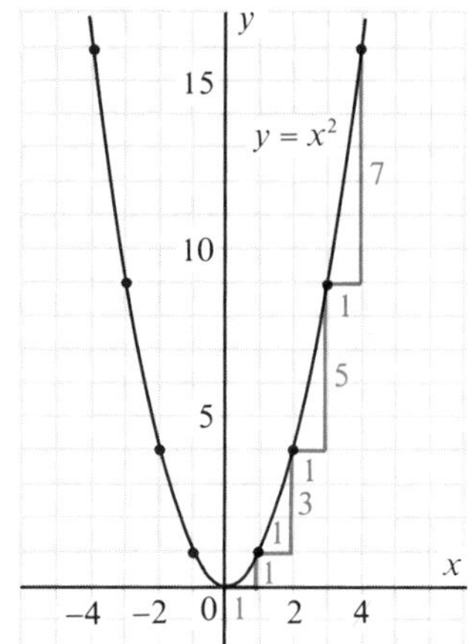

Starting at the vertex, points on the parabola can be found by moving: 1 right and 1 up;
then 1 right and 3 up;
then 1 right and 5 up;
and so on.

Other points are obtained by reflecting, in the axis of symmetry, those already found, or by repeating the above steps but moving 1 left each time.

This method can be used for any parabola which is congruent to $y = x^2$, and it can be modified to apply to parabolas congruent to $y = 2x^2$, $y = 3x^2$, $y = \frac{1}{2}x^2$, and so on.

1. Use the above method to graph:

a) $y = (x - 3)^2 + 5$; b) $y = (x + 1)^2 - 7$; c) $y = -(x - 2)^2 + 3$

2. Modify the above method to graph:

a) $y = 2x^2$; b) $y = 3x^2$;

c) $y = \frac{1}{2}x^2$ d) $y = 2(x - 4)^2 - 6$

e) $y = 3(x + 2)^2 - 10$; f) $y = -\frac{1}{2}(x + 2)^2 + 5$

8-10 GRAPHING $y = ax^2 + bx + c$

In the previous section, we developed a method of sketching the graph of an equation such as $y = 2(x - 3)^2 - 7$ using the geometric meaning of the three constants in the equation. In applications of quadratic functions, however, an equation is more likely to be encountered in the form: $y = 2x^2 - 12x + 11$. In this form, the constants useful in drawing the graph are not obvious. To obtain these constants, we use the method of *completing the square*.

Example 1.

Write $y = 2x^2 - 12x + 11$ in the form $y = a(x - p)^2 + q$, and sketch the graph.

Solution.

Step 1. Remove 2 as a common factor from the first two terms:

$$y = 2(x^2 - 6x) + 11$$

Step 2. Add and subtract the square of $\frac{1}{2}(-6)$ inside the brackets:

$$y = 2(x^2 - 6x + 9 - 9) + 11$$

Step 3. Remove the last term from the brackets and combine with the constant term:

$$y = 2(x^2 - 6x + 9) - 18 + 11$$
$$= 2(x^2 - 6x + 9) - 7$$

Step 4. Factor the expression in the brackets as a complete square:

$$y = 2(x - 3)^2 - 7$$

By inspection of this equation:
The coordinates of the vertex are $(3, -7)$. The equation of the axis of symmetry is $x - 3 = 0$. When $x = 0$, $y = 2(0)^2 - 12(0) + 11$, or 11. The y-intercept is 11. Since $x - 3 = 0$ is the axis of symmetry, $(6, 11)$ is also on the graph. Knowing the coordinates of the vertex, the point corresponding to the y-intercept and its reflection in the axis of symmetry, we can now sketch the curve.

To graph $y = ax^2 + bx + c$:
- Complete the square and write the equation in the form $y = a(x - p)^2 + q$.
- Draw the axis of symmetry $x - p = 0$.
- Draw a curve through the three points:
  1. the vertex (p, q);
  2. the point $(0, c)$ corresponding to the y-intercept;
  3. the reflection of $(0, c)$ in the axis of symmetry.

ompare the method of completing the square for the uadratic function:

$$y = 2x^2 + 8x - 9$$

ith the method of completing the square for the quadtic equation:

$$2x^2 + 8x - 9 = 0.$$

what ways are they the me? In what ways are they ifferent?

it possible to use the same ethod for both?

EXERCISES 8-10

1. Write in the form $y = a(x - p)^2 + q$:

   a) $y = x^2 - 6x + 8$ b) $y = x^2 + 10x + 14$
   c) $y = 2x^2 + 4x + 7$ d) $y = -2x^2 + 4x + 5$
   e) $y = 3x^2 - 24x + 40$ f) $y = -5x^2 - 20x - 30$

2. Sketch the graphs of the parabolas in Exercise 1.

3. Sketch each parabola showing:
   i) coordinates of the vertex;
   ii) equation of axis of symmetry;
   iii) coordinates of two other points on the graph.

   a) $y = x^2 - 6x + 10$ b) $y = 2x^2 + 8x + 7$
   c) $y = -x^2 + 10x - 13$ d) $r = 3t^2 - 6t + 8$
   e) $m = -4n^2 - 24n - 20$ f) $u = -2v^2 - 16v - 35$

(B)

4. Sketch each parabola showing:
   i) coordinates of the vertex;
   ii) equation of axis of symmetry;
   iii) coordinates of two other points on the graph.

   a) $y = \frac{1}{2}x^2 - 2x + 7$ b) $r = 4t^2 + 12t - 5$
   c) $k = -2j^2 + 14j - 12$ d) $y = 3x^2 - 4x - 6$
   e) $u = -4v^2 + 10v - 7$

5. Sketch each parabola showing:
   i) y-intercept;
   ii) coordinates of vertex;
   iii) coordinates of two other points on the graph.

   a) $y = 2x^2 - 5x - 3$ b) $y = 2x^2 - 9x - 18$
   c) $y = 0.4x^2 + 2x + 2.5$ d) $y = -2x^2 + 5x$
   e) $y = 3x^2 - 14x + 8$

6. a) Write $y = ax^2 + bx + c$ in the form: $y = a(x - p)^2 + q$.
   b) State the coordinates of the vertex, the axis of symmetry, and the y-intercept.

MATHEMATICS
PROJECT

Investigating b in: $y = ax^2 + bx + c$

In a quadratic function such as $y = x^2 + 4x + 3$, each of the constants has a geometric meaning. You already know two of them:

$$y = x^2 + 4x + 3$$

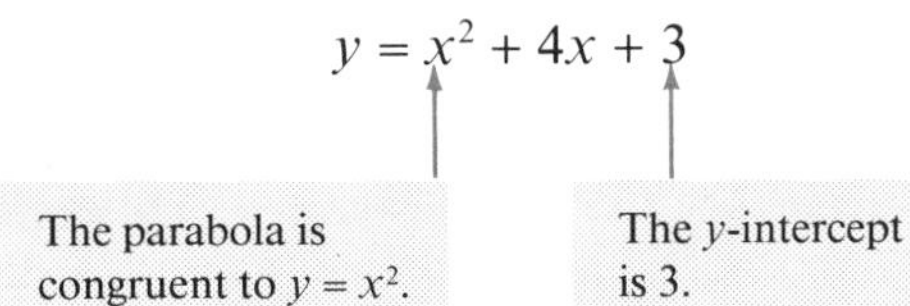
The parabola is congruent to $y = x^2$.
The y-intercept is 3.

The purpose of this project is to investigate the meaning of the coefficient of the linear term.

1. Use a calculator or computer to make tables of values and then graph the following parabolas on the same axes:

   a) $y = x^2 + 6x + 3$
   b) $y = x^2 + 4x + 3$
   c) $y = x^2 + 2x + 3$
   d) $y = x^2 + 3$
   e) $y = x^2 - 2x + 3$
   f) $y = x^2 - 4x + 3$
   g) $y = x^2 - 6x + 3$

2. Use the above results to describe the effect of varying the value of b in $y = x^2 + bx + 3$.
3. On the graph drawn for 1., what pattern is formed by the vertices of the parabolas?
4. Would the pattern be true for the general parabola $y = ax^2 + bx + c$, where a and c are constant and b varies?
5. Write a report of your findings.

8-11 MAXIMUM AND MINIMUM VALUES OF A QUADRATIC FUNCTION

When a quadratic function is graphed, the vertex is important because it is either the highest or lowest point on the curve. Consider these examples:

The parabola $y = 2(x - 3)^2 + 4$ has vertex (3,4) and opens up.

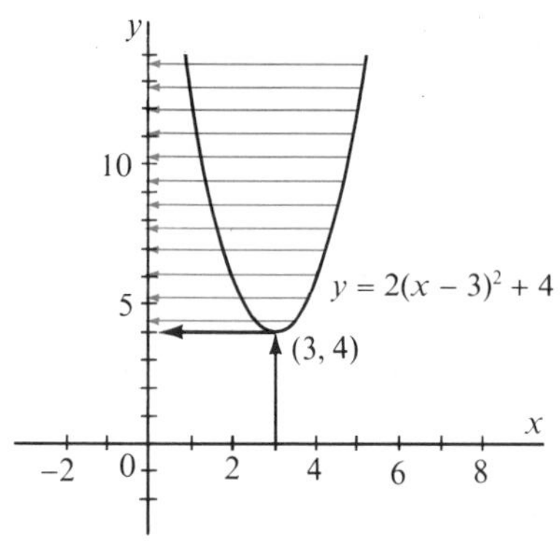

The graph shows that the values of y for points on the curve are never less than 4. That is, the function:

$$f(x) = 2(x - 3)^2 + 4$$

has a *minimum* value of 4 which occurs when $x = 3$.

The parabola $y = -2(x - 3)^2 + 4$ has vertex (3, 4) and opens down.

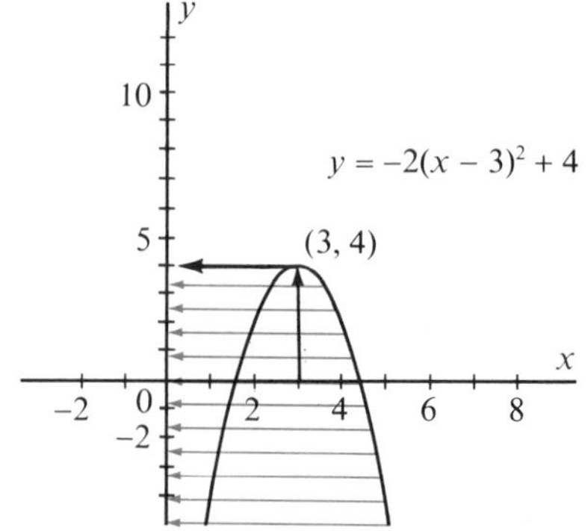

The graph shows that the values of y for points on the curve are never greater than 4. That is, the function:

$$f(x) = -2(x - 3)^2 + 4$$

has a *maximum* value of 4 which occurs when $x = 3$.

These characteristics of a quadratic function can be obtained from its equation without drawing its graph.

Positive—curve opens up.
There is a minimum value.

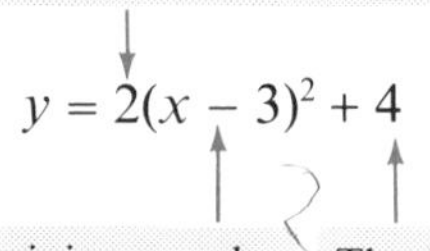

The minimum value occurs when $x - 3 = 0$, or $x = 3$.

The minimum value is 4.

Negative—curve opens down.
There is a maximum value.

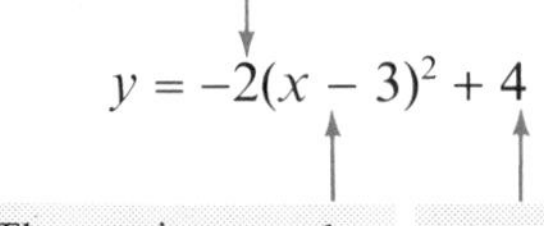

The maximum value occurs when $x - 3 = 0$, or $x = 3$.

The maximum value is 4.

Example 1.

Given: $y = -4x^2 - 12x + 5$

a) Find the maximum or minimum value of y and state which it is.

b) For what value of x does the maximum or minimum occur?

Solution.

a) Rearrange the expression by completing the square:

$$\begin{aligned} y &= -4x^2 - 12x + 5 \\ &= -4(x^2 + 3x) + 5 \\ &= -4\left(x^2 + 3x + \tfrac{9}{4} - \tfrac{9}{4}\right) + 5 \\ &= -4\left(x^2 + 3x + \tfrac{9}{4}\right) + 9 + 5 \\ &= -4\left(x + \tfrac{3}{2}\right)^2 + 14 \end{aligned}$$

The maximum value of y is 14.

b) The maximum value occurs when $x + \frac{3}{2} = 0$, or $x = -\frac{3}{2}$.

Many applications of quadratic functions involve finding the maximum or minimum value.

Example 2.

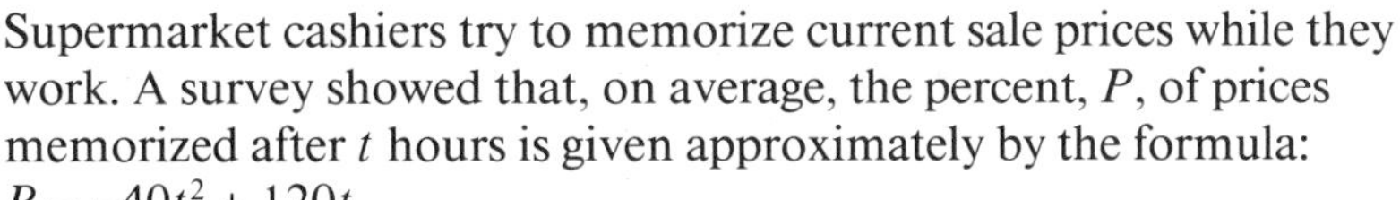

Supermarket cashiers try to memorize current sale prices while they work. A survey showed that, on average, the percent, P, of prices memorized after t hours is given approximately by the formula: $P = -40t^2 + 120t$.

a) What is the greatest percent of prices memorized?

b) How long does it take to memorize them?

Solution.

a) Since the coefficient of t^2 is negative, there is a maximum percent. To find this percent, rearrange the expression for P by completing the square:

$$\begin{aligned} P &= -40t^2 + 120t \\ &= -40(t^2 - 3t) \\ &= -40\left(t^2 - 3t + \tfrac{9}{4} - \tfrac{9}{4}\right) \\ &= -40\left(t^2 - 3t + \tfrac{9}{4}\right) + 90 \\ &= -40\left(t - \tfrac{3}{2}\right)^2 + 90 \end{aligned}$$

The greatest percent of prices memorized is 90%.

b) It takes $\frac{3}{2}$ h, or 1.5 h, to memorize 90% of the prices.

EXERCISES 8-11

1. Using the word maximum or minimum and data from the graph, complete this sentence: "The. . .value of y is. . .when $x =$. . ."

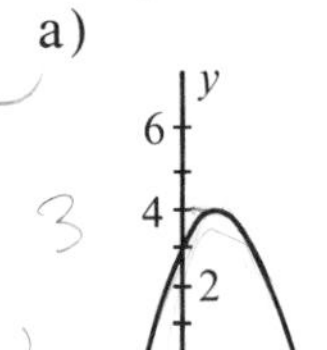

a)

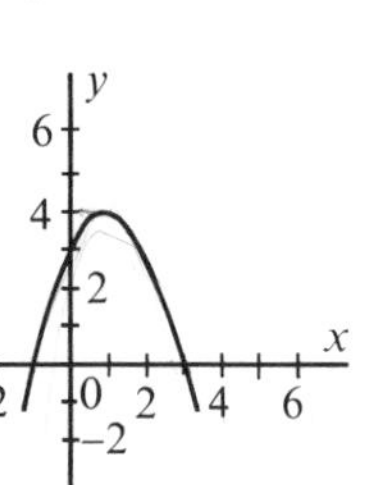

b)

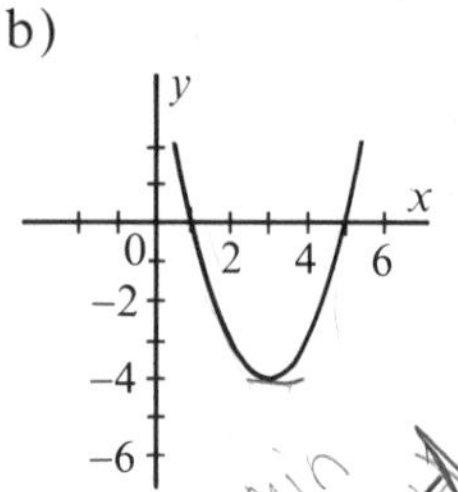

c)

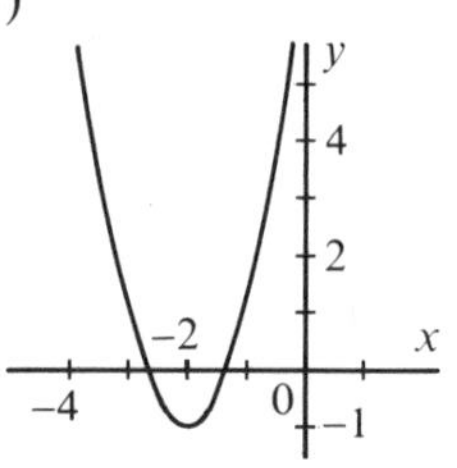

d)

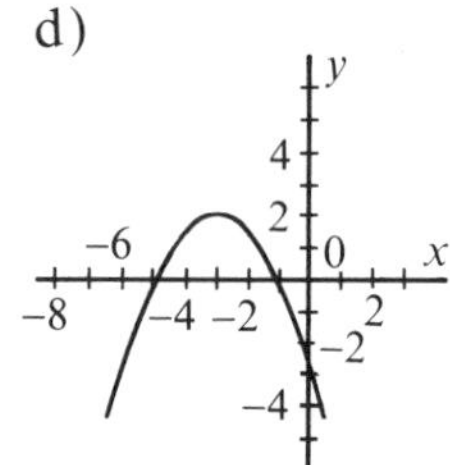

e)

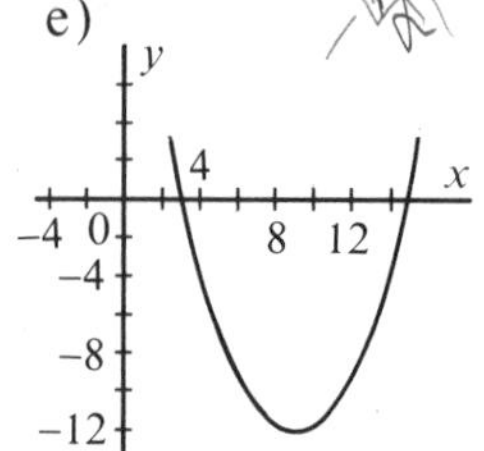

f)

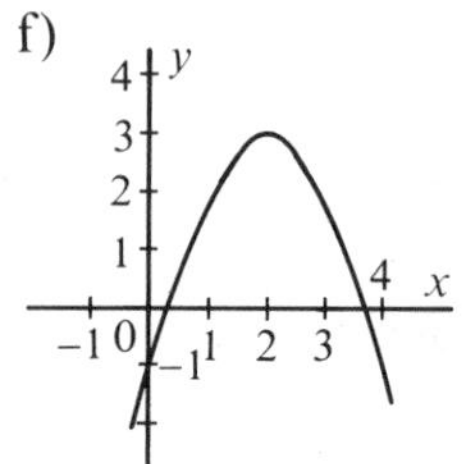

2. For each of the following state:
   i) the maximum or minimum value of y;
   ii) whether it is a maximum or minimum;
   iii) the value of x when it occurs.

   a) $y = (x - 3)^2 + 5$ b) $y = 2(x + 1)^2 - 3$
   c) $y = -2(x - 1)^2 + 4$ d) $y = -(x + 2)^2 - 6$
   e) $y = 0.5x^2 - 9$ f) $y = 7 - 2x^2$

3. Does the function have a maximum value? If it has, for what value of x does it occur?

   a) $y = -2(x + 5)^2 - 8$ b) $f(x) = \frac{1}{4}(x - 2)^2 - 9$
   c) $y = -0.5(x - 3)^2 + 7.5$ d) $y = 5 - 3x^2$
   e) $f(x) = 3\left(x - \frac{5}{2}\right)^2 + \frac{17}{2}$ f) $f(x) = -(x + 4)^2 - 19$

4. a) Write in the form $y = a(x - p)^2 + q$:
   i) $y = 2x^2 - 8x + 15$ ii) $y = 3x^2 + 12x - 7$
   iii) $y = x^2 - 6x + 7$ iv) $y = -2x^2 + 6x + 11$
   v) $y = -x^2 - 3x - 3$ vi) $y = 1.5x^2 - 9x + 10$

   b) For each function in (a), state:
   i) the maximum or minimum value;
   ii) the value of x for which the maximum or minimum occurs.

5. On a forward somersault dive, Greg's height, h, in metres, above the water is given approximately by: $h = -5t^2 + 6t + 3$, where t is the time in seconds after he leaves the board.
   a) Find Greg's maximum height above the water.
   b) How long does it take him to reach the maximum height?
   c) How long is it before he enters the water?
   d) How high is the board above the water?

B

6. The power, P, in watts, supplied to a circuit by a 9 V (volt) battery is given by the formula: $P = 9I - 0.5I^2$, where I is the current in amperes.
   a) For what value of the current will the power be a maximum?
   b) What is the maximum power?
7. A ball thrown vertically with a velocity of 18 m/s is h metres above the ground after t seconds, where $h = -5t^2 + 18t$. What is the maximum height of the ball, and when does it reach that height?
8. A ball is thrown into the air from the balcony of an apartment building and falls to the ground. The height, h, in metres, of the ball relative to the ground t seconds after being thrown is given by: $h = -5t^2 + 10t + 35$.
   a) Find the maximum height of the ball above the ground.
   b) How long does it take the ball to reach the maximum height?
   c) After how many seconds does the ball hit the ground?
   d) How high is the balcony above the ground?
   e) What would be the equation if heights were measured relative to the balcony rather than to the ground?
9. The rate of fuel consumption of an aircraft, f, in litres per hour, is given approximately by: $f = 0.01v^2 - 5v + 1000$, where v is the speed in kilometres per hour. At what speed is the rate of fuel consumption a minimum?
10. The approximate cost, C, in dollars, of driving a car from Calgary to Winnipeg is given as a function of the average speed, v, in kilometres per hour, by:
$$C = 0.02v^2 - 2.0v + 88, \text{ where } 20 \leq v \leq 120.$$
    a) Sketch a graph showing C as a function of v.
    b) What is the most economical speed for the trip?
    c) State the domain and range of the function.
11. The net income, I, in dollars, from a projected office building s storeys high is given by: $I = -40\ 000s^2 + 4\ 000\ 000s - 1\ 000\ 000$.
    a) How many storeys should the building have to maximize the income?
    b) What is the maximum income?

Ⓒ

12. A projectile is launched from a platform, and its height, h, in metres, is given as a function of the elapsed time, t, in seconds by: $h = -4.9t^2 + 180t + 2$. Draw a graph showing h as a function of t, and use it to estimate:
    a) the maximum height of the projectile;
    b) the time required for the projectile to reach its maximum height;
    c) the time required for the projectile to reach the ground.
13. If $f(x) = ax^2 + bx + c$ has a minimum value 0, what conditions must be satisfied by a, b, and c?

INVESTIGATE

Graph the parabola and the line on the same axes:

$y = x^2 - 4x + 3$

$y = -4x + 3$

Compare the graphs. Is there any geometric relation between the parabola and the line?

Determine if the relation holds for other parabolas.

Write a report of your findings.

An Analysis of Quadratic Functions

An analysis of a quadratic function, such as $y = -\frac{1}{2}x^2 + 4x - 5$, involves a combination of many algebraic and geometric skills.

$$\begin{aligned} y &= -\tfrac{1}{2}x^2 + 4x - 5 \\ &= -\tfrac{1}{2}(x^2 - 8x) - 5 \\ &= -\tfrac{1}{2}(x^2 - 8x + 16 - 16) - 5 \\ &= -\tfrac{1}{2}(x - 4)^2 + 3 \end{aligned}$$

common factors

completing the square

square of a binomial

The parabola opens down and is congruent to $y = \frac{1}{2}x^2$.

congruence

The maximum value of y is 3 and occurs when $x = 4$.

maximum and minimum values

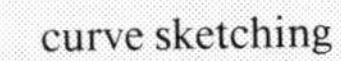

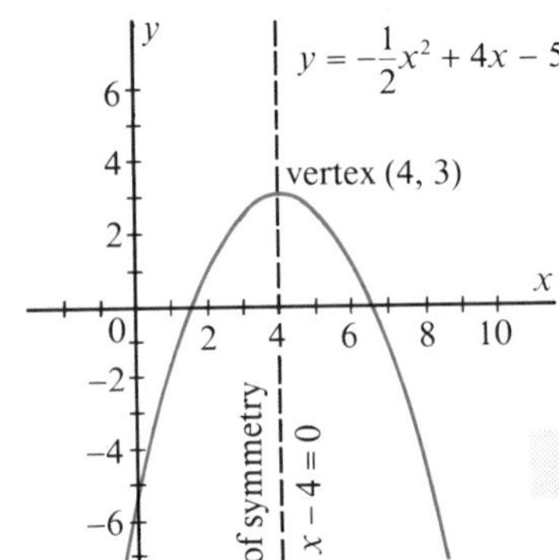

reflections

equation of a vertical line

Intercepts:

Let $x = 0$:

$$\begin{aligned} y &= -\tfrac{1}{2}(0)^2 + 4(0) - 5 \\ &= -5 \end{aligned}$$

The y-intercept is -5.

Let $y = 0$

$$0 = -\tfrac{1}{2}x^2 + 4x - 5$$

$$x^2 - 8x + 10 = 0$$

$$x = \frac{-b \pm \sqrt{b^2 - 4ac}}{2a} \qquad \begin{aligned} a &= 1 \\ b &= -8 \\ c &= 10 \end{aligned}$$

$$x = \frac{8 \pm \sqrt{24}}{2}, \text{ or } 4 \pm \sqrt{6}$$

The x-intercepts are approximately 6.45 and 1.55.

solving quadratic equations

working with radicals

finding intercepts

To analyze a quadratic function in the above manner means to determine all the following information about the function:

- the coordinates of the vertex
- the equation of the axis of symmetry
- the direction of opening
- congruent parabola
- sketch of the function
- the y-intercept
- the x-intercepts, if any
- the maximum or minimum value of y
- the value of x for which the maximum or minimum value occurs.

ANALYZE:

1. $y = x^2 - 6x + 5$
2. $y = -\frac{1}{2}x^2 + 5x - 9$
3. $f(x) = 2x^2 - 5x - 12$

8-12 MAXIMUM AND MINIMUM PROBLEMS

In many problems involving the maximum or minimum of a function, the function is not given; it has to be found from the data. Note the steps involved in the solutions of the following examples.

Example 1.

Two numbers have a difference of 10. What are the numbers if their product is a minimum?

Solution.

Step 1. *Identify the quantity to be maximized or minimized.*
The quantity to be minimized is the product, P, of two numbers.

Step 2. *Write the algebraic expression for this quantity.*
Let the two numbers be x and y. Then:

$$P = xy.$$

Step 3. *The expression must contain only one variable. If it contains more, use other information to write it in terms of one variable.*
Since the numbers have a difference of 10, $x - y = 10$, where x is the greater number.
Solve for y: $y = x - 10$
Substitute $x - 10$ for y in $P = xy$: $P = x(x - 10)$
$= x^2 - 10x$

Step 4. *The expression in Step 3 is a quadratic function. Rearrange it by completing the square.*

$$\begin{aligned} P &= x^2 - 10x \\ &= x^2 - 10x + 25 - 25 \\ &= (x - 5)^2 - 25 \end{aligned}$$

Step 5. *Determine the maximum or minimum value of the function and the value of the variable for which it occurs.*
The minimum value of P is -25 which occurs when $x = 5$.

Step 6. *Answer the question in the statement of the problem.*
Since $x = 5$ and $x - y = 10$, $y = -5$.
The two numbers are 5 and -5.

Example 2.

A rectangular lot is bounded on one side by a river and on the other three sides by a total of 80 m of fencing. Find the dimensions of the largest possible lot.

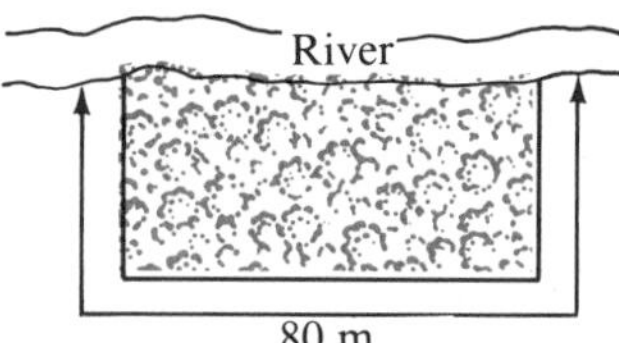

Solution.

Step 1. The quantity to be maximized is the area of the lot.

Step 2. Let x be the width of the lot and y the length, in metres.
Then, if A is the area:

$$A = xy.$$

Step 3. Since the total length of fencing is 80 m:

$$2x + y = 80$$

or,

$$y = 80 - 2x$$

Substitute $80 - 2x$ for y in $A = xy$: $A = x(80 - 2x)$
$= -2x^2 + 80x$

Step 4.

$$\begin{aligned} A &= -2(x^2 - 40x) \\ &= -2(x^2 - 40x + 400 - 400) \\ &= -2(x^2 - 40x + 400) + 800 \\ &= -2(x - 20)^2 + 800 \end{aligned}$$

Step 5. The maximum value of A is 800 and occurs when $x = 20$.

Step 6. Since $x = 20$ and $2x + y = 80$, $y = 40$.
The dimensions of the largest possible rectangular lot are 40 m by 20 m.

Example 3.

The cost of a ticket to a hockey arena seating 800 people is \$3. At this price every ticket is sold. A survey indicates that if the price is increased, attendance will fall by 100 for every dollar of increase. What ticket price results in the greatest revenue? What is the greatest revenue?

Solution.

Step 1. The quantity to be maximized is the total revenue, R, from the tickets to be sold.

Step 2. Let x be the increase in ticket price. Then:

$$\begin{aligned} R &= (\text{cost per ticket}) \times (\text{number of tickets sold}) \\ &= (3 + x)(800 - 100x) \\ &= -100x^2 + 500x + 2400 \end{aligned}$$

Step 3. The expression already contains only one variable.

Step 4.
$$\begin{aligned} R &= -100(x^2 - 5x) + 2400 \\ &= -100\left(x^2 - 5x + \frac{25}{4} - \frac{25}{4}\right) + 2400 \\ &= -100\left(x^2 - 5x + \frac{25}{4}\right) + 625 + 2400 \\ &= -100\left(x - \frac{5}{2}\right)^2 + 3025 \end{aligned}$$

Step 5. The maximum value of R is 3025 and occurs when $x = \frac{5}{2}$, or 2.5

Step 6. Since an increase in price of \$2.50 per ticket results in the greatest revenue, the ticket price should become \$5.50. The greatest revenue is \$3025.00.

EXERCISES 8-12

(B)

1. Two numbers have a difference of 8. Find the numbers if their product is a minimum.
2. The sum of two natural numbers is 12. If their product is a maximum, find the numbers.
3. The sum of two numbers is 60. Find the numbers if their product is a maximum.
4. Two numbers have a difference of 20. Find the numbers if the sum of their squares is a minimum.
5. The sum of two numbers is 16. Find the numbers if the sum of their squares is a minimum.
6. The sum of two numbers is 28. Find the numbers if the sum of their squares is a minimum.
7. The sum of a number and three times another number is 18. Find the numbers if their product is a maximum.
8. Two numbers have a difference of 16. Find the numbers if the result of adding their sum and their product is a minimum.
9. A rectangular lot is bordered on one side by a stream and on the other three sides by 600 m of fencing. Find the dimensions of the lot if its area is a maximum.

10. A lifeguard marks off a rectangular swimming area at a beach with 200 m of rope. What is the greatest area of water she can enclose?
11. 80 m of fencing are available to enclose a rectangular play area.
    a) What is the maximum area that can be enclosed?
    b) What dimensions produce the maximum area?
12. A rectangular area is enclosed by a fence and divided by another section of fence parallel to two of its sides, as shown. If the 600 m of fence used encloses a maximum area, what are the dimensions of the enclosure?

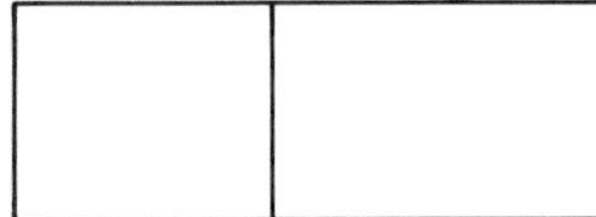

13. A theatre seats 2000 people and charges \$10 for a ticket. At this price, all the tickets can be sold. A survey indicates that if the ticket price is increased, the number sold will decrease by 100 for every dollar of increase. What ticket price would result in the greatest revenue?
14. A bus company carries about 20 000 riders per day for a fare of 90¢. A survey indicates that if the fare is decreased, the number of riders will increase by 2000 for every 5¢ of decrease. What ticket price would result in the greatest revenue?
15. A trough is made from a rectangular strip of sheet metal, 50 cm wide, by bending up at right angles a strip, x cm wide, along two sides. For what value of x is the cross-section area a maximum?

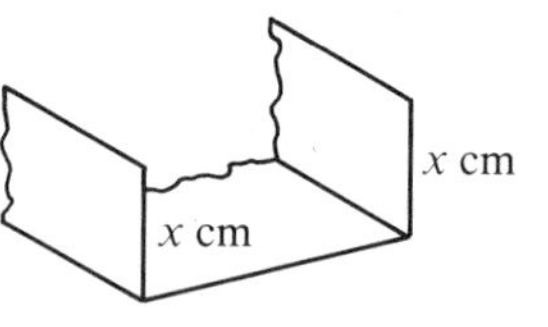

16. What is the maximum area of a triangle having 15 cm as the sum of its base and height?
17. A straight section of railroad track crosses two highways 400 m and 600 m from an intersection. Find the dimensions of the largest rectangular lot that can be laid out in the triangle formed by the railroad and highways.

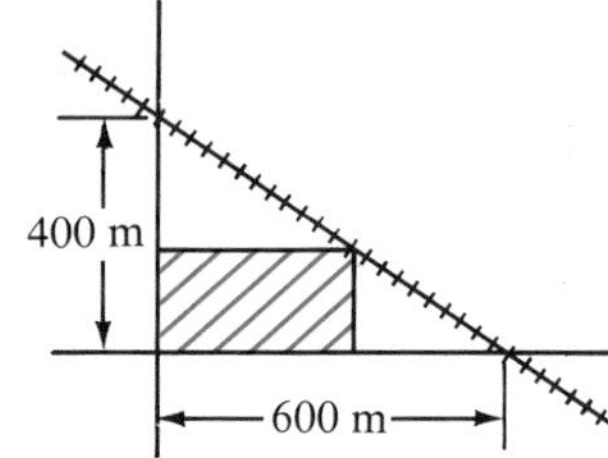

18. A 30 cm piece of wire is cut in two. One piece is bent into the shape of a square, the other piece into the shape of a rectangle with a length-to-width ratio of 2 : 1. What are the lengths of the two pieces if the sum of the areas of the square and rectangle is a minimum?

(C)

19. Find the number which exceeds its square by the greatest possible amount.
20. Find the maximum possible area of a rectangle with a given perimeter.
21. In $\triangle ABC$, $\angle B = 90°$ and AC has a constant length. Prove that the area of $\triangle ABC$ is a maximum when $AB = AC$.

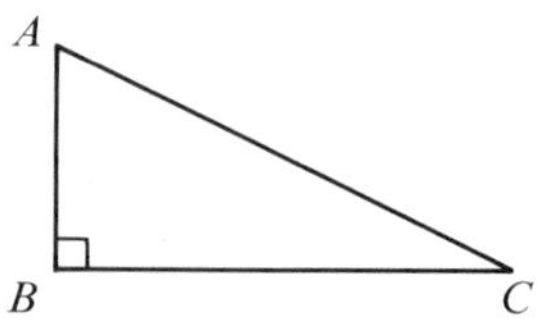

22. Find the minimum distance from (0, 0) to the line $3x + 2y - 12 = 0$.

Review Exercises

1. State the domain and range:

   a) $y = 3x - 2$ b) $y = \sqrt{2x - 1}$ c) $y = x^2 - 4x + 4$

2. State the domain and range:

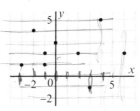

   a) b) c)

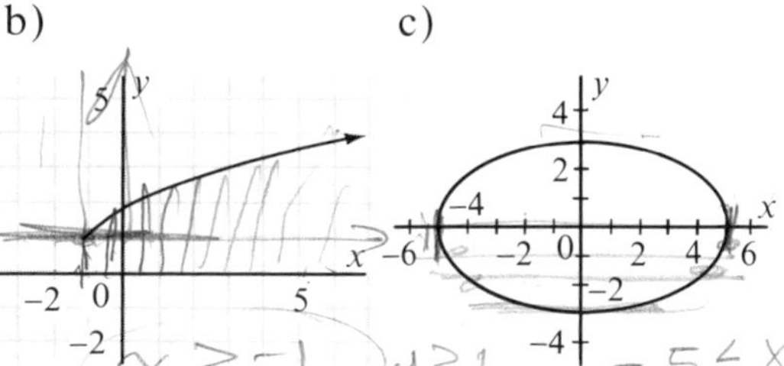

3. The area, A, of an equilateral triangle of side length d is given by: $A \doteq 0.433d^2$.
   a) Graph the relation. Is it a function?
   b) State the domain and range.
   c) If the area is 173.2 cm^2, what is the side length?

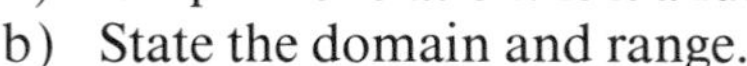

4. State the domain and range:

   a) $y = \sqrt{x + 2}$ b) $y = \frac{x}{3}$ c) $x - y = 5$

   d) $y = \frac{1}{1 - x}$ e) $y = 1 - x^2$ f) $y = (1.2)^x$

5. If $f(x) = 3x^2 - 4x + 5$, find:

   a) $f(x + 1)$; b) $f(2x - 1)$; c) $f(3x - 1)$.

6. If $f(x) = 2 - 5x$ and $g(x) = 3x - 2$, find a value of x such that:

   a) $f(x) = g(x)$; b) $f(x - 3) = g(x + 7)$;

   c) $f(4x + 1) = g(3 - x)$; d) $f(x^2) = g\left(\frac{5}{3}x - 2\right)$.

7. If $f(x) = x^2 + 5x - 14$, what values of x make:

   a) $f(x) = 0$? b) $f(x) = -20$? c) $f(x) = 10$?

8. Nancy works as a lifeguard and earns \$4.80/h for a 35 h week. She is paid time-and-a-half for any additional hours. Draw a graph showing Nancy's weekly earnings for up to a 50 h week.

9. If $g(x) = mx + b$, find m and b if the graph of the function:

   a) has slope $\frac{3}{5}$ and $g(10) = 17$;
   b) has y-intercept 3 and passes through $(-4, 7)$;
   c) passes through $(-2, 2)$ and $(4, 6)$;
   d) has $g(2) = -7$ and $g(-1) = 11$;

10. Graph, and state the domain and range:

    a) $f(x) = 3x^2 - 14x - 5$ b) $g(t) = 2 + t - 10t^2$

11. In a Test-Your-Strength booth at a fair a pad is struck with a hammer. This projects a weight up a vertical slide—to ring a bell if you have hit the pad hard enough. When the pad is struck with just sufficient force to ring the bell, the height of the weight, h, in metres, t seconds after the pad is struck is given by: $h = 8t - 4.9t^2$.
    a) How high is the weight 0.5 s after the pad is struck?
    b) How high is the bell?

12. Find the equation of the parabola:
    a) with vertex $(-2, 0)$, y-intercept 4;
    b) with vertex $(5, 0)$, y-intercept 25;
    c) with x-intercept -6, y-intercept 36, axis of symmetry $x + 6 = 0$.

13. Find the equation of the parabola with vertex $(0, 0)$ which passes through:

    a) $(2, 16)$; b) $(3, -18)$; c) $(2, 6)$; d) $(-3, 15)$;

    e) $\left(\frac{2}{3}, -\frac{2}{3}\right)$ f) $(4, 12)$; g) $\left(-\frac{5}{2}, 5\right)$; h) $\left(\frac{1}{2}, -\frac{1}{2}\right)$.

14. Write the equation of the parabola:
    a) with vertex $(-3, 4)$, y-intercept -5;
    b) with vertex $(2, -2)$, x-intercepts 1 and 3;
    c) with vertex $(4, -4)$, that opens up, and is congruent to $y = \frac{1}{2}x^2$.

15. Sketch each parabola showing:
    i) coordinates of the vertex;
    ii) equation of axis of symmetry;
    iii) coordinates of two other points on the graph.

    a) $y = x^2 - 6x + 5$ b) $w = 2z^2 - 8z - 5$

    c) $v = \frac{1}{2}t^2 + 10t + 21$ d) $p = -3q^2 + 18q - 20$

16. A producer of synfuel from coal estimates that the cost, C, in dollars per barrel for a production run of x thousand barrels is given by $C = 9x^2 - 180x + 940$. How many thousand barrels should be produced each run to keep the cost per barrel at a minimum? What is the minimum cost per barrel of synfuel?

17. Two numbers have a difference of 24. Find the numbers if the result of adding their sum and their product is a minimum.

18. A bus company carries about 40 000 riders per day for a fare of \$1.00. A survey indicates that if the fare is decreased, the number of riders will increase by 2500 for every 5¢ of decrease. What fare will result in the greatest revenue?

9 Transformations of Functions

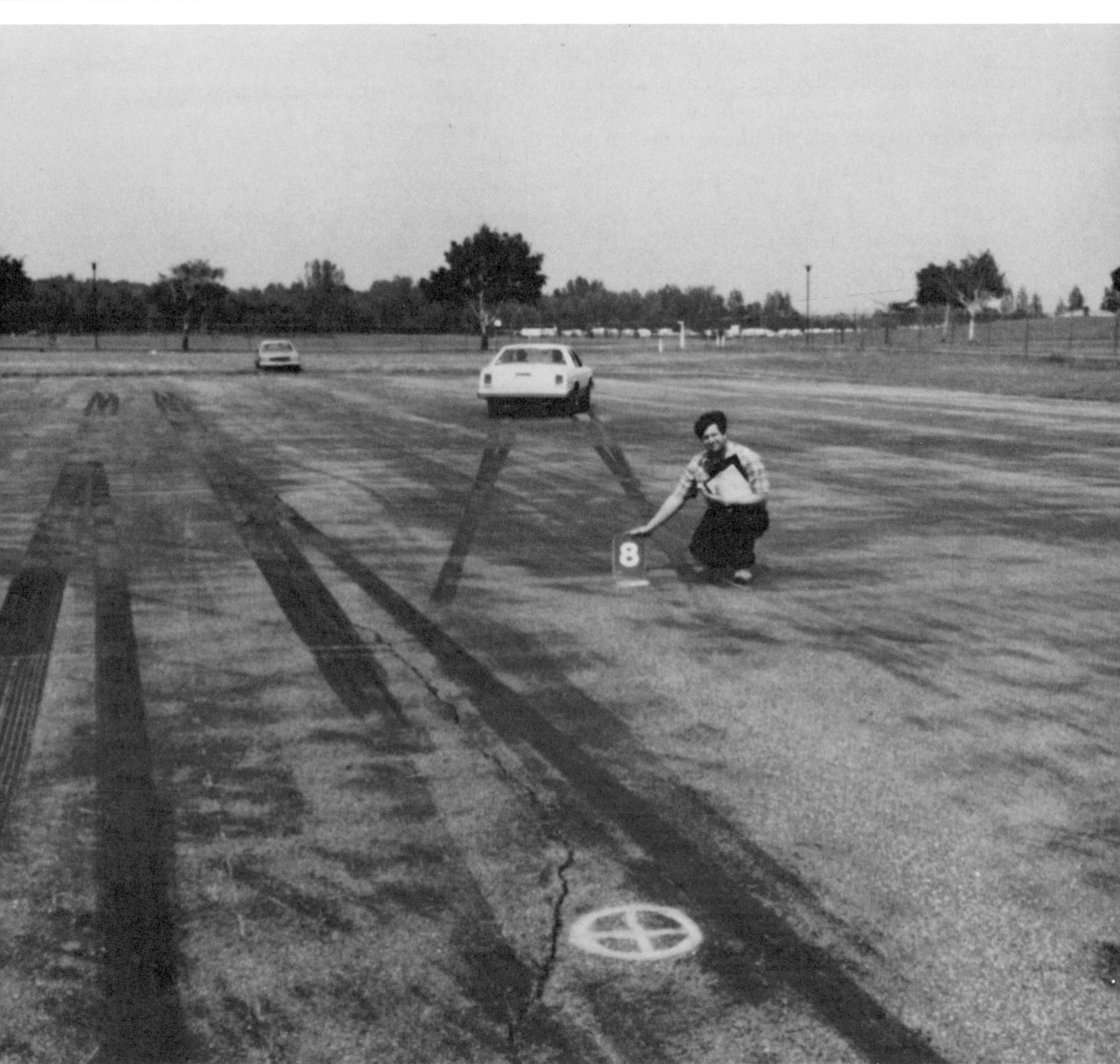

The speed of a vehicle, v, can be estimated from the length, d, of its skid marks. If

$$v = 12.6\sqrt{d} + 8,$$

sketch a graph of v as a function of d without making a table of values. (See *Example 2* in Section 9-5.)

9-1 SOME BASIC FUNCTIONS AND THEIR GRAPHS

In previous chapters the linear and quadratic functions were studied. The graphs of these functions have characteristic shapes—the graph of a linear function is a straight line and that of a quadratic function is a parabola. Examples are:

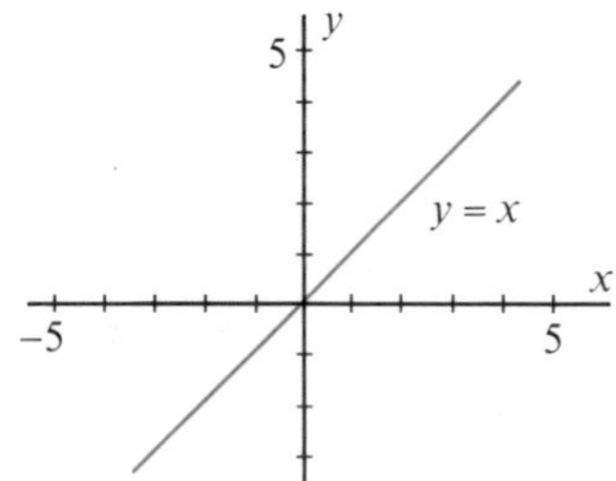

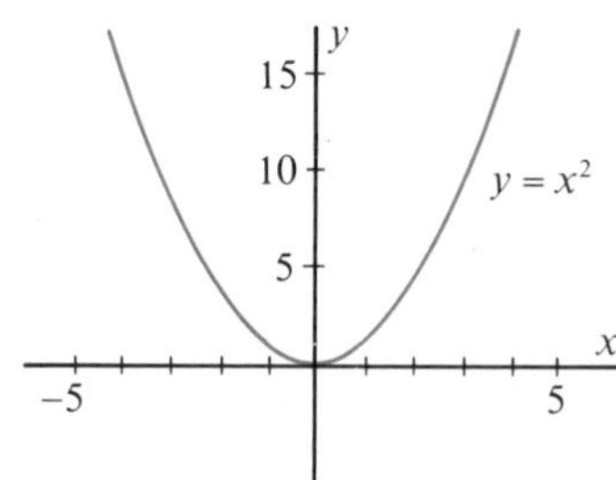

In this chapter, we investigate some other functions having graphs with characteristic shapes. The results will allow the graphs to be sketched *without* a table of values. Some of these functions are illustrated in this section.

Square Root Functions

The problem of finding a ship's longitude at sea was so important to exploration and trade in the sixteenth and seventeenth centuries that several countries offered substantial prizes for its solution. The solution that was eventually found required the accurate recording of time using pendulum clocks.

The period, T, in seconds, of a pendulum of length l metres is given approximately by the formula:

$$T \doteq 2\sqrt{l}$$

This function is an example of a **square root function.**

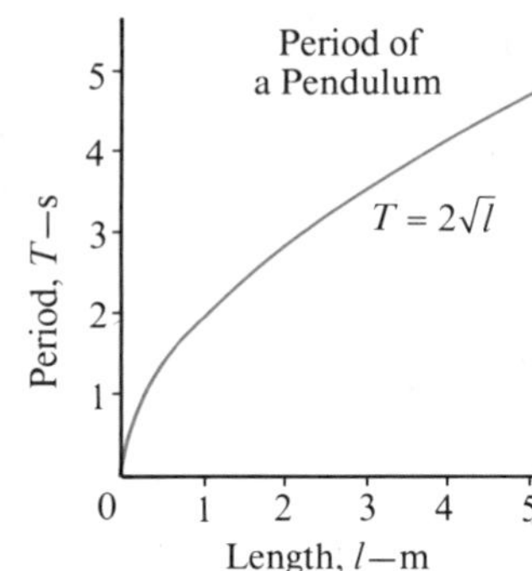

The basic square root function is $y = \sqrt{x}$. Since there are real values for $\sqrt{x}$ only when $x \geqslant 0$, the graph has an unusual property: it starts at a fixed point, (0, 0), and extends in one direction only.

The graphs of the two square root functions shown are drawn to the same scale. If they were drawn on the same axes, how would they be related?

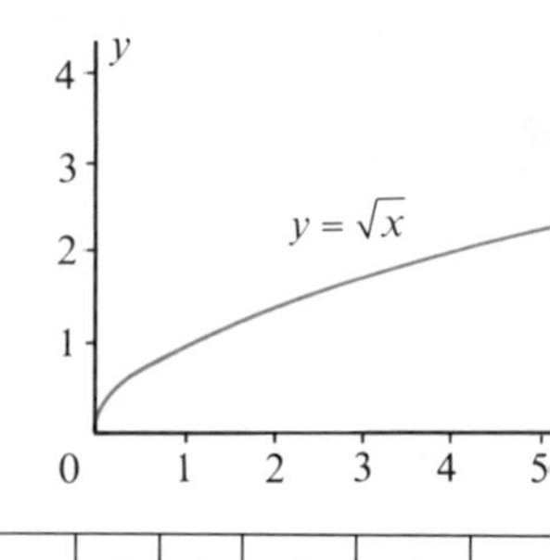

x	0	1	2	3	4
y	0	1	1.4	1.7	2.0

Other examples of square root functions are:

$y = 3\sqrt{x + 2}$ $\qquad$ $y = -\sqrt{x} + 5$ $\qquad$ $y = 0.6\sqrt{x - 1} + 3$

Reciprocal Functions

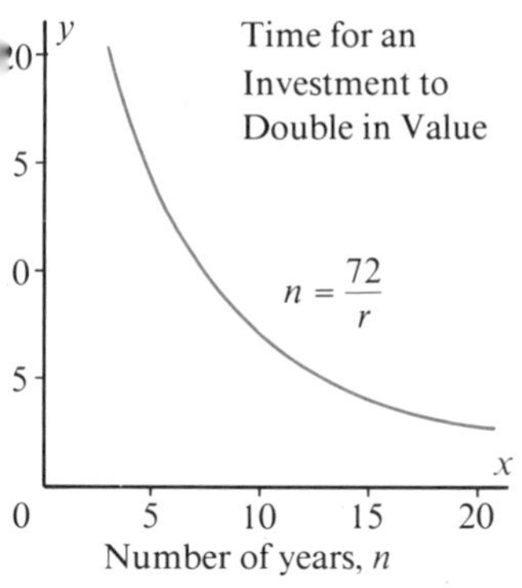

When money is invested at an interest rate of $r\%$, the approximate number of years, n, it takes to double is given by:

$$n = \frac{72}{r}$$

This is an example of a reciprocal function.

The basic reciprocal function is $y = \frac{1}{x}$. There is no point on the graph for $x = 0$, because $\frac{1}{x}$ is not defined when $x = 0$. Therefore, the curve, called a **hyperbola**, has two separate branches corresponding to positive and negative values of x. In most applications, the variables are positive and the graph consists of only one branch of the hyperbola.

x	y
-4	$-\frac{1}{4}$
-2	$-\frac{1}{2}$
-1	-1
$-\frac{1}{2}$	-2
$-\frac{1}{4}$	-4

x	y
$\frac{1}{4}$	4
$\frac{1}{2}$	2
1	1
2	$\frac{1}{2}$
4	$\frac{1}{4}$

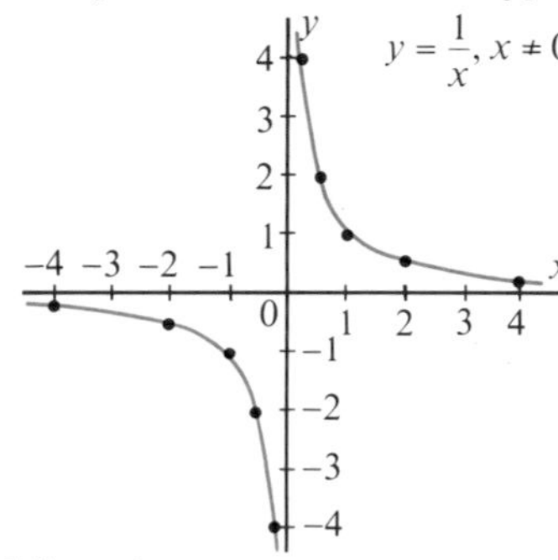

Other examples of reciprocal functions are:

$$y = \frac{1}{x-3} \qquad y = \frac{1}{x+4} - 1 \qquad V = \frac{100}{1+i}$$

Exponential Functions

Estimated World Population A.D. 1000–2000

Year

The graph shows estimates of the world's human population over the last one thousand years. This curve is called an **exponential curve**.

In equations of exponential functions, the variable occurs in an exponent. A simple example is the function $y = 2^x$. In this example the base is 2, but exponential functions can have any positive constant as a base.

x	y
-3	$\frac{1}{8}$
-2	$\frac{1}{4}$
-1	$\frac{1}{2}$
0	1

x	y
0	1
1	2
2	4
3	8

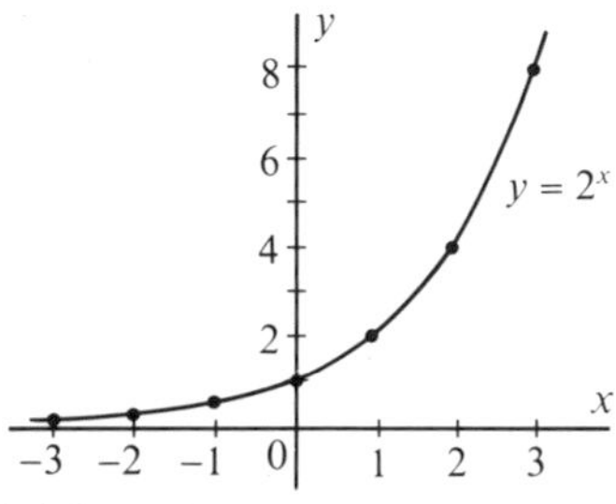

Other examples of exponential functions are:

$$P = 4.3e^{0.2(f-1980)} \qquad y = 2.5 \times 4^x \qquad y = 3^{x-1}$$

e, like π, is an irrational number and is approximately equal to 2.718.

Cubic functions and **absolute value functions** are two other types of functions.

x	y
−3	−27
−2	−8
−1	−1
0	0
1	1
2	8
3	27

x	y
−3	3
−2	2
−1	1
0	0
1	1
2	2
3	3

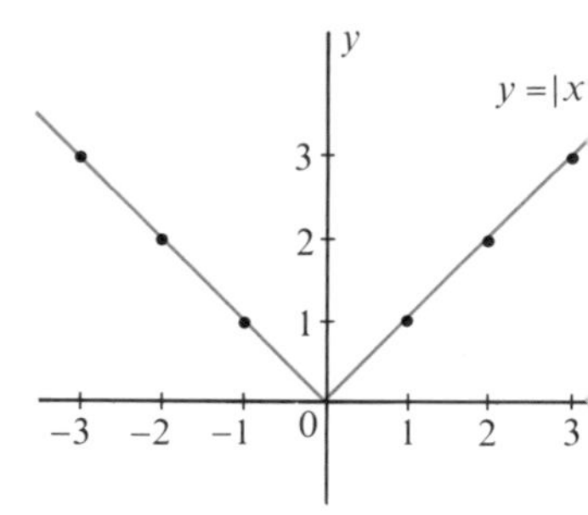

In chapter 8, we found that when certain changes were made in the equation of the quadratic function $y = x^2$, there were corresponding changes in the appearance and position of the parabola. Similarly, when certain changes are made in equations of other functions, the appearance and position of the graphs change but their characteristic shape does not change. In the following sections, we investigate how the changes in the equations are related to the changes in the graphs.

EXERCISES 9-1

Ⓐ

1. Classify each function as square root, reciprocal, exponential, absolute value, or cubic:

a)

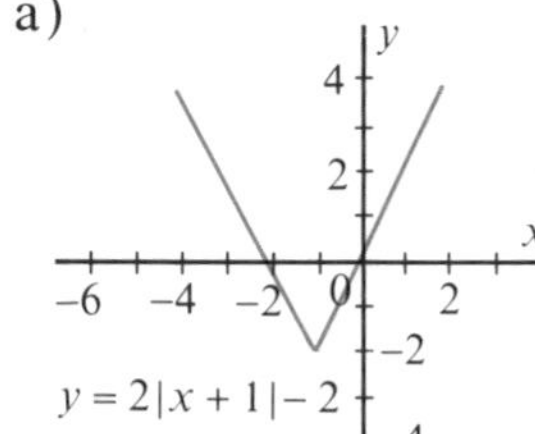

b)

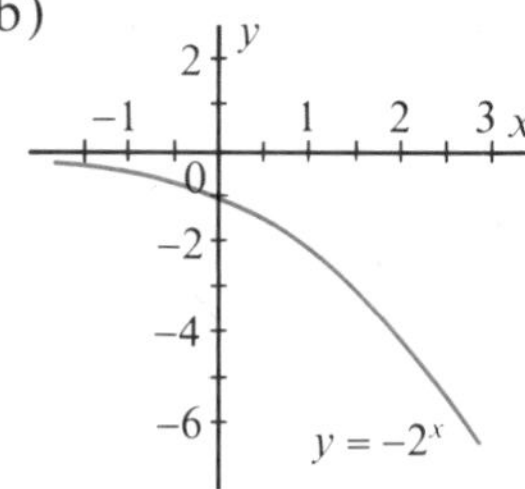

c)

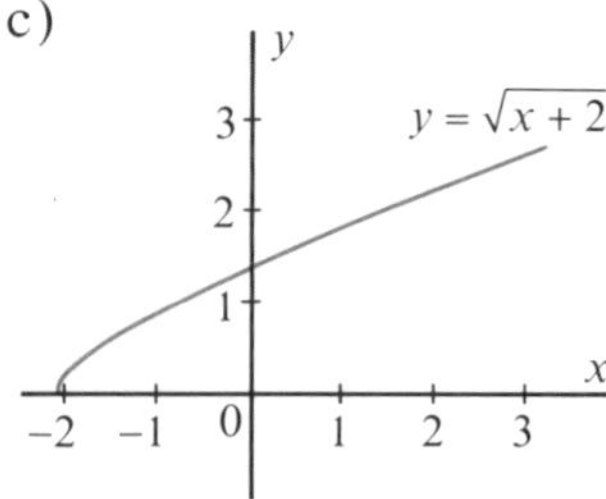

d)

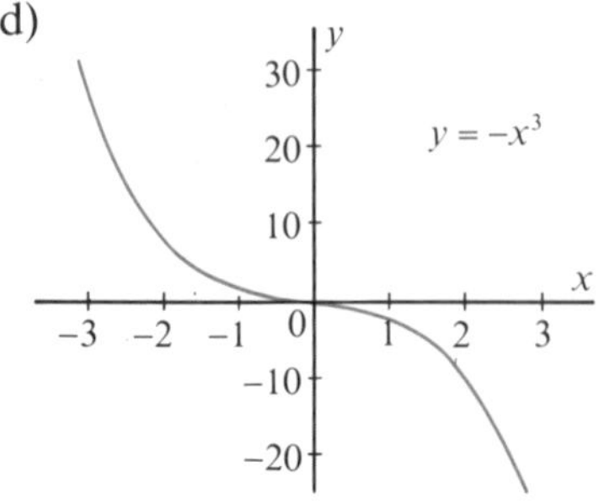

e)

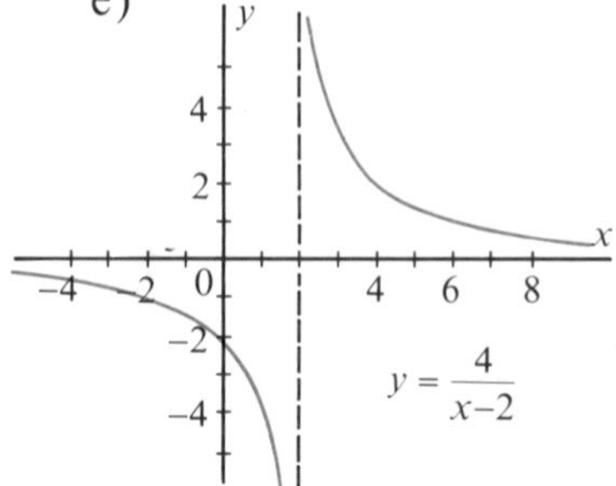

Ⓑ

2. Classify each function:
   a) The height, h, in metres, reached by a ball after n bounces is given by: $h = 2(0.7)^n$.
   b) A car begins to coast down a hill. The distance, d, in metres, it rolls in t seconds is: $d = 0.6t^2$.
   c) The length, L, in metres, of a steel girder is: $L = 8.5 + 0.000\,012(t - 20)$ where t is the temperature in °C.
   d) The free end of a diving board dips d cm when under a load of x kg. The relation is: $d = 0.000\,01x^3 + 0.0005x^2$.
   e) The value of \$100 when invested for n years at 10% compounded annually is: $A = 100(1.1)^n$.
   f) At an interest rate i, the amount that must be invested now to have \$100 in 1 year is: $P = \dfrac{100}{1 + i}$.
   g) The value, V, in dollars, of a car is given by: $V = \dfrac{12\,000}{n + 1} + 400$, where n is its age in years.
   h) The number of bacteria, N, in a culture t hours after midnight is given by: $N = 1000 \times 2^t$.
   i) In some rivers near an ocean, the incoming tide creates a single wave called a tidal bore. The speed of the bore, v, in kilometres per hour, is: $v = 11.27\sqrt{d}$, where d is the depth in metres.
   j) The percent, p, of surface light present in an ocean at a depth of d metres is given by: $p = 100e^{-0.023d}$, where e is a constant with the approximate value of 2.718.

3. Exponential Functions
   a) Using tables of values, graph:
      i) $y = (1.05)^x$; ii) $y = 2^x$; iii) $y = 3^x$.
   b) State the domain and range of the functions in (a).
   c) Describe how the graph of $y = a^x$ changes as a varies, $a > 0$.

4. Power Functions
   a) Using values of x between 0 and 2, graph on the same axes:
      i) $y = x^{0.5}$; ii) $y = x^{0.75}$; iii) $y = x^{1.0}$;
      iv) $y = x^{1.5}$; v) $y = x^{2.0}$; vi) $y = x^{2.5}$.
   b) State the domain and range of the functions in (a).
   c) Describe how the graph of $y = x^a$ changes as a varies, $a > 0$ and $x \geqslant 0$.

Ⓒ

5. Graph, and state if it is a function:
   a) $|y| = |x|$; b) $|x| + |y| = 1$; c) $|x + y| = 1$.

9-2 GRAPHING $y = f(x) + q$

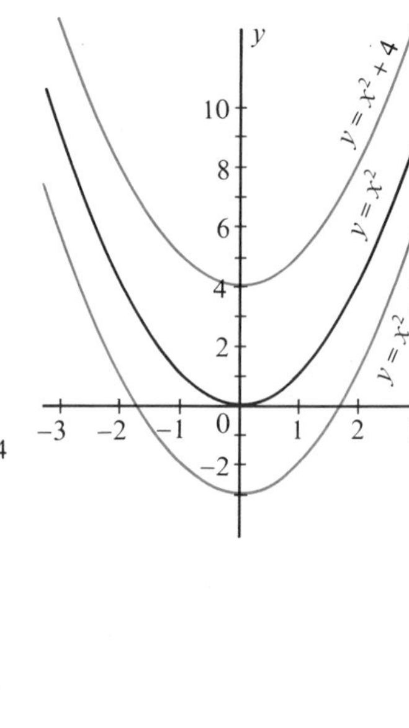

In the previous chapter, graphs of quadratic functions such as $y = x^2 + 4$ and $y = x^2 - 3$ were obtained from the graph of $y = x^2$ by a vertical translation. This result applies to other functions as well as quadratic functions.

Example 1.

Using a table of values, graph on the same axes:

$$y = 2^x \qquad y = 2^x + 4 \qquad y = 2^x - 3$$

Solution.

x	2^x	$2^x + 4$	$2^x - 3$
−2	0.25	4.25	−2.75
−1	0.5	4.5	−2.5
0	1	5	−2
1	2	6	−1
2	4	8	1
3	8	12	5

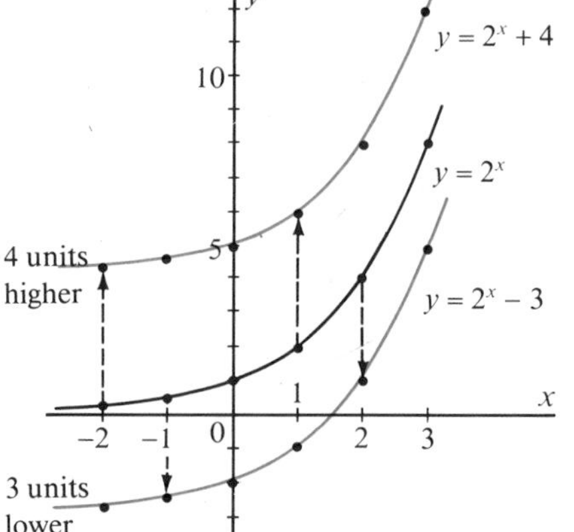

In *Example 1*, the y-coordinates of points on the curve $y = 2^x + 4$ are all 4 greater than those on $y = 2^x$. The curve has been translated 4 units up. Similarly, the y-coordinates of points on the curve $y = 2^x - 3$ are all 3 less than those on $y = 2^x$. The curve has been translated 3 units down. This result suggests how the graphs of other functions may be sketched without making tables.

Example 2.

Sketch the graph of $y = |x| - 5$.

Solution.

Sketch the graph of the absolute value function $y = |x|$. The graph of $y = |x| - 5$ is then obtained by translating this graph 5 units down.

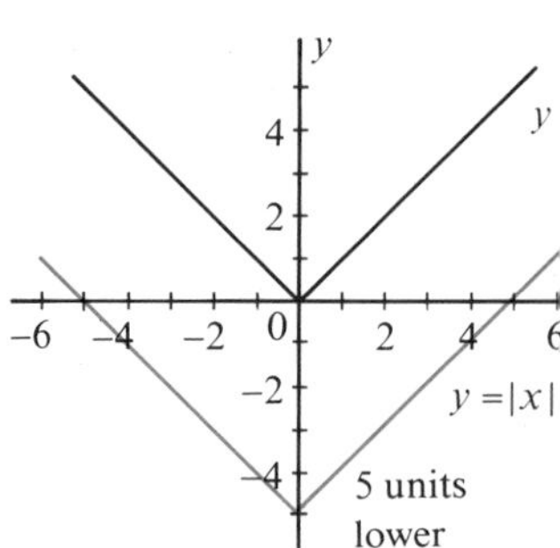

In general, adding a positive or negative constant to any function $y = f(x)$ causes a *vertical translation* of its graph.

The graph of $y = f(x) + q$ is related to that of $y = f(x)$ by a vertical translation.

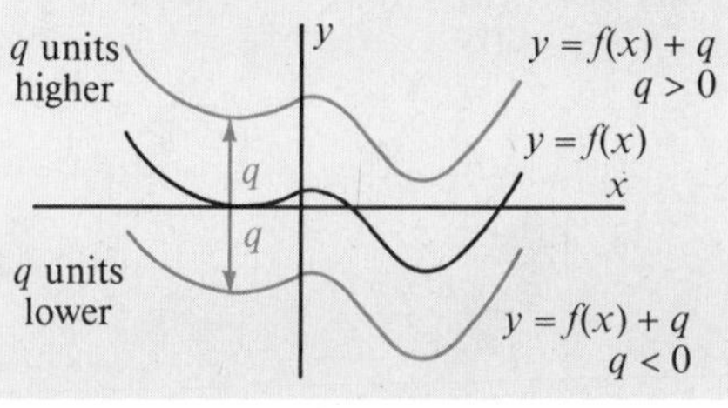

EXERCISES 9-2

Ⓐ

1. Which of the six graphs best represents:

a) $y = 2^x + 1$? b) $y = x^3 - 10$? c) $y = \frac{1}{x} + 2$?

i)
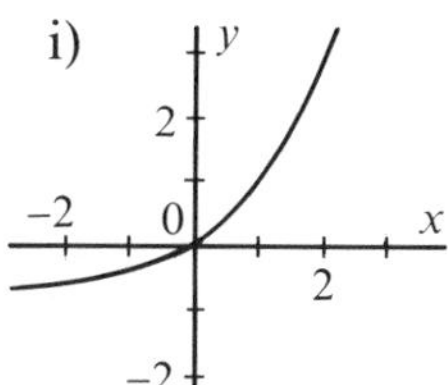

ii)
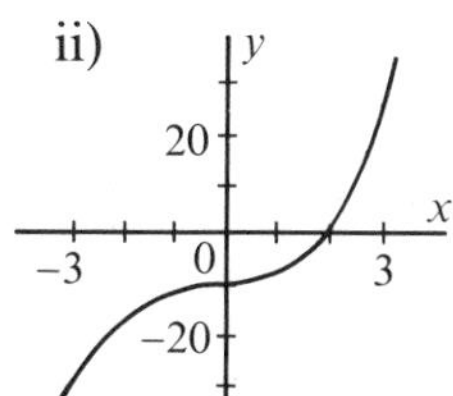

iii)
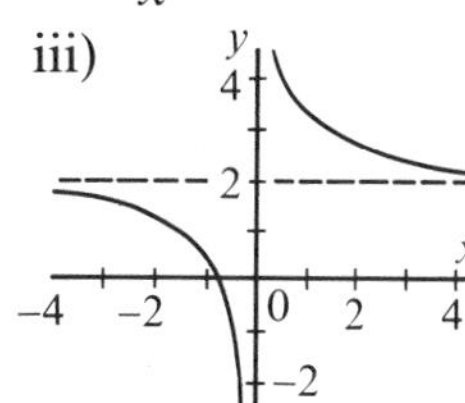

iv)
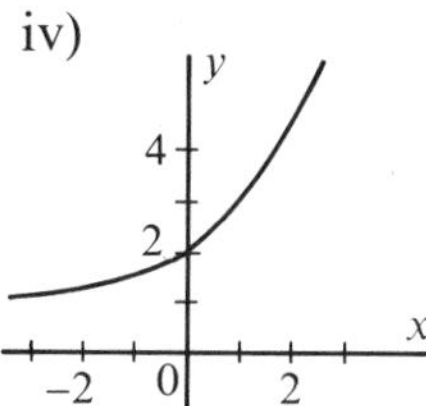

v)
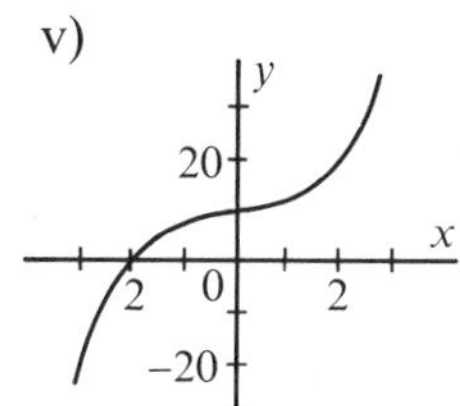

vi)
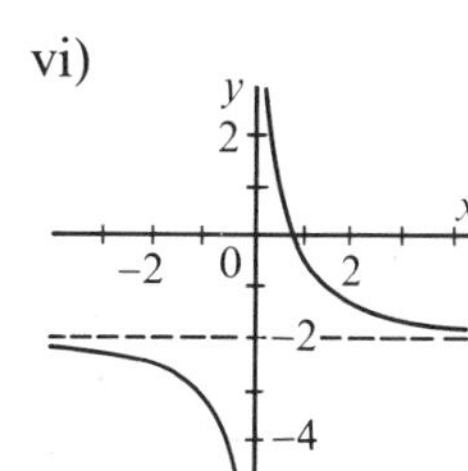

2. Without making a table of values, sketch the graphs of the following functions on the same axes:

a) $y = |x|$, $y = |x| + 5$, $y = |x| - 3$

b) $y = \sqrt{x}$, $y = \sqrt{x} + 5$, $y = \sqrt{x} - 3$

Ⓑ

3. Which of the four functions best represents each graph?

i) $y = |x| + 3$

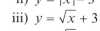

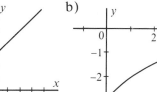

ii) $y = |x| - 3$

iii) $y = \sqrt{x} + 3$

iv) $y = \sqrt{x} - 3$

a)

b)
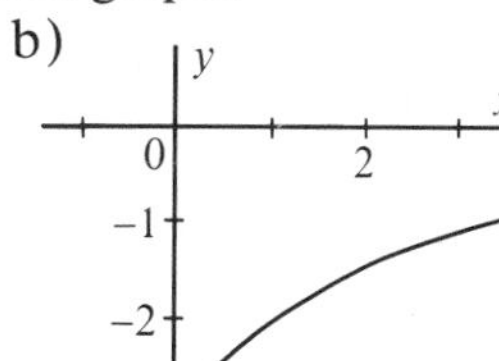

4. Sketch the graphs on the same axes:

a) $y = x^3$, $y = x^3 + 5$, $y = x^3 - 3$.

b) $y = 2^x$, $y = 2^x + 5$, $y = 2^x - 3$.

c) $y = \frac{1}{x}$, $y = \frac{1}{x} + 5$, $y = \frac{1}{x} - 3$.

5. Sketch the graph of:

a) $y = \sqrt{x} - 6$; b) $y = |x| + 2$; c) $y = 2^x - 5$;

d) $y = \frac{1}{x} + 1$; e) $y = x^3 - 4$.

Ⓒ

6. Copy the graph of $y = f(x)$ shown. On the same axes, sketch the graphs of $y = f(x) + 5$ and $y = f(x) - 3$.

9-3 GRAPHING $y = f(x - p)$

From earlier work, we know that the graphs of quadratic functions such as $y = (x - 5)^2$ and $y = (x + 2)^2$ can be obtained from the graph of $y = x^2$ by a horizontal translation. This result applies to other functions as well as quadratic functions.

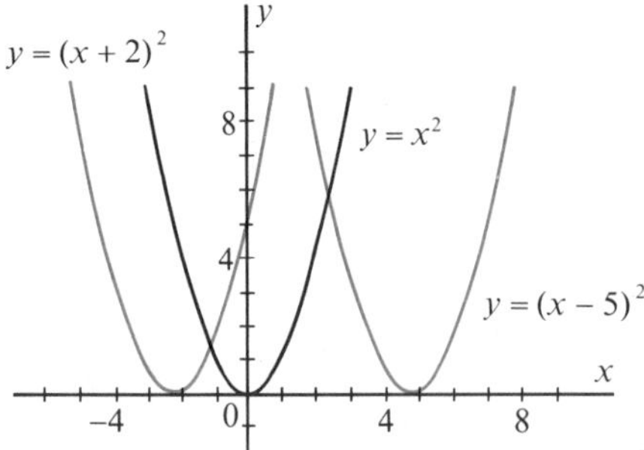

Example 1.

Using a table of values, graph on the same axes:
$y = \sqrt{x}, \quad y = \sqrt{x - 5}, \quad y = \sqrt{x + 2}.$

Solution.

$y = \sqrt{x}$ is defined when $x \geq 0$. Use values of x starting at 0 in the table.

x	0	1	2	3	4	5
y	0	1.0	1.41	1.73	2.0	2.23

$y = \sqrt{x - 5}$ is defined when $x - 5 \geq 0$, or $x \geq 5$. Use values of x starting at 5.

x	5	6	7	8	9	10
y	0	1.0	1.41	1.73	2.0	2.23

$y = \sqrt{x + 2}$ is defined when $x + 2 \geq 0$, or $x \geq -2$. Use values of x starting at -2.

x	−2	−1	0	1	2	3
y	0	1.0	1.41	1.73	2.0	2.23

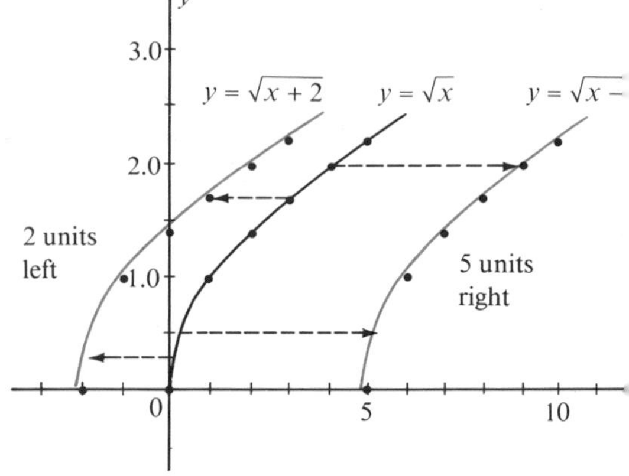

In *Example 1*, the x-coordinates of points on the curve $y = \sqrt{x - 5}$ are all 5 greater than those of the corresponding points on $y = \sqrt{x}$. The curve has been translated 5 units right. Similarly, the x-coordinates of points on $y = \sqrt{x + 2}$ are all 2 units less than those of the corresponding points on $y = \sqrt{x}$. The curve has been translated 2 units left. This result suggests how the graphs of other functions may be sketched without making tables.

Example 2.

Sketch the graph of $y = \dfrac{1}{x-3}$

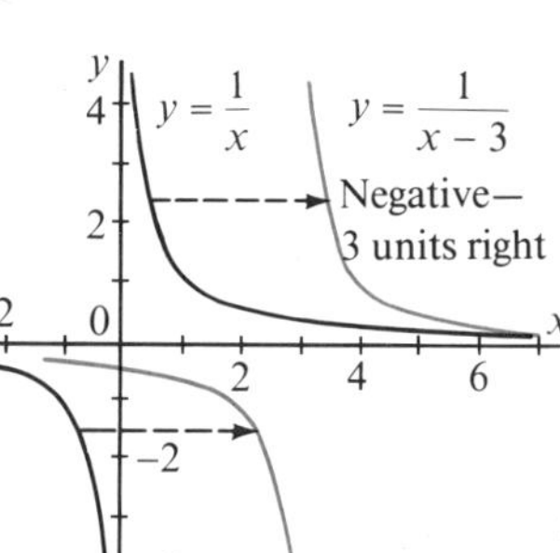

Solution.

Sketch the graph of the reciprocal function $y = \frac{1}{x}$. The graph of $y = \dfrac{1}{x-3}$ is then obtained by translating this graph 3 units right.

In general, adding a positive or negative constant to the variable x in any function $y = f(x)$ causes a *horizontal translation* of its graph.

The graph of $y = f(x - p)$ is related to that of $y = f(x)$ by a horizontal translation.

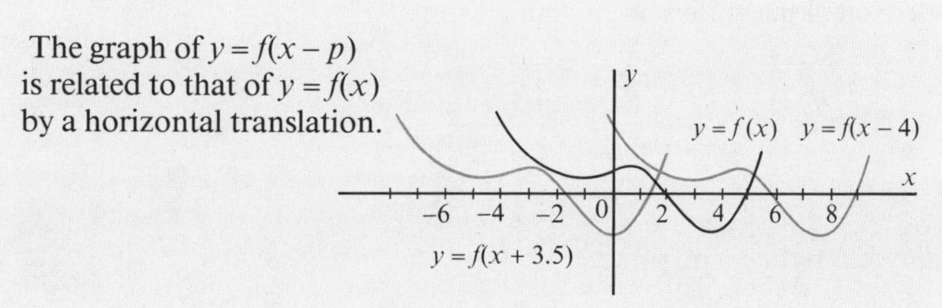

EXERCISES 9-3

(A)

1. Which of the six graphs best represents:

   a) $y = \sqrt{x+3}$? b) $y = 2^{x-3}$? c) $y = \dfrac{1}{x-2}$?

i)

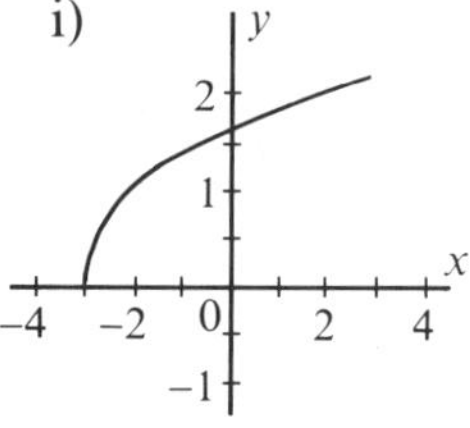

ii)

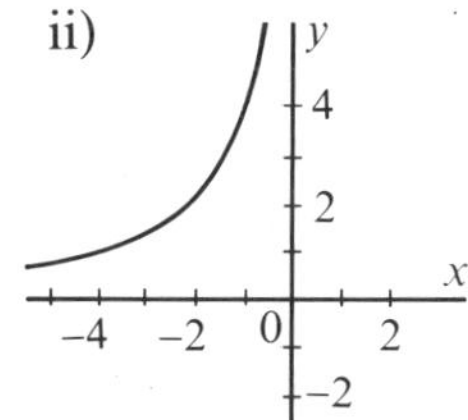

iii)

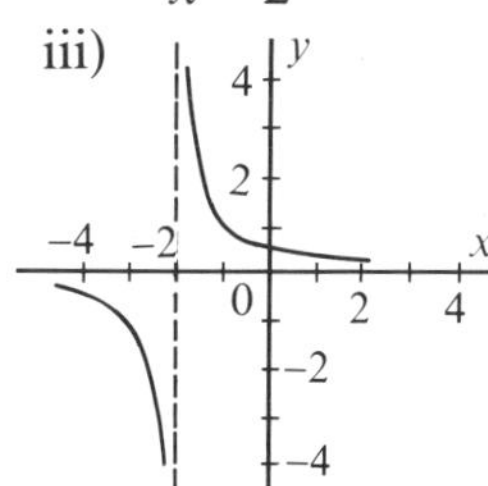

iv)

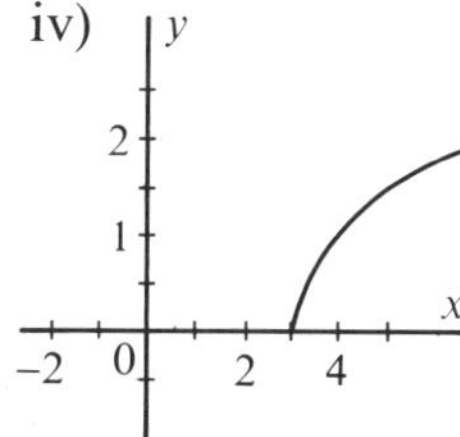

v)

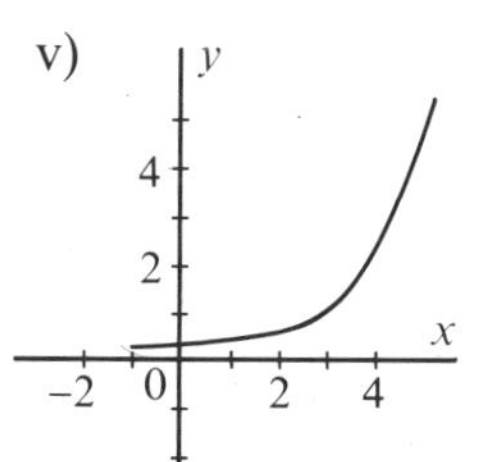

vi)

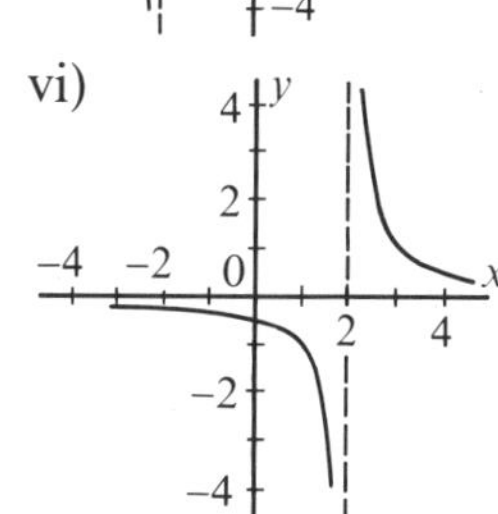

2. Without making a table, sketch the graphs on the same axes:

   a) $y = |x|$, $y = |x+2|$, $y = |x-5|$.

   b) $y = x^3$, $y = (x+2)^3$, $y = (x-5)^3$.

(B)

3. Which of the four functions best represents each graph?

i) $y = |x + 3|$
ii) $y = |x - 3|$
iii) $y = (x + 3)^3$
iv) $y = (x - 3)^3$

a) 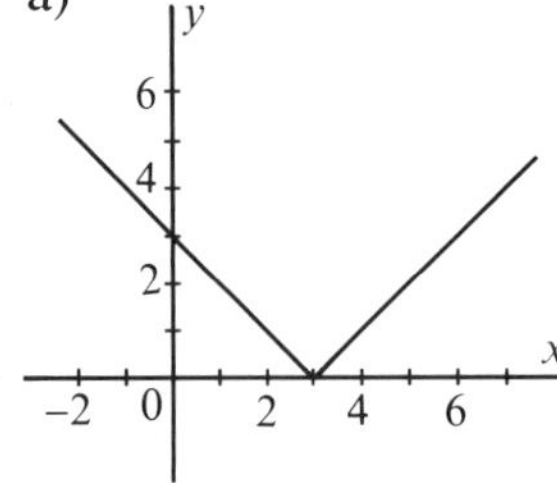

b) 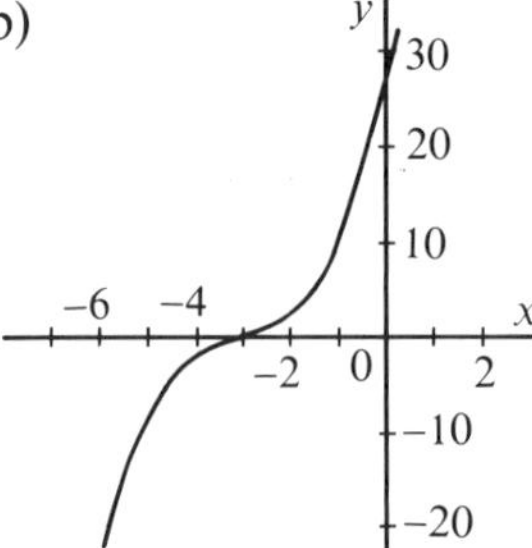

4. Sketch the graphs on the same axes:

a) $y = 2^x, \quad y = 2^{x+2}, \quad y = 2^{x-5}.$

b) $y = \dfrac{1}{x}, \quad y = \dfrac{1}{x+2}, \quad y = \dfrac{1}{x-5}.$

c) $y = \sqrt{x}, \quad y = \sqrt{x+2}, \quad y = \sqrt{x-5}.$

5. Sketch the graph of:

a) $y = (x - 1)^3$;
b) $y = |x + 7|$;
c) $y = \sqrt{x - 2}$;
d) $y = \dfrac{1}{x - 3}$;
e) $y = 2^{x+3}$.

6. Sketch the graph of:

a) $y = |x - 2| + 4$;
b) $y = \sqrt{x + 3} - 2$;
c) $y = (x + 5)^3 + 3$;
d) $y = \dfrac{1}{x - 4} - 1$.

(C)

7. Copy the graph of $y = f(x)$ shown. On the same axes, sketch the graphs of $y = f(x + 2)$ and $y = f(x - 5)$.

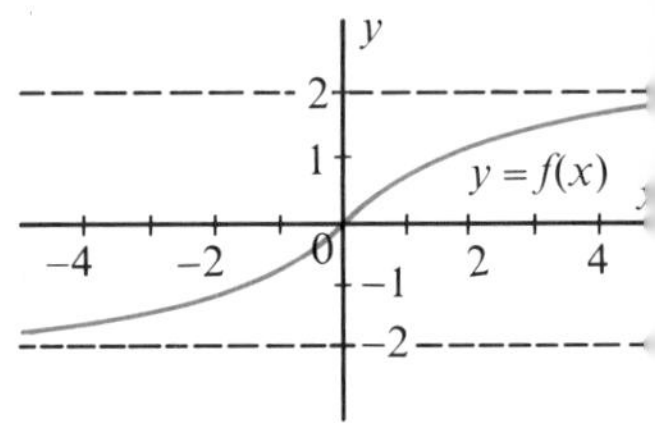

8. a) Using a table of values, graph: $y = \dfrac{1}{x^2 + 1}$.

b) Without using a table of values, sketch the graphs of:

i) $y = \dfrac{1}{(x - 3)^2 + 1}$;
ii) $y = \dfrac{1}{(x + 2)^2 + 1}$;
iii) $y = \dfrac{1}{x^2 + 10x + 26}$.

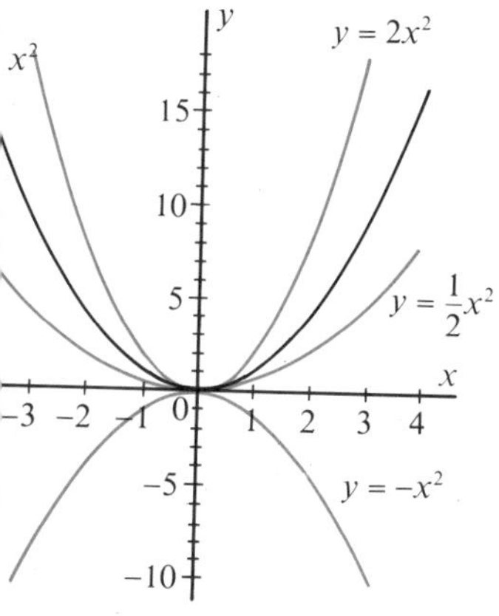

9-4 GRAPHING $y = af(x)$

We know that the graphs of quadratic functions such as $y = 2x^2$ and $y = \frac{1}{2}x^2$ can be obtained from the graph of $y = x^2$ by a vertical stretch or compression. Functions such as $y = -x^2$ involve a reflection in the x-axis. Similar results are obtained with functions other than quadratic functions.

Example 1.

Using a table of values, graph $y = x^3$ and $y = 2x^3$ on the same axes.

Solution.

x	x^3	$2x^3$
−3	−27	−54
−2	−8	−16
−1	−1	−2
0	0	0
1	1	2
2	8	16
3	27	54

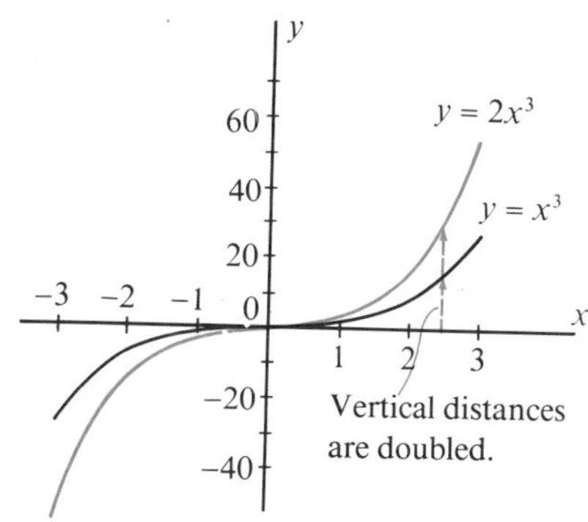

In *Example 1*, the y-coordinates of points on the curve $y = 2x^3$ are all twice as great as those on $y = x^3$. The curve has been stretched vertically. Similarly, a curve such as $y = \frac{1}{2}x^3$ is compressed vertically. A curve such as $y = -x^3$ is a reflection in the x-axis of $y = x^3$.

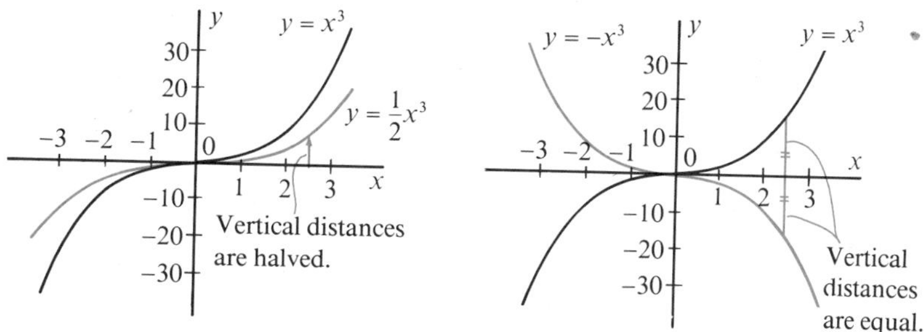

These results suggest how the graphs of other functions may be sketched without making tables.

Example 2.

Sketch the graph of $y = -\frac{2}{x}$, $x > 0$.

Solution.

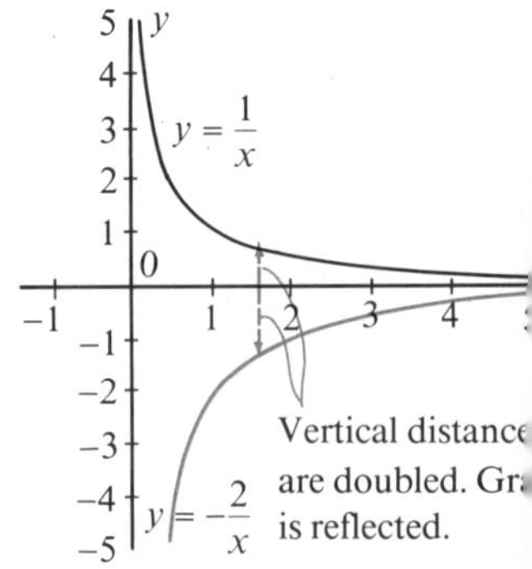

Sketch the graph of $y = \frac{1}{x}$. Since $-\frac{2}{x} = -2\left(\frac{1}{x}\right)$, the graph of $y = -\frac{2}{x}$ is obtained by a vertical stretch with a factor of 2 followed by a reflection in the x-axis.

In *Example 2*, since x was restricted to positive values, only one branch of the hyperbola is shown. This restriction is reasonable because in most applications of reciprocal functions the variables represent positive quantities.

The graph of $y = af(x)$ is related to that of $y = f(x)$ by a vertical stretch or compression and/or a reflection in the x-axis if a is negative. These are called *vertical magnifications*.

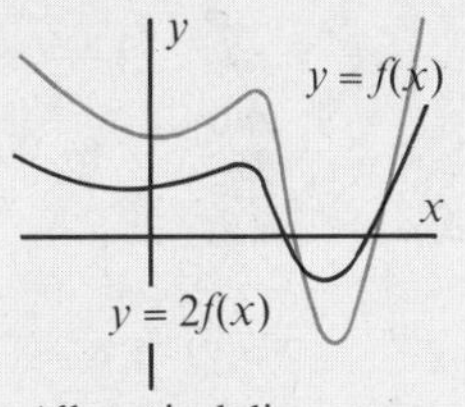

All vertical distances are doubled.

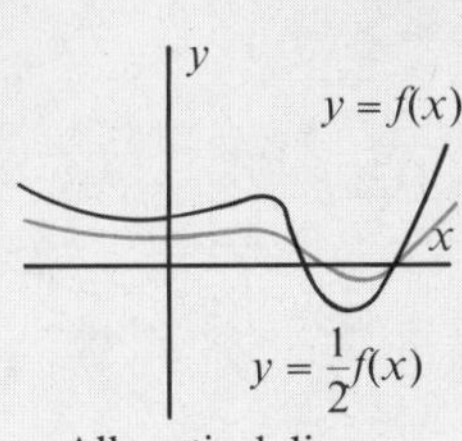

All vertical distances are halved.

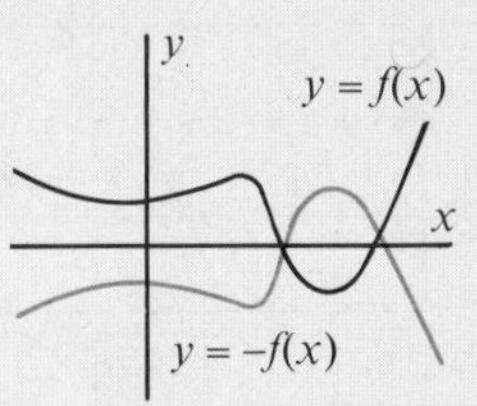

Graph is reflected in x-axis.

EXERCISES 9-4

Ⓐ

1. Which of the six graphs best represents:

a) $y = -\frac{1}{2}\sqrt{x}$?   b) $y = 0.25x^3$?   c) $y = -2^x$?

i)

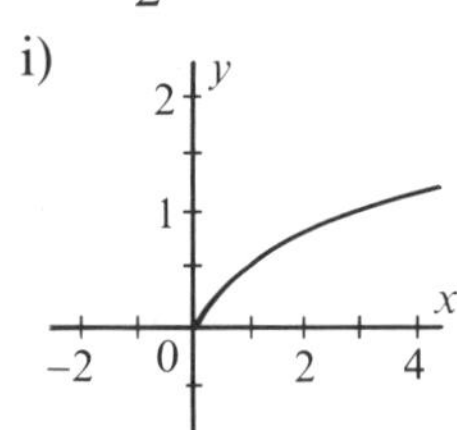

ii)

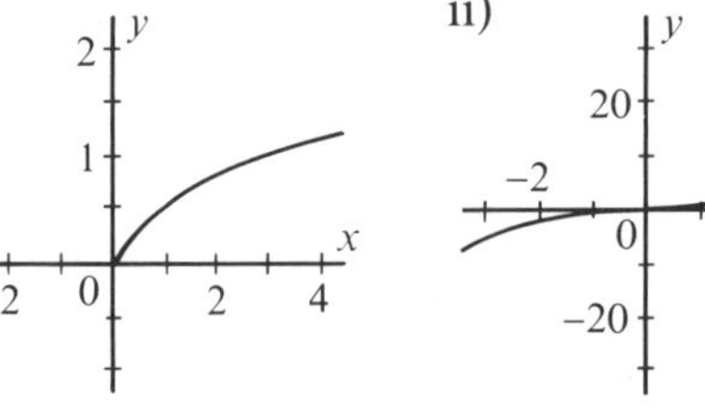

iii)

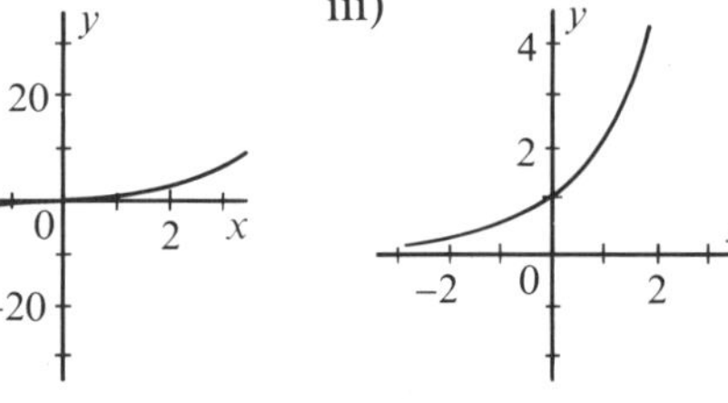

iv)

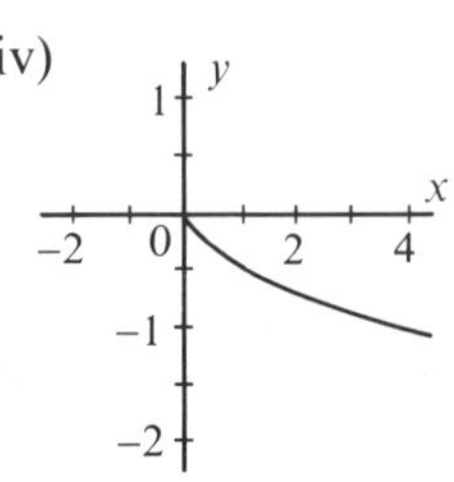

v)

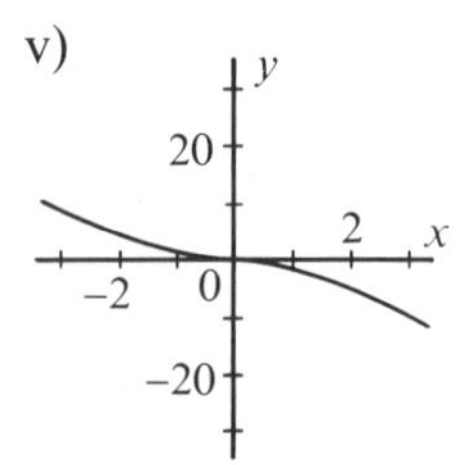

vi)

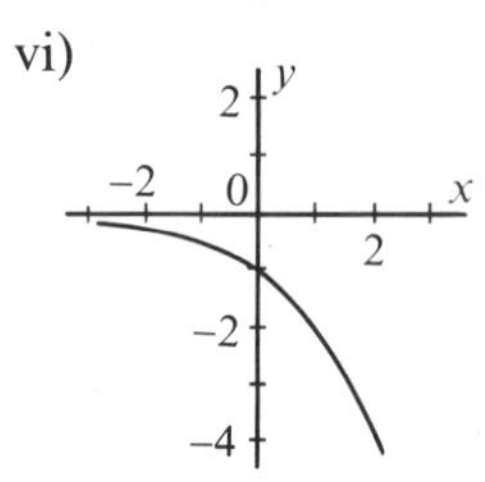

2. Without making a table, sketch the graphs on the same axes:

   a) $y = |x|$, $y = 3|x|$, $y = -\frac{1}{2}|x|$.

   b) $y = \frac{1}{x}$, $y = 3\left(\frac{1}{x}\right)$, $y = -\frac{1}{2}\left(\frac{1}{x}\right)$.

Ⓑ

3. Which of the four functions best represents each graph?

   i) $y = 2|x|$

   ii) $y = -2|x|$

   iii) $y = \frac{2}{x}$

   iv) $y = -\frac{2}{x}$

   a)

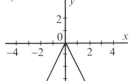

   b)

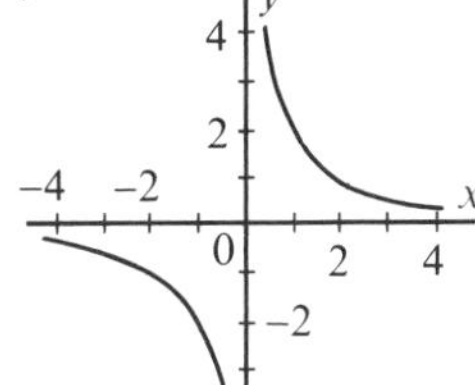

4. Sketch the graphs on the same axes:

   a) $y = x^3$, $y = 2x^3$, $y = -0.5x^3$.

   b) $y = \sqrt{x}$, $y = \frac{1}{3}\sqrt{x}$, $y = -2\sqrt{x}$.

   c) $y = 2^x$, $y = 0.5 \times 2^x$, $y = -2^x$.

5. Sketch the graph of:

   a) $y = \frac{3}{x}$; b) $y = -2|x|$; c) $y = 5\sqrt{x}$;

   d) $y = 1.5 \times 2^x$; e) $y = -x^3$.

6. Sketch the graph of:

   a) $y = 2|x| + 3$; b) $y = 2|x + 3|$;

   c) $y = \frac{2}{x} + 3$; d) $y = \frac{2}{x + 3}$.

Ⓒ

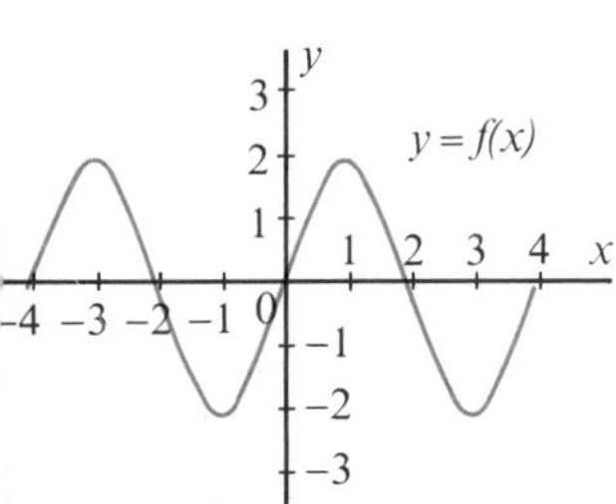

7. Copy the graph of $y = f(x)$ shown. On the same axes, sketch the graphs of $y = 2f(x)$, $y = 0.5f(x)$, and $y = -f(x)$.

8. a) Sketch on the same axes:

   $y = 2^x$, $y = 2 \times 2^x$, $y = 4 \times 2^x$.

   b) Describe two different transformations which relate:

   i) $y = 2 \times 2^x$ to $y = 2^x$;

   ii) $y = 4 \times 2^x$ to $y = 2^x$.

9-5 GRAPHING $y = af(x - p) + q$

In the previous three sections we investigated the effects of the constants a, p, and q on the graphs of such functions as $y = ax^3$, $y = 2^x + q$, and $y = \sqrt{x - p}$. We now consider the combined effects of these constants on the graph of a function such as $y = 2|x - 4| + 3$. The numbers in the equation indicate how to obtain its graph from the graph of $y = |x|$.

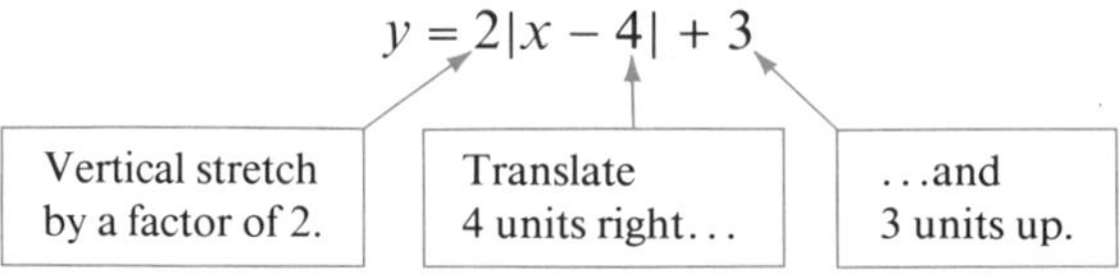

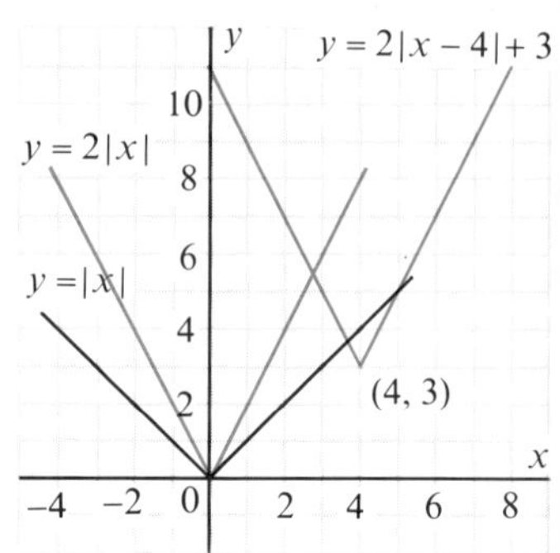

To graph the function, follow these steps:

Step 1. Graph $y = |x|$.

Step 2. Graph $y = 2|x|$.

Step 3. Translate all points on the graph, in Step 2, 4 units to the right and 3 units up.

The first two steps are useful because they aid in visualizing the appearance of the graph. They can often be omitted, as the next example shows.

Example 1.

Graph: $y = -\frac{1}{2}(x + 1)^3 + 2$

Solution.

The numbers in the equation indicate how the graph is obtained from the graph of the cubic function $y = x^3$.

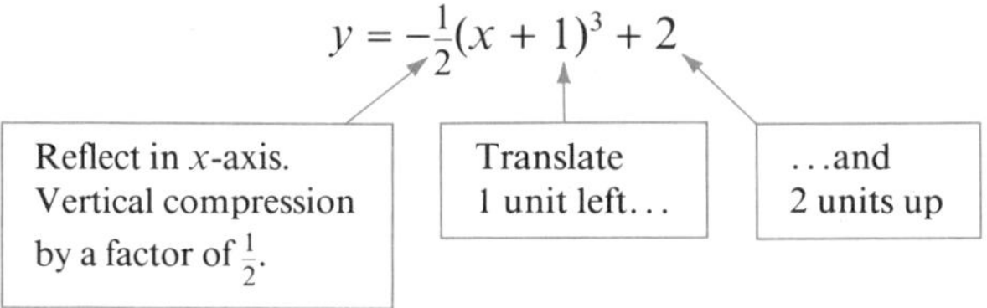

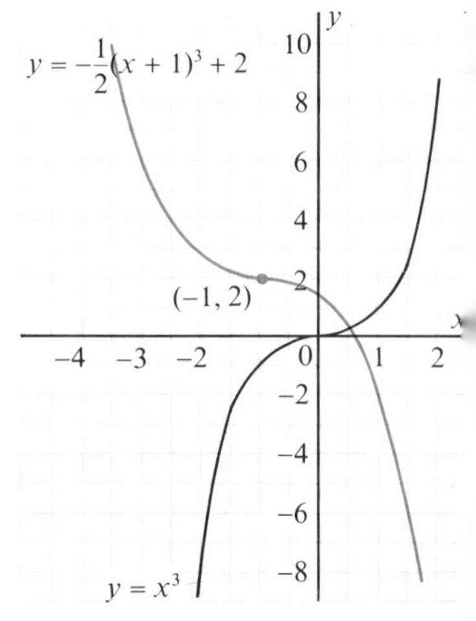

If only a reasonable sketch is required, it can be drawn on plain paper.

Example 2.

The speed of a vehicle, v, in kilometres per hour, can be estimated from the length, d, in metres, of the skid marks. If $v = 12.6\sqrt{d} + 8$, where $5 \leqslant d \leqslant 60$, sketch a graph of v as a function of d without making a table of values.

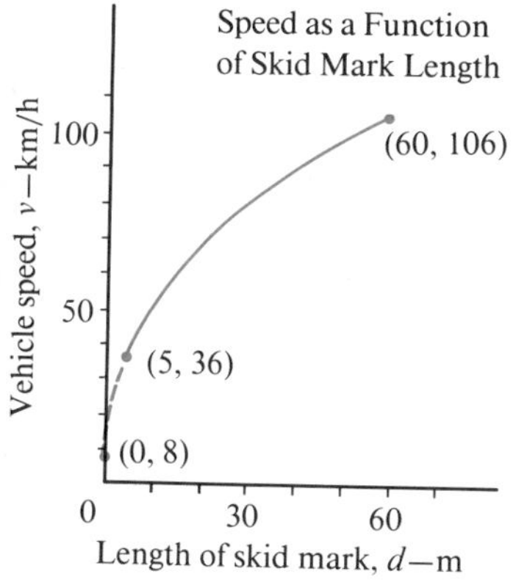

Solution.

The numbers in the equation indicate how the graph is obtained from the graph of the square root function $v = \sqrt{d}$:

$$v = 12.6\sqrt{d} + 8$$

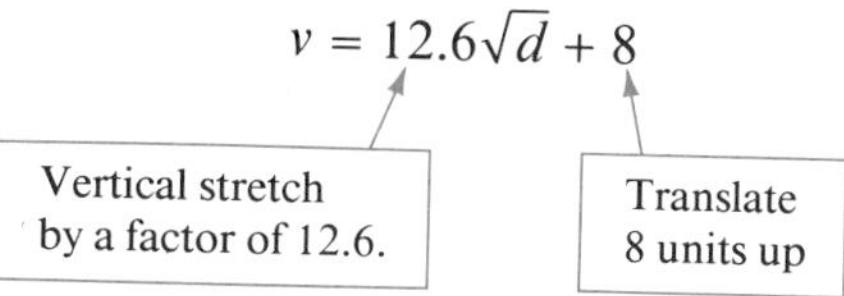

The second coordinates of the endpoints of the graph can be found with a calculator and serve to determine the scales for the axes. A third point, (0, 8), the maximum speed at which the vehicle leaves no skid marks, enables an approximation of the graph to be drawn.

The diagram below illustrates how the graph of the function defined by $y = af(x - p) + q$ is determined by the graph of $y = f(x)$ and the values of the constants a, p, and q.

Transformations of Functions

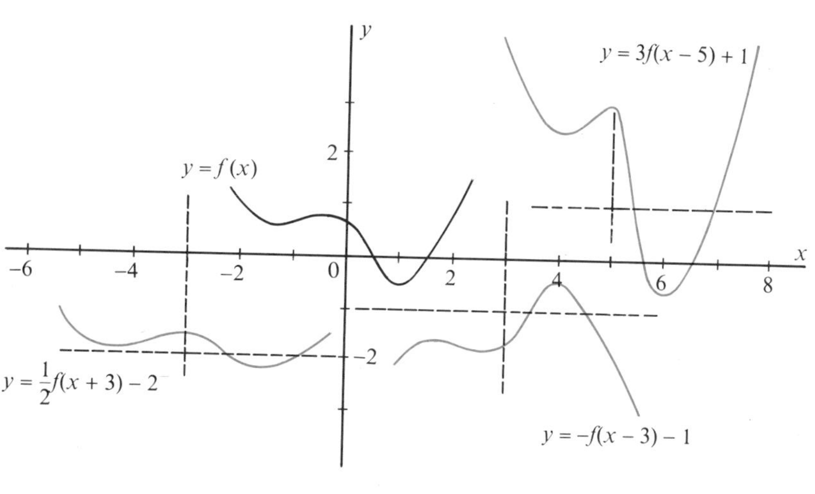

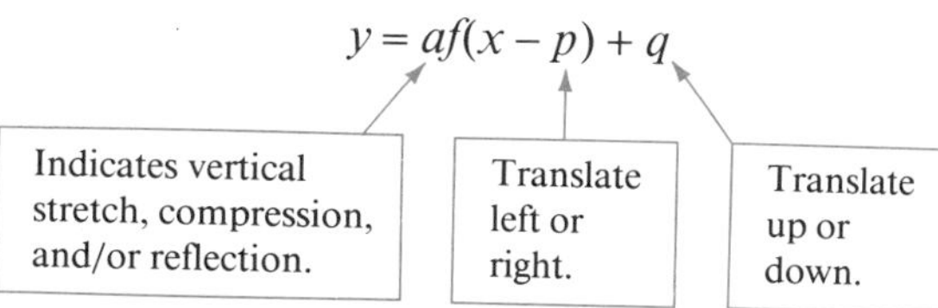

EXERCISES 9-5

Ⓐ

1. Which of the six graphs best represents:

   a) $y = 2\sqrt{x-2} + 2$? b) $y = \dfrac{-1}{x+3} - 1$? c) $y = 0.5(x+2)^3 + 10$?

i) 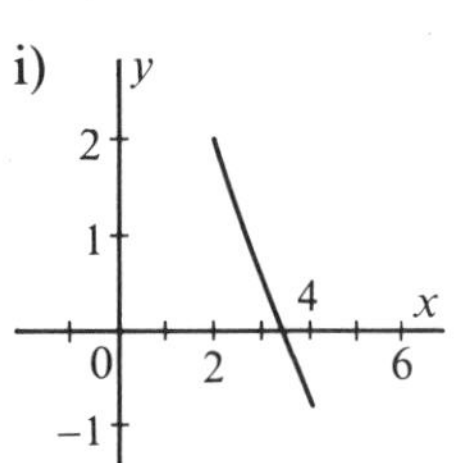

ii) 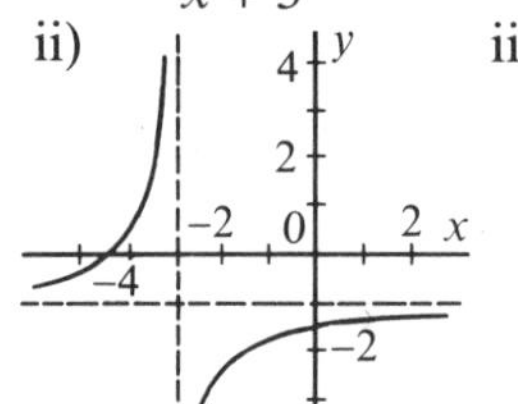

iii) 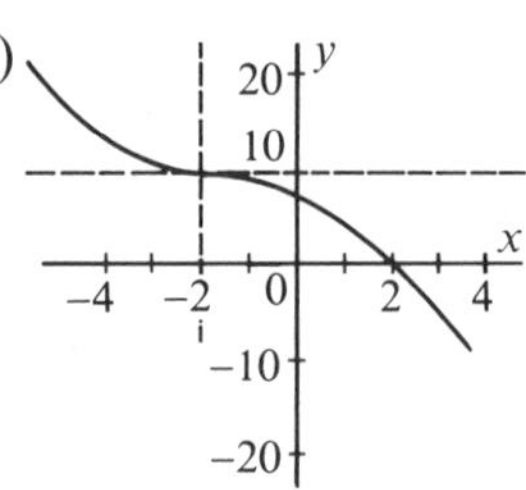

iv) 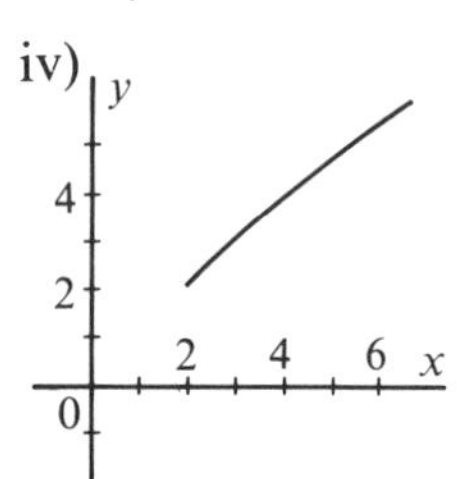

v) 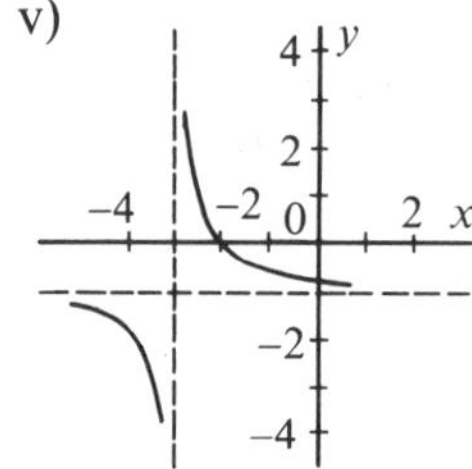

vi) 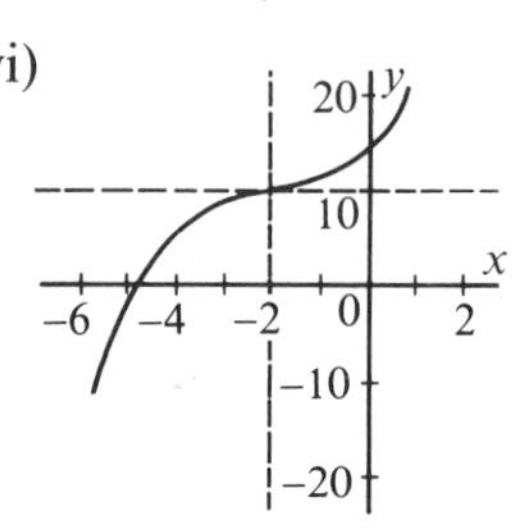

2. Sketch both graphs on the same axes without making a table:

   a) $y = 2|x+4| - 3$, $\quad y = \frac{1}{2}|x+4| - 3$.

   b) $y = 2 \times 2^x + 4$, $\quad y = \frac{1}{2} \times 2^x + 4$.

3. Which of the four functions best represents each graph?

   i) $y = 2|x+3| - 1$

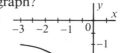

   ii) $y = -|x-2| + 4$

   iii) $y = 0.5 \times 2^{x-1} + 1$

   iv) $y = -2^{x+1} - 1$

a) 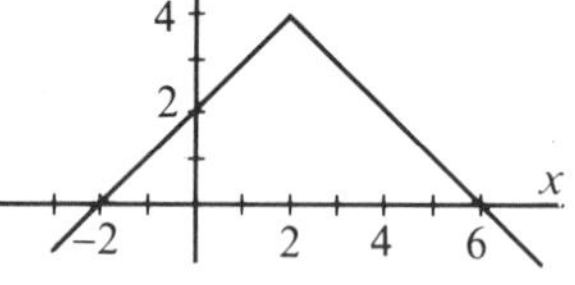

b)

4. Sketch both graphs on the same axes without making a table:

   a) $y = 3\sqrt{x+5} - 1$, $\quad y = -\sqrt{x-2} + 3$.

   b) $y = \frac{1}{2}(x+2)^3 - 4$, $\quad y = -x^3 + 2$.

5. Sketch the graphs:

   a) $y = \frac{1}{2}|x-6| + 1$, $\quad y = -|x+3| - 2$.

   b) $y = \dfrac{3}{x-2} + 1$, $\quad y = \dfrac{-1}{x+4} - 2$.

6. The cost per hour, C, of operating a power boat is given by the formula $C = 40 + 0.005v^3$, where v is the average speed in kilometres per hour. Which graph best represents this function?

a)

Cost/h, C

40

Speed, v

b)

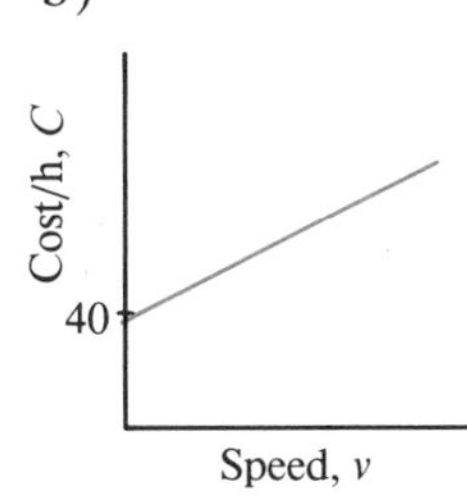

c)

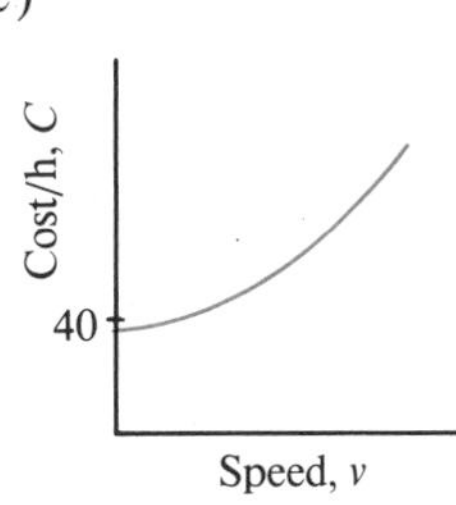

7. The value of a gravel pit, V, in millions of dollars, is given by the formula $V = \dfrac{24}{n + 1} + 1$, where n is the number of tonnes of gravel that have been removed from the pit. Which graph best represents this function?

a)

Value—$millions

25

Gravel removed, n—t

b)

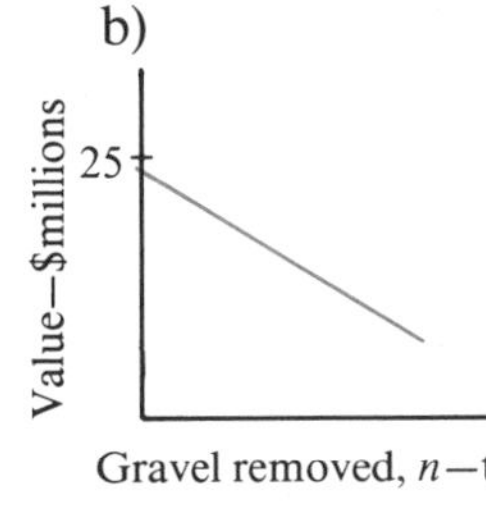

c)

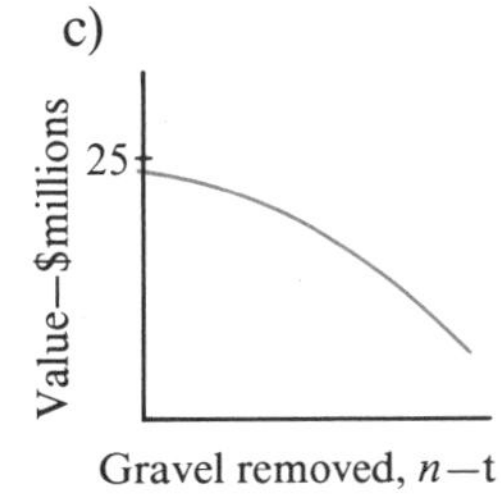

8. The amount of money, A, that must be invested now at an interest rate i in order to have $100 after one year is given by $A = \dfrac{100}{1 + i}$. Without making a table of values, sketch a graph showing A as a function of i.

9. The value, V, in hundreds of dollars, of a home computer system is given by $V = \dfrac{8}{n + 1} + 1$, where n is its age in years. Without making a table of values, sketch a graph showing V as a function of n.

Ⓒ

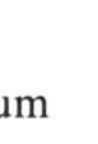

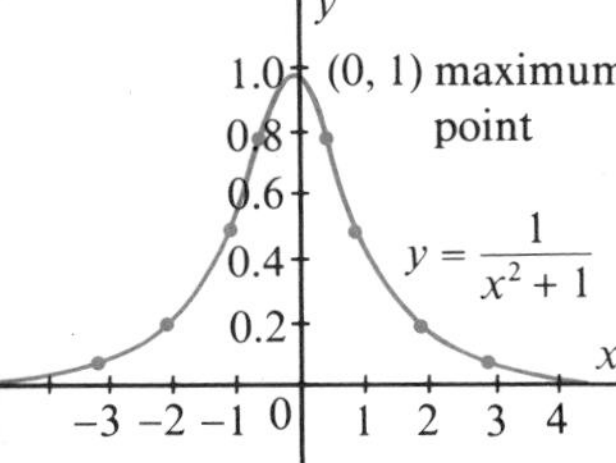

10. The graph of $y = \dfrac{1}{x^2 + 1}$ is shown. Sketch the graphs of the following functions, showing the coordinates of the maxium or minimum point.

a) $y = \dfrac{3}{x^2 + 1}$

b) $y = \dfrac{-1}{(x - 2)^2 + 1}$

c) $y = \dfrac{2}{(x + 1)^2 + 1} + 3$

d) $x^2y - 6xy + 10y - 1 = 0$

11. The graph of a function, $y = f(x)$, is shown. Sketch, on the same axes, graphs of:
    a) $y = f(x)$ and $y = f(x - 2) + 4$;
    b) $y = f(x)$ and $y = 3f(x + 1)$;
    c) $y = f(x)$ and $y = \frac{1}{2}f(x + 3) - 2$;
    d) $y = f(x)$ and $y = -f(x - 2) - 1$.

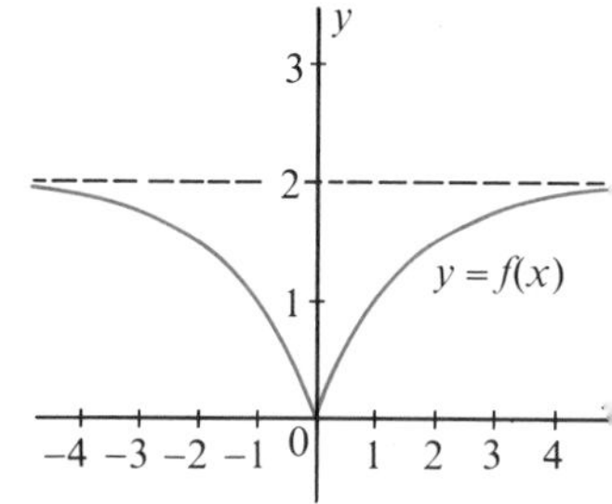

MATHEMATICS PROJECT

Classifying Functions

In earlier work, certain functions were classified as linear and others as quadratic. There are other ways that functions can be classified.

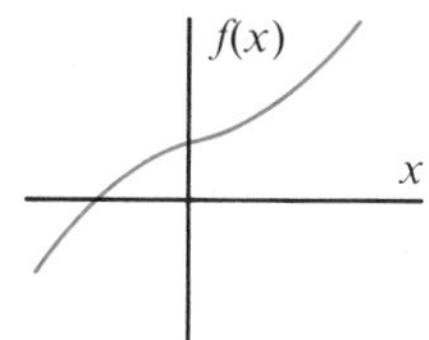

Increasing

As x increases, $f(x)$ increases.

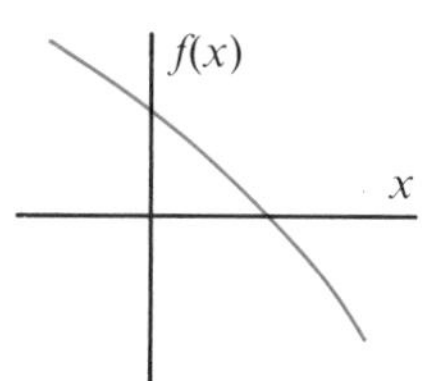

Decreasing

As x increases, $f(x)$ decreases.

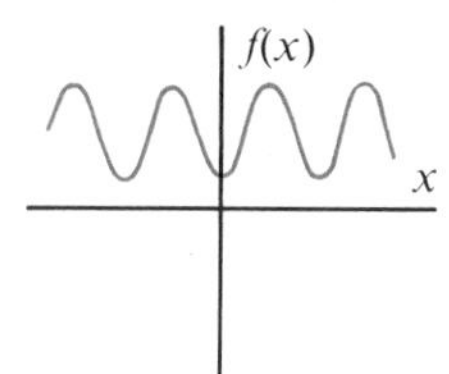

Periodic

There is a repeating pattern in the graph.

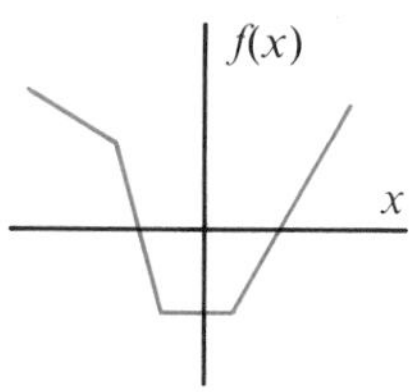

Piecewise Linear

The graph has parts all of which are linear.

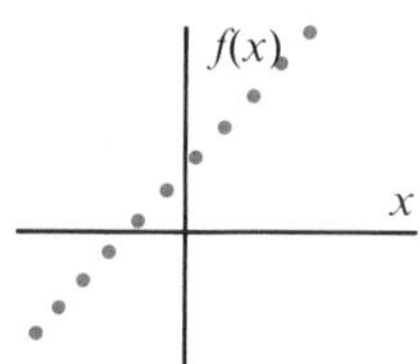

Discrete

The graph consists of separate points.

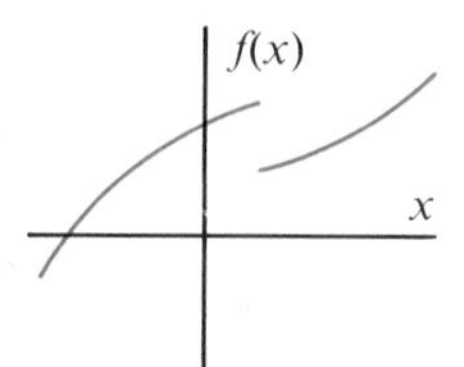

Discontinuous

The graph cannot be drawn without lifting the pencil.

Refer to the functions in the examples and exercises of Chapters 8 and 9.

1. Find at least two functions of each kind illustrated above.
2. Find an example of a function which has none of the above properties.

9-6 THE INVERSE OF A LINEAR FUNCTION

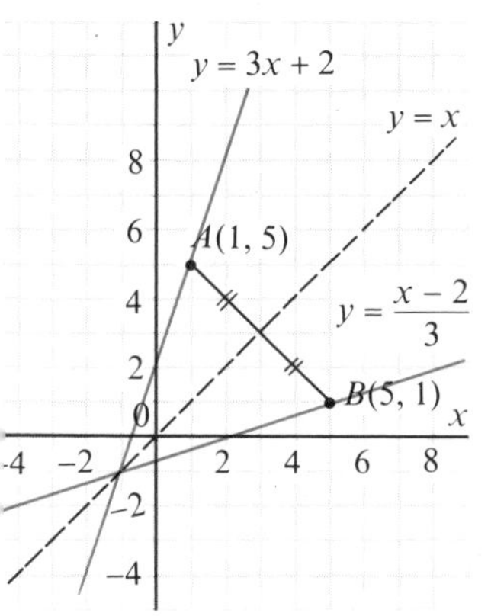

In previous sections we saw that when certain changes were made in the equation of a function, there was a corresponding change in its graph. We shall now investigate the effect of interchanging x and y in the equation of a function.

The graph shows the linear function $y = 3x + 2$. If x and y are interchanged, we get: $x = 3y + 2$.

Solving for y: $3y = x - 2$

$$y = \frac{x-2}{3}, \text{ or } \frac{1}{3}x - \frac{2}{3}$$

This is also a linear function.

Graphical Comparison of $y = 3x + 2$ and $y = \frac{x-2}{3}$

To compare the graphs of $y = 3x + 2$ and $y = \frac{x-2}{3}$, consider first their tables of values:

$y = 3x + 2$

x	y
0	2
1	5
2	8

$y = \frac{x-2}{3}$

x	y
2	0
5	1
8	2

The tables show that when x and y are interchanged in the equation $y = 3x + 2$, the coordinates of the points which satisfy the equation are interchanged as well.

The graph suggests that the line $y = \frac{x-2}{3}$ is the reflection of the line $y = 3x + 2$ in the line $y = x$. To verify this, consider the line segment AB joining corresponding points $A(1, 5)$ and $B(5, 1)$.

The midpoint of AB is $\left(\frac{1+5}{2}, \frac{5+1}{2}\right)$, or $(3, 3)$.

The slope of AB is $\frac{1-5}{5-1} = \frac{-4}{4}$, or -1.

$(3, 3)$ is on the line $y = x$ and -1 is the negative reciprocal of the line's slope. Therefore, the line $y = x$ is the perpendicular bisector of AB. Other pairs of corresponding points give similar results.

When x and y are interchanged in the equation of a function:

- the coordinates of the points which satisfy the equation of the function are interchanged;
- the graph of the function is reflected in the line $y = x$.

Algebraic Comparison of $y = 3x + 2$ and $y = \frac{x - 2}{3}$

Let x be any number, say 4.

When $x = 4$, $y = 3x + 2$ becomes:

$y = 3(4) + 2$, or 14 → When x = 14, $y = \frac{x-2}{3}$ becomes:

$y = (14 - 2) \div 3$, or 4

Multiply by 3. | Add 2. | Subtract 2. | Divide by 3.

Inverse operations

The function $y = \frac{x-2}{3}$ is called the **inverse** of the function $y = 3x + 2$.

> To find the inverse of a function:
> - Interchange x and y in the equation of the function.
> - Solve the resulting equation for y.

Example 1.

Find the inverse of $y = 3 - 7x$.

Solution.

Interchange x and y: $x = 3 - 7y$

Solve for y: $7y = 3 - x$

$$y = \frac{3 - x}{7}$$

The equation of the inverse function is $y = \frac{3 - x}{7}$.

To express the inverse of a function, $f(x)$, in function notation we use the symbol $f^{-1}(x)$, read "f inverse of x". In the last example, the result could be written: $f^{-1}(x) = \frac{3-x}{7}$.

$f^{-1}(x)$ does not mean $\frac{1}{f(x)}$.

When the graph of a function is given, its inverse can be graphed as a reflection in the line $y = x$.

Example 2.

Given the graph shown. Graph $y = f(x)$, $y = f^{-1}(x)$ and $y = x$ on the same axes.

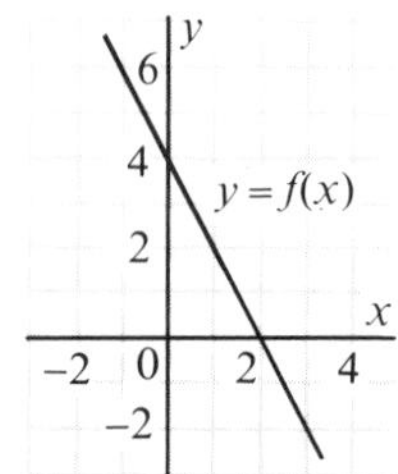

Solution.

Since $y = f(x)$ is linear, only two points are needed to graph $y = f^{-1}(x)$. The simplest ones to use are the intercepts: $(0, 4) \rightarrow (4, 0)$, and $(2, 0) \rightarrow (0, 2)$. The graph of the inverse function is the straight line through $(4, 0)$ and $(0, 2)$. This is the reflection of the given line in the line $y = x$.

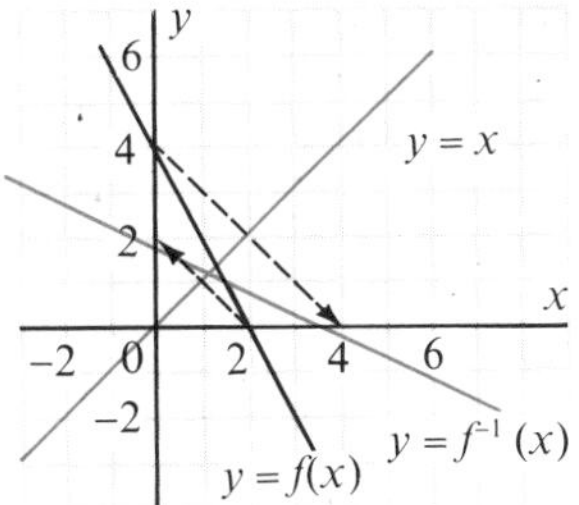

EXERCISES 9-6

Ⓐ

1. Are the two functions shown inverse functions?

a)

b)

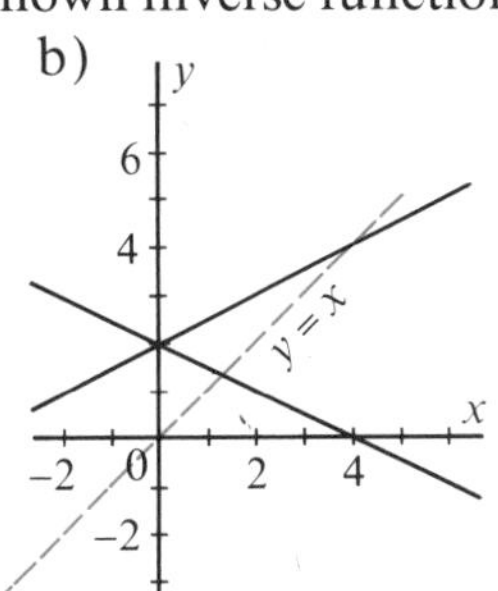

c)

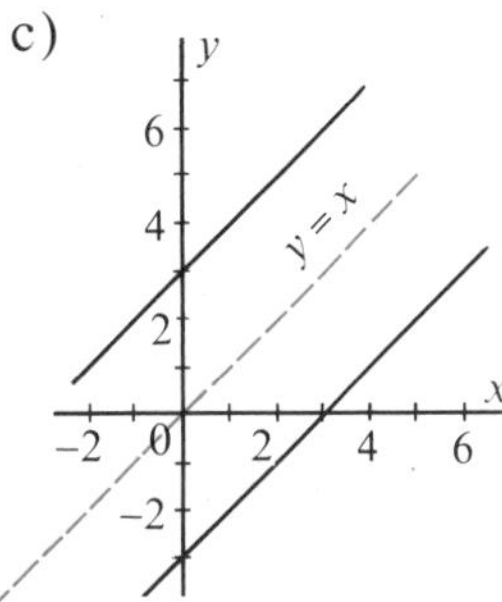

2. Find the inverse:

a) $y = x + 3$ b) $y = 4x - 1$ c) $y = 2x$

d) $y = 3x - 4$ e) $y = \frac{1}{2}x + 6$ f) $y = \frac{2}{3}x - 1$

3. Copy or graph the function, and graph its inverse and $y = x$ on the same axes:

a)

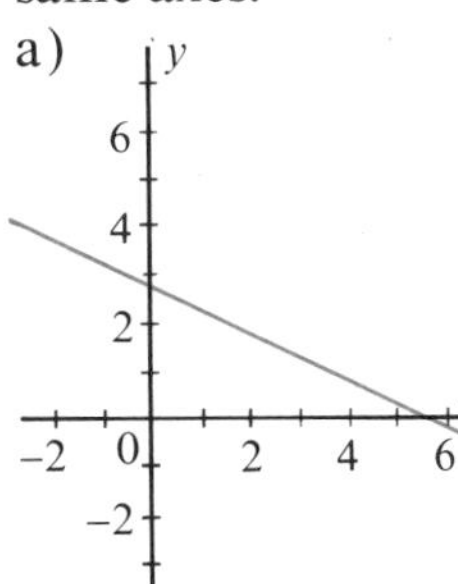

b)

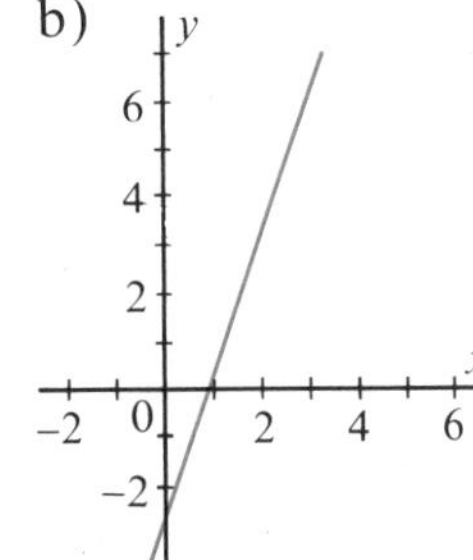

c)

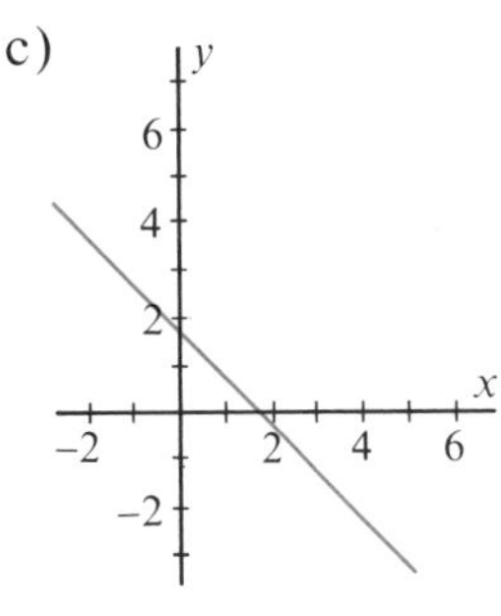

d) $y = 2x + 4$ e) $y = x + 5$ f) $y = 2x$

4. Two linear functions are described in words. Are they inverse functions?
   a) i) Multiply by 2, then add 5.
      ii) Subtract 5, then divide by 2.
   b) i) Multiply by 2, then add 5.
      ii) Divide by 2, then subtract 5.
   c) i) Add 1, then multiply by 6.
      ii) Subtract 1, then divide by 6.
   d) i) Add 1, then multiply by 6.
      ii) Divide by 6, then subtract 1.

(B)

5. Find the inverse:
   a) $f(x) = x + 6$ b) $f(x) = 2x$ c) $f(x) = 3 - x$
   d) $f(x) = \frac{1}{2}x - 3$ e) $f(x) = 5x + 1$ f) $f(x) = 2(1 + x)$

6. Determine if the functions are inverse:
   a) $y = 2x + 3$
      $y = 3x + 2$
   b) $y = \frac{1}{2}x - 4$
      $y = 2x - \frac{1}{4}$
   c) $y = 4x - 1$
      $y = \frac{x + 1}{4}$
   d) $y = 3x - 6$
      $y = \frac{1}{3}x + 2$

INVESTIGATE

Find a linear function which is its own inverse.

How many such functions are there? What properties do they have?

Write a report of your findings.

7. Which of the five functions given is the inverse of:
   a) $y = \frac{1}{2}x - 5$?
   b) $y = 2x + 5$?
   c) $y = 5(x - 2)$?

   i) $y = \frac{1}{2}x + 5$
   ii) $y = -\frac{1}{5}x + 2$
   iii) $y = 2x + 10$
   iv) $y = \frac{1}{5}x + 2$
   v) $y = \frac{1}{2}(x - 5)$

(C)

8. Show that the inverse of the linear function $y = mx + b$ is a function, provided that $m \neq 0$.

9. Since the inverse of a linear function is a linear function it, too, has an inverse. Find the inverse of the inverse of $f(x) = 2x + 5$.

9-7 THE INVERSE OF A QUADRATIC FUNCTION

The inverse of a quadratic function can be found using the same steps as for a linear function.

Example 1.

Given: $f(x) = x^2 + 4$.

a) Find the inverse of $f(x)$, and graph it and $y = f(x)$ on the same axes.

b) Is the inverse of $f(x)$ a function?

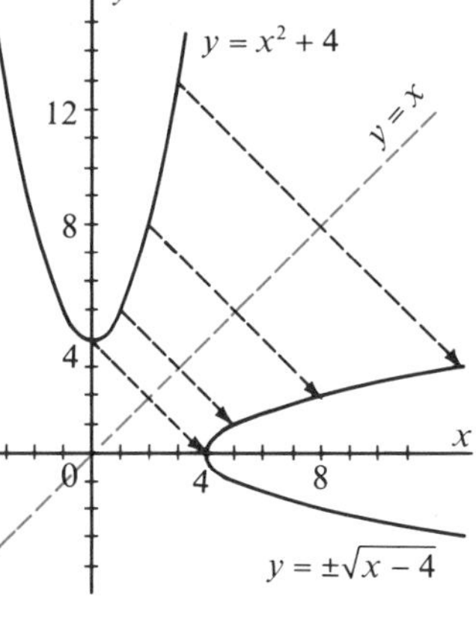

Solution.

a) To find the inverse of $f(x)$, interchange x and y in $y = x^2 + 4$: $x = y^2 + 4$.
Solve for y: $y^2 = x - 4$
$$y = \pm\sqrt{x-4}$$
$f(x) = x^2 + 4$ is a parabola with vertex (0, 4), opening up, with axis of symmetry the y-axis. The inverse, $y = \pm\sqrt{x-4}$, can be graphed by reflecting $y = f(x)$ in $y = x$.

b) The inverse is not a function because it fails the vertical line test.

As *Example 1* indicates, the graph of the inverse of a quadratic function is a parabola with a horizontal axis of symmetry. The example also shows that the inverse of a quadratic function is not necessarily a function.

It is sometimes convenient to restrict the domain of a quadratic function so that its inverse is a function. Since the graph is a parabola, the restriction requires limiting the values of x to those on one side or the other of the axis of symmetry.

Example 2.

Show two different ways of restricting the domain of $f(x) = x^2 + 4$ so that its inverse is a function. Illustrate both by a graph.

Solution

Domain of $y = x^2 + 4$ restricted to non-negative real numbers

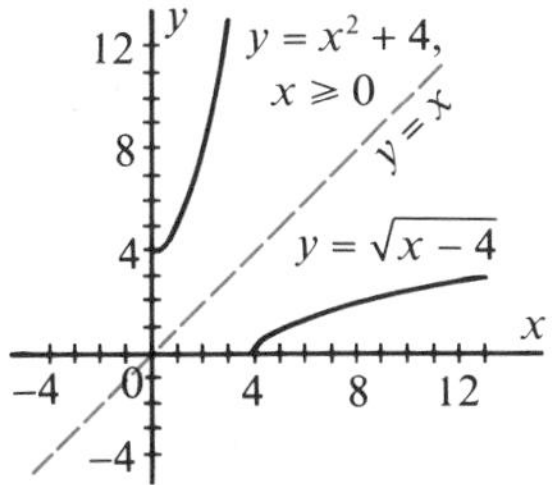

Domain of $y = x^2 + 4$ restricted to non-positive real numbers

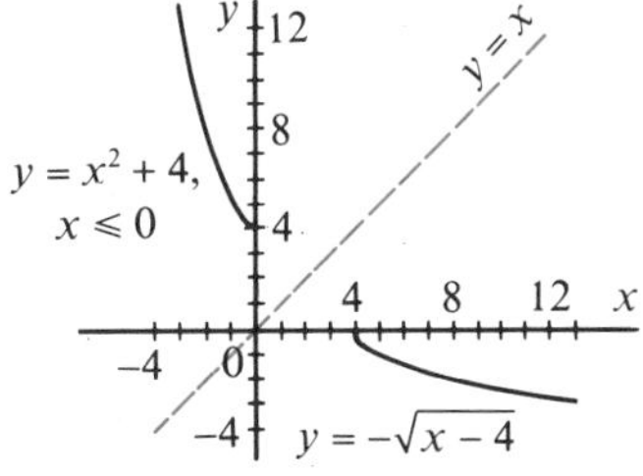

In both cases, the inverse is a function because it passes the vertical line test. The equations are: $y = \sqrt{x-4}$ and $y = -\sqrt{x-4}$.

EXERCISES 9-7

(A)

1. Find the inverse:

   a) $y = x^2$ b) $y = x^2 - 1$ c) $y = x^2 + 3$

   d) $y = 2x^2 + 5$ e) $y = \frac{1}{4}x^2 - 2$ f) $y = \frac{x^2 - 2}{4}$

2. Graph the function, its inverse, and $y = x$ on the same axes:

   a) 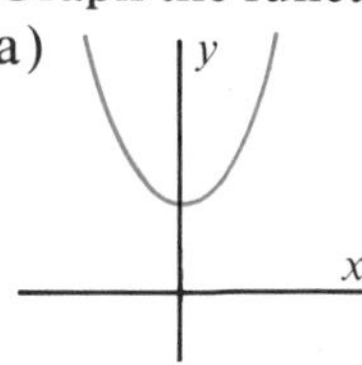

   b) 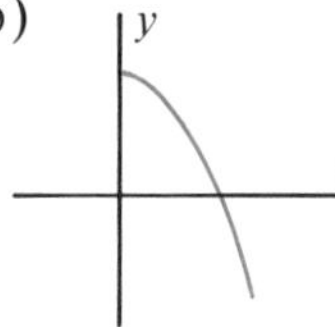

   c) 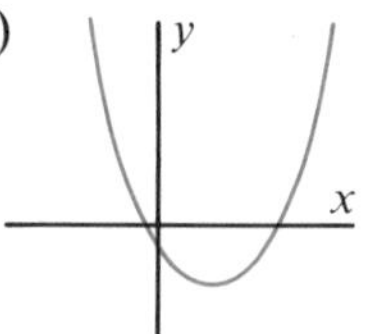

   d) $y = x^2 - 3$ e) $y = 2x^2 + 1$ f) $y = \frac{1}{3}x^2 - 2$

(B)

3. Find the inverse of $f(x)$ when:

   a) $f(x) = 4x^2$; b) $f(x) = 1 - x^2$; c) $f(x) = 2 - 3x^2$;

   d) $f(x) = (x + 3)^2$; e) $f(x) = 5(x - 2)^2$; f) $f(x) = \frac{1}{2}(x + 1)^2 - 3$.

4. Restrict the domain so that the inverse is a function, and illustrate on a graph:

   a) $y = x^2 - 1$ b) $y = x^2 + 2$ c) $y = (x + 1)^2$

   d) $y = (x - 2)^2 + 1$ e) $y = -2x^2 + 3$ f) $y = \frac{1}{3}(x - 1)^2 - 2$

5. Determine if the functions are inverse:

   a) $y = x^2 + 6, x \geqslant 0$
   $y = \sqrt{x + 6}$

   b) $y = 2x^2 - 3, x \leqslant 0$
   $y = -\sqrt{\frac{x + 3}{2}}$

   c) $y = 4(x + 1)^2, x \leqslant -1$
   $y = \frac{\sqrt{-x} - 2}{2}$

   d) $y = \frac{1}{3}(x - 2)^2 + 5, x \leqslant 2$
   $y = -\sqrt{3x + 3}$

6. Which of the five functions given is the inverse of:

   a) $y = x^2 - 12, x \geqslant 0$?

   b) $y = -\frac{1}{2}x^2 + 3, x \geqslant 0$?

   c) $y = 3(x - 1)^2 - 2, x \geqslant 1$?

   i) $y = \frac{1}{3}\sqrt{x + 3}$

   ii) $y = \sqrt{x + 12}$

   iii) $y = 2\sqrt{x - 3}$

   iv) $y = \sqrt{\frac{x + 2}{3}} + 1$

   v) $y = \sqrt{6 - 2x}$

(C)

7. Find the inverse, then graph the function, its inverse, and $y = x$:

   a) $y = 1 + \sqrt{x}$ b) $y = 3 - 2\sqrt{x}$

Review Exercises

1. a) Using tables of values, graph:

   i) $y = \dfrac{1}{x}$; ii) $y = \dfrac{1}{2x}$; iii) $y = \dfrac{1}{4x} + 1$.

   b) State the domain and range of the functions in (a).

2. Which of the four functions best represents each graph?

   i) $y = 2^x + 2$

   ii) $y = 2^x - 2$

   iii) $y = \dfrac{1}{x} - 2$

   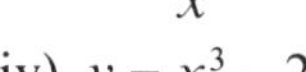

   iv) $y = x^3 - 2$

   a)

   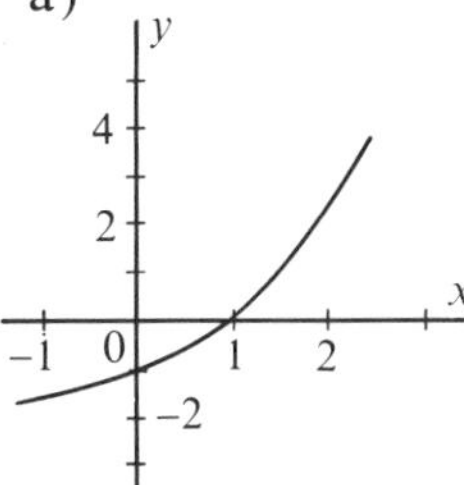

   b)

   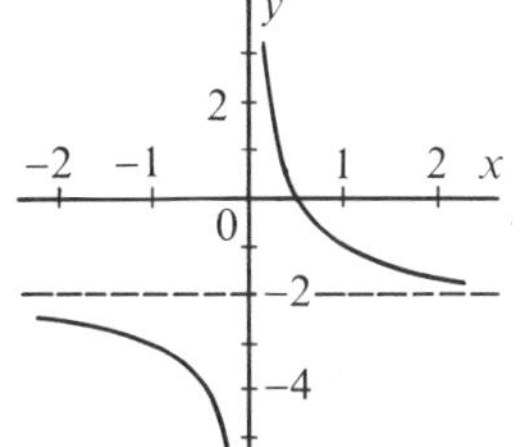

3. Without making a table of values, sketch the graphs:

   a) i) $y = |x|$ ii) $y = |x - 2|$ iii) $y = |x + 2|$

   b) i) $y = x^3$ ii) $y = (x - 2)^3$ iii) $y = (x + 2)^3$

4. Without making a table of values, sketch the graphs:

   a) i) $y = \dfrac{1}{x}$ ii) $y = \dfrac{2}{x}$ iii) $y = -\dfrac{2}{x}$

   b) i) $y = |x|$ ii) $y = 3|x|$ iii) $y = -3|x|$

5. Which of the four functions best represents each graph?

   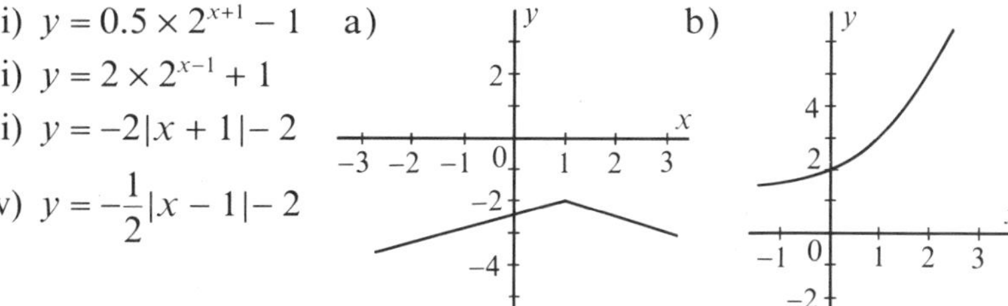

   i) $y = 0.5 \times 2^{x+1} - 1$

   ii) $y = 2 \times 2^{x-1} + 1$

   iii) $y = -2|x + 1| - 2$

   iv) $y = -\dfrac{1}{2}|x - 1| - 2$

6. The value, V, of a car in thousands of dollars is given by:
   $V = \dfrac{12}{n + 1} + 3$, where n is its age in years. Without making a table of values, sketch a graph showing V as a function of n.

7. Find the inverse:

   a) $f(x) = x + 3$ b) $f(y) = 3y$ c) $f(x) = 2 + x$

   d) $f(x) = \dfrac{1}{4}x + 1$ e) $f(y) = 4y + 3$ f) $f(x) = 3(2 - x)$

8. Determine if the functions are inverse:

a) $y = x - 7$
$y = x + 7$

b) $y = 7x - 6$
$y = \dfrac{x + 6}{7}$

c) $y = 2x + 9$
$y = \dfrac{x - 2}{9}$

d) $y = \dfrac{1}{3}x + 3$
$y = 3(x - 3)$

9. Find the inverse of $f(x)$ when:

a) $f(x) = 9x^2$; b) $f(x) = 4 - x^2$; c) $f(x) = 1 - 4x^2$;

d) $f(x) = (x - 2)^2$; e) $f(x) = 3(x - 1)^2$; f) $f(x) = \dfrac{1}{3}(x - 2)^2 + 5$.

10. Which of the five functions given is the inverse of:

a) $y = 4x^2 - 3, x \geqslant 0$?

b) $y = -\dfrac{1}{4}x^2 + \dfrac{1}{2}, x \leqslant 0$?

c) $y = 2(x - 2)^2 + 2, x \geqslant 2$?

i) $y = -\sqrt{2x + 1}$

ii) $y = -\sqrt{2 - 4x}$

iii) $y = \dfrac{1}{2}\sqrt{x + 3}$

iv) $y = \dfrac{1}{2}\sqrt{x - 3}$

v) $y = 2 + \sqrt{\dfrac{x - 2}{2}}$

Cumulative Review (Chapters 8 and 9)

1. State the domain and range:

a)

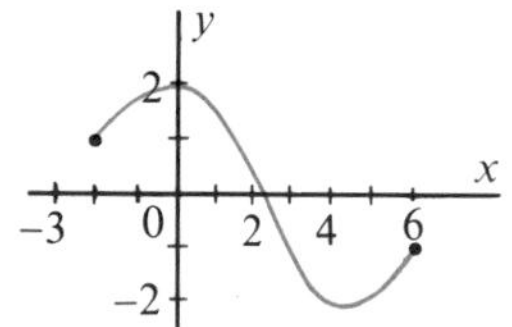

b) $y = 2x^2 + 4$

c) $y = \sqrt{3x - 4}$

d) $y = \dfrac{1}{x + 3}$

2. Which of the following represent a function?

a)

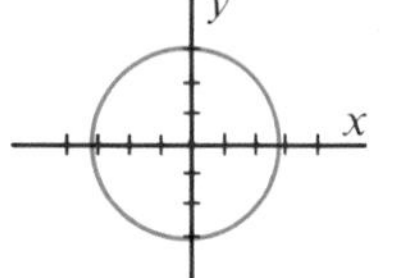

b) $\{(3, 6), (4, 5), (-2, 5), (-1, 5)\}$

c) $y = 6x - 2$

d) $y^2 - x - 4 = 0$

3. If $f(x) = 2x^2 + 3$ and $g(x) = 4 - 3x$, find:

a) $f(-4) + g(-1)$; b) $f(x) - g(x)$; c) $3f(2x) + 2g(3x)$.

4. If $g(x) = x^2 + 2x - 24$, for what values of x is:
   a) $g(x) = 0$? b) $g(x) = -9$? c) $g(x) = 11$?

Number of customers expected, n	Amount of batter cups, c
10	7
30	21
50	35

5. The table shows the amount of batter a cook prepares for his Pancake Special.
   a) Draw a graph showing the amount of batter as a function of the number of customers.
   b) Find the equation relating the amount of batter to the number of customers.
   c) How much batter is required for:
      i) 15 customers? ii) 35 customers? iii) 84 customers?
   d) The cook prepared 48 cups of batter. How many customers were expected?

6. The number of car accidents a driver is involved in is a function of his age. One insurance company uses the formula:
$$N = 0.4a^2 - 36a + 1000$$
where N is the number of accidents per 100 million kilometres, and a is the age of the driver ($16 \leqslant a \leqslant 85$).
   a) Graph the function.
   b) At what age do drivers have the fewest accidents?

7. On a running dive from a platform, Carolyn's height, h, in metres, above the water is given by $h = -4.9t^2 + 3t + 10$, where t is the time in seconds after she leaves the platform.
   a) Graph the function for appropriate values of t.
   b) Use the graph to determine:
      i) Carolyn's height above the water after 1.5 s;
      ii) the time it will take her to reach the water.
   c) State the domain and the range.

8. Sketch the graphs of the following on the same axes:
   a) $y = x^2$, $y = x^2 + 4$, $y = x^2 - 3$
   b) $y = x^2$, $y = 3x^2$, $y = \frac{1}{2}x^2$, $y = -x^2$
   c) $y = x^2$, $y = (x - 1)^2$, $y = (x + 3)^2$
   d) $y = x^2$, $y = 2(x + 1)^2 + 3$, $y = \frac{1}{2}(x - 2)^2 - 4$, $y = -(x - 3)^2 + 5$

9. For each parabola, state:
   i) coordinates of vertex; ii) axis of symmetry;
   iii) direction of opening; iv) y-intercept.
   a) $y = 3(x + 7)^2$ b) $y = -2(x - 3)^2 + 4$
   c) $y = -(x - \frac{1}{2})^2 - \frac{3}{4}$ d) $y = \frac{1}{2}(x + 6)^2 - 3$

10. Find the equation of the parabola:
    a) with vertex (0, 0), through (2, 7);
    b) with vertex (−1, 4) and y-intercept 16;
    c) with vertex (−3, −2), that opens down, and is congruent to $y = 3x$;
    d) with y-intercept 10, x-intercept 2, and axis of symmetry $x - 3 = 0$.

11. Sketch, showing:
    i) coordinates of vertex; ii) equation of axis of symmetry;
    iii) y-intercept; iv) any other point on the graph.
    a) $y = x^2 - 4x + 7$ b) $y = 2x^2 - 4x + 5$
    c) $y = \frac{1}{2}x^2 + 8x + 11$ d) $y = -3x^2 - 12x - 14$

12. A rectangular piece of land, bounded on one side by a hedge, is to be fenced on its other three sides. What is the maximum area that can be enclosed by 200 m of fencing?

13. Classify as square root, reciprocal, exponential, absolute value, or cubic:
    a) $y = \dfrac{2}{x + 6}$ b) $y = 3x^3 + 6x^2 + 4$ c) $y = 10^x + 2$
    d) 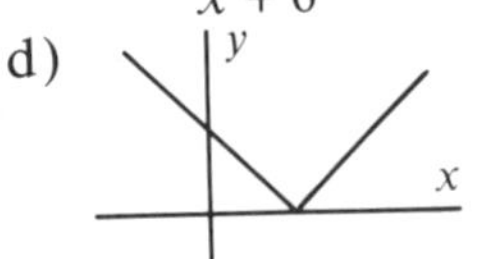

    e) 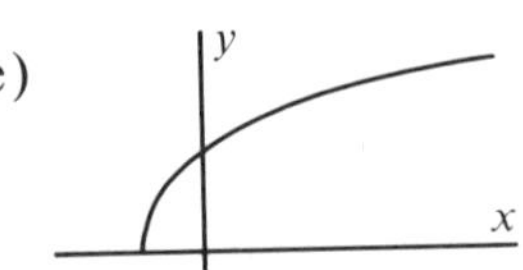

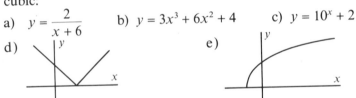

14. Sketch the graphs of the following on the same axes:
    a) $y = 3^x$, $y = 3^x - 1$, $y = 3^x + 4$
    b) $y = x^3$, $y = (x - 2)^3$, $y = (x + 3)^3$
    c) $y = |x|$, $y = 3|x|$, $y = \frac{1}{3}|x|$, $y = -|x|$
    d) $y = \sqrt{x}$, $y = 2\sqrt{x + 4} - 3$, $y = -\frac{1}{2}\sqrt{x - 3} + 2$

15. Sketch the graph: a) $y = \dfrac{4}{x + 1} + 3$ b) $y = -3|x - 2| + 4$

16. Find the inverse:
    a) $y = 3x - 11$ b) $y = -\frac{3}{5}x + 1$ c) $f(x) = 7 - 4x$

17. Graph the function, its inverse, and $y = x$ on the same axes:
    a) $y = -x + 3$ b) $f(x) = 2x - 1$

18. Find the inverse:
    a) $y = 4x^2 - 9$ b) $y = (x - 5)^2 + 9$ c) $f(x) = \frac{1}{4}(x - 7)^2 - 2$

19. Graph the function, its inverse, and $y = x$ on the same axes:
    a) $y = 2x^2 - 3$ b) $y = 3(x + 1)^2 + 2$

10 Sequences and Series

The Olympic Games are held every four years. The dates form an arithmetic sequence. Were they held the year you were born? (See *Example 4* in Section 10-2.)

10-1 WHAT IS A SEQUENCE?

"Sequence" and "series" are two words which are often used interchangeably in everyday language. In mathematics, however, they have precise and different meanings. We shall consider sequences first, and series in a later section.

In a sequence, the order in which the events or numbers occur is important. The following are some examples of sequences.

In football, the quarterback uses a sequence of audible signals which inform and direct his team but confuses the defensive team. One such sequence might be:

Red 5 29 6 Blue 4 14 2
Green 3 21 5

This tells player 4 to use play 14 and carry the ball through hole 2.

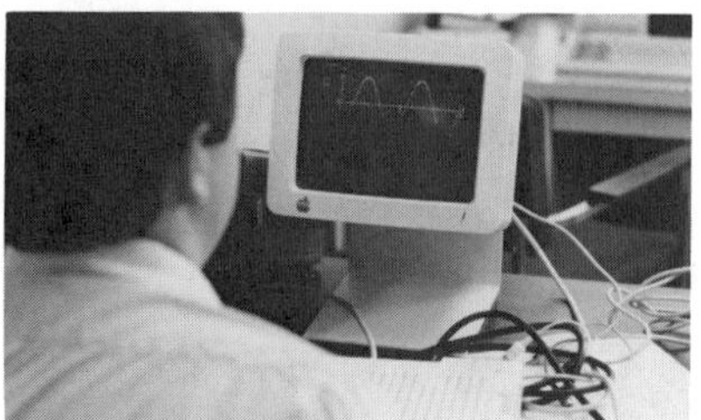

A computer program is a sequence of instructions. Here is one for finding the probability that, in a group of people, at least two have the same birthday.

```
100 REM *** BIRTHDAY PROBLEM ***
110 INPUT "HOW MANY PEOPLE? " ;N
120 T=365:X=1
130 FOR I=1 TO N
140 X=X*T/365:T=T-1
150 NEXT I
160 PRINT "PROBABILITY IS:
    ";1-X:END
```

IQ tests sometimes contain problems in which a sequence of letters, numbers, or geometric figures is given. The problem is to discover the pattern. Can you determine the next diagram?

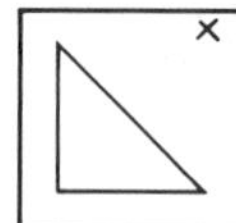 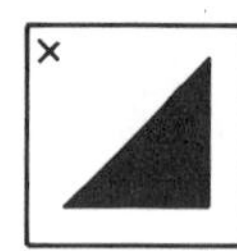 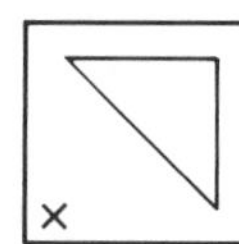 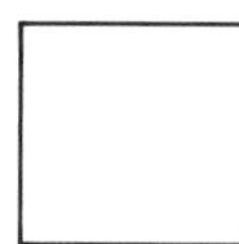

In mathematics, many sequences involve numbers. These numbers are called the **terms** of the sequence. Frequently, there is a pattern that is used to write the terms of the sequence.

Example 1.

Describe a pattern, and predict the next term:

a) 3, 7, 11, 15, — b) 2, 6, 18, 54, — c) 1, 1, 2, 3, 5, 8, —

INVESTIGATE

These sequences all start with 2, 3, 5,...
2, 3, 5, 7, 11, 13,...
2, 3, 5, 8, 12, 17,...
2, 3, 5, 8, 13, 21,...
2, 3, 5, 10, 20, 40,...
2, 3, 5, 6, 7, 8, 10,...
2, 3, 5, 14, 69, 965,...
What is the pattern in each?

Solution.

a) Add 4 to the preceding term. The next term is 19.
b) Multiply the preceding term by 3. The next term is 162.
c) Add the two preceding terms. The next term is 13.

Several sequences may begin with the same three or four terms. It is therefore necessary, when describing a sequence, to list enough terms to show the pattern which generates the succeeding terms.

The symbols, $t_1, t_2, t_3, \ldots$ are used to represent the terms of a sequence. Thus for the sequence of square numbers:

1, 4, 9, 16,...
$t_1 = 1$, or 1^2
$t_2 = 4$, or 2^2
$t_3 = 9$, or 3^2
$t_4 = 16$, or 4^2

The **general term** is n^2. That is, $t_n = n^2$.

INVESTIGATE

7
37
337
3337
33337
333337
3333337
....

The first six terms of this sequence are prime, the next term is not.

Find other sequences like this.

Write a report of your findings.

In many sequences, the formula for the general term can be used to generate the terms of the sequence.

Example 2.

Write the first four terms and 10th term for the sequence defined by:

$$t_n = \frac{n}{n+1}.$$

Solution.

Substitute 1, 2, 3, 4, and 10 for n in the formula for t_n:

$t_1 = \frac{1}{1+1}$, or $\frac{1}{2}$ $\quad t_2 = \frac{2}{2+1}$, or $\frac{2}{3}$

$t_3 = \frac{3}{3+1}$, or $\frac{3}{4}$, $\quad t_4 = \frac{4}{4+1}$, or $\frac{4}{5}$, $\quad t_{10} = \frac{10}{10+1}$, or $\frac{10}{11}$

The sequence is: $\frac{1}{2}, \frac{2}{3}, \frac{3}{4}, \frac{4}{5}, \ldots, \frac{10}{11}, \ldots$

When a few terms of a sequence are given, a formula for the general term can sometimes be found.

Example 3.

Describe each sequence and write an expression for the general term, t_n:

a) 101, 102, 103, 104,...
b) 2, 4, 6, 8,...
c) 6, 11, 16, 21, 26,...
d) 3, 9, 27, 81,...
e) 0, 3, 8, 15, 24,...

Solution.

a) The sequence is the positive integers greater than 100.
$t_n = 100 + n$

b) The sequence is the even numbers. $t_n = 2n$

c) The sequence is the multiples of 5 increased by 1. $t_n = 5n + 1$

d) The sequence is the powers of 3. $t_n = 3^n$

e) The sequence is the square numbers decreased by 1. $t_n = n^2 - 1$

EXERCISES 10-1

(A)

1. Explain how a sequence is involved:
   a) Opening a combination lock
   b) Dialing a telephone number
   b) Starting a car
   d) Writing a computer program
   e) Baking a cake
   e) Finding a word in a dictionary

2. What are the next three letters?
   a) $A\ C\ E\ G\ I$———
   b) $A\ B\ D\ G$———
   c) $A\ B\ C\ B\ D\ B\ E\ B$———
   d) $A\ B\ C\ B\ C\ D\ C\ D\ E$———

3. Describe a pattern and predict the next three terms:
   a) 2, 4, 6, 8,—,—,—
   b) 1, 3, 9, 27,—,—,—
   c) 5, 10, 15, 20,—,—,—
   d) 1, 2, 4, 7, 11,—,—,—
   e) 16, 8, 4, 2,—,—,—
   f) 2, 5, 8, 11,—,—,—
   g) 1, −2, 4, −8,—,—,—
   h) $4, 1, \frac{1}{4}, \frac{1}{16}$,—,—,—

4. The general term of a sequence is given. Write the first five terms.
   a) $t_n = 2n$
   b) $t_n = 10 + n$
   c) $t_n = 3n$
   d) $t_n = 2^n$
   e) $t_n = 10 - n$
   f) $t_n = n$

5. Describe each sequence and write an expression for the general term, t_n:
   a) 1, 3, 5, 7, 9,. . .
   b) 5, 10, 15, 20, 25,. . .
   c) 4, 9, 14, 19, 24,. . .
   d) 10, 100, 1000, 10 000,. . .
   e) 5, 50, 500, 5000,. . .

(B)

6. The general term of a sequence is given. Write the first five terms.
   a) $t_n = 3n - 2$
   b) $t_n = 2^n - 1$
   c) $t_n = 21 - 3n$
   d) $t_n = 2n + 5$
   e) $t_n = \frac{n}{3n + 1}$
   f) $t_n = 3 - \frac{1}{n}$

7. Find the indicated terms in the sequence:
   a) $t_n = 10 + 2n$, t_7 and t_{12}
   b) $t_n = 6n + 5$, t_2 and t_8
   c) $t_n = n^2 - 5$, t_4 and t_9
   d) $t_n = (-2)^n$, t_2 and t_5
   e) $t_n = \frac{n}{2n + 1}$, t_3 and t_6
   f) $t_n = 1 + \frac{1}{3^n}$, t_3 and t_4

8. Which of the general terms listed is the general term for:

a) 1, 5, 9, 13,...?
b) 20, 18, 16, 14,...?
c) 2, 8, 32, 128,...?
d) 1, 10, 100, 1000,...?

i) $t_n = 5n - 1$
ii) $t_n = 22 - 2n$
iii) $t_n = 10^{n-1}$
iv) $t_n = 2n - 20$
v) $t_n = 4n - 3$
vi) $t_n = 2 \times 4^{n-1}$

9. Find an expression for the general term of:

a) 2, 4, 6, 8, 10,...;
b) 5, 7, 9, 11, 13,...;
c) −3, −1, 1, 3, 5,...;
d) 2, 4, 8, 16, 32,...;
e) 1, 3, 7, 15, 31,...;
f) 16, 13, 10, 7, 4,...;
g) $1, \frac{2}{3}, \frac{3}{5}, \frac{4}{7}, \frac{5}{9}, \ldots$;
h) $\frac{1}{2}, \frac{2}{3}, \frac{3}{4}, \frac{4}{5}, \frac{5}{6}, \ldots$;
i) $\frac{1}{3}, \frac{3}{5}, \frac{5}{7}, \frac{7}{9}, \frac{9}{11}, \ldots$;
j) 2, 5, 10, 17, 26,....

10. Create as many different patterns as you can that start with: 1, 2, 3,...

11. Is the following a correct definition of a sequence of numbers?

a) A sequence is a set of numbers.
b) A sequence is a set of numbers written in a definite order.
c) A sequence is a function with domain the real numbers.
d) A sequence is a function with domain the positive integers.

12. Write the next two terms of this sequence of:

a) power functions: $f(x) = x^2$, $f(x) = x^3$, $f(x) = x^4$, ...
b) polynomial functions: $f(x) = ax + b$, $f(x) = ax^2 + bx + c$, $f(x) = ax^3 + bx^2 + cx + d, \ldots$

(C)

13. The least number of diagonals needed to divide a sequence of regular polygons into triangles also forms a sequence.

a) List the next three terms of the sequence shown.
b) Find a formula for the general term.

Polygon	Number of sides	Number of diagonals	Angle
△	3	0	60°
□	4	1	90°
⬠	5	2	108°

14. The angle measures in a sequence of regular polygons also form a sequence.
    a) List the next three terms of the sequence shown.
    b) Find a formula for the general term.
15. The diagram shows a system of one-way streets.
    a) How many different routes are there from A to B? to C? to D? to E?
    b) Explain how you could find the number of routes if there were more squares in the diagram.

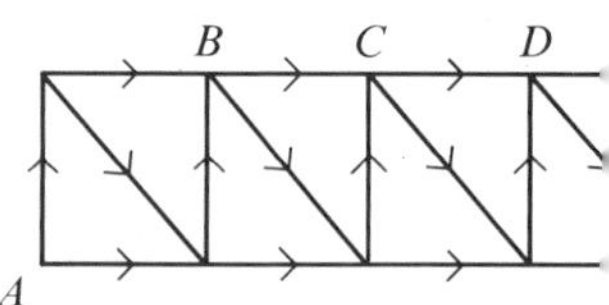

10-2 ARITHMETIC SEQUENCES

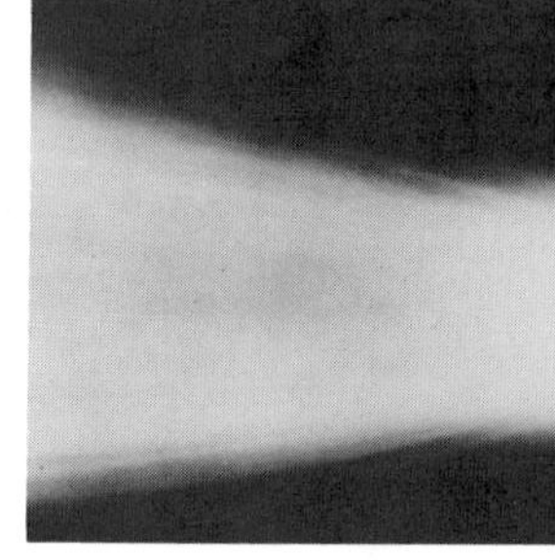

Throughout recorded history, comets have been associated with significant events such as famine, plague, and floods. In 1705, the English astronomer, Edmund Halley, noticed striking similarities in the records of major comets which had appeared in 1531, 1607, and 1682. He noticed also that these dates were almost the same number of years apart:

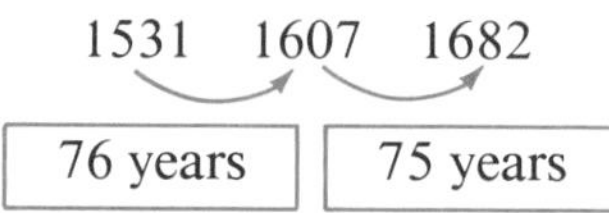

Halley concluded that the three appearances represented return visits of the same comet, which was in an extremely elongated orbit around the sun. He predicted it would return in 1758. The comet, now known as Halley's comet, returned in 1759, and records have since been found for every appearance of the comet since 239 B.C.

If it were not for the gravitational influence of the planets, the comet would always reappear every 77 years.

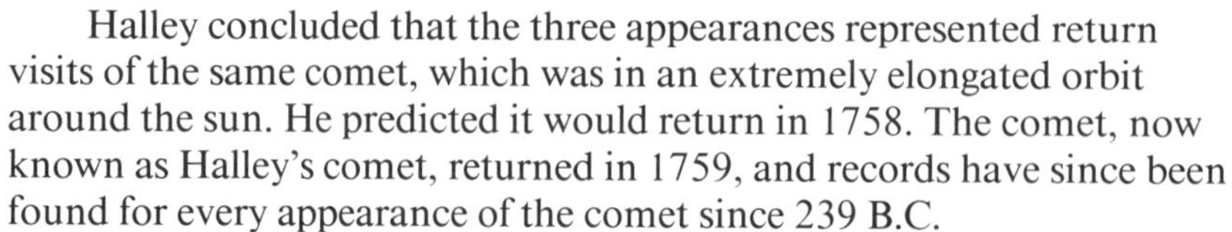

The sequence of numbers: 1531, 1608, 1685, 1762,...is an example of an **arithmetic sequence**. Each successive term is formed by adding the same number, 77. In an arithmetic sequence, the difference between consecutive terms is a constant. This constant is called the **common difference**.

These are arithmetic sequences:

3, 7, 11, 15,...	common difference 4
9, 4, −1, −6,...	common difference −5
1, 1.25, 1.5, 1.75, 2,...	common difference 0.25
$a, a + d, a + 2d, a + 3d, \ldots$	common difference d

Find, if possible, three or m perfect squares in arithmeti sequence.

If the first term and the common difference of an arithmetic sequence are known, any other term can be found.

Example 1.

In the arithmetic sequence: 2, 5, 8,. . ., find:

a) t_5; b) t_{20}; c) t_n.

Solution.

By inspection, the common difference is seen to be 3.

a) t_5 can be found by extending the sequence two more terms: 2, 5, 8, 11, 14.

t_5 is 14.

t_5 can also be found by adding four differences to the first term:

$$2 + 3 + 3 + 3 + 3 = 14$$

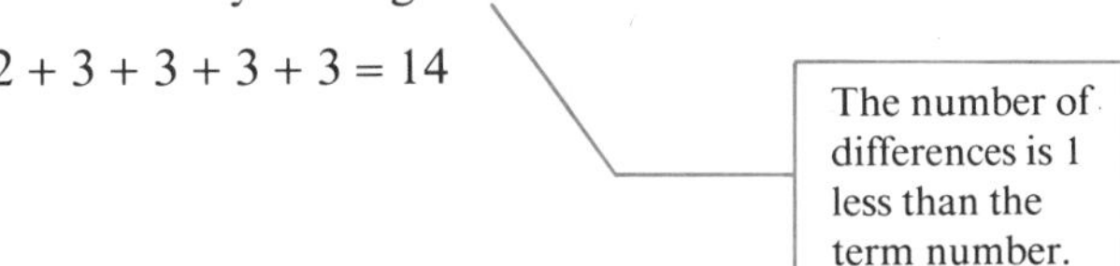

The number of
differences is 1
less than the
term number.

b) To find t_{20} add 19 differences to the first term:

$$\begin{aligned} t_{20} &= 2 + 19 \times 3 \\ &= 2 + 57, \text{ or } 59 \end{aligned}$$

c) An expression for t_n can be found by adding $(n - 1)$ differences to the first term:

$$\begin{aligned} t_n &= 2 + (n - 1) \times 3 \\ &= 2 + 3n - 3, \text{ or } 3n - 1 \end{aligned}$$

The general arithmetic sequence has the first term represented by a and the common difference by d. The first few terms are:

$$\begin{aligned} t_1 &= a \\ t_2 &= a + d \\ t_3 &= a + 2d \\ t_4 &= a + 3d \\ &\cdot \quad \cdot \\ &\cdot \quad \cdot \\ t_n &= a + (n - 1)d \end{aligned}$$

The general term of an arithmetic sequence is given by:

$$t_n = a + (n - 1)d$$

where a is the first term, n the number of the term, and d is the common difference.

Example 2.

Given the arithmetic sequence: 8, 14, 20, 26,. . .,

a) find the 20th term;

b) which term is 236 ?

Solution.

By inspection, the common difference is seen to be 6.
Using the formula: $t_n = a + (n - 1)d$:

a) $$t_{20} = 8 + (20 - 1) \times 6$$
$$= 8 + 19 \times 6, \text{ or } 122$$

The 20th term is 122.

b) $$236 = 8 + (n - 1) \times 6$$
$$= 2 + 6n$$
$$6n = 234$$
$$n = 39$$

236 is the 39th term of the sequence.

Given the position of any two terms of an arithmetic sequence, the first term and the common difference can be found.

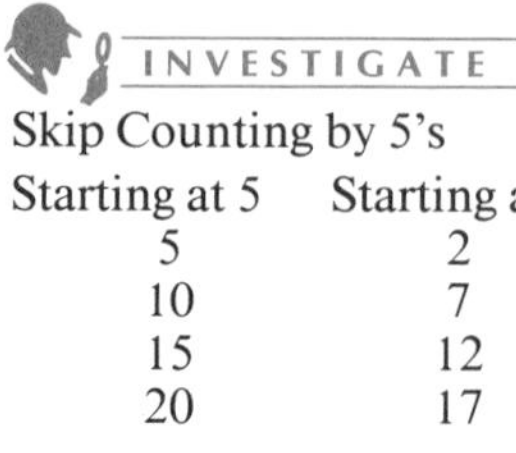

INVESTIGATE

Skip Counting by 5's

Starting at 5	Starting at
5	2
10	7
15	12
20	17
.	.
.	.

What is the general term of each sequence?

What is the significance of coefficients in each general term?

Can this idea be used to wr the general term of any arit metic sequence?

Write a report of your findings.

Example 3.

In an arithmetic sequence, the third term is 8 and the tenth term is 4.5. Find the sequence.

Solution.

Let the first term be a and the common difference d.

Since the third term is 8: $8 = a + 2d \ldots$ ①

Since the tenth term is 4.5: $4.5 = a + 9d \ldots$ ②

Solve the linear system ① and ② to find a and d.

Subtract ② from ①: $3.5 = -7d$
$d = -0.5$

Substitute -0.5 for d in ①: $8 = a + 2(-0.5)$
$a = 9$

The first term is 9 and the common difference is -0.5.

The sequence is: 9, 8.5, 8, 7.5,...

Example 4.

The Olympic Games are held every four years. The dates form an arithmetic sequence. Were they held the year you were born?

Solution.

The Olympic Games were held in Los Angeles in 1984. Write the sequence: 1984, 1980, 1976,...as far as necessary to determine if they were held in the year you were born.

EXERCISES 10-2

(A)

1. Is the sequence arithmetic? If it is, what is the common difference?
   a) 3, 5, 9, 15, 23,...
   b) −4, −1, 2, 5, 8, 11,...
   c) 2, 1, 0, −1, −2,...
   d) $1, \frac{1}{2}, \frac{1}{3}, \frac{1}{4}, \ldots$
   e) 4, 4, 4, 4, 4,...
   f) 3, 11, 19, 27, 35,...
2. State the common difference and list the next three terms of the arithmetic sequence:
   a) 1, 4, 7, 10,...;
   b) −5, −1, 3, 7,...;
   c) 16, 14, 12, 10,...;
   d) −2, −8, −14, −20,...;
   e) 2, 7, 12, 17,...;
   f) 6, 3, 0, −3,....
3. Write the first five terms of the arithmetic sequence with:
   a) $a = 2, d = 3$;
   b) $a = 7, d = 4$;
   c) $a = -1, d = -3$;
   d) $a = 12, d = -4$;
   e) $a = -8, d = 5$;
   f) $a = 25, d = -5$.
4. In the arithmetic sequence 3, 5, 7, 9,..., find:
   a) t_8;
   b) t_{25};
   c) t_n.
5. In the arithmetic sequence 11, 8, 5, 2,..., find:
   a) t_6;
   b) t_{20};
   c) t_n.
6. The disappearance of the dinosaurs about 65 million years ago is one of the great mysteries of science. Scientists have recently found that mass extinctions of Earth's creatures are separated by periods of roughly 26 million years.
   a) About when did other mass extinctions occur?
   b) If the theory is correct, estimate when the next mass extinction should occur.
7. The years in which the Olympic Games are held form an arithmetic sequence. The sequence since 1968 is: 1968, 1972, 1976, 1980, 1984,...
   a) Will the Olympic Games be held in 1998? in 2000?
   b) The modern Olympics began in 1896. Explain why the 1988 Olympics, in Seoul, Korea, is referred to as the XXIV Olympiad.

(B)

8. Which of the general terms listed is the general term for:
   a) 5, 8, 11, 14,...?
   b) 17, 14, 11, 8,...?
   c) 5, 7, 9, 11,...?
   d) 10, 8, 6, 4,...?

   i) $t_n = 3 + 2n$
   ii) $t_n = 2 + 3n$
   iii) $t_n = 1 + 4n$
   iv) $t_n = 20 - 3n$
   v) $t_n = 12 - 2n$
   vi) $t_n = 1 + 3n$

9. Write the first five terms of the arithmetic sequence defined by:
   a) $t_1 = 3, \quad t_2 = 10$ b) $t_1 = -3, \quad t_2 = 1$
   c) $t_n = 2n + 3$ d) $t_n = -5n + 21$
   e) $t_n = -7 + 3n$ f) $t_n = -4n - 6$
10. For the arithmetic sequence 2, 5, 8, 11, 14,..., find:
    a) t_{24} and t_{35};
    b) which term is 152.
11. For the arithmetic sequence −8, −3, 2, 7,..., find:
    a) t_{17} and t_{43};
    b) which term is 322.
12. Write a formula for t_n and use it to find the indicated term:
    a) 1, 5, 9, 13,... t_{17} b) 3, 6, 9, 12,... t_{21}
    c) −4, 1, 6, 11,... t_{13} d) 41, 35, 29, 23,... t_{18}
    e) −2, −5, −8, −11,... t_{10} f) 9, 1, −7, −15,... t_{46}
13. In an arithmetic sequence, the third term is 11 and the eighth term is 46. Find the sequence.
14. The 10th term of an arithmetic sequence is 39. If the first term is 3, find the next three terms.
15. The 8th term of an arithmetic sequence is 45. If the common difference is −6, find the first three terms.
16. In an arithmetic sequence, the 11th term is 53 and the sum of the 5th and 7th terms is 56. Find the sequence.
17. The sum of the first two terms of an arithmetic sequence is 15, and the sum of the next two terms is 43. Find the sequence.
18. How many terms are in each sequence?
    a) 2, 6, 10,..., 94 b) −9, −4, 1,..., 171
    c) 4, 15, 26,..., 213 d) 18, 13, 8,..., −102
    e) 5, 12, 19,..., 222 f) 42, 29, 16,..., −673
19. Find the missing terms in the arithmetic sequence:
    a) —, 9, 16,—,—; b) —,—, 8, 2,—;
    c) 12,—, 22,—,—; d) 3,—,—, 24,—;
    e) —, 4,—,—, −8; f) 15,—,—,—, −21.
20. If $5 + x$, 8, and $1 + 2x$ are consecutive terms in an arithmetic sequence, find x.
21. If $2x + y + 3$, $4x - y - 2$, and $x + 5y - 8$ are consecutive terms in an arithmetic sequence, find the relation between x and y.
22. Every appearance of Halley's comet has been recorded since 239 B.C. How many times has it been recorded?

23. On the Bayeux tapestry, which records the events of 1066, there is a crowd of people pointing to a comet in the border. Could the comet be Halley's comet?

(C)

24. The sum of the first three terms of an arithmetic sequence is 12. The sum of their squares is 66. Find the fourth term.

25. Find an expression for the general term of the sequence. Is the sequence arithmetic?

a) $1 \times 1, 3 \times 4, 5 \times 7, 7 \times 10, \ldots$ b) $2 \times 3, 4 \times 6, 6 \times 9, 8 \times 12, \ldots$

c) $\frac{1}{3}, \frac{2}{5}, \frac{3}{7}, \frac{4}{9}, \ldots$ d) $\frac{1 \times 3}{2 \times 4}, \frac{3 \times 5}{4 \times 6}, \frac{5 \times 7}{6 \times 8}, \frac{7 \times 9}{8 \times 10}, \ldots$

26. The diagram below (left) shows a pattern of positive integers in five columns. If the pattern is continued, in which column will the following numbers appear?

a) 49 b) 117 c) 301 d) 8725

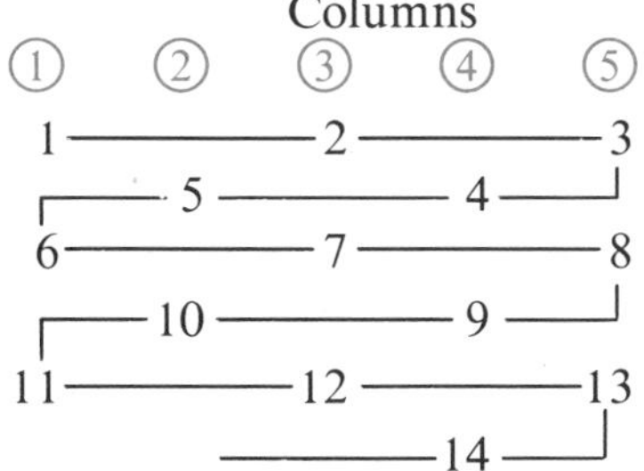

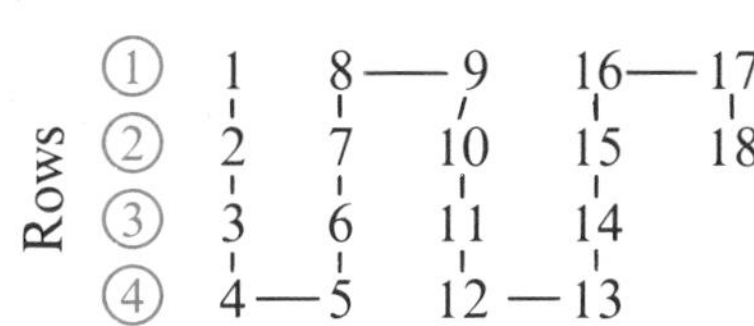

27. The diagram above (right) shows a pattern of positive integers in four rows. If the pattern is continued,

a) what are the first ten numbers in row 3?

b) in which row will the following numbers appear?

i) 75 ii) 93 iii) 259 iv) 3267

Prime Sequences

Prime numbers have always interested mathematicians. This interest has increased in recent years because many investigations can now be carried out with a computer. One of these investigations concerns prime numbers which are in arithmetic sequence. 11, 17, 23, 29 is an example. In this sequence, $a = 11$ and $d = 6$.

In 1983, Paul A. Pritchard of Cornell University programmed a computer to find, in its free time, long arithmetic sequences of prime numbers. After about a month, the longest sequence the computer had found was one with 18 terms. The first term of this sequence is 107 928 278 317 and the common difference is 9 922 782 870. At the time, this was the longest known arithmetic sequence of primes.

1. Using primes less than 100, find some that are in arithmetic sequence.
2. The following program can be used to find primes in arithmetic sequence.
   a) Run the program several times and try to find sequences with six or more terms.
   b) What is the longest arithmetic sequence of primes you can find?

```
100 REM *** PRIME SEQUENCES ***
110 INPUT "WHAT IS THE FIRST NUMBER? ";A
120 INPUT "WHAT IS THE COMMON DIFFERENCE? ";D
130 PRINT:IF A=3 THEN 180
140 IF A>2 AND A/2=INT(A/2) THEN 200
150 FOR I=3 TO SQR(A) STEP 2
160 IF ABS(A/I-INT(A/I))<0.0000001 THEN 200
170 NEXT I
180 PRINT A
190 A=A+D:GOTO 140
200 PRINT:PRINT A" IS COMPOSITE"
210 PRINT:INPUT "PRESS S TO STOP, RETURN TO CONTINUE ";Y$
220 PRINT:IF Y$<>"S" THEN 110:END
```

Arithmetic sequences of primes tend to have common differences that are multiples of 6, 30, or 210.

3. The first term of an arithmetic sequence of seven primes is less than 10. Find the sequence if its common difference is a multiple of 30 and less than 200.

4. Primes which differ by 2, such as 29 and 31, are called twin primes.
   a) Find two arithmetic sequences of twin primes in primes less than 100.
   b) Two long arithmetic sequences of twin primes have first terms less than 50 and common differences that are multiples of 210. Find the sequences.

The next two exercises concern the arithmetic sequence of 18 primes found by the computer in Paul Pritchard's investigation.

5. Find the last prime in the longest known arithmetic sequence of primes.
6. Express the common difference, 9 922 782 870, as a product of prime factors. Do the same with the suggested differences given above. The results may suggest possible differences to use in your search for long arithmetic sequences of primes.

10-3 GEOMETRIC SEQUENCES

More potatoes are grown on Prince Edward Island than in any other province of Canada. The industry is so large that an entire farm is devoted to producing the seed potatoes for the other farms in the province.

Part of the eye of a potato is allowed to grow and is then cut to produce six more. When this is done again and again, the number of potato plants increases according to this pattern:

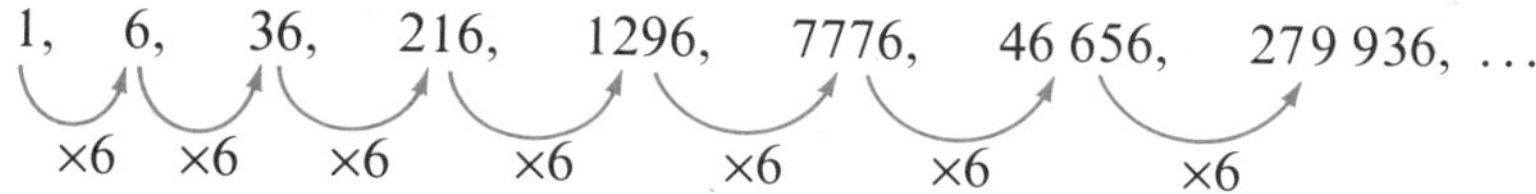

This sequence of numbers is an example of a **geometric sequence**. Each successive term is formed by multiplying by the same number, 6. In a geometric sequence, the ratio of consecutive terms is a constant. This constant is called the **common ratio**.

Each successive term is formed by multiplying by the same number, the **common ratio**.

These are geometric sequences

2, 10, 50, 250,...	common ratio 5
12, 6, 3, 1.5, 0.75,...	common ratio $\frac{1}{2}$
3, −12, 48, −192,...	common ratio −4
$a, ar, ar^2, ar^3, \ldots$	common ratio r

If the first term and the common ratio of a geometric sequence are known, any other term can be found.

Example 1.

In the geometric sequence: 5, 15, 45,..., find:
a) t_5; b) t_{10}; c) t_n.

Solution.

By inspection, the common ratio is seen to be 3.

a) The 5th term can be found by extending the sequence:

5, 15, 45, 135, 405,.... The 5th term is 405.

The 5th term can also be found by multiplying the first term successively by 3 four times:

The number of factors is 1 less than the term number.

$$5 \times 3 \times 3 \times 3 \times 3 = 405$$

b) Similarly, the 10th term is found by multiplying the first term successively by 3 nine times:

$$5 \times 3 \times 3 \times \ldots \times 3 = 5 \times 3^9, \text{ or } 98\,415$$

c) An expression for the nth term can be found by multiplying the first term successively by $(n - 1)$ factors of 3:

$$t_n = 5 \times 3^{n-1}$$

The general geometric sequence has its first term represented by a and the common ratio by r. The first few terms are:

$$t_1 = a$$
$$t_2 = ar$$
$$t_3 = ar^2$$
$$t_4 = ar^3$$
$$\vdots$$
$$t_n = ar^{n-1}$$

The general term of a geometric sequence is given by:

$$t_n = ar^{n-1},$$

where a is the first term, n the number of the term, and r is the common ratio.

Example 2.

Given the geometric sequence: 3, 6, 12, 24,. . .,
a) find the 14th term; b) which term is 384?

Solution.

Using the formula: $t_n = ar^{n-1}$

a) $t_{14} = 3 \times 2^{13}$ $a = 3$
$= 3 \times 8192$ $r = 2$
$= 24\ 576$ $n = 14$

The 14th term is 24 576.

b) $384 = 3 \times 2^{n-1}$ $a = 3$
$128 = 2^{n-1}$ $r = 2$
$t_n = 384$

Since $128 = 2^7$, $n - 1 = 7$, and $n = 8$.

384 is the 8th term of the sequence.

If any two terms of a geometric sequence are known, the first term and the common ratio can be found.

Example 3.

In a geometric sequence, the 3rd term is 20 and the 6th term is −540. Find the first six terms.

Solution.

Let the first term be a and the common ratio be r.

Since the 3rd term is 20: $ar^2 = 20$ . . . ①

Since the 6th term is −540: $ar^5 = -540$. . . ②

To solve this system, divide each side of equation ② by the corresponding side of equation ①.

$$\frac{ar^5}{ar^2} = \frac{-540}{20}$$

$$r^3 = -27$$

$$r = -3$$

Substitute −3 for r in ①: $a(-3)^2 = 20$

$$a = \frac{20}{9}$$

The first term is $\frac{20}{9}$ and the common ratio is −3.

The first six terms of the sequence are:

$$\frac{20}{9}, -\frac{20}{3}, 20, -60, 180, -540.$$

EXERCISES 10-3

Ⓐ

1. Is the sequence geometric? If it is, what is the common ratio?
   a) 1, 2, 4, 8, 16,...
   b) 2, 4, 6, 10, 16,...
   c) $4, -2, 1, -\frac{1}{2}, \frac{1}{4},\ldots$
   d) 0.6, 0.06, 0.006,...
   e) −3, 2, 7, 12, 17,...
   f) $1, -\frac{1}{3}, \frac{1}{9}, -\frac{1}{27},\ldots$
2. State the common ratio and list the next three terms of the geometric sequence:
   a) 1, 3, 9, 27,...;
   b) 5, −15, 45, −135,...;
   c) 3, 6, 12, 24,...;
   d) $6, 2, \frac{2}{3}, \frac{2}{9},\ldots;$
   e) $36, 9, \frac{9}{4}, \frac{9}{16},\ldots;$
   f) $\frac{1}{2}, -2, 8, -32,\ldots.$
3. Write the first five terms of the geometric sequence with:
   a) $a = 2, r = 3$;
   b) $a = 5, r = 2$;
   c) $a = 3, r = -5$;
   d) $a = 60, r = \frac{1}{2}$;
   e) $a = -4, r = -2$;
   f) $a = 8, r = 3$.
4. In the geometric sequence, 3, 6, 12,..., find:
   a) t_6;
   b) t_{11};
   c) t_n.
5. Which of the general terms listed is the general term for:
   a) 2, 10, 50,...?
   b) 3, −12, 48,...?
   c) 3, 9, 27,...?
   d) 5, 15, 45,...?

   i) $5(2)^{n-1}$
   ii) $2(5)^{n-1}$
   iii) $3(3)^{n-1}$
   iv) $3(-4)^{n-1}$
   v) $4(-3)^{n-1}$
   vi) $5(3)^{n-1}$
6. Is the sequence geometric?
   a) Camera shutter speeds (seconds): $1, \frac{1}{2}, \frac{1}{4}, \frac{1}{8}, \frac{1}{15}, \frac{1}{30}, \frac{1}{60},\ldots$
   b) Frequencies of a piano's A notes in hertz (cycles per second): 27.5, 55, 110, 220, 440, 880, 1760, 3520
   c)

Type of sediment	Grain size mm
Very fine sand	1/16–1/8
Fine sand	1/8–1/4
Medium sand	1/4–1/2
Coarse sand	1/2–1
Very coarse sand	1–2
Granules	2–4
Pebbles	4–64
Cobbles	64–256

d) The electromagnetic spectrum

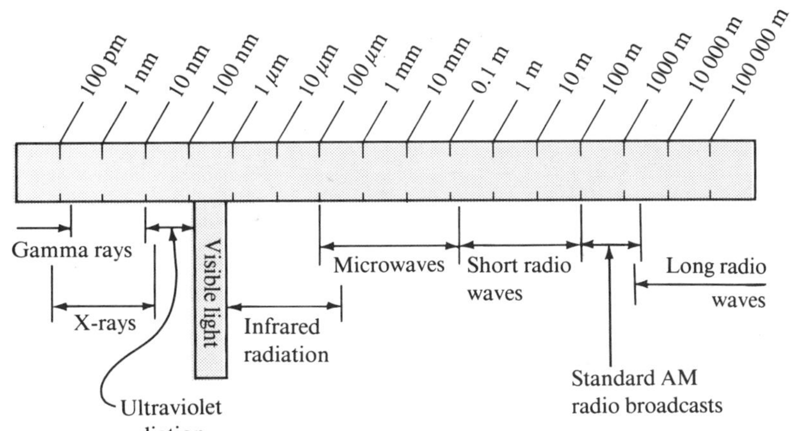

(B)

7. Write the first five terms of the geometric sequence defined by:
   a) $t_1 = 2, \quad t_2 = -6$
   b) $t_1 = 20, \quad t_2 = 10$
   c) $t_n = 3(2)^{n-1}$
   d) $t_n = 7(3)^{n-1}$
   e) $t_n = \frac{1}{8}(4)^{n-1}$
   f) $t_n = -2(-5)^{n-1}$

8. Write a formula for t_n and use it to find the indicated term:
   a) 2, 4, 8, 16,... t_{10}
   b) 5, 10, 20, 40,... t_{13}
   c) −3, 15, −75, 375,... t_8
   d) 12, 6, 3, $\frac{3}{2}$,... t_{12}
   e) 6, −2, $\frac{2}{3}$, $-\frac{2}{9}$,... t_9
   f) 3, 18, 108, 648,... t_7

9. For the sequence 3, 12, 48, 192,..., find:
   a) the 9th term;
   b) which term is 12 288.

10. Find the first five terms of the geometric sequence with the 3rd term 18 and the 7th term 1458.

11. Find the first four terms of the geometric sequence with the 5th term 1536 and the 10th term 48.

INVESTIGATE

Is it possible to find three numbers that are in arithmetic sequence and also in geometric sequence?

12. Find the missing numbers in the geometric sequence:
   a) 4, _, 16, _;
   b) 2, 12, _, _;
   c) 3, _, 12, _;
   d) _, 5, _, 125;
   e) _, _, 2, 1;
   f) 3, _, _, 375.

13. In a geometric sequence, $t_3 = 20$ and $t_6 = 1280$. Find the sequence.

14. In a geometric sequence, $t_1 = 2$ and $t_5 = 162$. Find the common ratio and the terms between t_1 and t_5.

15. How many terms are in the sequence?

a) 2, 6, 18,..., 486

b) $12, 4, \frac{4}{3}, \ldots, \frac{4}{729}$

c) 3, 6, 12,..., 3072

d) $64, 32, 16, \ldots, \frac{1}{256}$

e) 5, −10, 20,..., 1280

f) 50, 5, 0.5,..., 0.000 05

16. If $x - 3$, $x + 1$, and $4x - 2$ are consecutive terms in a geometric sequence, find x.

17. If $m + 2$, $m + 4$, and $2m + 11$ are consecutive terms in a geometric sequence, find m.

18. The population of Mexico City is 16 million and is increasing at about 4% per year. Show that the yearly populations form a geometric sequence and predict the population in 10 years time.

(C)

19. The sum of the first two terms of a geometric sequence is 3. The sum of the next two terms is $\frac{4}{3}$. Find the first four terms of the sequence.

20. In a geometric sequence, $t_3 + t_4 = 36$, and $t_4 + t_5 = 108$. Find the sequence.

21. In a geometric sequence, $t_1 + t_2 + t_3 = 3$, and $t_3 + t_4 + t_5 = 12$. Find the sequence.

22. A geometric sequence has positive terms. The sum of the first three terms of a geometric sequence is 13. The sum of the reciprocals of the first three terms is $\frac{13}{9}$. Find the sequence.

23. The aperture markings on a camera lens are:
1.4 2 2.8 4 5.6 8 11 16 22
They form a geometric sequence but the numbers have been rounded for convenience. Determine the common ratio as accurately as possible.

24. The following sequences start with the same two terms:

arithmetic sequence: 3, 12, 21,... ①
geometric sequence: 3, 12, 48,... ②

a) Show that t_3 of ② is the same as t_6 of ①.

b) Which term in ① is the same as t_4 in ②?

c) Show that every term in the geometric sequence is also a term in the arithmetic sequence.

10-4 WHAT IS A SERIES?

In mathematics, sequences and series have separate and distinct meanings. The following examples illustrate how they differ.

These are sequences:	These are series:
$1, 2, 3, 4, 5, \ldots$	$1 + 2 + 3 + 4 + 5 + \ldots$
$2, 4, 8, 16, 32, \ldots$	$2 + 4 + 8 + 16 + 32 + \ldots$
$1, 0.1, 0.01, 0.001, \ldots$	$1 + 0.1 + 0.01 + 0.001 + \ldots$
$1, \frac{1}{2}, \frac{1}{3}, \frac{1}{4}, \frac{1}{5}, \ldots$	$1 + \frac{1}{2} + \frac{1}{3} + \frac{1}{4} + \frac{1}{5} + \ldots$

A series is obtained from a sequence by writing addition signs between the terms to indicate that the terms are to be added. A **series**, then, is the indicated sum of the terms of a sequence.

The symbols $S_1, S_2, S_3, \ldots, S_n$ are used to represent the sum of the terms of a series. S_3 means the sum of the first three terms and S_n denotes the sum of the first n terms. We can sometimes find an expression for the first n terms of a series by looking for a pattern.

Example 1.

Find a possible expression for the sum of the first n terms of the series of odd numbers: $1 + 3 + 5 + \ldots + (2n - 1)$.

Solution.

Evaluate $S_1, S_2, S_3, \ldots$.

The first term, S_1:	1, or 1^2
Sum of first two terms, S_2:	$1 + 3 = 4$, or 2^2
Sum of first three terms, S_3:	$1 + 3 + 5 = 9$, or 3^2
Sum of first four terms, S_4:	$1 + 3 + 5 + 7 = 16$, or 4^2

The resulting numbers are all perfect squares. This pattern suggests that a possible expression for the sum of the first n terms is: $S_n = n^2$

INVESTIGATE

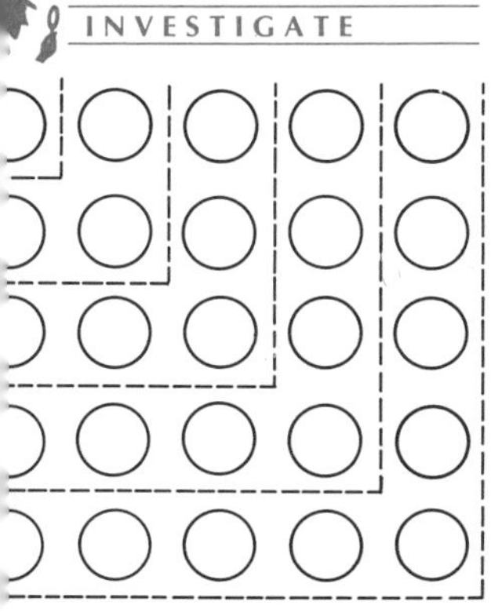

ow does this diagram demnstrate that the sum of concutive odd numbers, starting 1, is a perfect square?

In *Example 1,* the expression is called "possible" because there is no guarantee that the pattern of perfect squares will continue to hold if more than four terms of the series are added.

In the same example, the values of S_3, and S_4 could have been found with fewer additions. For example, S_4 is the sum of the first three terms and the fourth term:

$$\begin{aligned} S_4 &= S_3 + t_4 \\ &= 9 + 7, \text{ or } 16 \end{aligned}$$

If an expression for the sum of the first n terms of a series is known, the series can easily be found.

Example 2.

Given: $S_n = 4n^2 + n$
a) Find the first four terms of the series.
b) Find the nth term of the series.

Solution.

a) Substitute 1, 2, 3, 4, in turn, in $S_n = 4n^2 + n$ to find the values of S_1, S_2, S_3, and S_4:

$S_1 = 4(1)^2 + 1$, or 5 $\quad t_1 = 5$

$S_2 = 4(2)^2 + 2$, or 18
Since $5 + t_2 = 18$, $t_2 = 18 - 5$, or 13

$S_3 = 4(3)^2 + 3$, or 39
Since $18 + t_3 = 39$, $t_3 = 39 - 18$, or 21

$S_4 = 4(4)^2 + 4$, or 68
Since $39 + t_4 = 68$, $t_4 = 68 - 39$, or 29

The first four terms of the series are:
$5 + 13 + 21 + 29$.

b) The terms of the series appear to form an arithmetic sequence with first term 5 and common difference 8. Therefore, the nth term is:

$$\begin{aligned} t_n &= a + (n-1)d \\ &= 5 + (n-1)8 \\ &= 8n - 3 \end{aligned}$$

In *Example 2b*, the general term can also be found by subtracting the sum of $(n - 1)$ terms from the sum of n terms:

$$\begin{aligned} t_n &= S_n - S_{n-1} \\ &= [4n^2 + n] - [4(n-1)^2 + (n-1)] \\ &= [4n^2 + n] - [4n^2 - 8n + 4 + n - 1] \\ &= 8n - 3 \end{aligned}$$

$t_1 + t_2 + t_3 + \dots t_{n-1} + t_n$
← S_{n-1} →
← S_n →

In any series:
- the general term is the difference between the sum of the first n terms and the sum of the first $(n - 1)$ terms:
$$t_n = S_n - S_{n-1} \quad (n > 1)$$
- the first term is the same as S_1: $t_1 = S_1$

Example 3.

Given: $\frac{1}{1 \times 3} + \frac{1}{3 \times 5} + \frac{1}{5 \times 7} + \frac{1}{7 \times 9} + \dots + \frac{1}{(2n-1)(2n+1)}$

a) Find S_1, S_2, S_3, and from the pattern predict S_4.

b) Find a possible expression for S_n.

Solution.

a) $S_1 = \frac{1}{3}$

$S_2 = \frac{1}{3} + \frac{1}{15} = \frac{5+1}{15} = \frac{6}{15}$, or $\frac{2}{5}$

$S_3 = S_2 + \frac{1}{35} = \frac{2}{5} + \frac{1}{35} = \frac{14+1}{35} = \frac{15}{35}$, or $\frac{3}{7}$

Since the sums are $\frac{1}{3}, \frac{2}{5}, \frac{3}{7}, \ldots$, S_4 might be $\frac{4}{9}$.

b) A possible expression for S_n is: $S_n = \frac{n}{2n+1}$

The above method of finding an expression for the sum of the first n terms of a series applies only when we can see a pattern in the values of $S_1, S_2, S_3, S_4, \ldots$. If no pattern can be seen, an expression for S_n must be found by other methods. Some of these will be presented in the following sections.

EXERCISES 10-4

(A)

1. Write the series corresponding to the sequence:
   a) 2, 6, 10, 14, 18,...
   b) $9, 3, 1, \frac{1}{3}, \frac{1}{9}, \ldots$

2. Is the following a sequence or a series?
   a) 2, 6, 18, 54,...
   b) $1 + 3 + 5 + 7$
   c) $3 + 6 + 12 + 24 + \ldots$
   d) $3 + 6 + 9 + 12 + \ldots$
   e) $12, 7, 2, -3, -8, \ldots$
   f) $-2 + 3 + 1 + 4 + 5 + \ldots$

3. The sum of the first four terms of a series is 24. Find the 4th term if the sum of the first three terms is:
   a) 20; b) 10; c) 8; d) 30.

4. For a given series, $S_4 = 36$. Find t_5 if S_5 equals:
   a) 40; b) 60; c) 76; d) 30.

5. Find the first five terms of a series for which:
   a) $S_n = 3n$;
   b) $S_n = 2n^2 - n$;
   c) $S_n = n^2 - 3n$;
   d) $S_n = 5n - 2$;
   e) $S_n = n^2 + 2n$;
   f) $S_n = 15 - 2n^2$.

INVESTIGATE

If $S_n = an + b$, where a and b are constants, what are the terms of the series?

What happens if $b = 0$?

Write a report of your findings.

(B)

6. Which of the expressions for S_n is the sum of the first n terms of:
   a) $3 + 5 + 7 + 9 + 11 + \ldots$?
   b) $1 + 5 + 9 + 13 + 17 + \ldots$?
   c) $3 + 7 + 11 + 15 + 19 + \ldots$?
   d) $-3 - 1 + 1 + 3 + 5 + \ldots$?

   i) $S_n = 2n^2 - n$
   ii) $S_n = n^2 + 4n$
   iii) $S_n = n^2 + 2n$
   iv) $S_n = n^2 - 4n$
   v) $S_n = 2n^2 + n$

7. A formula for the sum of the first n terms of a series is given.

   Find: i) S_{n-1}; ii) t_n.

   a) $S_n = n^2 + n$ b) $S_n = 3n^2 - 5n$ c) $S_n = 2^n - 1$
   d) $S_n = 2n^2 - 3n$ e) $S_n = 2(3^n - 1)$ f) $S_n = n^2 - 4n$

8. For a certain series, $S_n = an$, where a is a constant. Find the series.

9. Which of the given expressions for S_n is the sum of the first n terms of:

   a) $1 \times 2 + 2 \times 3 + 3 \times 4 + \ldots + n(n + 1)$?

   b) $1 \times 2 \times 3 + 2 \times 3 \times 4 + 3 \times 4 \times 5 + \ldots + n(n + 1)(n + 2)$?

   c) $1 \times 1 + 2 \times 2 + 3 \times 2^2 + 4 \times 2^3 + \ldots + n \times 2^{n-1}$?

   d) $\dfrac{1}{2 \times 5} + \dfrac{1}{5 \times 8} + \dfrac{1}{8 \times 11} + \ldots + \dfrac{1}{(3n - 1)(3n + 2)}$?

   i) $S_n = \dfrac{n}{6n + 4}$
   ii) $S_n = n^2(n + 1)$
   iii) $S_n = \dfrac{n(n + 1)(n + 2)(n + 3)}{4}$
   iv) $S_n = 2^n - 1$
   v) $S_n = \dfrac{n(n + 1)(n + 2)}{3}$
   vi) $S_n = (n - 1)2^n + 1$

10. Find a possible expression for the sum of the first n terms of:

    a) $-1 + 1 + 3 + 5 + 7 + \ldots$; b) $1 + 2 + 4 + 8 + 16 + \ldots$;

    c) $1 + \frac{1}{2} + \frac{1}{4} + \frac{1}{8} + \frac{1}{16} + \ldots$; d) $1 + 7 + 19 + 37 + 61 + 91 + \ldots$.

(C)

11. a) Find S_n if t_n is equal to: i) $2n + 1$; ii) $2n + 3$; iii) $2n + 5$.
    b) Using the results of (a), predict S_n if $t_n = 2n + 7$. Show that your prediction is correct.

12. Show that only two terms of this sequence are perfect squares:

$$1$$
$$1 + (1 \times 2)$$
$$1 + (1 \times 2) + (1 \times 2 \times 3)$$
$$1 + (1 \times 2) + (1 \times 2 \times 3) + (1 \times 2 \times 3 \times 4)$$

Proving Series Expressions

In *Example 1* of Section 10-4, we found that a possible expression for the sum of the first n terms of the series $1 + 3 + 5 + 7 + \ldots + (2n - 1)$ is $S_n = n^2$. We can show that this expression is correct by evaluating $S_n - S_{n-1}$. It should simplify to the expression for the general term of the series.

$$S_n - S_{n-1} = n^2 - (n - 1)^2$$
$$= n^2 - (n^2 - 2n + 1)$$

That is, $S_n - S_{n-1} = 2n - 1$ .... (1)

This equation is correct for all integral values of $n > 1$.

We now know the following about the possible formula $S_n = n^2$:

When $n = 1$	S_1	$= 1$	All terms on the left side add to 0 except the one term, S_n.
When $n = 2$, ① becomes:	$S_2 - S_1$	$= 3$	
When $n = 3$, ① becomes:	$S_3 - S_2$	$= 5$	
When $n = 4$, ① becomes:	$S_4 - S_3$	$= 7$	
		$\vdots$	
For any value of n	$S_n - S_{n-1}$	$= 2n - 1$	
Add:	S_n	$= 1 + 3 + 5 + \ldots + (2n - 1)$	

That is, S_n is the sum of the first n terms of the series

This suggests a method of showing that a possible formula for the sum of the first n terms of a series is correct.

If S_n is a possible formula for the sum of the first n terms of a series, it is the correct formula if both the following conditions are satisfied:

- S_1 is the first term;
- $S_n - S_{n-1}$ is equal to the general term.

1. Given: $2 + 7 + 19 + 37 + \ldots + (3n^2 - 3n + 1)$.
   Show that $S_n = n^3 + 1$.
2. Given: $1 \times 4 + 2 \times 7 + 3 \times 10 + \ldots + n(3n + 1)$.
   Show that $S_n = n(n + 1)^2$.
3. Determine a possible expression for the sum of the first n terms of the following series, and then show the expression is correct:

   a) $2 + 4 + 6 + \ldots + 2n$ b) $1 + 2 + 4 + 8 + \ldots + 2^{n-1}$

   c) $\frac{1}{1 \times 2} + \frac{1}{2 \times 3} + \frac{1}{3 \times 4} + \ldots + \frac{1}{n(n+1)}$

   d) $\frac{1}{1 \times 4} + \frac{1}{4 \times 7} + \frac{1}{7 \times 10} + \ldots + \frac{1}{(3n-2)(3n+1)}$
4. Given: $1^2 + 2^2 + 3^2 + \ldots + n^2$. Show that $S_n = \frac{n(n+1)(2n+1)}{6}$
5. Given: $1^3 + 2^3 + 3^3 + \ldots + n^3$. Show that $S_n = \frac{n^2(n+1)^2}{4}$.

THE MATHEMATICAL MIND

Staircase Series

More than two thousands years ago, the ancient Greeks knew the sums for certain series. Though their algebraic development was not sufficiently advanced to be of much help, they were able to give geometric representations of such series.

For the series of natural numbers: $1 + 2 + 3 + 4 + \ldots$, they could find the sum of any number of terms geometrically. For example, the sum of the first 8 terms can be represented by the squares in a *staircase* pattern:

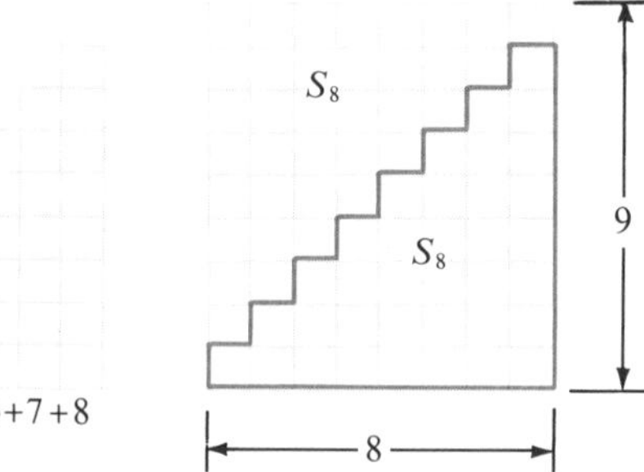

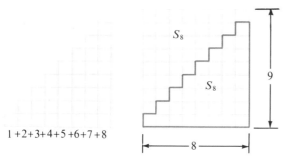

They arranged two of these patterns to form an 8 by 9 rectangle, as in the diagram. If S_8 represents the sum of the first 8 terms, then $2S_8$ represents the area of the rectangle.

$$2S_8 = 8 \times 9$$
$$= 72$$
$$S_8 = 36$$

The sum of the first 8 terms is 36.

With the efficiency of algebra available, if S_n represents the sum of the first n terms, then $2S_n$ represents the area of the rectangle.

$$2S_n = n(n + 1)$$
$$S_n = \frac{n(n + 1)}{2}$$

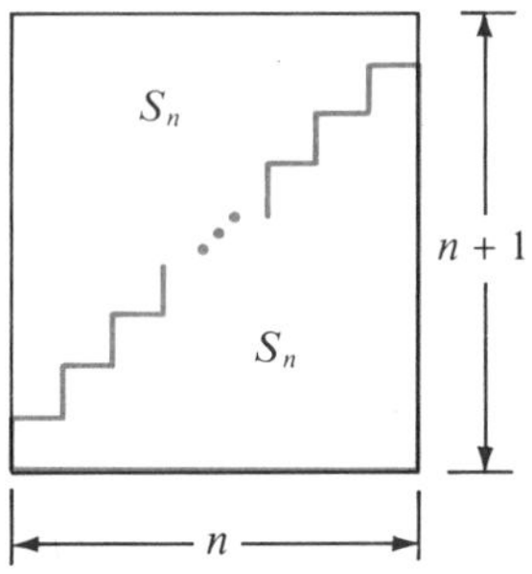

1. a) Represent geometrically the sum of the series: $1 + 3 + 5 + 7$.
   b) If the **n**th odd number can be written $2n - 1$, find an expression for the sum of the first **n** odd numbers.

2. a) Represent geometrically the sum of the series: $2 + 4 + 6 + 8$.
   b) If the nth even number can be written $2n$, find an expression for the sum of the first n even numbers.

3. a) Represent geometrically the sum of the series: $3 + 6 + 9 + 12$.
   b) If the nth multiple of 3 can be written $3n$, find an expression for the sum of the first n multiples of 3.

10-5 ARITHMETIC SERIES

Each of two summer jobs is for 3 months, or 12 weeks.

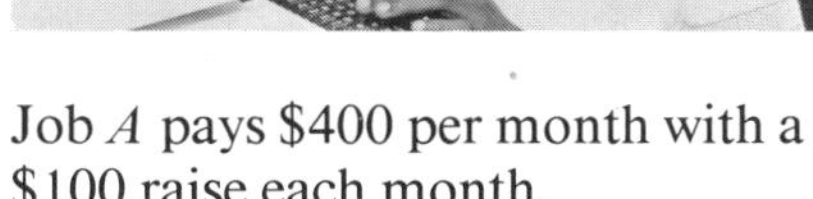

Job A pays \$400 per month with a \$100 raise each month.

Job B pays \$100 per week with a \$5 raise each week.

Which is the better paying job?

Job A. Total salary for 3 months, in dollars:

$$400 + 500 + 600 = 1500$$

Job B. Payments, in dollars: 100, 105, 110,..., t_{12}

This is an arithmetic sequence with t_{12} representing the last payment.

$$t_{12} = t_1 + (n - 1)d,$$

where n is the number of payments, and d the weekly increase.

$$\begin{aligned} t_{12} &= 100 + (11)5 \\ &= 155 \end{aligned}$$

Total salary for Job B: \$100 + \$105 + \$110 +...\$155

This expression is an example of an **arithmetic series** because it indicates that the terms of an arithmetic sequence are to be added. Instead of adding the twelve numbers, the sum can be found as follows:

Let S represent the sum of the series:

$$S = 100 + 105 + 110 + \ldots + 145 + 150 + 155 \qquad \ldots①$$

Write the series in reverse order:

$$S = 155 + 150 + 145 + \ldots + 110 + 105 + 100 \qquad \ldots②$$

Adding ① and ②:

$$\begin{aligned} 2S &= 255 + 255 + 255 + \ldots + 255 + 255 + 255 \\ &= 12 \times 255 \text{ (since there are 12 terms)} \\ &= 3060 \\ S &= 1530 \end{aligned}$$

Job B pays a total of \$1530. It is the better paying job.

This method can be used to find the sum of any number of terms of an arithmetic series.

Formulas for t_n can be used with both sequences and series.

Example 1.

Find the sum of the first 25 terms of the arithmetic series:
$2 + 9 + 16 + 23 + \ldots$

Solution.

Find the 25th term using $t_n = a + (n-1)d$:

$$t_{25} = 2 + 24 \times 7$$
$$= 170$$

$a = 2$
$d = 7$
$n = 25$

Let S represent the sum of the series.

$$\begin{aligned} \text{Then} \quad S &= 2 + 9 + 16 + \ldots + 170 \\ \text{Reversing:} \quad S &= 170 + 163 + 156 + \ldots + 2 \\ \text{Adding:} \quad 2S &= 172 + 172 + 172 + \ldots + 172 \end{aligned}$$

Since there are 25 terms: $2S = 25 \times 172$

$$S = \frac{25 \times 172}{2}, \text{ or } 2150$$

The sum of the first 25 terms of the series is 2150.

The method of *Example 1* can be used to find a formula for the sum of the first n terms of the general arithmetic series:

$$\begin{aligned} S_n &= a + a+d + a+2d + \ldots + a+(n-1)d \\ S_n &= a+(n-1)d + a+(n-2)d + a+(n-3)d + \ldots + a \\ 2S_n &= 2a+(n-1)d + 2a+(n-1)d + 2a+(n-1)d + \ldots + 2a+(n-1)d \end{aligned}$$

Since there are n terms on the right side:

$$2S_n = n[2a + (n-1)d]$$
$$S_n = \frac{n}{2}[2a + (n-1)d]$$

For the general arithmetic series:

$$a + a+d + a+2d + \ldots + a+(n-1)d$$

the sum of the first n terms is:

$$S_n = \frac{n}{2}[2a + (n-1)d]$$

What happens if $d = 0$?

Example 2.

Find the sum of the first 50 terms of the arithmetic series:
$3 + 4.5 + 6 + 7.5 + \ldots$

Solution.

Using the formula $S_n = \frac{n}{2}[2a + (n - 1)d]$: $\quad a = 3$, $d = 1.5$, $n = 50$

$$S_{50} = \frac{50}{2}[2 \times 3 + (50 - 1) \times 1.5]$$
$$= 25[6 + 49 \times 1.5]$$
$$= 25 \times 79.5, \text{ or } 1987.5$$

The sum of the first 50 terms is 1987.5

Example 3.

Find the sum of the arithmetic series: $6 + 10 + 14 + \ldots + 50$

Solution.

The number of terms must be found before a formula for S_n can be used. Let 50 be the nth term.
Using $t_n = a + (n - 1)d$: $\quad a = 6$, $d = 4$, $t_n = 50$

$$50 = 6 + (n - 1)4$$
$$= 6 + (n - 1)4$$
$$4n = 48$$
$$n = 12$$

There are 12 terms in the series.

To find the sum of the series, use $S_n = \frac{n}{2}[2a + (n - 1)d]$: $\quad a = 6$, $d = 4$, $n = 12$

$$S_{12} = 6[12 + 11 \times 4]$$
$$= 6[12 + 44]$$
$$= 6 \times 56, \text{ or } 336$$

The sum of the series is 336.

EXERCISES 10-5

Ⓐ

1. Find the sum of the first ten terms of the arithmetic series:

a) $3 + 7 + 11 + \ldots$
b) $5 + 12 + 19 + \ldots$
c) $2 + 8 + 14 + \ldots$
d) $45 + 39 + 33 + \ldots$
e) $6 + 18 + 30 + \ldots$
f) $21 + 15 + 9 + \ldots$

2. Find the sum of the arithmetic series:
a) $3 + 12 + 21 + 30 + 39 + 48 + 57 + 66$
b) $6 + 13 + 20 + 27 + 34 + 41 + 48 + 55 + 62 + 69$
c) $13 + 19 + 25 + 31 + 37 + 43 + 49 + 55 + 61 + 67 + 73 + 79$
d) $19 + 31 + 43 + 55 + 67 + 79 + 91 + 103 + 115 + 127 + 139 + 151$

3. Which of the expressions for S_n is the sum of the first n terms of:

   a) $2 + 6 + 10 + \ldots$?

   b) $2 + 5 + 8 + \ldots$?

   c) $7 + 11 + 15 + \ldots$?

   d) $5 + 11 + 17 + \ldots$?

   i) $S_n = \dfrac{3n^2 + 5n}{2}$

   ii) $S_n = 2n^2$

   iii) $S_n = 3n^2 + 2n$

   iv) $S_n = 5n^2 - 2n$

   v) $S_n = 2n^2 + 5n$

   vi) $S_n = \dfrac{3n^2 + n}{2}$

4. For the arithmetic series $6 + 8 + 10 + 12 + \ldots$, find:

   a) the 50th term; b) the sum of the first 50 terms.

5. For the arithmetic series $44 + 41 + 38 + 35 + \ldots$, find the sum of the first:

   a) 15 terms; b) 30 terms; c) 60 terms.

6. For the three summer months (12 weeks), Job A pays \$325 per month with a monthly raise of \$100. Job B pays \$50 per week with a weekly raise of \$10. Which is the better-paying job?

7. In a supermarket, cans of apple juice are displayed in a pyramid containing 12, 11, 10, ..., 5 cans. How many cans are displayed?

8. *Tasty Treats* finds its profit from the sale of ice cream increases by \$5 per week during the 15-week summer season. If the profit for the first week is \$30, find the profit for the season.

(B)

9. Find the sum of the arithmetic series:

   a) $2 + 7 + 12 + \ldots + 92$ b) $4 + 11 + 18 + \ldots + 88$

   c) $3 + 5.5 + 8 + \ldots + 133$ d) $20 + 14 + 8 + \ldots + (-70)$

10. The sum of the first 5 terms of an arithmetic series is 85 and the sum of the first 6 terms is 123. Find the series.

11. The sum of the first 9 terms of an arithmetic series is 162 and the sum of the first 12 terms is 288. Find the series.

12. The 5th term of an arithmetic series is 16 and the sum of the first 10 terms is 145. Find the series.

13. In an arithmetic series, $t_1 = 6$ and $S_9 = 108$. Find the common difference and the sum of the first 20 terms.

14. Find the arithmetic series with $S_{10} = 210$ and $S_{20} = 820$.

15. If $S_n = -441$ for the series $19 + 15 + 11 + \ldots + t_n$, find n.

16. Find an expression for the sum of:

    a) the first n even integers; b) the first n odd integers.

17. Given: $3 + 7 + 11 + 15 + \ldots$

    a) Find: i) t_{20} and t_n; ii) S_{20} and S_n.

    b) How many terms:

       i) are less than 500? ii) have a sum less than 500?

18. For an arithmetic series, find S_n if t_n is equal to:
 a) $5 + (n - 1)2$; b) $-8 + (n - 1)6$; c) $4n + 1$;
 d) $5n - 2$; e) $12 - 3n$; f) $7n + 4$.

Ⓒ

19. a) Verify each statement:

$$1 = 1^3$$
$$3 + 5 = 2^3$$
$$7 + 9 + 11 = 3^3$$
$$13 + 15 + 17 + 19 = 4^3$$

 b) Use the pattern to write the next line.
 c) If the pattern continues, what is the first number on the nth line?
 d) Show that the sum of the numbers on the nth line is n^3.

20. a) Verify each statement:

$$1 = 1$$
$$2 + 3 = 5$$
$$4 + 5 + 6 = 15$$
$$7 + 8 + 9 + 10 = 34$$
$$11 + 12 + 13 + 14 + 15 = 65$$

 b) What is the first number on the nth line?
 c) What is the sum of the numbers on the nth line?
 d) What is the general term of the sequence: 1, 5, 15, 34, 65,...?

INVESTIGATE

17 + 2 = 19
19 + 4 = 23
23 + 6 = 29
29 + 8 = 37
37 + 10 = 47
47 + 12 = 59
.
.

How long does this list continue to give primes?
Find other lists like this.

INVESTIGATE

How many letters are in this snowball sentence?

I
do
not
know
where
family
doctors
acquired
illegibly
perplexing
handwriting;
nevertheless,
extraordinary
pharmaceutical
intellectuality,
counterbalancing
indecipherability,
transcendentalizes
intercommunications'
incomprehensibleness.

Create your own snowball sentence.

Create a reverse snowball sentence.

THE MATHEMATICAL MIND

The Prince of Mathematicians

About 200 years ago in Brunswick (West Germany), a schoolmaster asked his class to find the sum of all the whole numbers from 1 to 100. He had barely finished speaking when a ten-year-old boy handed in his answer, but with no calculation. Other students worked on the problem for up to an hour, but this boy's answer was the only correct one. The boy was Carl Friedrich Gauss. He had begun teaching himself arithmetic at the age of three and would become one of the greatest mathematicians of all time.

Gauss had mentally summed the numbers this way:

$1 + 100 = 101, 2 + 99 = 101, 3 + 98 = 101$, and so on up to $50 + 51 = 101$. Since there are 50 such pairs, all adding to 101, the sum of the whole numbers to 100 is 50×101, or 5050.

In the above arithmetic, 101 is the sum of the first and last numbers added. This suggests that the sum of n terms of an arithmetic series is equal to half the number of terms multiplied by the sum of the first and last terms.

For the general arithmetic series:
$a + a + d + a + 2d + \ldots + a + (n - 1)d$,
the sum of the first n terms is:

$$S_n = \frac{n}{2}(t_1 + t_n)$$

where $t_1 = a$ and $t_n = a + (n - 1)d$

Gauss is credited with many important discoveries in astronomy, geography, physics, and mathematics. At the age of 19 he was the first to publish the proof of an important theorem in number theory. Other mathematicians knew the theorem but had never been able to prove it. In his lifetime, Gauss published eight different proofs of this particular theorem.

Carl Friedrich Gauss
1777–1855

At the age of 20,Gauss wrote that he had so many mathematical ideas there was not enough time to write them down. He was constantly revising and improving his proofs, but he left little to guide succeeding mathematicians into an understanding of his methods.

1. Use Gauss's method to find the sum of the series:
   a) $1 + 2 + 3 + \ldots + 10$
   b) $1 + 2 + 3 + \ldots + 20$
   c) $1 + 2 + 3 + \ldots + 30$
   d) $1 + 2 + 3 + \ldots + 40$
2. Can Gauss's method be used for a series of non-consecutive numbers which start with a number other than 1? Illustrate with examples.
3. Can Gauss's method be used for a series with an odd number of terms? Illustrate with examples.
4. Show that the formula for S_n above is equivalent to the formula on page 374.

10-6 GEOMETRIC SERIES

A favorite pastime of some people is to construct their family tree. Some families have succeeded in tracing their roots as far back as ten generations. If you go back through ten generations, how many ancestors will you find that you have?

Every person has 2 parents, 4 grandparents, 8 great-grandparents, and so on. The number of ancestors through ten generations is:

$$2 + 4 + 8 + 16 + 32 + 64 + 128 + 256 + 512 + 1024$$

Let S represent the sum of this series:

$$S = 2 + 4 + 8 + 16 + \ldots + 512 + 1024 \qquad \ldots ①$$

Multiplying by common ratio 2

$$\text{Then } 2S = 4 + 8 + 16 + \ldots + 512 + 1024 + 2048 \quad \ldots ②$$

$$S = -2 \qquad\qquad + 2048$$

Subtracting ① from ②

$$= 2046$$

The sum of the first ten terms of the series is 2046. Going back through ten generations, each person has 2046 ancestors.

In the above example, the expression for S is a **geometric series** because it indicates that the terms of a geometric sequence are to be added.

The above method can be used to find the sum of any number of terms of a geometric series.

Example 1.

Find the sum of the first 9 terms of the geometric series:
$2 + 6 + 18 + 54 + \ldots$.

Solution.

Find t_9 using $t_n = ar^{n-1}$:

$$t_9 = 2 \times 3^8 \qquad a = 2$$
$$= 2 \times 6561 \qquad r = 3$$
$$= 13\ 122 \qquad n = 9$$

Let S represent the sum of the series:

$$S = 2 + 6 + 18 + \ldots + 13\ 122 \qquad \ldots ①$$

Multiplying by common ratio 3

$$\text{Then } 3S = 6 + 18 + \ldots + 13\ 122 + 39\ 366 \ldots ②$$

$$2S = -2 \qquad\qquad + 39\ 366$$

Subtracting ① from ②

$$= 39\ 364$$
$$S = 19\ 682$$

The sum of the first 9 terms of the series is 19 682.

The method of *Example 1* can be used to find a formula for the sum of the first n terms of the general geometric series.

Let $\qquad S_n = a + ar + ar^2 + \ldots + ar^{n-1} \qquad \ldots①$

Multiplying ① by r: $\qquad rS_n = \quad ar + ar^2 + \ldots + ar^{n-1} + ar^n \qquad \ldots②$

Subtracting ① from ②: $\qquad rS_n - S_n = -a \qquad + ar^n$

$$S_n(r-1) = a(r^n - 1)$$

$$S_n = \frac{a(r^n - 1)}{r - 1}$$

For the general geometric series: $a + ar + ar^2 + \ldots + ar^{n-1}$

the sum of the first n terms is: $S_n = \dfrac{a(r^n - 1)}{r - 1}, \quad r \neq 1$

Example 2.

Find the sum of the first seven terms of the series:

a) $5 + 10 + 20 + 40 + \ldots;$

b) $12 + 6 + 3 + \frac{3}{2} + \ldots;$

c) $100 - 50 + 25 - 12.5 + \ldots.$

Solution.

a) Using the formula $S_n = \dfrac{a(r^n - 1)}{r - 1}$:

$a = 5$
$r = 2$
$n = 7$

$$S_7 = \frac{5(2^7 - 1)}{2 - 1}$$

$$= 5(128 - 1)$$

$$= 5(127), \text{ or } 635$$

The sum of the first seven terms is 635.

b) Using the formula $S_n = \dfrac{a(r^n - 1)}{r - 1}$

$a = 12$
$r = \frac{1}{2}$
$n = 7$

$$S_7 = \frac{12\left[\left(\frac{1}{2}\right)^7 - 1\right]}{\frac{1}{2} - 1}$$

$$= -24[0.007\,812\,5 - 1]$$

$$= -24[-0.992\,187\,5]$$

$$= 23.8125$$

The sum of the first seven terms is 23.8125

c) Using the formula $S_n = \dfrac{a(r^n - 1)}{r - 1}$ $\qquad a = 100$

$$S_7 = \frac{100\left[\left(-\frac{1}{2}\right)^7 - 1\right]}{-\frac{1}{2} - 1} \qquad r = -\frac{1}{2}, \quad n = 7$$

$$= -\frac{100}{\frac{3}{2}}[-0.007\,812\,5 - 1]$$

$$= 67.1875$$

The sum of the first seven terms is 67.1875.

When a calculator is used to find the value of S_n for some series, certain values of n and r may lead to a decimal approximation for the sum. This is usually sufficient for most purposes.

EXERCISES 10-6

(A)

1. Using the method of *Example 1*, find the sum of:
   a) $1 + 2 + 4 + 8 + 16 + 32$; b) $3 + 9 + 27 + 81 + 243 + 729$;
   c) $2 + 8 + 32 + 128 + 512$; d) $40 + 20 + 10 + 5 + 2.5$.
2. Use the formula for S_n to find the sum of the first five terms of:
   a) $2 + 10 + 50 + \ldots$ b) $4 + 12 + 36 + \ldots$
   c) $3 + 6 + 12 + \ldots$ d) $24 + 12 + 6 + \ldots$
   e) $5 + 15 + 45 + \ldots$ f) $6 + 12 + 24 + \ldots$
3. Which of the expressions for S_n is the sum of the first n terms of:
   a) $2 + 12 + 72 + \ldots$?
   b) $6 + 12 + 24 + \ldots$?
   c) $3 + 12 + 48 + \ldots$?
   d) $4 + 8 + 16 + \ldots$?

   i) $S_n = \dfrac{2(1 - 6^n)}{3}$ ii) $S_n = -(1 - 4^n)$
   iii) $S_n = \dfrac{5(3^n - 1)}{2}$ iv) $S_n = \dfrac{2(1 - 6^n)}{-5}$
   v) $S_n = 4(2^n - 1)$ vi) $S_n = 6(2^n - 1)$
4. For the geometric series $6 + 3 + 1.5 + 0.75 + \ldots$, find:
   a) the 7th term; b) the sum of the first 7 terms.
5. For the geometric series $6 + 18 + 54 + \ldots$, find:
   a) the 6th term; b) the sum of the first 6 terms.
6. a) How many ancestors does a person have in:
      i) 12 generations? ii) 15 generations?
   b) Write a formula for the number of ancestors a person has in n generations.

7. A doctor prescribes 200 mg of medication on the first day of treatment. The dosage is halved on each successive day for one week. To the nearest milligram, what is the total amount of medication administered?

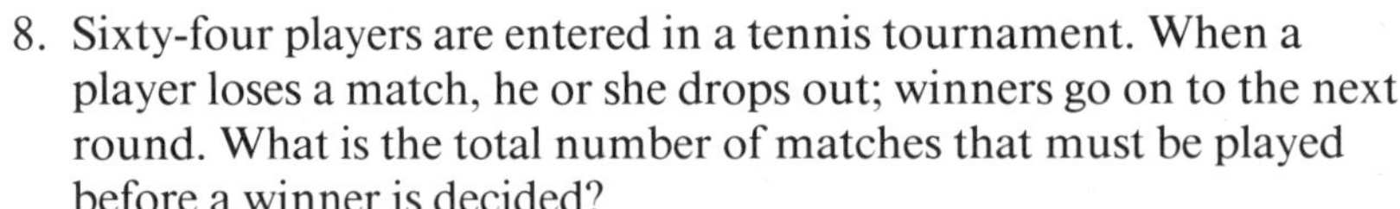

8. Sixty-four players are entered in a tennis tournament. When a player loses a match, he or she drops out; winners go on to the next round. What is the total number of matches that must be played before a winner is decided?

9. If you are paid \$0.01 on the first day, \$0.02 on the second day, \$0.04 on the third day, \$0.08 on the fourth day, and so on, how much money would you have at the end of a 30-day month?

Ⓑ

10. Find the sum of:
    a) $2 + 6 + 18 + \ldots + 1458$;
    b) $1 + 5 + 25 + \ldots + 3125$;
    c) $3 + 6 + 12 + \ldots + 768$;
    d) $\frac{1}{3} + 1 + 3 + \ldots + 6561$;
    e) $5 + 20 + 80 + \ldots + 20\,480$;
    f) $32 + 16 + 8 + \ldots + \frac{1}{8}$.

11. How many generations must a person go back to have at least 1000 ancestors?

12. The sum of the first two terms of a geometric series is 12 and the sum of the first three terms is 62. Find the series.

13. In a geometric series, $t_1 = 3$ and $S_3 = 21$. Find the common ratio and the sum of the first 7 terms.

14. The second term of a geometric series is 15 and the sum of the first three terms is 93. Find the series.

15. Find S_n for a series with t_n equal to:
    a) $2(3^{n-1})$;
    b) $5(2^{n-1})$;
    c) $3(4^{n-1})$;
    d) 2^{n+1}

Ⓒ

16. Show that for the series $1 + \frac{1}{2} + \frac{1}{4} + \frac{1}{8} + \ldots$, S_n is never greater than 2.

17. Find the sum of the factors of 2^{10}.

SIDE TRIP Counting Methods IV

Extending the counting rule allows us to solve many interesting problems.

How many three-digit numbers greater than 500 can be formed from the digits 2, 4, 7, and 8 if no repetitions are allowed?

The first digit can be chosen in only 2 ways, since it must be either 7 or 8. The second digit can be any of the remaining 3. The third digit can be either of the remaining 2 digits.

There are $2 \times 3 \times 2$, or 12 ways to get a three-digit number greater than 500.

Suppose repetition of digits is allowed, how many three-digit numbers greater than 500 can be formed?

First digit : 2 ways
Second digit : 4 ways
Third digit : 4 ways

There are $2 \times 4 \times 4$, or 32 possible three-digit numbers.

1. How many four-digit numbers greater than 5000 can be formed:
   a) from 1, 3, 5, 7 if:
      i) no repetitions are allowed? ii) repetitions are allowed?
   b) from 2, 4, 6, 7, 8 if no repetitions are allowed?
2. a) How many four-digit numbers greater than 5000 can be formed from the digits 2, 3, 4, 6, 7, 8 if no repetition is allowed?
   b) How many numbers in (a):
      i) are even? ii) end in 7?
3. There are eight doors to the outside in a school building. In how many ways can a student enter one door and
   a) leave by a different door?
   b) leave by any door?
4. Of his nine players, a baseball manager insists on having his best hitter bat fourth and the pitcher bat last. How many batting orders are possible?

1. a) 12 b) 128 c) 72 2. a) 180 b) i) 120 ii) 24
3. a) 56 b) 64 4. 5040

THE MATHEMATICAL MIND

Population and Food

Thomas R. Malthus was a man of many talents. A mathematics graduate of Cambridge University, he was also a minister of the Church of England and a professor of history and political economy. In 1798, he published his famous "Essay on the Principle of Population As It Affects the Future Improvement of Society".

Thomas R. Malthus
1766 - 1834

In this essay, Malthus set forth his theory that the rate of increase of the world's population was fast exceeding the development of food supplies. He reasoned that population, if left unchecked, doubles about every 25 years, or increases geometrically. But the food supply increases, at best, only arithmetically. Thus, sooner or later, there will be widespread starvation unless a limit is placed on the population.

Waiting for food

Malthus' essay provoked considerable controversy because it offended those who believed that society would eventually be perfect; they thought a time would come when suffering, crime, disease, and war would be eliminated. Malthus held the opposite view, and felt that the basic structure of society would always remain unchanged. Although his essay was written almost two hundred years ago, the truth of his theory is even more evident today than in his time. The following is an excerpt from Malthus' essay:

> "Taking the whole earth....and, supposing the present population to equal a thousand millions, the human species would increase [every 25 years] as the numbers 1, 2, 4, 8, 16, 32, 64, 128, 256, and subsistence as 1, 2, 3, 4, 5, 6, 7, 8, 9. In two centuries the population would be to the means of subsistence as 256 to 9; in three centuries as 4096 to 13; and in two thousand years the difference would be almost incalculable."

1. Use Malthus' figures to predict the ratio of population to food supply after:
   a) four centuries; b) five centuries.
2. If Malthus' reasoning and figures were correct, the world population today would be about 256 billion.
   a) Give reasons why this is far in excess of the present world population.
   b) Does this negate the essential validity of his theory?
3. Use a scientific calculator to find the "almost incalculable" figures for the ratio of population to food supply after two thousand years.

10-7 SIGMA NOTATION FOR A SERIES

There is a special notation that is used to represent a series. For example, the arithmetic series with 6 terms:

$$1 + 4 + 7 + 10 + 13 + 16$$

has general term $t_n = a + (n - 1)d$
$= 1 + (n - 1)3$
$= 3n - 2$

Each term in the series can be expressed in this form:

$t_1 = 3(1) - 2$ $\quad$ $t_2 = 3(2) - 2$ $\quad$ $t_3 = 3(3) - 2$

$t_4 = 3(4) - 2$ $\quad$ $t_5 = 3(5) - 2$ $\quad$ $t_6 = 3(6) - 2$

The series is the sum of all the terms. This is abbreviated to:

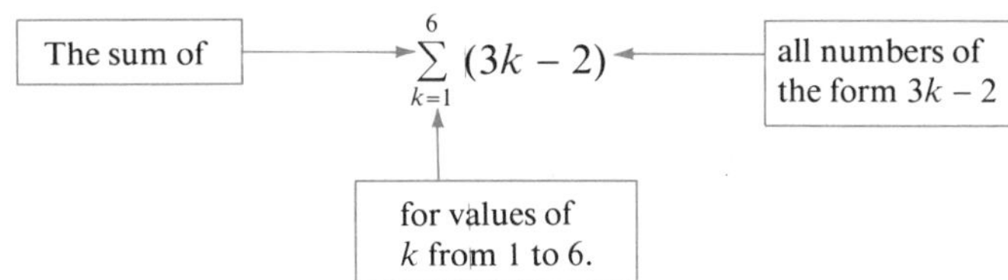

The symbol Σ is the capital Greek letter *sigma*, which corresponds to S, the first letter of *Sum*. When Σ is used as shown, it is called **sigma notation.** In sigma notation, k is often used as the variable under the Σ sign and in the expression following it. Although any letter can be used for this purpose, n should be avoided because n usually represents the number of terms in a series.

Example 1.

Write the series corresponding to $\sum_{j=1}^{3} (j^2 + 2j + 5)$

Solution.

Substitute values from 1 to 3, in turn, for j in the expression $j^2 + 2j + 5$ and add the results:

$$\sum_{j=1}^{3} (j^2 + 2j + 5) = [1^2 + 2(1) + 5] + [2^2 + 2(2) + 5] + [3^2 + 2(3) + 5]$$
$$= 8 + 13 + 20$$

Example 2.

Write the series using sigma notation:

a) $3 + 9 + 15 + 21 + 27$

b) $5 + 10 + 20 + 40 + 80 + 160$

Solution.

a) This is an arithmetic series with $a = 3$ and $d = 6$.

The general term is: $t_n = a + (n - 1)d$
$= 3 + (n - 1)6$
$= 6n - 3$

Since there are 5 terms, the series can be written:

$$\sum_{k=1}^{5} (6k - 3)$$

b) This is a geometric series with $a = 5$ and $r = 2$.

The general term is: $t_n = ar^{n-1}$
$= 5 \times 2^{n-1}$

Since there are 6 terms, the series can be written:

$$\sum_{k=1}^{6} 5 \times 2^{k-1}$$

The formulas for the sum of an arithmetic series or a geometric series can sometimes be used to simplify expressions involving sigma notation.

Example 3.

Simplify: a) $\sum_{i=1}^{20} (3i + 1)$

b) $\sum_{k=1}^{7} 2^k$

Solution.

a) $\sum_{i=1}^{20} (3i + 1) = 4 + 7 + 10 + \ldots + 61$

This is an arithmetic series with $a = 4$, $d = 3$, $n = 20$.

The sum of the series is:

$$S_n = \frac{n}{2}[2a + (n - 1)d]$$

$$S_{20} = \frac{20}{2}[8 + 19 \times 3]$$

$$= 10[65], \text{ or } 650$$

Therefore, $\sum_{i=1}^{20} (3i + 1) = 650$

b) $\sum_{k=1}^{7} 2^k = 2 + 2^2 + 2^3 + \ldots + 2^7$

This is a geometric series with $a = 2, r = 2, n = 7$.

The sum of the series is:

$$S_n = \frac{a(r^n - 1)}{r - 1}$$

$$S_7 = \frac{2(2^7 - 1)}{2 - 1}$$

$$= 2(2^7 - 1)$$

$$= 2 \times 127, \text{ or } 254$$

Therefore, $\sum_{k=1}^{7} 2^k = 254$

EXERCISES 10-7

(A)

1. Write the series corresponding to:

a) $\sum_{k=1}^{5} (k + 3)$; b) $\sum_{j=1}^{4} (4j + 1)$; c) $\sum_{m=1}^{6} 2m$;

d) $\sum_{j=1}^{5} (3j - 8)$; e) $\sum_{i=1}^{7} (9 - 2i)$ f) $\sum_{k=1}^{4} (5k - 12)$.

2. Write the series using sigma notation:

a) $2 + 5 + 8 + 11 + \ldots + 20$ b) $3 + 5 + 7 + 9 + 11 + 13$
c) $1 + 5 + 9 + \ldots + 21$ d) $24 + 18 + 12 + 6$
e) $2 + 8 + 14 + \ldots + 44$ f) $15 + 11 + 7 + \ldots + (-9)$

3. Which of the expressions in sigma notation is correct for:

a) $5 + 7 + 9 + 11 + 13$?
b) $-1 + 1 + 3 + 5 + 7$?
c) $1 + 4 + 7 + 10 + 13$?
d) $4 + 9 + 14 + 19 + 24$?

i) $\sum_{k=1}^{5} (3k + 1)$ ii) $\sum_{k=1}^{5} (2k - 3)$
iii) $\sum_{k=1}^{5} (3k - 2)$ iv) $\sum_{k=1}^{5} (2k + 3)$
v) $\sum_{k=1}^{5} (3 - 2k)$ vi) $\sum_{k=1}^{5} (5k - 1)$

4. Simplify:

a) $\sum_{k=1}^{12} (2k + 3)$ b) $\sum_{j=1}^{8} (j - 2)$ c) $\sum_{k=1}^{10} (4k - 1)$

5. Simplify:

a) $\sum_{j=1}^{7} 3(2^j)$ b) $\sum_{k=1}^{6} 2^{k+1}$ c) $\sum_{i=1}^{6} 3^i$

(B)

6. Write the series corresponding to:

   a) $\sum_{j=1}^{5} (j^2 - 2j)$; b) $\sum_{i=1}^{7} (i^2 + 3)$; c) $\sum_{k=1}^{4} (3k^2 + 2k - 5)$;

   d) $\sum_{m=1}^{6} (2m^2 - 5m)$; e) $\sum_{k=1}^{5} (3k - k^2)$ f) $\sum_{i=1}^{7} (i^2 + 5i - 2)$

7. Write using sigma notation:

   a) $2 + 5 + 8 + \ldots + (3n - 1)$ b) $18 + 13 + 8 + \ldots + (23 - 5n)$

   c) $3 + 9 + 15 + \ldots + 93$ d) $2 + 6 + 10 + \ldots + 46$

   e) $2 + 6 + 18 + \ldots + 1458$ f) $3 + 6 + 12 + \ldots + 768$

8. Write the series corresponding to:

   a) $\sum_{k=1}^{4} a^k$; b) $\sum_{k=1}^{4} ka^k$; c) $\sum_{k=1}^{4} ak^k$; d) $\sum_{k=1}^{4} (-ak)^k$.

Π, the capital Greek letter *P*, is the first letter of *Product*. Make up some examples to show what pi notation would mean.

9. Write using sigma notation:

   a) $3 + 6 + 9 + 12 + 15$ b) $2 + 4 + 8 + 16 + 32 + 64$

   c) $1 + \frac{1}{2} + \frac{1}{3} + \frac{1}{4} + \frac{1}{5}$ d) $-3 + 6 - 12 + 24 - 48$

10. Simplify:

    a) $\sum_{j=3}^{15} (3j - 1)$ b) $\sum_{k=2}^{11} (2k + 5)$ c) $\sum_{i=4}^{14} (4i - 3)$

11. Simplify:

    a) $\sum_{i=2}^{6} 2^{i-1}$ b) $\sum_{j=3}^{7} 2^{2j-3}$ c) $\sum_{k=1}^{5} 2^{1-k}$

12. Write using sigma notation:

    a) $1 + 2 + 3 + 4 + \ldots + n$ b) $1 + 4 + 9 + 16 + \ldots + n^2$

    c) $1 + 4 + 27 + 256 + \ldots + n^n$ d) $3 + 6 + 12 + \ldots + 3(2)^{n-1}$

13. Find the sum of the series $\sum_{i=1}^{n} (-1)^i$ if:

    a) n is odd; b) n is even.

(C)

14. Write using sigma notation:

    a) $a + a + d + a + 2d + a + 3d + \ldots + a + (n - 1)d$

    b) $a + ar + ar^2 + ar^3 + \ldots + ar^{n-1}$

Review Exercises

1. Write the first four terms of the sequence defined by:
   a) $t_n = 3n + 1$ b) $t_n = (n - 1)^2$
   c) $t_n = 5n^2 - 2n$ d) $t_n = \frac{n-2}{n+1}$

2. Find the indicated terms of each sequence:
   a) $t_n = 3 + 5n$, t_4 and t_{11} b) $t_n = 2^n - 3$, t_5 and t_{10}
   c) $t_n = \frac{n}{3n-1}$, t_3 and t_8 d) $t_n = 10 - 2^{n-1}$, t_4 and t_7

3. Write the first four terms of the sequence with:
   a) $a = 2, d = 7$; b) $a = 1, r = 3$;
   c) $a = 21, d = -4$; d) $a = -2, r = 5$.

4. Classify each sequence as arithmetic or geometric, and find the value of d or r:
   a) 13, 9, 5, 1,... b) $\frac{1}{4}, \frac{1}{2}, 1, 2, \ldots$
   c) $18, -9, 4\frac{1}{2}, -2\frac{1}{4}, \ldots$ d) 5, 13, 21, 29,...

5. Find an expression for the general term:
   a) 2, 6, 10, 14,... b) 2, 6, 18, 54,...
   c) 1, 8, 27, 64,... d) $1\frac{1}{2}, 2\frac{2}{3}, 3\frac{3}{4}, 4\frac{4}{5}, \ldots$

6. Find an expression for the general term:
   a) 2, 9, 16, 23,... b) 2, 8, 32, 128,...
   c) 1, 5, 25, 125,... d) 19, 14, 9, 4,...

7. Find x and y if 2, 8, x, y are consecutive terms of:
   a) an arithmetic sequence; b) a geometric sequence.

8. Find t_5 in the sequence 5, 2,... if the sequence is:
   a) arithmetic; b) geometric.

9. In the arithmetic sequence 5, 9, 13, 17,..., find:
   a) t_7; b) t_{20}; c) t_n.

10. Find the 10th and nth terms of: 25, 23.5, 22, 20.5,...

11. In the sequence 4, 12, 36, 108,..., find: a) t_7; b) t_{15}; c) t_n.

12. Find the 6th and nth terms of: 2, 12, 72, 432,...

13. How many terms are in the sequence?
    a) 1, 4, 16,..., 4096 b) 9, 13, 17,..., 121
    c) 35, 29, 23,..., −91 d) $27, 9, 3, \ldots, \frac{1}{243}$

14. How many multiples of 12 are there from 36 to 252 inclusive?

15. Find the middle term of the sequence: 3, 8, 13, 18,. . ., 303.

16. In an arithmetic sequence, the third term is 19 and the fifteenth term is −17. Find the sequence.

17. In a geometric sequence, the third term is 50 and the sixth term is 6250. Find the sequence.

18. In an arithmetic sequence, $t_4 + t_5 + t_6 = 300$, and $t_{15} + t_{16} + t_{17} = 201$. Find t_{18}.

19. In a geometric sequence, $t_1 + t_2 + t_3 = 21$, and $t_4 + t_5 + t_6 = 168$. Find the sequence.

20. Classify each series as arithmetic, geometric, or other:
    a) $1 + 7 + 13 + 19 + \ldots$
    b) $1 + 4 + 9 + 16 + \ldots$
    c) $1 + 3 + 9 + 27 + \ldots$
    d) $64 + 32 + 16 + 8 + \ldots$
    e) $21 + 13 + 5 + (-3) + \ldots$
    f) $\frac{1}{2} + \frac{2}{3} + \frac{3}{4} + \frac{4}{5} + \ldots$

21. The sum of the first three terms of a series is 32. Find the fourth term if the sum of the first four terms is:
    a) 40;
    b) 55;
    c) 25.

22. Write the first four terms of the series for which:
    a) $S_n = 2n$;
    b) $S_n = n^2 + 2n$;
    c) $S_n = 3n + 1$;
    d) $S_n = 2n^2 - n$.

23. Find S_5 and S_n:
    a) $2 + 5 + 8 + \ldots$
    b) $12 + 5 + (-2) + \ldots$
    c) $6 + 10 + 14 + \ldots$
    d) $5 + 10 + 20 + \ldots$
    e) $12 + 6 + 3 + \ldots$
    f) $2 + 6 + 18 + \ldots$

24. For the series $-3 + 1 + 5 + 9 + \ldots$, find: a) t_{10}; b) S_{16}.

25. For the series $1 + 2 + 4 + 8 + \ldots$, find: a) t_8; b) S_{21}.

26. How many terms of the series $1 + 3 + 5 + 7 + \ldots$ add to 144?

27. How many terms of the series $3 + 6 + 12 + 24 + \ldots$ add to 765?

28. In an arithmetic series, if the fifth term is 74 and the twelfth term is 116, find:
    a) the series;
    b) the sum of the first 30 terms.

29. In a geometric sequence, $t_3 = 18$ and $t_6 = 486$. Find:
    a) the series;
    b) S_{17}.

30. Find the sum of the first fifteen terms of an arithmetic series if the middle term is 92.

31. A tractor-trailer worth $84 000 depreciates 20% the first year and 10% each year thereafter. How much is it worth after 5 years?

11 Mathematics of Investment

Used cars are often sold through advertisements that read: "Low Down Payment", and "Low Monthly Payments". Are buyers really aware of the interest rate they are being charged in such sales? (See *Example 2* in Section 11-8.)

11-1 SIMPLE INTEREST

When you deposit money in a bank account, you are actually lending the money to the bank. In return, the bank pays you **interest**, which is money paid for the use of money. Since banks compete with one another to get the use of your money, they offer you many different kinds of accounts to choose from. Some of these accounts have special features, such as daily interest, which computers have made possible.

In this chapter, we will describe some of the current practices of financial institutions, and indicate how they can affect the customer. For simplicity, we shall assume that, in any problem, interest rates remain constant though, in practice, they change fairly frequently.

Marsha has $120 with which to open a savings account. She has to decide between these two accounts:

Daily Interest Savings Account annual rate 7%	Regular Savings Account annual rate $7\frac{1}{2}$%
• Interest is calculated for each day on the final daily balance.	• Interest is calculated for each month on the minimum monthly balance.
• Interest is credited to the account on the last day of each month, and when the account is closed.	• Interest is credited to the account on April 30 and October 31, and when the account is closed.

If Marsha opens a daily interest account on May 10, then on May 31 she will receive interest for 22 days. If she makes no further deposits or withdrawals, her interest for May will be:

$$\$120 \times 0.07 \times \frac{22}{365} = \$0.51$$

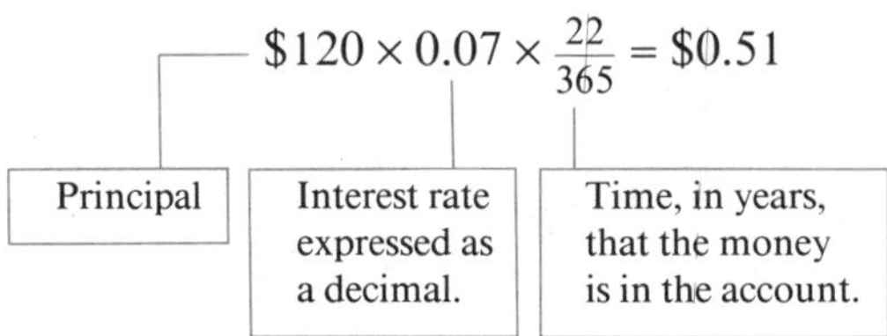

Both May 10 and May 31 are counted. The number of days is therefore: 31 − 10 + 1, or 22

$0.51 will be credited to her account on May 31. If she makes no deposits or withdrawals in June, her interest for June will be:

$$\$120.51 \times 0.07 \times \frac{30}{365} = \$0.69$$

Therefore, her balance on June 30 will be $120.51 + $0.69, or $121.20. The sum of the principal and the interest is called the *accumulated amount*.

If Marsha opens a regular savings account on May 10, she will receive no interest for May since the balance before that date was \$0. In June the interest is:

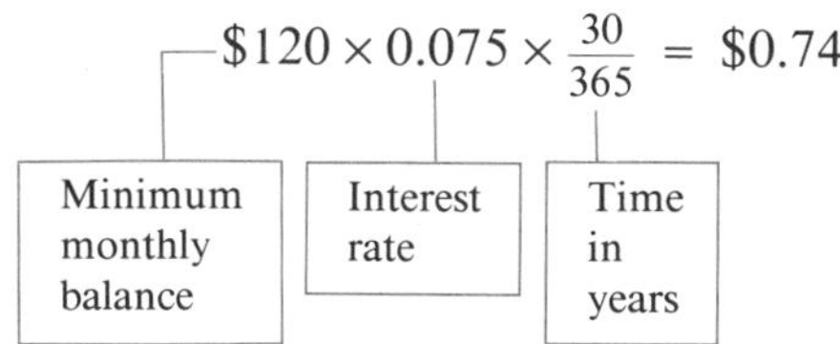

This will be added to her account, with the interest from succeeding months, on October 31. However, if she closed the account in July she would receive \$120.74. This compares with \$121.20 in the daily interest account. It would seem that a daily interest account is the better choice for Marsha.

In the foregoing examples, the interest, I, was calculated using the formula:

$I = P \times r \times t$ P: principal t: time in years
r: annual interest rate

Interest calculated in this way is called **simple interest**. As the examples suggest, simple interest is commonly used in many banking transactions, but the calculations are done by computers.

Example.

Calculate the missing information:

	Principal P	Interest rate, r	Time t	Simple interest I
a)	\$500.00	$9\frac{1}{2}\%$	25 days	
b)	\$ 38.50		149 days	\$ 1.65
c)	\$1750.00	$8\frac{3}{4}\%$		\$39.85
d)		$7\frac{1}{8}\%$	64 days	\$ 3.07

Solution.

a) Using the formula $I = Prt$:

$I = \$500 \times 0.095 \times \frac{25}{365}$

$\doteq \$3.25$

The interest earned is \$3.25.

$P = 500$
$r = 0.095$
$t = \frac{25}{365}$

b) Solving $I = Prt$ for r: $r = \frac{I}{Pt}$ $\quad I = 1.65$, $P = 38.50$, $t = \frac{149}{365}$

$$= \frac{1.65}{38.50 \times \frac{149}{365}}$$

$$\doteq 0.105$$

The interest rate is 10.5%.

c) Solving $I = Prt$ for t: $t = \frac{I}{Pr}$ $\quad I = 39.85$, $P = 1750$, $r = 0.0875$

$$= \frac{39.85}{1750 \times 0.0875}$$

$$\doteq 0.2602$$

The time is 0.2602 years, or 95 days.

d) Solving $I = Prt$ for P: $P = \frac{I}{rt}$ $\quad I = 3.07$, $r = 0.07125$, $t = \frac{64}{365}$

$$= \frac{3.07}{0.07125 \times \frac{64}{365}}$$

$$\doteq 245.73$$

The principal is about $245.73.

EXERCISES 11-1

Ⓐ

1. If you open a bank account that pays 7% interest by depositing $100, give as many reasons as you can why you may not receive $7.00 interest after one year.
2. A daily interest account usually has a lower interest rate than a regular savings account. When would it be better to have:
   a) a daily interest account? b) a regular savings account?
3. Calculate the missing information:

	Principal P	Interest rate, r	Time t	Simple interest I
a)	$627.00	$6\frac{1}{2}$%	27 d	
b)		$9\frac{1}{4}$%	58 d	$ 5.72
c)	$265.50		120 d	$ 16.50
d)	$575.00	$8\frac{1}{2}$%		$ 33.28
e)		7%	215 d	$126.25
f)	$183.12	$6\frac{7}{8}$%	47 d	

4. Calculate the simple interest on:
   a) $210.00 at 8% for 91 d (days);
   b) $465.00 at $7\frac{1}{2}$% for 150 d;
   c) $78.50 at $8\frac{1}{4}$% for 240 d;
   d) $1245.00 at $6\frac{3}{4}$% for 450 d.
5. The balance in Lynda's daily interest account on February 1 is $137.25. If the interest rate is $9\frac{1}{4}$% and no deposits or withdrawals are made, find the accumulated amount on February 28.

(B)

How to make your money earn its daily bread.

Typical example of how you can earn $25.91 more through our Daily Interest Account.

Date	Account Balance	7¾% Monthly Interest	7¾% Daily Interest
Oct. 1	2 000.	$13.16	$ 1.70
Oct. 5	8 000.		22.08
Oct. 18	6 000.		12.74
Oct. 28	3 000.		2.55
		$13.16	$39.07

6. On May 7, a daily interest account earning $8\frac{3}{8}$% is opened with a deposit of $2178.65. Find the accumulated amount at the end of May if:
   a) there are no further deposits and no withdrawals;
   b) there is a further deposit of $345.18 on May 23.
7. The newspaper advertisement shows how the amount of interest earned in a daily interest account can be much greater than in a regular savings account. Carry out calculations to confirm that the figures in the table are correct.
8. How long does it take $500 to grow to $510 at 9% simple interest?
9. What rate of simple interest results in $350 growing to $362.76 in 5 months?
10. Find the interest at $8\frac{1}{2}$% on $328 in a daily interest account:
    a) from April 15 to May 27;
    b) from March 20 to May 15;
    c) from March 6 to August 31;
    d) from October 12 to February 20.
11. On October 11, Jenny opens a daily interest account with a deposit of $415.40. If the interest rate is $7\frac{3}{4}$%, find the accumulated amount on:
    a) October 31;
    b) November 30;
    c) December 20.
12. A bank ran a contest in which the prizes were the interest on a million dollars. If the annual interest rate was $8\frac{1}{2}$%, calculate the value of each prize.

WIN: the interest on $1 000 000
1st prize: one week's interest
2nd prize: one day's interest
3rd prize: one hour's interest

Ⓒ

13. A payment of \$650 is due in 10 months. How much should be invested now at $7\frac{1}{2}\%$ simple interest to meet the payment?
14. What amount invested now will grow to \$3500 in 8 months at 9% simple interest?
15. The table gives the interest rates for the Royal Bank's Signature account.

How Signature works:

Daily closing balance	
up to \$999.99	—you earn 3%† on all your money
\$1,000.00 to \$2,999.99	—you earn $7\frac{1}{2}\%$† on all your money
\$3,000.00 to \$4,999.99	—you earn 8%† on all your money
\$5,000.00 and over	—you earn $9\frac{1}{2}\%$† on all your money

†Rates quoted on a per annum basis, as at Oct. 26, 1984 and subject to change.

Calculate the interest to be credited to the account below at the end of September.

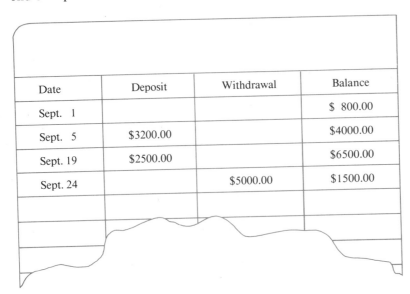

Date	Deposit	Withdrawal	Balance
Sept. 1			\$ 800.00
Sept. 5	\$3200.00		\$4000.00
Sept. 19	\$2500.00		\$6500.00
Sept. 24		\$5000.00	\$1500.00

Canada Savings Bonds

11.25% interest

Maturity: 9 years

Choose between:

- **Regular Interest Bond** Interest payable by cheque on November 1 each year.
- **Compound Interest Bond** Interest accumulates at $11\frac{1}{4}$% compounded annually.

Available in the following amounts:

$100, $300, $500, $1000, and up.

11-2 COMPOUND INTEREST: ACCUMULATED AMOUNT

Each November the federal government offers a new issue of Canada Savings Bonds for sale to the public. This is a form of investment with an interest rate which is usually slightly greater than that of a savings account. Unlike a savings account, the interest rate is guaranteed never to be lower than the advertised rate for the year of issue, and it may even increase if interest rates rise generally. When you purchase a Canada Savings Bond, you are actually lending your money to the federal government. Although there are no deposits or withdrawals, the bond can be redeemed for cash plus accumulated interest at any time.

There are two types of Canada Savings Bonds — Regular Interest Bonds and Compound Interest Bonds. Those who purchase the Regular Interest Bonds advertised receive annual interest payments of $\$500 \times 0.1125$, or $56.25. With a Compound Interest Bond, the interest earned each year is added to the value of the bond. Then, in the following year this interest also earns interest. That is, the bond earns "interest on the interest". Interest calculated in this manner is called **compound interest**.

If you buy a $500 Canada Savings Compound Interest Bond as advertised, you can determine its value each year as follows:

1st year: Interest earned: $\$500.00 \times 0.1125 = \$56.25$
Value of bond on November 1: $\$500.00 + \$56.25 = \$556.25$

2nd year: Interest earned: $\$556.25 \times 0.1125 = \$62.58$
Value of bond on November 1: $\$556.25 + \$62.58 = \$618.83$

3rd year: Interest earned: $\$618.83 \times 0.1125 = \$69.62$
Value of bond on November 1: $\$618.83 + \$69.62 = \$688.45$

If the value at the beginning of any year is P:
Interest earned during the year: $0.1125P$
Value of bond at the end of any year: $P + 0.1125P$, or $1.1125P$
That is:

Value of bond at the end of any year.	=	Value at the beginning of the year.	× 1.1125

Using this principle, we can obtain a formula for the value of the bond after n years.

Value, in dollars, at end of:

year 1: 500×1.1125
year 2: $500 \times 1.1125 \times 1.1125$, or $500(1.1125)^2$
year 3: $500(1.1125)^2 \times 1.1125$, or $500(1.1125)^3$
nth year: $500(1.1125)^n$

The advertisement states that the bond matures in 9 years. After that time, no further interest is paid and the bond should be redeemed.

The *maturity value* will be:

$$\$500(1.1125)^9 = \$1305.18$$

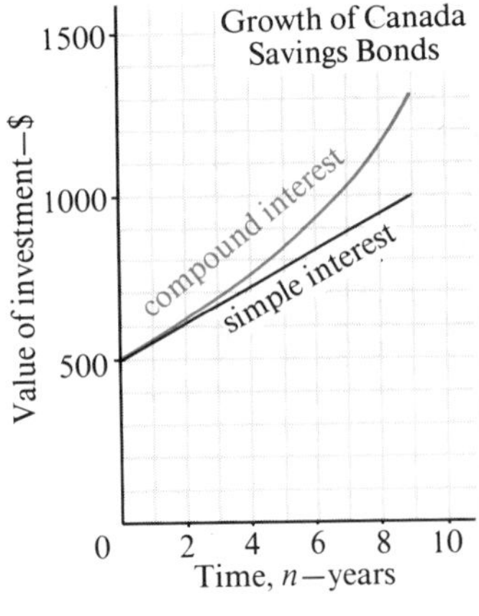

The graph shows how the value of the bond grows over the 9 years. The graph was drawn using a table of values of the expression $500(1.1125)^n$ for values of n from 0 to 9. Also shown is the growth of the investment in the Regular Interest Bond assuming that the interest payments are not reinvested.

The growth of the value of the Compound Interest Bond can also be represented by a **time diagram**:

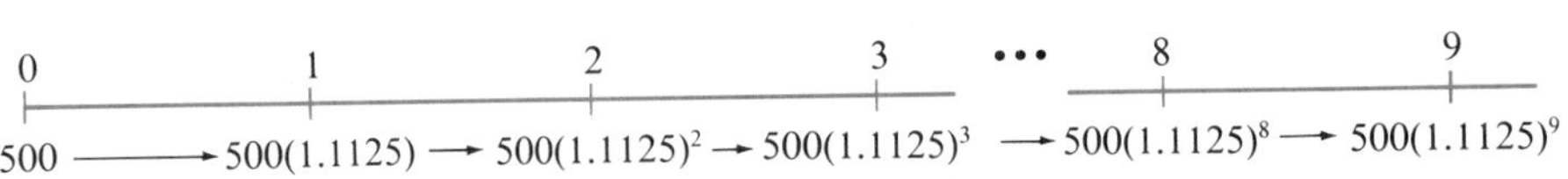

On this time diagram, moving one unit to the right corresponds to multiplying by 1.1125.

When an amount of money, P (the **principal**) is invested at an interest rate, i, compounded annually, the **accumulated amount**, A, after n years is given by the formula:

$$A = P(1 + i)^n$$

Example 1.

Find the accumulated amount of \$5000 invested at 13.5% compounded annually for 10 years.

Solution.

Using the formula $A = P(1 + i)^n$:

$$\begin{aligned} A &= 5000(1.135)^{10} \\ &= 5000(3.547\ 795\ 8) \\ &= 17\ 738.98 \end{aligned}$$

$P = 5000$
$i = 0.135$
$n = 10$

The accumulated amount is \$17 738.98.

The formula for accumulated amount can be used to determine the interest rate necessary for an investment to grow to a certain amount in a given number of years.

Example 2.

If \$200 grows to \$300 in 4 years, what is the interest rate?

Solution.

Let the required interest rate be denoted by i.

Using the formula $A = P(1 + i)^n$: 	$A = 300$, $P = 200$, $n = 4$

$$300 = 200(1 + i)^4$$

$$(1 + i)^4 = 1.5$$

Take the fourth root of both sides:

$$1 + i = (1.5)^{\frac{1}{4}}$$

The expression on the right side can be simplified with a scientific calculator using a key sequence such as:

The result is 1.106 6819.

$$1 + i = 1.106\,6819$$
$$i = 0.106\,6819$$

$200 will grow to $300 in 4 years if invested at about 10.67% compounded annually.

At a given interest rate, the number of years for an investment to grow to a certain amount can be found.

Example 3.

How many years will it take $400 to grow to $1000 if it is invested at 15% compounded annually?

Solution.

Using the formula $A = P(1 + i)^n$: 	$A = 1000$, $P = 400$, $i = 0.15$

$$1000 = 400(1.15)^n$$

$$(1.15)^n = 2.5$$

We solve this equation by *systematic trial* using a scientific calculator. Values of $(1.15)^n$ are found for various values of n:

n	5	6	7
$(1.15)^n$	2.011	2.313	2.660

$400 will grow to $1000 in slightly less than 7 years.

EXERCISES 11-2

Ⓐ

1. Compare the advantages and disadvantages of savings accounts and Canada Savings Bonds as forms of investment.

2. Use a time diagram to show the growth in value of:
   a) a \$500 bond at $11\frac{1}{4}\%$ for 5 years;
   b) a \$300 bond at 9% for 6 years;
   c) a \$1000 bond at $10\frac{1}{2}\%$ for 4 years.

3. Find the accumulated amount:
   a) \$1000 for 6 years at 7% compounded annually;
   b) \$500 for 20 years at 9% compounded annually;
   c) \$215 for 3 years at 10% compounded annually;
   d) \$720 for 8 years at $7\frac{1}{2}\%$ compounded annually;

4. Find the value of a \$1000 Canada Savings Compound Interest Bond at $10\frac{1}{4}\%$ after: a) 3 years; b) 5 years; c) 8 years.

5. Bonds of a particular issue earn $10\frac{1}{2}\%$ interest compounded annually and mature in 7 years. Find the maturity value of
   a) a \$100 bond; b) a \$500 bond; c) a \$2500 bond.

6. A person 20 years old deposits \$1000 in an account that accumulates at 12% compounded annually. Find the accumulated amount when the person is 65 years old.

(B)

7. A donor gave \$75 000 to a town council stipulating that it was to be invested for 10 years and the accumulated amount used to enlarge the public library. If the money earned 8% interest compounded annually, how much was available to spend on the library?

8. A debenture is a certificate entitling the owner to receive interest and the principal after a specified time. Use the information in the advertisement to determine the maturity value of:
   a) a \$5000 1-year debenture;
   b) a \$2000 3-year debenture;
   c) a \$10 000 5-year debenture.

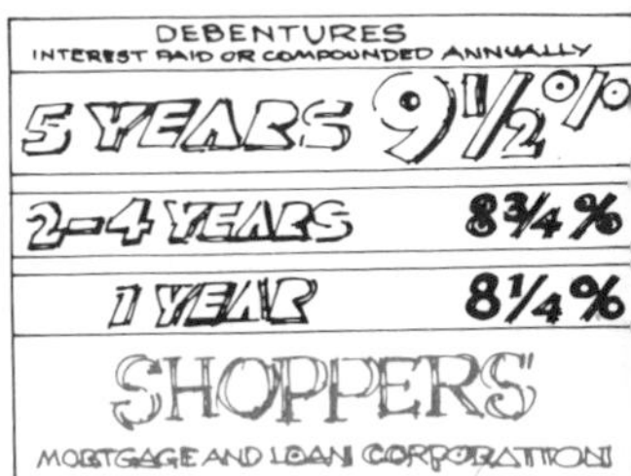

9. The graph shows the accumulated amount of \$100 when invested at interest rates of 10% and 20% compounded annually for up to 20 years. Use the graph to answer these questions:
   a) What is the accumulated amount of \$100 after 15 years when invested at: i) 10%? ii) 20%?
   b) About how many years does it take \$100 to grow to \$500 when invested at: i) 10%? ii) 20%?
   c) How many more years does it take \$100 to double at 10% than at 20%?

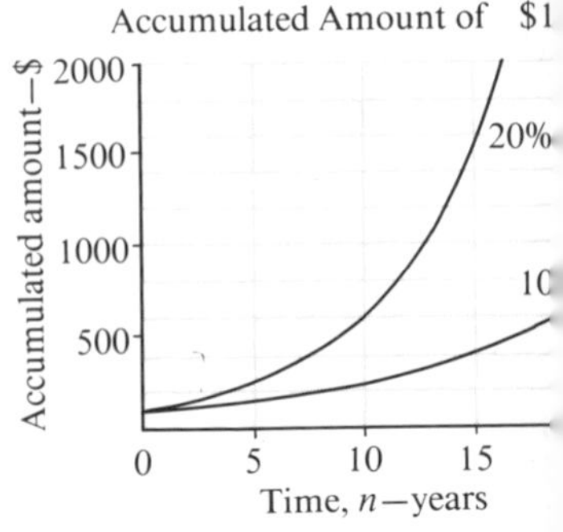

10. In about how many years will \$500 grow to \$1000 at an interest rate of 7% compounded annually?
11. At what interest rate compounded annually will:
    a) \$350 accumulate to \$637.15 in 6 years?
    b) \$3500 accumulate to \$6195.50 in 7 years?
12. If interest is compounded annually, how much is earned by:
    a) \$462.50 invested for 3 years at $9\frac{1}{2}$%?
    b) \$1500 invested for 8 years at $11\frac{1}{4}$%?
    c) \$600 invested for 5 years at $10\frac{3}{4}$%?
    d) \$1435 invested for 11 years at $7\frac{7}{8}$%?

> Vancouver (UPI). Last week a local resident sent the city a cheque for \$7.15 to repay a 40-year old debt. Due to the special circumstances, the mayor decided not to charge the \$3000 in interest that was owing.

13. In the news item, if a constant interest rate compounded annually had been used to calculate the amount owing, what rate was used? Do you think that this was a reasonable assessment?
14. At what interest rate would a sum of money double in 7 years?
15. About how many years will it take a sum of money to double when invested at 12% compounded annually?
16. The annual interest rate for a daily interest account is $8\frac{1}{2}$%. In the first 6 months after opening her account, Sheila makes the following transactions:

    Jan. 12—deposits \$450 | Feb. 6—deposits \$1280
    Apr. 20—deposits \$742 | May 8—withdraws \$1385
    June 10—deposits \$195

    Calculate the balance in her account at the end of each of the first 6 months.

Number of Years for Money to Double

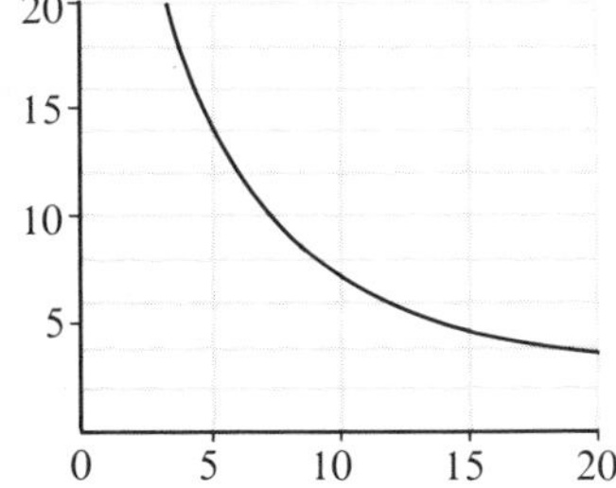

17. The graph shows the number of years required for money to double when invested at different interest rates. Use the graph to answer these questions:
    a) About how long does it take money to double when invested at:
       i) 10%? ii) 15%?
    b) What interest rate is needed if an investment is to double in value in: i) 6 years? ii) 10 years?

(C)

18. A sum of \$1000 earns interest at an annual rate i. At the end of 10 years, the original \$1000 plus the accumulated interest, compounded annually, has grown to an amount, A.
    a) Express A as a function of i.
    b) Graph the function in (a).
    c) From the graph, estimate:
       i) the amount after 10 years at 14.5%;
       ii) the interest rate necessary to triple the original investment in 10 years.

19. A \$6 billion issue of Canada Savings Bonds bears interest at $12\frac{1}{4}\%$. To remain competitive with other investments, the government increases the interest rate to $15\frac{1}{2}\%$ on March 1. How much additional interest will the government have to pay that year on account of the increase?

MATHEMATICS PROJECT

Tribune Media Services

1. If Broom Hilda had invested ten dollars 1500 years ago, what would it be worth now? Try different rates of interest.
2. Is Gaylord right when he says that it would amount to trillions?

11-3 COMPOUND INTEREST: PRESENT VALUE

Banks and trust companies offer Guaranteed Investment Certificates which mature over different periods of time. They pay higher interest rates than savings accounts and, unlike Canada Savings Bonds, they can be bought at any time. However, the money cannot be obtained before the maturity date without penalty.

An attractive feature of Guaranteed Investment Certificates is that they can be purchased for any amount, usually above a specified minimum. This enables a purchaser to invest an amount which will give a definite accumulated value in a given time. For example: you wish to buy a Guaranteed Investment Certificate, as advertised, that will provide you with $1000 in 5 years time. How much must you invest? We can calculate the amount as follows:

Using the formula $A = P(1 + i)^n$: $1000 = P(1.0975)^5$

$A = 1000$, $i = 0.0975$, $n = 5$

Solving for P:

$$P = \frac{1000}{(1.0975)^5}$$

$$= \frac{1000}{1.592\,291\,7}$$

$$= 628.03$$

You must invest $628.03 now to receive $1000 in 5 years.
Check: The accumulated value is: $\$628.03(1.0975)^5 = \$1000.00$

We say that the **present value** of $1000.00 due in 5 years at $9\frac{3}{4}\%$ compounded annually is $628.03.

The amount of money, P, which accumulates after n years to the amount A when invested at an interest rate i, compounded annually, is called the **present value** of A. The present value may be found by solving the formula $A = P(1 + i)^n$ for P:

$$P = \frac{A}{(1 + i)^n}$$

Example.

What is the present value of $3000 due in 4 years at $9\frac{1}{2}\%$ compounded annually?

Solution.

Using the formula $P = \dfrac{A}{(1+i)^n}$:

$A = 3000$
$i = 0.095$
$n = 4$

$$P = \frac{3000}{(1.095)^4}$$

$$= \frac{3000}{1.437\,661\,0}, \text{ or } 2086.72$$

The present value is \$2086.72.

The example can be illustrated by a time diagram:

Time—years

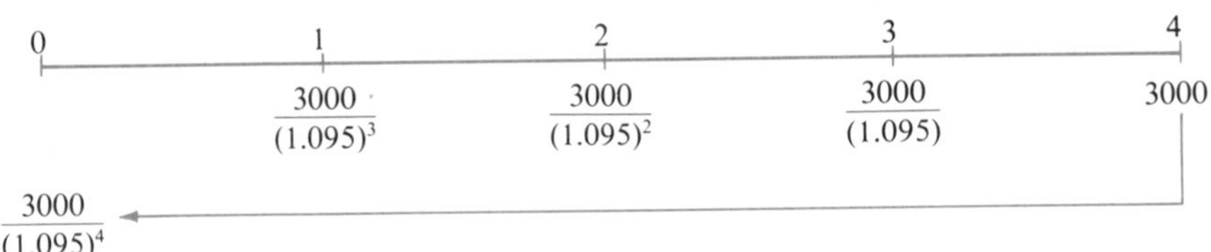

On this time diagram, moving one year to the left corresponds to dividing by 1.095. Therefore, moving 4 years to the left corresponds to dividing by $(1.095)^4$.

Summary

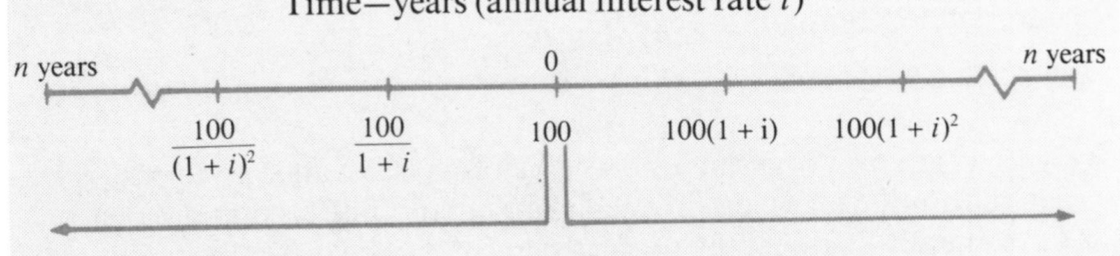

Present Value
- move to the left;
- divide by $(1 + i)$ for each year;
- the present value of \$100 due in n years is: $\dfrac{100}{(1+i)^n}$.

Accumulated Amount
- move to the right;
- multiply by $(1 + i)$ for each year;
- the accumulated amount of \$100 after n years is: $100(1 + i)^n$.

EXERCISES 11-3

Ⓐ

1. Compare the advantages and disadvantages of Canada Savings Bonds and Guaranteed Investment Certificates as forms of investment.

2. Use a time diagram to illustrate the present value of:
   a) \$1000 due in 4 years at 8% compounded annually;
   b) \$1650 due in 6 years at $10\frac{1}{2}\%$ compounded annually;
   c) \$5750 due in 5 years at $12\frac{1}{4}\%$ compounded annually;

3. If interest is compounded annually, find the present value of:
   a) \$500 due in 7 years at 10%;
   b) \$1625 due in 5 years at $11\frac{1}{2}\%$;
   c) \$410 due in 3 years at $13\frac{1}{4}\%$;
   d) \$2700 due in 6 years at $10\frac{1}{2}\%$;
   e) \$4650 due in 8 years at $9\frac{3}{4}\%$.

4. At $12\frac{1}{2}\%$ compounded annually, how much should be invested now to amount to \$10 000 in:
   a) 3 years? b) 5 years? c) 8 years?

5. How much should Michelle, age 16, invest now at $9\frac{1}{4}\%$ in order to have \$4500 at age 25?

(B)

6. Mark estimates that the cost of his first year at college will be \$3860. How much should he invest now at 12% compounded annually so that he will have the required amount in 3 years?

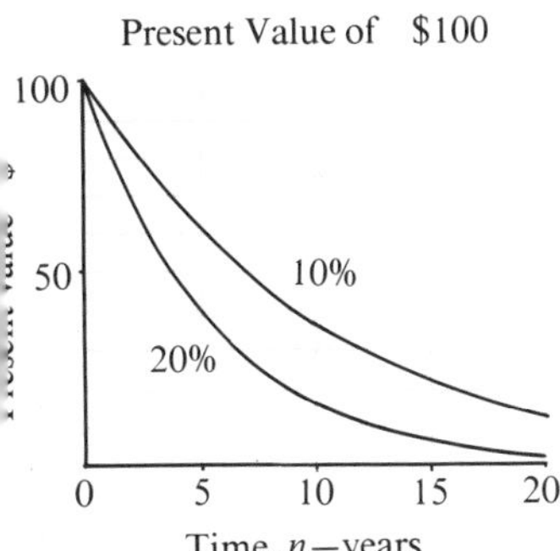

7. The graph shows the present value of \$100 for periods up to 20 years at interest rates of 10% and 20% compounded annually. Use the graph to answer these questions:
   a) What is the present value of \$100 due in 5 years at:
      i) 10%? ii) 20%?
   b) How long is the period of investment for \$100 to have a present value of \$40 with the interest rate: i) 10%? ii) 20%?
   c) Estimate the present value of \$4000 due in 7 years at 10%.

8. If the present value of \$500 due in 8 years is \$196.61, find the interest rate.

9. If the present value of \$2850 invested at $10\frac{3}{4}\%$ is \$1895, how long is the period of investment?

10. Mr. and Mrs. Slimmon wish to provide their daughter with \$10 000 on her eighteenth birthday. How much should they invest on her first birthday at $9\frac{3}{4}\%$ compounded annually?

11. Car City Sales agrees to pay \$25 000 now and \$75 000 in 4 years time for a parcel of real estate. If money is worth $10\frac{1}{2}\%$ compounded annually, what sum of money would settle the account now?

Ⓒ

12. A sum of money, P, is invested at an interest rate i. At the end of 10 years, the investment plus accumulated interest amounts to \$1000.
    a) Express P as a function of i.
    b) Graph the function in (a).
    c) From the graph, estimate:
        i) the amount invested if the interest rate was 12%;
        ii) the interest rate if the amount invested was \$500.

11-4 COMPOUNDING PERIODS LESS THAN ONE YEAR

Interest is often charged or credited more frequently than once a year. The two most common compounding periods are semi-annually and monthly.

Semi-annual Compounding

A regular savings account pays interest at the rate of 8% per annum but the interest is credited every 6 months, on April 30 and October 31. If \$1000 is deposited on May 1 and no further withdrawals or deposits are made, the balance next April 30 may be found as follows:

Interest for first 6 months (to October 31): $I = Prt$

$$= 1000 \times 0.8 \times \frac{1}{2}$$

$$= 1000 \times 0.4, \text{ or } 40$$

Balance on October 31: \$1000 + \$40 = \$1040

Interest for second 6 months (to April 30): $I = 1040 \times 0.8 \times \frac{1}{2}$

$$= 1040 \times 0.4, \text{ or } 41.60$$

Balance on April 30: \$1040 + \$41.60 = \$1081.60

The total interest earned over the year is \$81.60. This is \$1.60 greater than it would have been had the interest been credited just once a year, because the interest for the first period, \$40, earns interest during the second period. We say that the interest rate is 8% compounded *semi-annually*. This means that the earned interest rate is 4% compounded every 6 months. That is, the calculation of the balance can be made as follows:

$$\$1000(1.04)^2 = \$1081.60$$

When interest is compounded semi-annually, in the formula $A = P(1 + i)^n$, n is double the number of years and i is half the stated interest rate.

INVESTIGATE

Instead of using $\frac{1}{2}$ for semi-annual, banks use fractions corresponding to the actual number of days in each interest period.

How does this affect the calculations?

Why do you think banks do this?

Example 1.

Find the accumulated amount after 7 years if \$2000 is invested at $9\frac{1}{2}\%$ per annum compounded semi-annually.

Solution.

Using the formula $A = P(1+i)^n$:

$P = 2000$, $i = \dfrac{0.095}{2}$, $n = 7 \times 2$

$$A = 2000\left(1 + \frac{0.095}{2}\right)^{7\times 2}$$

$$= 2000(1.0475)^{14}$$

$$= 3829.89$$

The accumulated amount after 7 years is \$3829.89.

Monthly Compounding

A daily interest savings account pays interest at the rate of 8% per annum, but the interest is credited every month. That is, the interest is compounded *monthly*. If \$1000 is deposited on May 1 and no further deposits or withdrawals are made, the balance next April 30 may be found using the formula $A = P(1+i)^n$, where n is the total number of months and i is the stated interest rate divided by 12.

$$A = 1000\left(1 + \frac{0.08}{12}\right)^{12}, \text{ or } \$1083.00$$

This balance is \$1.40 greater than that obtained with semi-annual compounding because interest is credited to the account more frequently.

Example 2.

Find the present value of \$325 in 2 years if the annual interest rate is $6\frac{3}{4}\%$ compounded monthly.

Solution.

Using the formula $A = P(1+i)^n$:

$A = 325$, $i = \dfrac{0.0675}{12}$, $n = 12 \times 2$

$$325 = P\left(1 + \frac{0.0675}{12}\right)^{12\times 2}$$

$$P = \frac{325}{\left(1 + \frac{0.0675}{12}\right)^{24}}$$

$$= 284.07$$

The present value is \$284.07.

Present values and accumulated amounts can be found for other compounding periods, such as quarterly, weekly, and daily, but these are rarely used in business transactions.

EXERCISES 11-4

(A)

1. If interest is compounded semi-annually, find the value of:
   a) \$80 for 9 years at 10%;
   b) \$100 for 10 years at 12%;
   c) \$260 for 4 years at $9\frac{1}{2}$%;
   d) \$1200 for 15 years at $7\frac{1}{4}$%.
2. If interest is compounded monthly, find the value of:
   a) \$150 for 3 years at 12%;
   b) \$800 for 5 years at 9%;
   c) \$325 for 2 years at $10\frac{1}{2}$%;
   d) \$2740 for 7 years at $8\frac{1}{2}$%.
3. Find the interest on \$1000 after one year at 12% compounded:
   a) semi-annually;
   b) monthly.
4. Calculate the accumulated amount if \$250 is invested for 3 years at 9% compounded: a) monthly: b) semi-annually.
5. How much money should be deposited today to accumulate to \$1000 in 3 years at 8% compounded:
   a) semi-annually? b) monthly?

(B)

6. Find the interest rate for \$150 to accumulate to \$275 in 8 years with interest compounded semi-annually.
7. On May 1, 1986, Marcie deposits \$500 in an account paying $8\frac{3}{4}$% compounded semi-annually. On May 1, 1987, she deposits another \$500. If there are no other deposits and no withdrawals, determine the balance in the account on May 1, 1988.
8. What amount invested today at $9\frac{1}{2}$% compounded semi-annually will amount to \$2500 in 6 years?
9. On his 21st birthday, Henry received \$5000, the accumulated amount of an investment his parents made for him when he was born. What was the amount of their investment if the interest rate was $8\frac{3}{4}$% compounded: a) semi-annually? b) monthly?
10. Find the present value of:
    a) \$800 in 4 years at $10\frac{1}{2}$% compounded monthly;
    b) \$750 in 6 years at 9% compounded semi-annually;
    c) \$1260 in 9 years at $13\frac{1}{2}$% compounded monthly.
11. Find, correct to the nearest half year, how long it will take \$100 to amount to \$500 at $13\frac{1}{2}$% compounded semi-annually.
12. Find, correct to the nearest month, how long it will take \$300 to accumulate to \$1000 at 8% compounded monthly.
13. Find how long it takes money to double
    a) at 10%, and at $9\frac{1}{4}$% compounded semi-annually;
    b) at $11\frac{1}{2}$% compounded monthly.

INVESTIGATE

The money for a scholarship is provided by the interest on an investment.

- For a given investment, how can the value of the scholarship be determined?
- For a given scholarship award, how can the necessary investment be determined?

Write a report of your findings.

A sequence of payments which lasts forever is called a **perpetuity**.

Ⓒ

14. What equal deposits, one made now and another made in 6 months time, will accumulate to $1000 one year from now at $7\frac{1}{2}\%$ compounded semi-annually?
15. A merchant buys goods worth $3000. She pays a certain amount down and agrees to pay $1000 in 6 months and another $1000 after a further 6 months. If money is worth $9\frac{1}{2}\%$ compounded semi-annually, find the down payment required.

11-5 COMPARING INTEREST RATES

When buying Guaranteed Investment Certificates, we are often faced with a choice of two different rates for the same period of investment. For example, the rates for a two-year certificate might be:

11% compounded semi-annually

$11\frac{1}{4}\%$ compounded annually

Which is the greater rate?

The answer is: the one which provides the greater return.

We compare the rates by considering the interest on $100 over a period of a year.

In one year, at 11% compounded semi-annually, $100 grows to:

$$\$100\left(1 + \frac{0.11}{2}\right)^2 = \$111.30$$

In one year, at $11\frac{1}{4}\%$ compounded annually, $100 grows to:

$$\$100(1 + 0.1125) = \$111.25$$

Since 11% compounded semi-annually gives a slightly greater return, it is the greater rate.

While the difference in the two rates is insignificant for an investment of $100, compounding periods are very important to people who invest or borrow large amounts of money. For example, an investment of $1 000 000 for one year at 11% compounded semi-annually earns $525 more interest than it would at $11\frac{1}{4}\%$ compounded annually. Compounded monthly, it would earn $3219 more.

To compare interest rates having different compounding periods, find the accumulated amount of any sum over one year at each rate.

Two rates of interest with different compounding periods can have the same effect on a given sum of money. Such rates are called *equivalent rates*.

Example 1.

Show that the following rates are equivalent:
12% compounded semi-annually
12.36% compounded annually

Solution.

Assume that $100 is invested at each rate.
The accumulated amounts at the end of 1 year are:
$\$100\,(1.06)^2 = \$112.36$
$\$100(1.1236) = \$112.36$
Since the results are the same, the two interest rates are equivalent.

Although interest rates are often compounded semi-annually or monthly, it is customary to name them as annual rates. A rate may be quoted as 12% compounded semi-annually but, as *Example 1* shows, this is equivalent to 12.36% compounded annually. This rate is called the *effective rate* because it is the rate at which interest is actually earned.

Example 2.

An investment pays interest at 9% compounded semi-annually. What is the effective rate of interest?

Solution.

The accumulated amount of $1 in one year at the quoted rate is:

$$1\left(1 + \frac{0.09}{2}\right)^2 = (1.045)^2$$
$$= 1.09203$$

In one year, $1 would grow to $1.09203. If the principal of $1 is subtracted, the difference represents the interest earned on $1. Therefore, the effective rate is 9.203%.

Example 3.

What annual interest rate compounded monthly is equivalent to an effective rate of 18% per annum?

Solution.

Let the quoted annual rate be i% compounded monthly.

In one year, the accumulated amount of $1,

at the quoted rate of i% is: $\$1\left(1 + \frac{i}{12}\right)^{12}$;

at the effective rate of 18% is: $1.18.

Since the rates are equivalent: $1\left(1 + \frac{i}{12}\right)^{12} = 1.18$

Taking the 12th root of both sides: $1 + \frac{i}{12} = (1.18)^{\frac{1}{12}}$

Using a scientific calculator: $1 + \frac{i}{12} = 1.013\ 888\ 4$

Solving for i: $\frac{i}{12} = 0.013\ 888\ 4$

$i = 0.166\ 660\ 8$

An annual rate of about 16.67% compounded monthly is equivalent to an effective rate of 18% per annum.

Example 4.

The credit service charge rate of a large department store is 2.4% per month.

a) What annual rate of interest is being charged?

b) Assuming that any interest charged is added to the next month's balance, determine the effective rate that is being charged.

Solution.

a) Since $2.4 \times 12 = 28.8$, the annual rate of interest is 28.8%.

b) The accumulated amount of $1 in one year at the quoted rate is: $1(1.024)^{12} = 1.329\ 23$
This indicates that the effective annual interest rate is about 32.9%.

In *Example 4,* what arguments might the management of the store make to justify such a high effective interest rate?

EXERCISES 11-5

1. Show that the rates are equivalent:
   a) 10% compounded semi-annually
   10.25% compounded annually
   b) 13% compounded semi-annually
   13.4225% compounded annually
   c) 12% compounded monthly
   12.6825% compounded annually
   d) 9% compounded monthly
   9.380 69% compounded annually
2. What is the accumulated amount of $100 after one year at each rate? Which is the greater rate?
   a) i) 9% compounded semi-annually
   ii) $9\frac{1}{4}$% compounded annually

b) i) $12\frac{1}{4}$% compounded semi-annually
ii) $12\frac{1}{2}$% compounded annually

c) i) $10\frac{1}{2}$% compounded monthly
ii) $11\frac{1}{4}$% compounded annually

3. Which is the greater rate?
a) i) $11\frac{3}{4}$% compounded semi-annually
ii) 12% compounded annually

b) i) $6\frac{1}{2}$% compounded annually
ii) $6\frac{1}{4}$% compounded semi-annually

c) i) $9\frac{1}{4}$% compounded monthly
ii) $9\frac{3}{4}$% compounded semi-annually

d) i) $11\frac{1}{4}$% compounded annually
ii) $10\frac{1}{2}$% compounded monthly

4. What annual rate is equivalent to:
a) $8\frac{1}{2}$% compounded semi-annually?
b) $12\frac{1}{4}$% compounded semi-annually?
c) $10\frac{3}{4}$% compounded monthly?
d) $9\frac{1}{2}$% compounded monthly?

(B)

5. Which is the greater rate?
a) i) $12\frac{1}{2}$% compounded semi-annually
ii) $11\frac{3}{4}$% compounded monthly
b) i) $10\frac{1}{4}$% compounded annually
ii) $9\frac{3}{4}$% compounded monthly
c) i) 16% compounded monthly
ii) 17% compounded semi-annually

6. Express as an equivalent annual rate:
a) 16%, and $13\frac{1}{4}$% compounded semi-annually
b) 9%, and $12\frac{1}{4}$% compounded monthly

7. Find the effective rate of interest:
a) of 8%, and of $12\frac{1}{4}$% compounded semi-annually
b) of 15%, and of $9\frac{1}{2}$% compounded monthly

8. What interest rate compounded i) semi-annually, ii) monthly: is equivalent to an effective rate of.
a) 14%? b) 9%? c) $10\frac{1}{2}$%?

(C)

9. Express as an equivalent semi-annual rate:
a) 12% compounded monthly b) 12% compounded annually

10. The credit terms shown appeared on a bank-card statement.
a) If the daily rate 0.05094% is correct, is the rate of 18.6% per annum correct? What effective annual interest rate is being charged on overdue accounts?

INTEREST CHARGES

No interest is charged on purchases that appear on your statement for the first time provided full payment is received by the Due Date. Purchases not paid in this manner incur interest from the Statement Date until full payment is received. Interest is calculated at a daily rate of 0.05094% (18.6% per annum).

b) If the annual rate of 18.6% is correct, is the daily rate of 0.05094% correct?

11. On a given investment, interest compounded semi-annually requires a slightly lower rate than interest compounded annually to yield the same amount. If the semi-annual rate is i and the annual rate is r,
   a) express r as a function of i;
   b) graph the function for reasonable values of i;
   c) use the graph to estimate:
      i) the annual rate equivalent to 10% compounded semi-annually,
      ii) the semi-annual rate equivalent to 18% compounded annually.

11-6 ANNUITIES: ACCUMULATED AMOUNT

What do the following financial situations have in common?

- Marcia makes car payments of $250 at the end of each month for 3 years.
- A scholarship fund provides an annual scholarship of $500.
- An insurance policy provides a pensioner with an income of $2000 a month for life.

In each situation, equal payments are made at equally spaced intervals of time. For this reason, they are called **annuities**.

An **annuity** is a sequence of equal payments made at equally spaced intervals of time.

The following example shows how to calculate the accumulated amount of the payments of an annuity.

Example 1.

Lisa plans to deposit $500 at the end of the year for 5 years in a special savings account. If the account pays interest at the rate of 9% compounded annually, what will be the accumulated amount at the end of 5 years?

Solution.

The accumulated amount of each deposit is shown on the diagram:

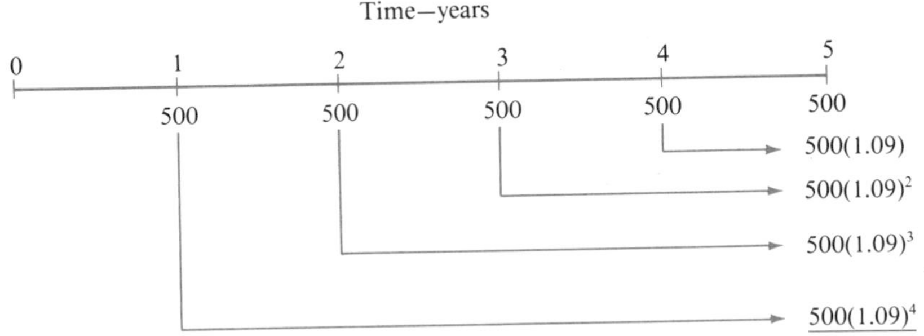

The accumulated amount, A, of all the deposits at the end of the five-year term is:

$$500 + 500(1.09) + 500(1.09)^2 + 500(1.09)^3 + 500(1.09)^4$$

This is a geometric series with first term 500 and common ratio 1.09. Using the formula for the sum of the first n terms of a geometric series $S = \dfrac{a(r^n - 1)}{r - 1}$:

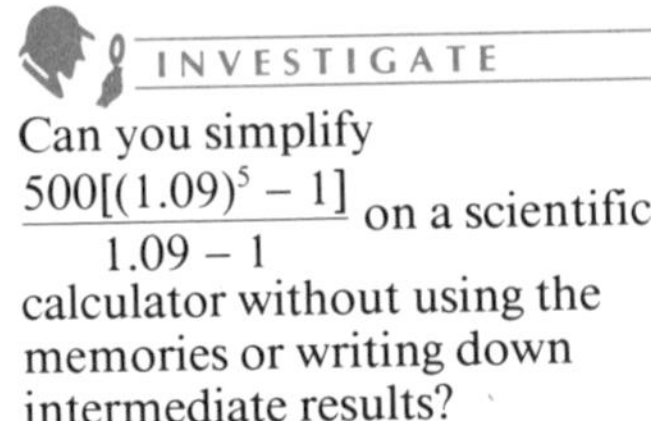

INVESTIGATE

Can you simplify $\dfrac{500[(1.09)^5 - 1]}{1.09 - 1}$ on a scientific calculator without using the memories or writing down intermediate results?

$$A = \frac{500[(1.09)^5 - 1]}{1.09 - 1} \qquad a = 500,\; r = 1.09,\; n = 5,\; S = A$$

$$= \frac{500[0.538\,623\,955]}{0.09}$$

$$= 2992.36$$

The accumulated amount at the end of 5 years is \$2992.36

In *Example 1*, \$2992.36 is called the *accumulated amount* of the annuity. The time between successive payments is the *payment interval*.

When the amount of an annuity is calculated, the payment interval must be the same as the compounding period.

In this chapter, only ordinary annuities are considered These have all annuity payments made at the end of the payment intervals.

Example 2.

An annuity of semi-annual payments of \$3000 is for 4 years at 10% compounded semi-annually. If the first payment is in 6 months time, what is the amount of the annuity?

Solution.

10% compounded semi-annually is equivalent to 5% compounded every 6 months. This is the same as the payment interval. The payments and accumulated amounts are shown on the time diagram:

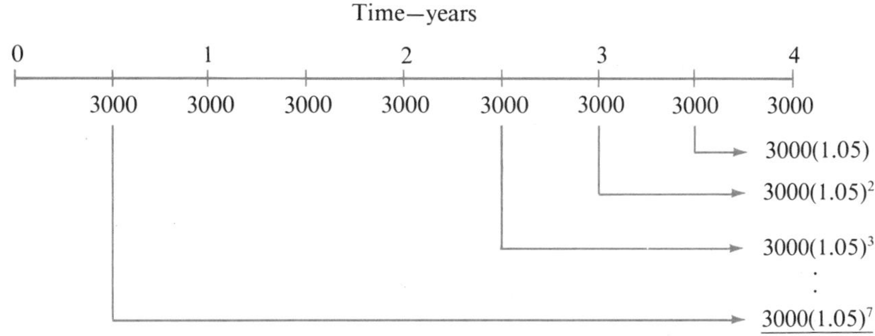

The amount of the annuity, A, is:
$3000 + 3000(1.05) + 3000(1.05)^2 + \ldots + 3000(1.05)^7$

Using the formula for the sum of a geometric series $S = \dfrac{a(r^n - 1)}{r - 1}$:

$$A = \frac{3000[(1.05)^8 - 1]}{1.05 - 1}$$
$$= 28\,647.33$$

$a = 3000$
$r = 1.05$
$n = 8$
$S = A$

The amount of the annuity is \$28 647.33.

Sometimes a specified amount is required in a certain number of years and it is necessary to find what the annuity payments need to be.

Example 3.

Henry plans to make an equal deposit at the end of each year for 10 years in a trust account that pays interest at 12% compounded annually. If he expects to have \$100 000 at the end of 10 years, what must be his annual deposit?

Solution.

Let the annual deposits be x dollars. The time diagram shows the accumulated amounts of the deposits:

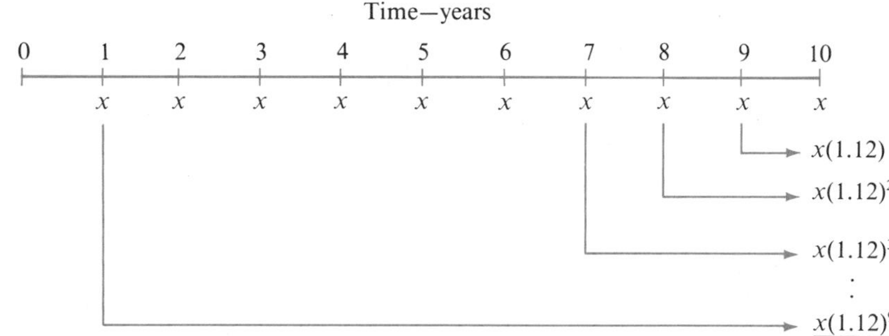

The accumulated amount, A, of the payments is:
$x + x(1.12) + x(1.12)^2 + x(1.12)^3 + \ldots + x(1.12)^9$

Using the formula for the sum of a geometric series $S = \frac{a(r^n - 1)}{r - 1}$:

$$A = \frac{x[(1.12)^{10} - 1]}{1.12 - 1} \qquad a = x,\ r = 1.12$$

$$= x[17.548\,735] \qquad n = 10,\ S = A$$

Since the amount of the annuity is $100 000:

$$x[17.548\,735] = 100\,000$$

$$x = \frac{100\,000}{17.548\,735}$$

$$= 5698.42$$

The required annuity payment is $5698.42.

EXERCISES 11-6

(A)

1. Gerry deposits $1000 at the end of each year for 5 years in a daily interest savings account that pays interest at 12% compounded monthly. She makes no further deposits and no withdrawals. The graph shows the balance in her account during the 5 year period. Use the graph to answer these questions:
   a) What was the balance in her account after $3\frac{1}{2}$ years?
   b) How long did it take the balance to reach $5000?
   c) About how much interest was earned over the 5 years?

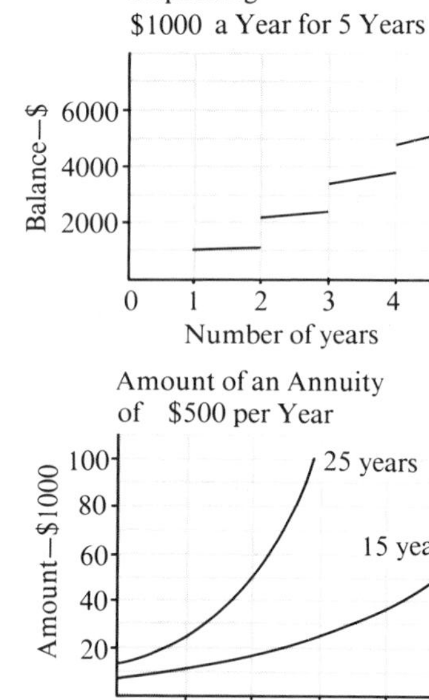

2. The graph shows the effect of depositing $500 at the end of each year for 15 years and for 25 years at different interest rates. Using the graph:
   a) estimate the amount of an annuity of $500 per year for 15 years at: i) 10%, ii) 15%.
   b) estimate the amount of an annuity of $500 per year for 25 years at: i) 10%, ii) 15%.
   c) what interest rate is necessary for an annual deposit of $500 to accumulate to $40 000 in: i) 15 years? ii) 25 years?

3. Draw a time diagram to represent the amount of:
   a) $1000 deposited at the end of each year for 4 years in an account paying 8% annually;
   b) $450 deposited after every 6 months for 3 years in an account paying 12% compounded semi-annually;
   c) $25 deposited at the end of each month for a year in a daily interest account paying 9% compounded monthly.

4. In Exercise 3, find the balance after the last deposit for each account.

(B)

5. Find the amount of an annuity of \$300 at the end of each year for 6 years at 9% compounded annually.
6. Find the amount of an annuity of \$500 after every 6 months for 4 years at 8% compounded semi-annually.
7. Sheri deposits \$25 at the end of each month for 3 years in an account paying 12% compounded monthly. If she makes no further deposits and no withdrawals, find the balance after 3 years.
8. One month after their daughter was born, Mr. and Mrs. Chilton opened an account paying 8% compounded monthly with a \$10 deposit. If they deposit \$10 each month, how much will be available on their daughter's:
   a) 10th birthday? b) 15th birthday? c) 18th birthday?
9. What amount must be deposited at the end of each year in an account paying 10% compounded annually in order to have an accumulated amount of \$1000 after 4 years?
10. How much money would you have to invest at the end of every 6 months for the next 5 years in order to accumulate:
    a) \$5000 if money is worth 8% compounded semi-annually?
    b) \$2000 if money is worth $8\frac{1}{2}$% compounded semi-annually?
11. How much money would you have to deposit at the end of every month in an account which pays 9% compounded monthly in order to accumulate \$2500 in 4 years?

(C)

12. If you deposit \$50 on the first of each month in an account paying 9% compounded monthly, how much will you have after 5 years?
13. Beginning November 1, 1988 and ending May 1, 1994, semi-annual deposits of \$150 are made into an account earning $11\frac{3}{4}$% compounded semi-annually. If the deposits remain untouched until November 1, 1998, what will be the amount in the account?
14. If \$1000 is deposited at the end of each year in an account that pays 13% compounded annually, about how many years will it take to accumulate to \$20 000?
15. If you deposit \$100 at the end of each year in an account that pays $7\frac{1}{2}$% compounded semi-annually, what will be the balance in your account after 9 years?

16. The annual payment, P, required to discharge a loan of \$10 000 after n years at 12% interest compounded annually is given by:

$$P = \frac{1200}{1 - (1.12)^{-n}}$$

a) Graph P as a function of n.
b) Use the graph to determine:
   i) the payment required to discharge the loan in 5 years;
   ii) the number of years required if the payment is \$1500.

11-7 ANNUITIES: PRESENT VALUE

In the previous section, we found how to calculate the amount of an annuity. This is the accumulated amount of all the payments at the time the last payment is made. We calculate the **present value** of an annuity the same way. This is the total present value of the payments.

Example 1.

Donna plans to deposit a sum of money in an account which pays 9% compounded annually so that she can make five equal annual withdrawals of \$500. How much should she deposit if the first withdrawal is one year later?

Solution.

The time diagram shows the present value of each withdrawal.

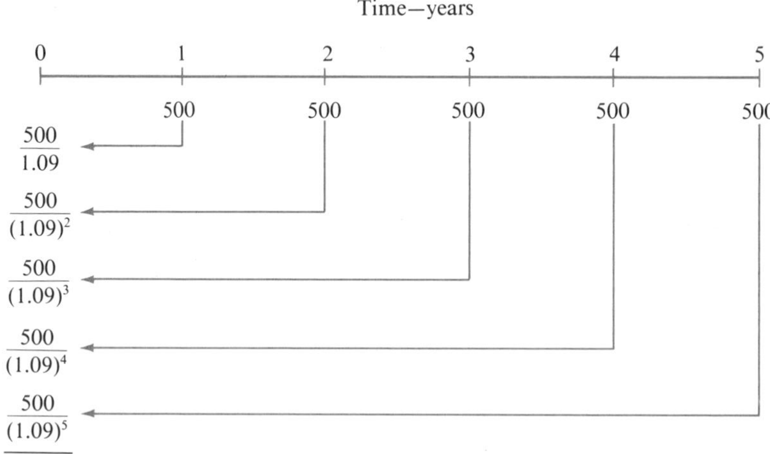

The total present value, P, of the five withdrawals is:

$$\frac{500}{1.09} + \frac{500}{(1.09)^2} + \frac{500}{(1.09)^3} + \frac{500}{(1.09)^4} + \frac{500}{(1.09)^5}$$

This is a geometric series. We avoid difficulties with fractions if we reverse the order of the terms.

$$\frac{500}{(1.09)^5}+\frac{500}{(1.09)^4}+\frac{500}{(1.09)^3}+\frac{500}{(1.09)^2}+\frac{500}{1.09}$$

The first term is now $\frac{500}{(1.09)^5}$ and the common ratio 1.09. Using the formula for the sum of a geometric series $S=\frac{a(r^n-1)}{r-1}$:

$$P=\frac{500}{(1.09)^5}\times\frac{(1.09)^5-1}{1.09-1}$$
$$=(324.965\,693\,1)(5.984\,710\,6)$$
$$=1944.83$$

$a=\frac{500}{(1.09)^5}$

$r=1.09$

$n=5$

$S=P$

Donna should deposit $1944.83.

INVESTIGATE

Can you simplify the expression for P on a scientific calculator without using the memories or writing down the intermediate results?

Sometimes a person wishes to invest a sum of money in an annuity which will deplete the investment in a series of equal payments over a chosen period of time. In this case it is necessary to determine the size of the payments corresponding to a given interest rate.

Example 2.

Mrs. Talbot's life savings total $280 000. She wishes to use this money to purchase an annuity earning interest at 12% compounded semi-annually which will provide her with equal semi-annual payments for 20 years. How much is each semi-annual payment if the first is 6 months from the date of purchase?

Solution.

Let each semi-annual payment be x dollars. Since 12% compounded semi-annually is equivalent to 6% every 6 months, there will be 40 payments at 6-month intervals. The time diagram shows their present value:

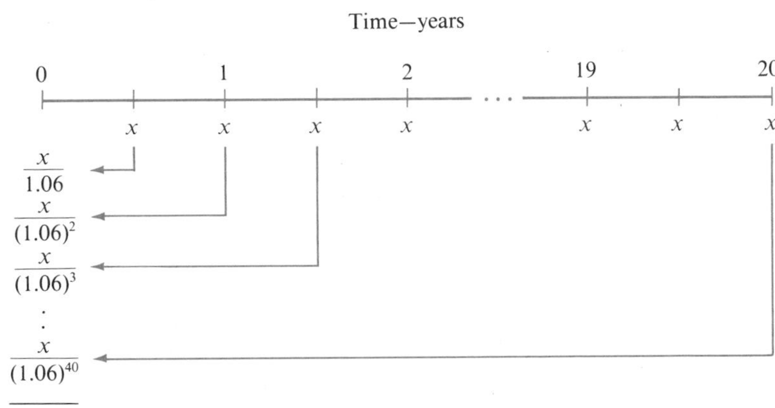

The present value of the annuity is:

$$\frac{x}{(1.06)^{40}} + \frac{x}{(1.06)^{39}} + \ldots + \frac{x}{(1.06)^{2}} + \frac{x}{1.06}$$

Using the formula for the sum of a geometric series $S = \frac{a(r^n - 1)}{r - 1}$:

$$280\,000 = \frac{x}{(1.06)^{40}} \times \frac{(1.06)^{40} - 1}{1.06 - 1}$$

$$= \frac{x}{10.285\,718} \times 154.761\,97$$

$$= 15.046\,297x$$

$$x = 18\,609.23$$

$a = \frac{x}{(1.06)^{40}}$
$r = 1.06$
$n = 40$
$S = 280\,000$

Mrs. Talbot will receive \$18 609.23 every 6 months for 20 years.

EXERCISES 11-7

(A)

1. Tom deposits \$1000 in an account that pays 12% interest compounded monthly. At the end of each year for 5 years he withdraws equal amounts. The graph shows the balance in his account during the 5 year period. Using the graph:
   a) what was the balance in the account after $2\frac{1}{2}$ years?
   b) when did the balance drop to \$500?
   c) about how much did Tom withdraw each year?

2. The graph shows the present values of two annuities of \$500 per year at different rates, for 15 years, and for 25 years. Using the graph:
   a) estimate the present value of an annuity of \$500 per year for 15 years at: i) 10%; ii) 15%.
   b) estimate the present value of an annuity of \$500 per year for 25 years at: i) 10%; ii) 15%.
   c) what interest rate would provide a \$500 per year annuity for \$4000 over a period of: i) 15 years? ii) 25 years?

3. The graph shows the annual 5-year and 10-year annuities that can be purchased for \$100 at different interest rates. Use the graph to determine, for an investment of \$1000, the annual annuity that can be purchased at 15% for:
   a) 5 years; b) 10 years.

4. Draw a time diagram to show the present value of:
   a) \$1200 paid at the end of each year for 4 years, if money is worth 10% compounded annually;

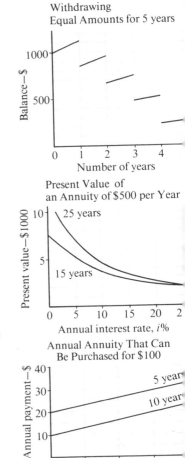

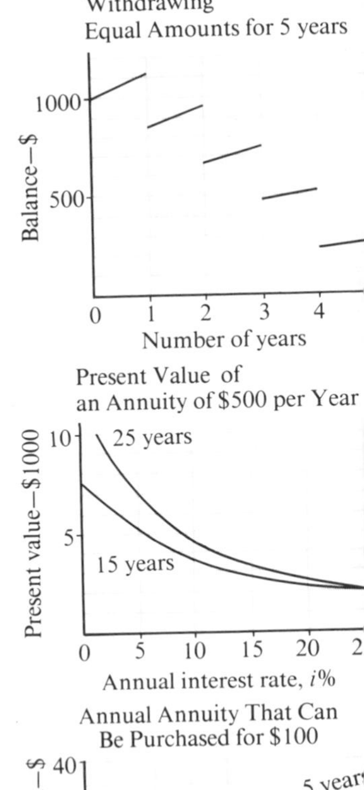

b) \$200 received after every 6 months for $3\frac{1}{2}$ years from a fund earning 11% compounded semi-annually;

c) \$100 received at the end of each month for 1 year from an account paying 12% compounded monthly.

5. In Exercise 4, find the present value of each annuity.

(B)

6. How much money should be deposited in an account which pays 8% compounded annually in order to be able to withdraw \$500 at the end of each year for the next 6 years?
7. You plan to buy an 8-year annuity which pays \$10 000 annually. The first payment will be 1 year from the date of purchase, and money is worth 14% compounded annually. What price should you pay?
8. A retiring teacher wishes to establish a scholarship that pays \$100 at the end of each year for 10 years. How much money must he deposit in a trust account that pays $7\frac{3}{4}$% compounded annually?
9. Find the present value of an annuity of \$1200 a year for 15 years at $10\frac{1}{2}$% compounded annually. The first payment is 1 year from now.
10. You deposit \$1000 in an account paying $7\frac{1}{2}$% compounded semi-annually. What equal withdrawals could you make every 6 months for the next 4 years?
11. The purchase price of a new car, including taxes, is \$14 387.45. What down payment will allow the balance to be paid off by monthly instalments of \$250 for 36 months, when interest is charged at 15% compounded monthly?

(C)

12. To assist with your college expenses, your parents deposit \$10 000 in an account when you enter college. If the account pays 9% compounded semi-annually, what equal amounts can you withdraw every 6 months over the next 3 years?
13. A trust account pays $8\frac{1}{4}$% compounded semi-annually. What deposit now would enable you to withdraw \$250 at the end of each year for the next 6 years?
14. You borrow \$2000 and agree to repay it in semi-annual instalments of \$325 at $12\frac{1}{2}$% compounded semi-annually. How many payments must you make?
15. An account pays 9% compounded annually. What deposit on November 1, 1988 will allow you to make 10 annual withdrawals of \$5000 beginning November 1, 2000?

MATHEMATICS AROUND US

Teacher Wins Free Groceries Until She Is 65

In September 1978, Mrs. Jane Lawson, a Bramalea, Ontario school teacher, won the Groceries-for-Life lottery at the Canadian National Exhibition. Her prize was the equivalent of \$204 500 in groceries from Loblaws Ltd. over the next 42 years.

Under the contest rules she had the option of receiving the cash equivalent in the form of annual redeemable certificates. The first year's certificate would be worth \$4000, and each subsequent year the certificate would be worth \$100 more until the yearly gift is \$5000.

QUESTIONS

1. Show how the value of the prize was calculated to be \$204 500.
2. What single piece of additional information is needed to determine the cash equivalent of the prize?
3. Using an 8% rate of interest compounded annually, estimate the cash equivalent that Mrs. Lawson might have been offered.

11-8 ANNUITIES: DETERMINING THE INTEREST RATE

It is sometimes useful, in financial planning or when considering a loan, to determine the interest rate for an annuity from other data given. The simplest case occurs with annual payments.

Example 1.

David has \$2000 to invest in an annuity. What interest rate must he obtain in order to receive payments of \$500 at the end of each year for the next 5 years?

Solution.

Let i represent the annual interest rate. The time diagram shows the present value of the payments.

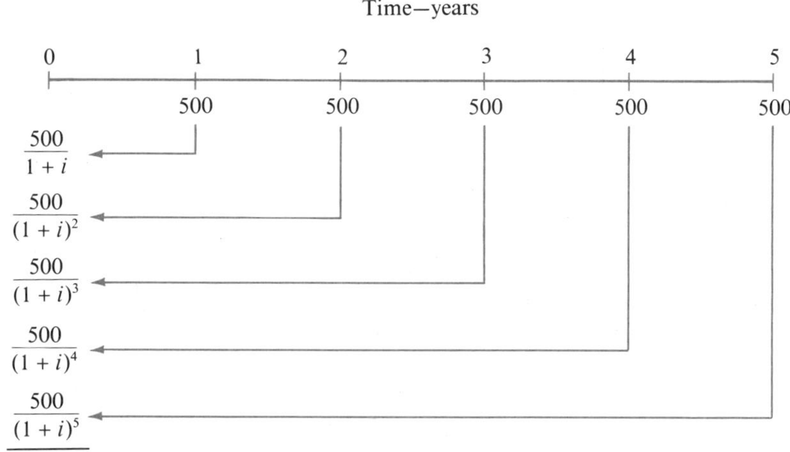

The total present value of the payments is \$2000. That is,

$$\frac{500}{(1+i)^5}+\frac{500}{(1+i)^4}+\frac{500}{(1+i)^3}+\frac{500}{(1+i)^2}+\frac{500}{1+i}=2000$$

Using the formula for the sum of a geometric series $S=\frac{a(r^n-1)}{r-1}$:

$$\frac{\frac{500}{(1+i)^5}\left[(1+i)^5-1\right]}{(1+i)-1}=2000 \qquad a=\frac{500}{(1+i)^5}$$

$$r=(1+i)$$

$$\frac{500}{(1+i)^5}\times\left[\frac{(1+i)^5-1}{i}\right]=2000 \qquad n=5$$

$$S=2000$$

The only way to solve this equation is by systematic trial using a scientific calculator or computer.

Using a scientific calculator: The table shows values of the left side of the equation for various values of i.

i	0.09	0.08	0.07
$\frac{500}{(1+i)^5}$	324.965 70	340.291 60	356.493 09
$\frac{(1+i)^5-1}{i}$	5.984 710 6	5.866 601 0	5.750 739 0
Product	1944.83	1996.36	2050.10

This shows that David must obtain an interest rate of about 8%.

Using a computer: The following BASIC program can be used to find the value of i to as many decimal places as desired. Run the program and enter different interest rates until one is found which gives a value of the expression very close to 4.

```
100 REM *** FINDING INTEREST RATES ***
110 INPUT "WHAT ARE THE PAYMENTS? ";P
120 INPUT "HOW MANY PAYMENTS? ";N
130 INPUT "ESTIMATED RATE? ";I
140 A=(P/(1+I)∧N)*((1+I)∧N-1)/I
150 PRINT:PRINT I,A
160 PRINT:INPUT "PRESS S TO STOP, RETURN TO REPEAT ";Y$
170 PRINT:IF Y$<>"S" THEN 130:END
```

Using this program, these results were obtained. They show that David must obtain an interest rate of not less than 7.93%.

i	$\frac{500}{(1+i)^5} \times \left[\frac{(1+i)^5 - 1}{i}\right]$
0.09	1944.825 63
0.08	1996.355 02
0.07	2050.098 73
0.079	2001.627 75
0.0793	2000.043 61
0.0794	1999.516 00

Since loan repayments are usually made on a monthly basis, the interest rate must be considered as a monthly rate.

Example 2.

Determine the effective interest rate being charged for the loan to purchase the 1979 Mercedes.

Low Monthly Payments

'79 Mercedes
Full Price $399
This is your chance to buy a great car—
6 cylinder, rust-proofed, air conditioned, stereo, only 85 000 km
Test drive now!
Down Payment $25
Monthly, for 36 months $12

Solution.

Since the payments are made monthly, let i represent the monthly interest rate. The time diagram shows the present values of the loan payments.

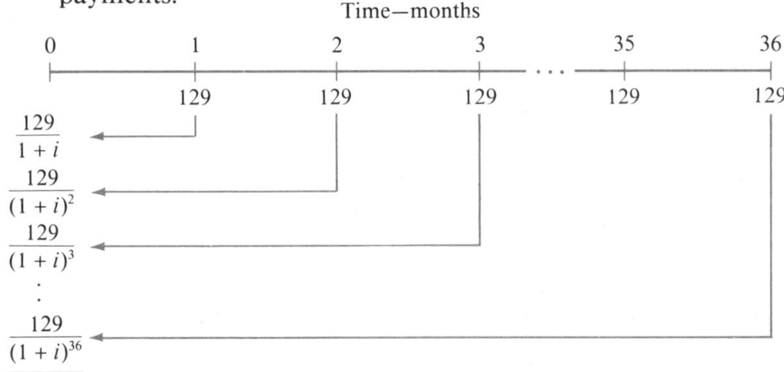

The total present value of the payments is the price of the car less the down payment. That is,

$$\frac{129}{(1+i)^{36}} + \frac{129}{(1+i)^{35}} + \ldots + \frac{129}{(1+i)^{2}} + \frac{129}{1+i} = 3995 - 250$$
$$= 3745$$

Using the formula for the sum of a geometric series, $S = \frac{a(r^n - 1)}{r - 1}$:

$$\frac{\frac{129}{(1+i)^{36}}[(1+i)^{36} - 1]}{(1+i) - 1} = 3745$$

$$\frac{129}{(1+i)^{36}} \times \left[\frac{(1+i)^{36} - 1}{i}\right] = 3745$$

$a = \frac{129}{(1+i)^{36}}$
$r = (1 + i)$
$n = 36$
$S = 3745$

Solve this equation by systematic trial.

Using a scientific calculator: The table shows values of the left side of the equation for various values of i.

i	0.010	0.012	0.013
$\frac{129}{(1+i)^{36}}$	90.161 318	83.963 640	81.030 716
$\frac{(1+i)^{36} - 1}{i}$	43.076 878	44.698 276	45.537 607
Product	3883.87	3753.03	3689.94

753.03 ≐ 3745

y using values of i with 4 ecimal places, a more accu- te value for the interest rate n be found.

This shows that the interest rate being charged is about 1.2% per month. The effective annual interest rate is approximated by finding the accumulated amount of $1 in 12 months.

$$1(1.012)^{12} \doteq 1.153\,894\,6$$

The effective annual rate is about 15.4%.

Using a computer: The same BASIC program yields these results. They show that the interest rate being charged is about 1.213% per month.

$$1(1.012\,13)^{12} \doteq 1.155\,674\,6$$

The effective annual rate is about 15.6%

i	$\frac{129}{(1+i)^{36}} \times \left[\frac{(1+i)^{36} - 1}{i}\right]$
0.010	3883.868 10
0.012	3753.029 97
0.013	3689.945 00
0.0121	3746.652 82
0.01213	3744.742 85
0.01212	3745.379 29

EXERCISES 11-8

Ⓐ

Monthly Payments on a $1000 Loan

Monthly payments—$ 100, 50; 1 year, 2 years, 3 years; 0, 5, 10, 15, 20; Effective annual rate—%

1. The graph shows the monthly payments of a $1000 loan for 1, 2, or 3 years at interest rates up to 25%. Use the graph to estimate the monthly payment for a loan of:

   a) $3000 for 2 years at: i) 10%, ii) 15%, iii) 20%;

   b) $5000 at 15% for: i) 1 year, ii) 2 years, iii) 3 years.

2. Use a scientific calculator or a computer to solve for i using systematic trial:

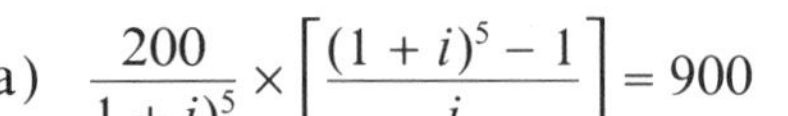

   a) $\frac{200}{1+i)^5} \times \left[\frac{(1+i)^5 - 1}{i}\right] = 900$ b) $\frac{500}{(1+i)^4} \times \left[\frac{(1+i)^4 - 1}{i}\right] = 1700$

   c) $\frac{1500}{1+i)^9} \times \left[\frac{(1+i)^9 - 1}{i}\right] = 8700$ d) $\frac{250}{(1+i)^{12}} \times \left[\frac{(1+i)^{12} - 1}{i}\right] = 1550$

3. Sheila has $6000 to invest in an annuity. If she wishes to receive $1500 at the end of each year for the next 5 years, what interest rate should she obtain?

4. An insurance company sells a 20-year annuity with annual payments of $3000 for $33 000. Determine the interest rate the company is offering if the first payment is 1 year from the date of purchase.

Ⓑ

5. Mr. Tucker wishes to invest $100 000 in an annuity which will provide $12 000 at the end of each year for the next 20 years. What interest rate must he obtain?

6. Connie invests her $100 000 inheritance in a 40-year annuity. What interest rate must she obtain if she wishes to receive $13 100 at the end of each year?

7. An $89 900 home sells for a down payment of $4900 and a semi-annual mortgage payment of $5392.76 for 25 years. If the first mortgage payment is 6 months from the date of purchase, what interest rate, compounded semi-annually, is used?

8. A used car, priced at $5500, sells for a down payment of $550 and monthly instalments of $161.59 for 3 years. Calculate:
   a) the monthly interest rate;
   b) the effective annual interest rate.

Ⓒ

9. Malcolm invests $500 at the end of each year for 10 years and accumulates $10 000. What rate of interest provides this amount?

10. The table shows some examples of bank loan rates. Determine the effective annual interest rate being charged.

Term months	Amount Required	Cost of Borrowing	Amount to be Repaid	Monthly Payments
36	$5000.00	$ 999.76	$ 5 999.76	$166.66
48	7500.00	2024.16	9 524.16	198.42
60	9500.00	3250.60	12 750.60	212.51

11. You decide to accumulate $1600 in 2 years by depositing $60 at the end of each month in a savings account. Calculate the necessary:
    a) monthly interest rate;
    b) effective annual interest rate.

11-9 BONDS: PRICE FOR A GIVEN YIELD

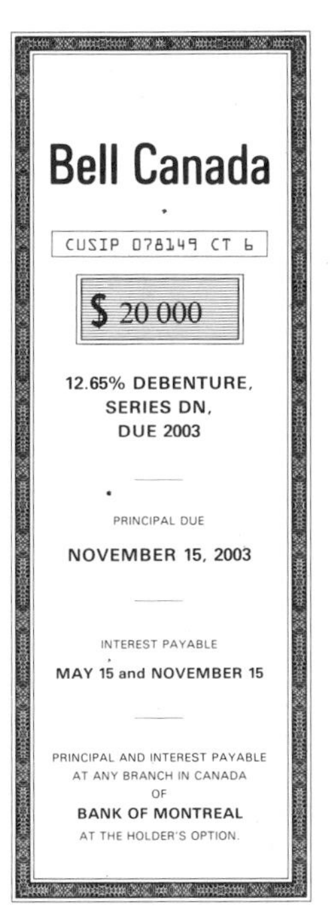

ed with permission of Bell Canada

It is common for governments and large business corporations to borrow millions of dollars to finance special projects. Since it is difficult to find a single institution prepared to lend this much money, the government or corporation may print *bonds* which are issued to many small lenders in exchange for money.

Bell Canada
CUSIP 078149 CT 6
$ 20 000
12.65% DEBENTURE, SERIES DN, DUE 2003
PRINCIPAL DUE
NOVEMBER 15, 2003
INTEREST PAYABLE
MAY 15 and NOVEMBER 15
PRINCIPAL AND INTEREST PAYABLE AT ANY BRANCH IN CANADA OF
BANK OF MONTREAL
AT THE HOLDER'S OPTION.

To finance the construction of a new office building, Bell Canada issued bonds like the one shown. This bond is a promise by Bell Canada to pay the owner the *face value* of $20 000 on November 15, 2003 (the *maturity date*). To compensate the owner for the use of the money, Bell Canada will pay interest at 12.65% compounded semi-annually (the *bond rate*). Unlike a Canada Savings Bond, this bond cannot be redeemed at any time. It can only be redeemed for its face value on the maturity date. However, the bond can be bought and sold in the financial marketplace. When this happens, the *price* of the bond may be higher or lower than the face value.

For example, if interest rates rise above 12.65%, investors would require an incentive to buy the bond. Those wishing to sell might offer it for $19 500, or $18 000, or less. Conversely, if interest rates fall below 12.65%, there would be an increased demand for the bond. It might then sell for $21 000, $22 500, or more.

Suppose the bond is sold on November 15, 1991. The new owner would then be entitled to receive from Bell Canada:

- the remaining semi-annual interest payments of $\$20\ 000 \times \frac{0.1265}{2}$, or $1265.00, from May, 1992 to November 15, 2003. There would be 24 such payments.
- the face value of $20 000 on November 15, 2003.

Suppose that the price the new owner paid for the bond represents an investment which will earn 14% interest compounded semi-annually. To find what this price is, we find the present value of the above amounts.

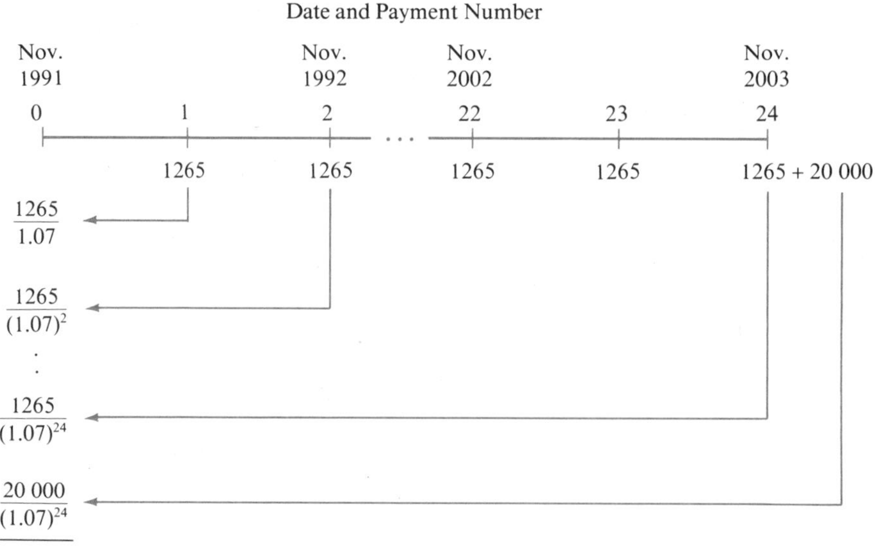

Using the formula for the sum of a geometric series $S = \dfrac{a(r^n - 1)}{r - 1}$, the present value of the 24 interest payments is:

$$\frac{\frac{1265}{(1.07)^{24}}[(1.07)^{24} - 1]}{1.07 - 1} \doteq \frac{(249.390\,47)(4.072\,367\,0)}{0.07} \doteq 14\,508.71$$

$$a = \frac{1265}{(1.07)^{24}} \quad r = 1.07 \quad n = 24$$

The present value of the \$20 000 payment is:

$$P = \frac{A}{(1 + i)^n} = \frac{20\,000}{(1.07)^{24}} = 3942.93$$

$$A = 20\,000 \quad i = 0.07 \quad n = 24$$

The present value of all payments at 14% compounded semi-annually is \$14 508.71 + \$3942.93, or \$18 451.64. This is the price the new owner paid for the bond. At this price, the investment yields a return of 14% compounded semi-annually. This rate is called the *yield rate.*

The financial pages of a daily newspaper list bond prices. For example, a bond listed under Provincials might show the information:

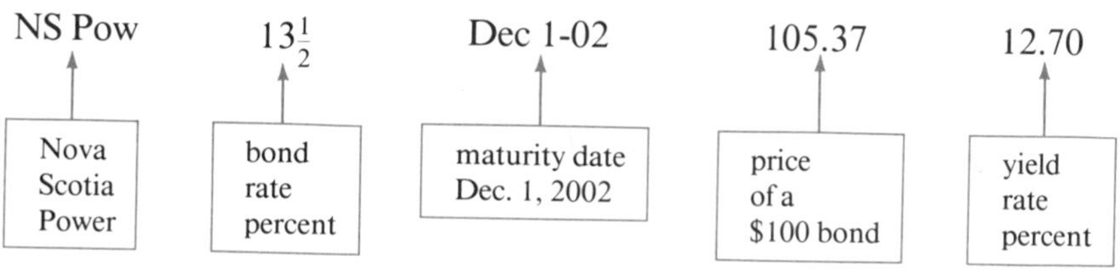

EXERCISES 11-9

(A)

1. For each bond, issued November 1, 1987, state:
   i) the face value; ii) the bond rate;
   iii) the interest payment; iv) the number of payments.
   a) a $10 000 $12\frac{3}{4}$% bond maturing November 1, 1997
   b) a $6000 13% bond maturing November 1, 2001
   c) a $2500 12% (compounded semi-annually) bond maturing November 1, 2009

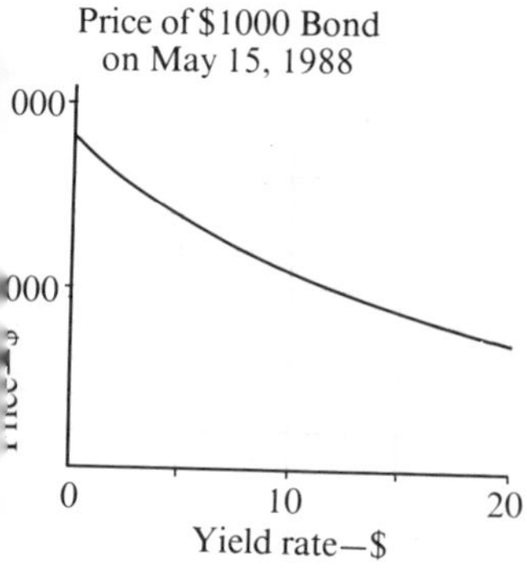

2. A $10 000 Ontario Hydro bond pays 12% interest annually, and has a maturity date of May 15, 1995. It is offered for sale on May 15, 1988. The graph shows the price of the bond for yield rates up to 20%. Use the graph to answer these questions:
   a) What bond price produces a yield rate of 14%?
   b) What yield rate corresponds to a purchase price of $12 000?
   c) How does the graph show that the bond rate is 12%?

(B)

3. You buy a $5000 $10\frac{1}{2}$% Ontario Hydro bond November 30, 1987. The maturity date is November 30, 1992. What purchase price yields:
   a) 12% ? b) 10% ?
4. A $12 000 $11\frac{1}{2}$% Alberta Oil bond, maturing September 1, 1995, is purchased September 1, 1988. What is the purchase price if the yield rate is: a) 14% ? b) $11\frac{1}{4}$% ?
5. How are the bond rate and the yield rate related if a bond is offered for sale at a price which is:
   a) less than the face value? b) greater than the face value?
   c) equal to the face value?
6. A $20 000 Bank of Montreal bond, maturing September 1, 2001, is purchased September 1, 1988. What purchase price yields 14% if the bond rate is $12\frac{1}{2}$% compounded:
   a) annually? b) semi-annually?

Ⓒ

7. An \$8000 $11\frac{1}{2}$% (compounded semi-annually) Quebec Hydro bond, maturing December 31, 2010, is purchased June 30, 1987. If the yield is 13%, what is the purchase price?
8. To raise money for a major expansion, Imperial Scientific floats a \$1 000 000 issue of 20-year bonds to be redeemed at \$104. The bond rate is 12% compounded semi-annually. If the bonds sell to yield 15% compounded semi-annually, how much did the company raise by their sale?
9. AKAS Corporation issues a special 20-year bond, the interest payments of which accumulate at 12% for the life of the bond. At maturity, the face value of the bond plus accumulated interest will be paid. If a 14% yield is desired, how much should be paid for a \$1000 bond?

11-10 BONDS: YIELD FOR A GIVEN PRICE

In the preceding section we calculated the price of a bond from its yield rate. When we buy a bond, however, the price is already fixed and it is necessary to compute the yield rate to determine which of the several bonds provides the greatest return. Though there is no direct method for computing the yield rate, we can find it as accurately as desired.

Example.

A \$1000 bond pays 9.5% interest annually and its maturity date is October 1, 1996. If it is purchased on October 1, 1987 for \$940, what is the approximate yield rate?

Solution.

From October 1, 1987 to October 1, 1996 is 9 years. Let the yield rate be i.
The price of the bond is the present value of the 9 interest payments of \$95 and the face value of \$1000 as shown by this time diagram:

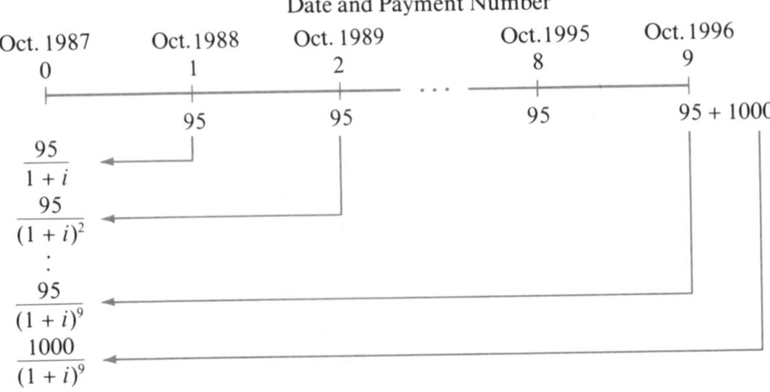

Using the formula for the sum of a geometric series, $S = \dfrac{a(r^n - 1)}{r - 1}$, the present value of the 9 interest payments is:

$$\frac{\frac{95}{(1+i)^9}[(1+i)^9 - 1]}{(1+i) - 1} = \frac{95}{(1+i)^9} \times \left[\frac{(1+i)^9 - 1}{i}\right] \qquad a = \frac{95}{(1+i)^9}$$

$$r = 1 + i$$

$$n = 9$$

The present value of the \$1000 payment is: $\dfrac{1000}{(1+i)^9}$

The price of the bond is the present value of all payments:

$$\frac{95}{(1+i)^9} \times \left[\frac{(1+i)^9 - 1}{i}\right] + \frac{1000}{(1+i)^9} = 940$$

The only way to solve this equation is by systematic trial using a scientific calculator or a computer.

Using a scientific calculator: The table shows the evaluation of the L.S. of the equation for various values of i. Since the price is less than the face value, the yield rate is greater than the bond rate. Therefore, only values of i greater than 0.095 have been used.

i	0.105	0.106	0.1056
$\frac{95}{(1+i)^9}$ ①	38.677 919	38.364 316	38.489 417
$\frac{(1+i)^9 - 1}{i}$ ②	13.868 398	13.926 976	13.903 513
$\frac{1000}{(1+i)^9}$ ③	407.135 99	403.834 91	405.151 76
① × ② + ③	943.54	938.13	940.29

The L.S. of the equation approximates the R.S., 940, when i is slightly greater than 0.1056. That is, the yield rate of the bond is about 10.6%.

Using a computer: The following BASIC program can be used to find the value of i to as many decimal places as desired. Run the program and enter different interest rates until one is found which gives a value of the expression very close to 940.

```
100 REM *** BOND YIELD RATES ***
110 INPUT "FACE VALUE OF THE BOND? ";A
120 INPUT "ANNUAL INTEREST PAYMENT? ";R
130 INPUT "HOW MANY ANNUAL INTEREST PAYMENTS? ";N
140 INPUT "ESTIMATED RATE? ";I
150 X=(1+I)^N
160 P=(R/X)*((1+I)^N-1)/I+A/X
170 PRINT:PRINT I,P
180 PRINT:INPUT "PRESS S TO STOP, RETURN TO CONTINUE ";Y$
190 PRINT:IF Y$<>"S" THEN 140:END
```

Using this program, these results were obtained. They show that the yield rate is approximately 10.57%.

i	$\frac{95}{(1+i)^9} \times \left[\frac{(1+i)^9 - 1}{i}\right] + \frac{1000}{(1+i)^9}$
0.105	943.536 761
0.106	938.133 811
0.1056	940.289 855
0.10563	940.127 914
0.10565	940.019 975
0.10566	939.966 013

EXERCISES 11-10

(B)

1. A $5000 9% bond, maturing May 1,1992, is bought for $4800 on May 1, 1986. Find the approximate yield.
2. A $9000 12% bond, maturing March 31, 2001, is bought on March 31, 1986, for $9650. What is the yield?
3. A $100 $10\frac{1}{2}$% bond, maturing August 31, 1998, sells for $109.50 on August 31, 1986. Find the approximate yield.
4. A $20 000 $9\frac{1}{2}$% bond, maturing in 18 years, sells for $18 400 now. Find the approximate yield.
5. A $3000 13% bond matures in 15 years. Find the yield if it sells now for: a) $2752 b) $3286.
6. The $100 bonds of SAKA Company pay $10\frac{1}{2}$% and are due December 31, 1999. If an investor pays $68 for them on December 1, 1985, what yield will she get?

Ⓒ

7. On March 1, 1987, Jennifer pays \$8250 for a \$10 000 bond which matures September 1, 2002. If the bond rate is $9\frac{1}{2}\%$ compounded semi-annually, what yield does she get?

> Department of Finance Canada
> issue of
> \$1 200 000 000 non-callable
> Government of Canada Bonds
> Dated December 15, 1984
>
> The Bank of Canada is authorized by the Minister of Finance to receive subscriptions for a loan to be issued for cash as follows:
>
> $11\frac{1}{2}\%$ bonds due December 15, 1991
>
> Issue Price: 99.50% yielding about 11.61% to maturity
>
> Interest payable June 15 and December 15.

8. A \$1 000 000 Government of Canada bond is purchased December 15, 1984.
   a) From the information in the advertisement,
      i) determine the price of the bond;
      ii) find the interest payable on June 15 and December 15 each year.
   b) Verify that the bonds yield about 11.61% to maturity.
   c) If \$1.2 billion of the bonds are sold, what total interest payments must the government make each June and December?

LEADERS IN MATHEMATICS

Charlotte Scott

Charlotte Angas Scott
(1858-1931)

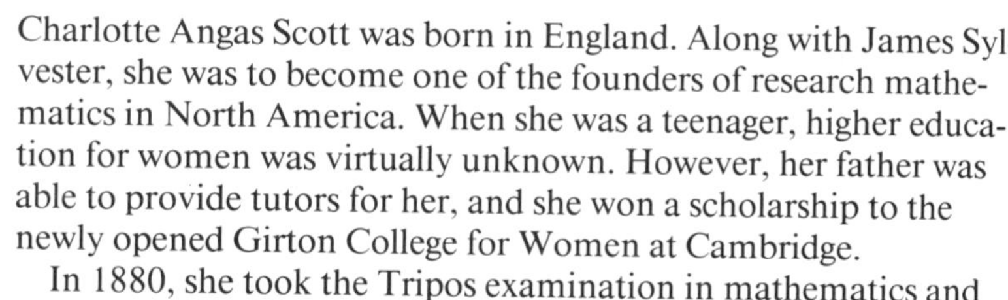

Charlotte Angas Scott was born in England. Along with James Sylvester, she was to become one of the founders of research mathematics in North America. When she was a teenager, higher education for women was virtually unknown. However, her father was able to provide tutors for her, and she won a scholarship to the newly opened Girton College for Women at Cambridge.

In 1880, she took the Tripos examination in mathematics and was placed eighth among all Cambridge students. But because she was a woman, she could not be present at the award ceremony or even have her name read. When the name of another student was read in eighth place instead of hers, irate male students shouted, "Scott of Girton! Scott of Girton!" throughout the hall. This publicity enabled subsequent female students to take the exam and have their names posted with those of the men. As Cambridge would not award her a degree, she applied to the University of London, obtaining her doctorate from there in 1885.

Despite her qualifications, there were no opportunities for her at English institutions, so she turned to the United States. She received an appointment to the faculty of Bryn Mawr College in Pennsylvania, and remained there for almost forty years.

In 1894, she wrote a textbook on analytic geometry. It was so popular, it was reprinted by another publisher thirty years later.

MONTHLY PAYMENT TO AMORTIZE A LOAN OF $10 000

Years	10%	11%	12%	13%	14%	15%	16%	17%	18%
1	878.22	882.68	887.13	891.58	896.03	900.47	904.90	909.33	913.76
2	460.52	464.95	469.38	473.83	478.28	482.74	487.20	491.68	496.15
3	321.72	326.23	330.76	335.31	339.88	344.46	349.06	353.68	358.32
4	252.66	257.27	261.92	266.60	271.30	276.04	280.80	285.60	290.42
5	211.48	216.21	220.98	225.80	230.66	235.55	240.49	245.46	250.47
6	184.24	189.09	194.00	198.96	203.97	209.02	214.13	219.28	224.47
7	164.97	169.94	174.98	180.08	185.24	190.46	195.73	201.06	206.44
8	150.67	155.77	160.94	166.18	171.49	176.87	182.31	187.81	193.37
9	139.69	144.91	150.21	155.60	161.05	166.58	172.18	177.85	183.58
10	131.03	136.37	141.80	147.32	152.92	158.60	164.36	170.19	176.08
11	124.06	129.51	135.07	140.72	146.46	152.29	158.19	164.18	170.23
12	118.34	123.92	129.60	135.37	141.25	147.21	153.26	159.39	165.60
13	113.60	119.28	125.08	130.99	136.99	143.09	149.28	155.55	161.89
14	109.61	115.41	121.32	127.35	133.48	139.70	146.02	152.42	158.89
15	106.23	112.13	118.16	124.30	130.55	136.90	143.34	149.86	156.46
16	103.33	109.35	115.48	121.74	128.10	134.56	141.12	147.75	154.46
17	100.84	106.96	113.20	119.56	126.03	132.61	139.27	146.01	152.83
18	98.69	104.90	111.24	117.71	124.28	130.96	137.72	144.56	151.47
19	96.81	103.12	109.56	116.12	122.79	129.56	136.42	143.35	150.35
20	95.17	101.56	108.10	114.75	121.52	128.38	135.32	142.34	149.42
21	93.72	100.21	106.83	113.58	120.43	127.37	134.40	141.49	148.65
22	92.45	99.02	105.73	112.56	119.49	126.51	133.62	140.78	148.00
23	91.33	97.98	104.77	111.67	118.68	125.78	132.95	140.18	147.47
24	90.33	97.06	103.93	110.91	117.99	125.15	132.39	139.68	147.01
25	89.45	96.25	103.19	110.24	117.39	124.61	131.91	139.25	146.64
26	88.66	95.54	102.54	109.66	116.87	124.15	131.50	138.89	146.32
27	87.96	94.90	101.97	109.15	116.42	123.76	131.15	138.59	146.06
28	87.33	94.34	101.47	108.71	116.03	123.41	130.85	138.33	145.84
29	86.77	93.84	101.03	108.32	115.69	123.12	130.60	138.11	145.65
30	86.27	93.39	100.64	107.98	115.39	122.87	130.38	137.93	145.49
31	85.82	93.00	100.29	107.68	115.14	122.65	130.20	137.77	145.36
32	85.41	92.64	99.99	107.42	114.92	122.46	130.04	137.64	145.25
33	85.05	92.33	99.72	107.19	114.72	122.30	129.90	137.53	145.16
34	84.72	92.05	99.48	106.99	114.55	122.16	129.79	137.43	145.08
35	84.42	91.80	99.27	106.81	114.41	122.04	129.69	137.35	145.01

Table 1

11-11 MORTGAGES: DETERMINING THE PAYMENTS AND TOTAL INTEREST

The largest investment most people ever make is buying a house. Since the price of many houses in urban areas exceeds $100 000, it is usually necessary to borrow a large sum of money. Money borrowed with property as security is called a **mortgage**.

Mortgage payments to repay the loan are made, usually monthly, over an extended period of time—20, 25, 35 years—called the *amortization period*. However, since interest rates can vary widely, a mortgage agreement is usually only for a short *term*. For example, a $60 000 25-year mortgage may be for 3 years at 13%, after which time it must be renegotiated at the rates then current.

The monthly payment is determined by three factors:
- the amount of the mortgage (**principal**)
- the interest rate
- the amortization period

The method of calculating the monthly payment for any mortgage is given on page 446. Or, reference can be made to a book of mortgage tables. Table 1 is similar to a page of those tables.

Example 1.

a) What is the monthly payment on a $60 000 mortgage amortized over 25 years at 13%?

b) About what amount of interest is paid over the 25 years?

Solution.

a) From the table, the monthly payment for a $10 000 25-year mortgage at 13% is $110.24. Since a $60 000 mortgage is 6 times as great, the monthly payment is 6 × $110.24, or $661.44.

b) The total amount paid over 25 years is:

$$25 \times 12 \times \$661.44, \text{ or about } \$198\ 000.$$

Of this amount, $60 000 repays the principal. Therefore the total amount of interest paid is about $198 000 – $60 000, or about $138 000.

As *Example 1* indicates, the total interest usually far exceeds the principal. It can be reduced in the following ways:
- By borrowing less money or repaying some of the principal early, as allowed;
- By obtaining a mortgage with a lower interest rate;
- By choosing a shorter amortization period, even though this increases the monthly payment.

Unless otherwise stated, we assume that the interest rate is constant during the amortization period. In practice, the rate changes each time the mortgage is renewed.

Example 2.

How much would the holder of the mortgage in *Example 1* save by paying $30 more each month?

Solution.

The monthly payment becomes $661.44 + $30, or $691.44. Monthly payments of this amount on a $60 000 mortgage are equivalent to payments of $\frac{1}{6} \times$ $691.44, or $115.24 on a $10 000 mortgage. From Table 1, the amortization period, at 13%, for this payment is about 20 years. That is, monthly payments of $691.44 would repay the $60 000 mortgage in about 20 years.

The total amount paid in 20 years would be:

$$20 \times 12 \times \$691.44, \text{ or about } \$166\,000.$$

By increasing the monthly payments by $30, the mortgage holder saves about $198 000 – $166 000, or $32 000 in interest.

Example 2 shows that even a modest increase in the monthly payment can result in large savings in interest.

You hold a mortgage and by early repayment of some of the principal, are able to:
- reduce the monthly paymen[t] keeping the amortization period the same;

or
- reduce the amortization period keeping the monthly payment the same.

Which would you choose? Illustrate which is the better choice with a numerical example.

Example 3.

If the mortgage in *Example 1* is renewed after 2 years, the principal outstanding is $59 229.47. Determine the new monthly payment if the new interest rate is:

a) 15%; b) 11%.

Solution.

a) Since 2 years have elapsed, the amortization period of the renewed mortgage is 23 years. From Table 1, the monthly payment for a $10 000 23-year mortgage at 15% is $125.78. Since the renewed mortgage is 5.922 947 times as great, the new monthly payment is 5.922 947 × $125.78, or $744.99.

b) Similarly, at 11%, the new monthly payment is 5.922 947 × $97.98, or $580.33.

EXERCISES 11-11

(A)

1. What is the monthly payment on a $40 000 mortgage amortized at 14% over:
   a) 15 years? b) 25 years? c) 35 years?
2. What is the monthly payment on a $30 000 mortgage amortized over 25 years at:
   a) 12%? b) 15%? c) 18%?
3. A $50 000 mortgage is amortized at 12% over 20 years. What is:
   a) the monthly payment?
   b) the total amount of interest paid over the 20 years?
4. A $60 000 mortgage is amortized at 15% over 25 years. What is:
   a) the monthly payment?
   b) the total amount of interest paid over the 25 years?
5. A $30 000 mortgage is being arranged at 16%.
   a) What are the monthly payments for amortization periods of:
      i) 15 years? ii) 25 years? iii) 35 years?
   b) What total amount of interest would be paid in each case?
   c) What are the advantages and disadvantages of the different amortization periods?

(B)

6. A $45 000 mortgage is amortized at 16% over 30 years. Calculate:
   a) the monthly payment;
   b) the total amount of interest paid over the 30 years;
   c) the savings if the mortgage is amortized over 20 years instead of 30 years.
7. A $75 000 mortgage is amortized at 12% over 25 years. Calculate:
   a) the monthly payment;
   b) the total amount of interest paid over the 25 years;
   c) the savings if the borrower pays $50 more each month.
8. A $35 000 mortgage is amortized at 12% over 30 years. Calculate:
   a) the monthly payment;
   b) the savings if the borrower pays $100 more each month.
9. If you can pay $600 per month, about how many years would it take to amortize a mortgage of $50 000 at:
   a) 10%? b) 12%? c) 14%?
10. a) What is the monthly payment on a $20 000 mortgage amortized at 18% over 15 years?
    b) If the mortgage is renewed after 2 years, the principal outstanding is $19 328.75. Determine the new monthly payment if interest rates have fallen to 14%.

11. You purchase the house advertised for $125 000 and make a $50 000 down payment.
    a) If the balance is mortgaged over 25 years at 14%, what is the monthly payment?
    b) After 3 years, when the principal outstanding is $73 679.96, the mortgage is renewed. Determine the new monthly payment if the interest rate is:

       i) 16%; ii) 12%.

12. The graph shows how the monthly payment on a $40 000 mortgage at 13% depends on the amortization period.
    a) Use the graph to compare the advantages and disadvantages of choosing, instead of 25 years, an amortization period of:
       i) 35 or 40 years; ii) 10 or 15 years.
    b) How does the graph change if the interest rate is
       i) higher than 13%? ii) lower than 13%?

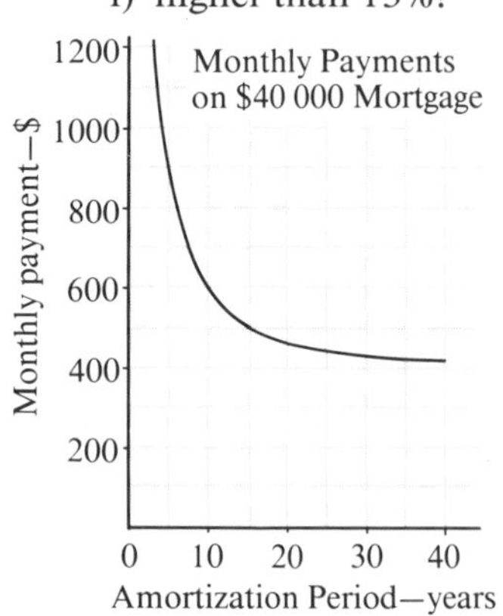

13. a) Draw a graph showing how the monthly payment on a $40 000 25-year mortgage depends on the interest rate.
    b) How does the graph change if the amortization period is:
       i) longer than 25 years? ii) shorter than 25 years?

Ⓒ

14. A \$40 000 25-year mortgage at 13% has a 5-year term.
    a) Calculate the monthly payment.
    b) At renewal, the principal outstanding is \$38 426.96 and mortgage rates have risen to 16%. Calculate the new monthly payment.
    c) To reduce the monthly payment, the bank suggests renewing the mortgage for a 25-year period. Calculate the monthly payment for this plan.
    d) Calculate the monthly payment if a 15-year amortization period is chosen instead.
    e) About how much interest is saved if the 15-year period is chosen instead of the 25-year period?
15. Estimate the monthly payment for a mortgage of:
    a) \$65 000 for 15 years at $12\frac{1}{2}$%;
    b) \$25 000 for 23 years at $15\frac{1}{4}$%;
    c) \$42 000 for 17 years at $13\frac{3}{4}$%.

Amortization Schedule

Amount	$50 000	Interest Rate	14.00%
Period	20 years	Monthly Payment	$607.59
		Interest Factor	0.011340268

No.	Interest Paid	Principal Paid	Principal Outstanding	No.	Interest Paid	Principal Paid	Principal Outstanding	No.	Interest Paid	Principal Paid	Principal Outstanding	No.	Interest Paid	Principal Paid	Princip Outstanc
1	567.01	40.58	49 959.42	61	527.76	79.83	46 459.11	121	450.55	157.04	39 573.50	181	298.67	308.92	26 028.
2	566.55	41.04	49 918.38	62	526.85	80.74	46 378.37	122	448.77	158.82	39 414.68	182	295.16	312.43	25 716.
3	566.08	41.51	49 876.87	63	525.94	81.65	46 296.72	123	446.97	160.62	39 254.06	183	291.62	315.97	25 400.
4	565.61	41.98	49 834.89	64	525.01	82.58	46 214.14	124	445.15	162.44	39 091.62	184	288.04	319.55	25 080.
5	565.14	42.45	49 792.44	65	524.08	83.51	46 130.63	125	443.30	164.29	38 927.33	185	284.41	323.18	24 757.
6	564.65	42.94	49 749.50	66	523.13	84.46	46 046.17	126	441.44	166.15	38 761.18	186	280.75	326.84	24 430.
7	564.17	43.42	49 706.08	67	522.17	85.42	45 960.75	127	439.56	168.03	38 593.15	187	277.04	330.55	24 099.
8	563.67	43.92	49 662.16	68	521.20	86.39	45 874.36	128	437.65	169.94	38 423.21	188	273.29	334.30	23 765.
9	563.18	44.41	49 617.75	69	520.22	87.37	45 786.99	129	435.72	171.87	38 251.34	189	269.50	338.09	23 427.
10	562.67	44.92	49 572.83	70	519.23	88.36	45 698.63	130	433.78	173.81	38 077.53	190	265.67	341.92	23 085.
11	562.16	45.43	49 527.40	71	518.23	89.36	45 609.27	131	431.80	175.79	37 901.74	191	261.79	345.80	22 739.
12	561.65	45.94	49 481.46	72	517.22	90.37	45 518.90	132	429.81	177.78	37 723.96	192	257.87	349.72	22 390.
13	561.13	46.46	49 435.00	73	516.19	91.40	45 427.50	133	427.79	179.80	37 544.16	193	253.91	353.68	22 036.
14	560.60	46.99	49 388.01	74	515.15	92.44	45 335.06	134	425.76	181.83	37 362.33	194	249.89	357.70	21 678.
15	560.07	47.52	49 340.49	75	514.11	93.48	45 241.58	135	423.69	183.90	37 178.43	195	245.84	361.75	21 317.
16	559.53	48.06	49 292.43	76	513.05	94.54	45 147.04	136	421.61	185.98	36 992.45	196	241.74	365.85	20 951.
17	558.98	48.61	49 243.82	77	511.97	95.62	45 051.42	137	419.50	188.09	36 804.36	197	237.59	370.00	20 581.
18	558.43	49.16	49 194.66	78	510.89	96.70	44 954.72	138	417.37	190.22	36 614.14	198	233.39	374.20	20 206.
19	557.88	49.71	49 144.95	79	509.79	97.80	44 856.92	139	415.21	192.38	36 421.76	199	229.15	378.44	19 828.
20	557.31	50.28	49 094.67	80	508.68	98.91	44 758.01	140	413.03	194.56	36 227.20	200	224.86	382.73	19 445.
21	556.74	50.85	49 043.82	81	507.56	100.03	44 657.98	141	410.82	196.77	36 030.43	201	220.52	387.07	19 058.
22	556.16	51.43	48 992.39	82	506.43	101.16	44 556.82	142	408.59	199.00	35 831.43	202	216.13	391.46	18 667.
23	555.58	52.01	48 940.38	83	505.28	102.31	44 454.51	143	406.33	201.26	35 630.17	203	211.69	395.90	18 271.
24	554.99	52.60	48 887.78	84	504.12	103.47	44 351.04	144	404.05	203.54	35 426.63	204	207.20	400.39	17 870.
25	554.40	53.19	48 834.59	85	502.95	104.64	44 246.40	145	401.74	205.85	35 220.78	205	202.66	404.93	17 466.
26	553.79	53.80	48 780.79	86	501.76	105.83	44 140.57	146	399.41	208.18	35 012.60	206	198.06	409.53	17 056.
27	553.18	54.41	48 726.38	87	500.56	107.03	44 033.54	147	397.05	210.54	34 802.06	207	193.42	414.17	16 642.
28	552.56	55.03	48 671.35	88	499.35	108.24	43 925.30	148	394.66	212.93	34 589.13	208	188.72	418.87	16 223.
29	551.94	55.65	48 615.70	89	498.12	109.47	43 815.83	149	392.24	215.35	34 373.78	209	183.97	423.62	15 799.
30	551.31	56.28	48 559.42	90	496.88	110.71	43 705.12	150	389.80	217.79	34 155.99	210	179.17	428.42	15 371.
31	550.67	56.92	48 502.50	91	495.62	111.97	43 593.15	151	387.33	220.26	33 935.73	211	174.31	433.28	14 938.
32	550.03	57.56	48 444.94	92	494.35	113.24	43 479.91	152	384.84	222.75	33 712.98	212	169.40	438.19	14 499.
33	549.37	58.22	48 386.72	93	493.07	114.52	43 465.39	153	382.31	225.28	33 487.70	213	164.43	443.16	14 056.
34	548.71	58.88	48 327.84	94	491.77	115.82	43 249.57	154	379.75	227.84	33 259.86	214	159.40	448.19	13 608.
35	548.05	59.54	48 268.30	95	490.46	117.13	43 132.44	155	377.17	230.42	33 029.44	215	154.32	453.27	13 155.
36	547.37	60.22	48 208.08	96	489.13	118.46	43 013.98	156	374.56	233.03	32 796.41	216	149.18	458.41	12 696.
37	546.69	60.90	48 147.18	97	487.78	119.81	42 894.17	157	371.91	235.68	32 560.73	217	143.98	463.61	12 233.
38	546.00	61.59	48 085.59	98	486.43	121.16	42 773.01	158	369.24	238.35	32 322.38	218	138.72	468.87	11 764.
39	545.30	62.29	48 023.30	99	485.05	122.54	42 650.47	159	366.54	241.05	32 081.33	219	133.41	474.18	11 290.
40	544.59	63.00	47 960.30	100	483.66	123.93	42 526.54	160	363.81	243.78	31 837.55	220	128.03	479.56	10 810.
41	543.88	63.71	47 896.59	101	482.26	125.33	42 401.21	161	361.04	246.55	31 591.00	221	122.59	485.00	10 325.
42	543.15	64.44	47 832.15	102	480.84	126.75	42 274.46	162	358.25	249.34	31 341.66	222	117.09	490.50	9 835.
43	542.42	65.17	47 766.98	103	479.40	128.19	42 146.27	163	355.42	252.17	31 089.49	223	111.53	496.06	9 339.
44	541.68	65.91	47 701.07	104	477.94	129.65	42 016.62	164	352.56	255.03	30 834.46	224	105.90	501.69	8 837.
45	540.94	66.65	47 634.42	105	476.47	131.12	41 885.50	165	349.67	257.92	30 576.54	225	100.21	507.38	8 330.
46	540.18	67.41	47 567.01	106	474.99	132.60	41 752.90	166	346.74	260.85	30 315.69	226	94.46	513.13	7 816.
47	539.42	68.17	47 498.84	107	473.48	134.11	41 618.79	167	343.78	263.81	30 051.88	227	88.64	518.95	7 298.
48	538.64	68.95	47 429.89	108	471.96	135.63	41 483.16	168	340.79	266.80	29 785.08	228	82.76	524.83	6 773.
49	537.86	69.73	47 360.16	109	470.42	137.17	41 345.99	169	337.77	269.82	29 515.26	229	76.80	530.79	6 242.
50	537.07	70.52	47 289.64	110	468.87	138.72	41 207.27	170	334.71	272.88	29 242.38	230	70.79	536.80	5 705.
51	536.27	71.32	47 218.32	111	467.30	140.29	41 066.98	171	331.61	275.98	28 966.40	231	64.70	542.89	5 162.
52	535.46	72.13	47 146.19	112	465.71	141.88	40 925.10	172	328.48	279.11	28 687.29	232	58.54	549.05	4 613.
53	534.65	72.94	47 073.25	113	464.10	143.49	40 781.61	173	325.32	282.27	28 405.02	233	52.31	555.28	4 058.
55	533.82	73.77	46 999.48	114	462.47	145.12	40 636.49	174	322.12	285.47	28 119.55	234	46.02	561.57	3 496.
55	532.98	74.61	46 924.87	115	460.82	146.77	40 489.72	175	318.88	288.71	27 830.84	235	39.65	567.94	2 928.
56	532.14	75.45	46 849.42	116	459.16	148.43	40 341.29	176	315.60	291.99	27 538.85	236	33.21	574.38	2 354.
57	531.28	76.31	46 773.11	117	457.48	150.11	40 191.18	177	312.29	295.30	27 243.55	237	26.70	580.89	1 773.
58	530.41	77.18	46 695.93	118	455.77	151.82	40 039.36	178	308.94	298.65	26 944.90	238	20.11	587.48	1 186.
59	529.54	78.05	46 617.88	119	454.05	153.54	39 885.82	179	305.56	302.03	26 642.87	239	13.45	594.14	591.
60	528.65	78.94	46 538.94	120	452.31	155.28	39 730.54	180	302.13	305.46	26 337.41	240	6.71	591.96	0
												Total Interest Paid:			95 812.
												Total Principal Paid:			50 000.

Table 2

11-12 MORTGAGES: AMORTIZATION SCHEDULES

Table 2 is an example of an **amortization schedule**. Such a schedule can be computed for any mortgage. It shows the two parts of each monthly payment: the part which is the payment of interest and the part which goes toward reducing the principal. The schedule also shows the principal outstanding after each payment.

Example 1.

For the amortization schedule shown (Table 2),

a) how much principal is repaid in the first 3 years?
b) what is the total interest paid in the first 3 years?

Solution.

a) The principal repaid in the first 3 years can be found as follows:

Original principal:	\$50 000.00
Less principal outstanding after 36 months:	\$48 208.08
Principal repaid in the first 3 years:	\$ 1 791.92

b)

Amount paid in 3 years: 36 × \$607.59, or	\$21 873.24
Less principal repaid:	\$ 1 791.92
Interest paid in the first 3 years:	\$20 081.32

As *Example 1* shows, almost all of each payment in the early years of a mortgage is payment of interest. This is because the outstanding balance is so large.

Some mortgages permit the borrower to make a lump sum payment against the principal at specified times. These are called *open mortgages*. The next example shows that this is a very desirable feature.

Example 2.

For the amortization schedule shown (Table 2), what amount of interest would be saved if a \$5000 payment is made against the principal at the end of the first year?

Solution.

At the end of the 12th month the outstanding principal is \$49 481.46. A lump sum payment of \$5000 reduces this to \$44 481.46. The figure closest to this in the Principal Outstanding column is \$44 454.51 opposite the 83rd payment. That is, the principal repaid between the 12th and 83rd months is approximately \$5000. The interest saved is the amount of interest paid from the 13th to the 83rd payments.

Total of payments: 71 × \$607.59, or	\$43 138.89
Less principal repaid:	\$ 5 000.00
Interest saved:	\$38 138.89

A payment of \$5000 against the principal after the first year will save about \$38 000 in interest.

In *Example 2*, when the $5000 payment is made the table is recalculated, but the effect is about the same as continuing from the 83rd month.

On the amortization schedule, there is a figure called an *interest factor*. This factor is used to calculate the interest portion of any monthly payment. Table 3 gives interest factors for a few interest rates. The method of calculating interest factors is given in the Computer Power on page 446.

Monthly Interest Factors	
10%	0.008 164 846
11%	0.008 963 394
12%	0.009 758 794
13%	0.010 551 074
14%	0.011 340 260
15%	0.012 126 379
16%	0.012 909 457
17%	0.013 689 519
18%	0.014 466 592

Interest for one month on any amount can be obtained by multiplying by this factor.

Table 3

Example 3.

Use the interest factor to check the first three numbers in the Interest Paid column of Table 2.

Solution.

Multiply the previous principal outstanding by 0.011 340 260:

1. $50\ 000.00 \times 0.011\ 340\ 260 = 567.01$
2. $49\ 959.92 \times 0.011\ 340\ 260 = 566.56$
3. $49\ 918.38 \times 0.011\ 340\ 260 = 566.09$

Example 4.

If the mortgage in Table 2 has a 3-year term,

a) determine the principal outstanding at the time of the first renewal;

b) what is the new monthly payment if the new rate of interest is 16%?

c) prepare an amortization schedule for the first four payments of the renewed mortgage.

Solution.

a) From Table 2, the principal outstanding after 3 years is $48 208.08.

b) Since 3 years have elapsed, the amortization period of the renewed mortgage is 17 years. From Table 1, the monthly payment for a $10 000 17-year mortgage at 16% is $139.27. Since the renewed mortgage is $48 208.08, the new monthly payment is:

$$4.820\ 808 \times \$139.27, \text{ or } \$671.39.$$

c) From Table 3, the interest factor for 16% is 0.012 909 457. Using a calculator, we construct this table:

Payment Number	① Interest Paid ③ × 0.012 909 457	② Principal Repaid 671.39 − ①	③ Principal Outstanding ③ − ②
			48 208.08
1	622.34	49.05	48 159.03
2	621.71	49.68	48 109.35
3	621.07	50.32	48 059.03
4	620.42	50.97	48 008.06

EXERCISES 11-12

The exercises refer to the amortization schedule of Table 2.

(A)

1. a) What is the principal outstanding after:
   i) the first year? ii) the fifth year?
   iii) the tenth year? iv) the sixteenth year?
   b) How many years does it take to repay:
   i) $10 000 of the principal?
   ii) half the principal?
2. a) How much principal is repaid in the first year?
   b) About how much interest is paid in the first year?
3. a) How much principal is repaid in the 20th year?
   b) About how much interest is paid in the 20th year?
4. Estimate the amount of interest saved if a payment of $1000 is made at the end of:
   a) the first year; b) the second year;
   c) the third year; d) the tenth year.
5. Draw a graph showing the principal outstanding after each year during the amortization period.

(B)

6. a) Why are the interest portions of the early payments so great?
   b) Why do the interest portions decrease over the amortization period?
   c) How long does it take until half of each payment goes to reducing the principal?
7. Which graph best represents the interest and principal portions of the monthly payments during the amortization period?

a)

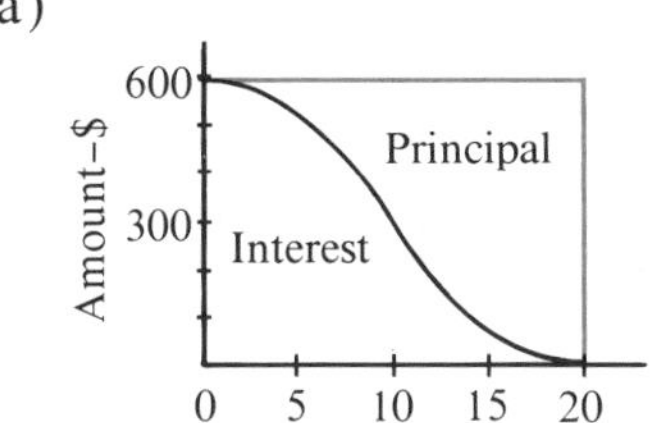

b)

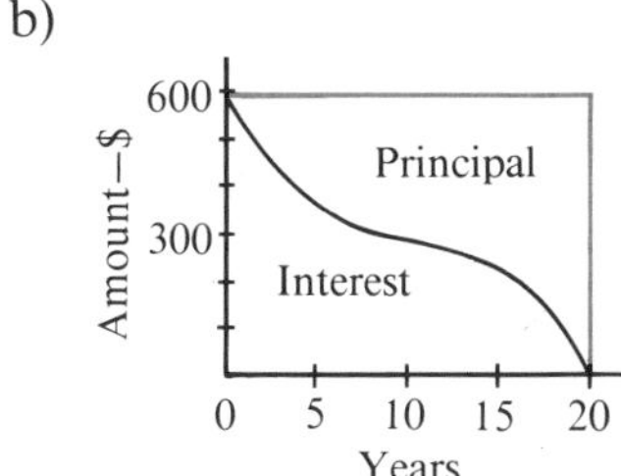

c)

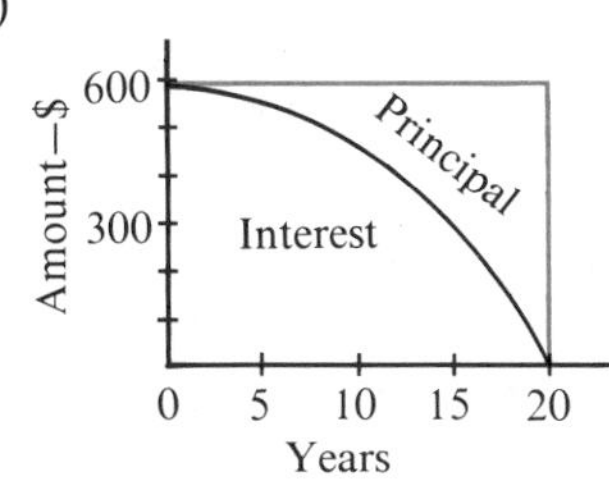

d)

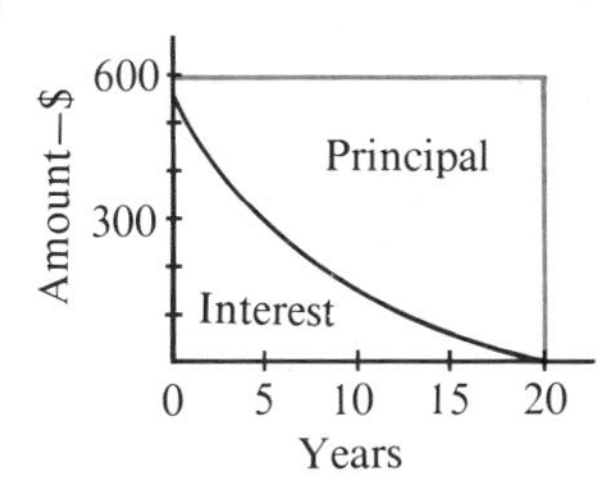

8. If the mortgage of Table 2 has a 1-year term,
   a) determine the new monthly payment if the new interest rate is 12%;
   b) prepare an amortization schedule for the first four payments of the renewed mortgage.
9. If the mortgage of Table 2 has a 5-year term,
   a) determine the new monthly payment if the new interest rate is 17%;
   b) prepare an amortization schedule for the first four payments of the renewed mortgage.
10. The graphs show the principal outstanding for three different plans which include a lump sum payment in the repayment of the principal.
    a) Estimate the amount of each lump sum payment and when it was made.
    b) Which is the best plan? Why?

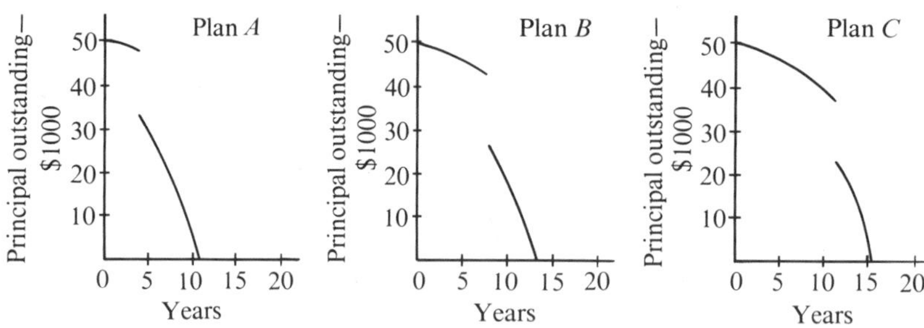

11. Which is the better plan?

Plan *A*	Plan *B*
Make a lump sum payment of $3000 at the end of the second year.	Make a lump sum payment of $4000 at the end of the fifth year.

12. If a lump sum payment of $1000 is made at the end of the first year and also at the end of the second year, how much interest is saved?
13. Make calculations to check that the amount of Total Interest Paid in Table 2 is correct.

Ⓒ

14. Financial institutions compete for customers by offering a variety of mortgage repayment plans designed to save borrowers thousands of dollars. The saving is made by reducing the principal outstanding and the amortization period more quickly than a regular mortgage does. Some typical plans are:

    Weekly payments: The monthly payment is divided into four equal parts which are paid weekly. Since there are 52 weeks in a year, the effect is to make 13 monthly payments in a 12-month period. The extra payment reduces the principal outstanding.

INVESTIGATE

Some banks offer a *variable rate* mortgage. The interest rate changes with current market rates, but the monthly payment remains the same for the term of the mortgage.

What are the advantages and disadvantages of this type of mortgage?

Write a report of your findings.

Double-up payment: The payment made in any month can be doubled. The second payment reduces the principal outstanding.

10 + 10: a) Each year, the monthly payment can be increased by up to 10%.
b) Each year, up to 10% of the original principal can be repaid.

The following are examples of how these plans affect the mortgage in Table 2.

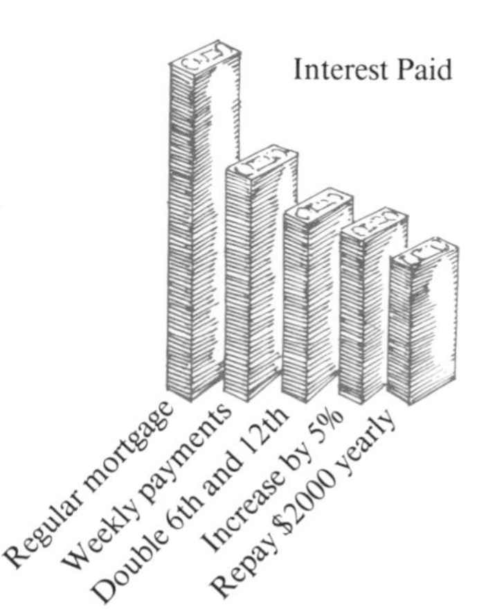

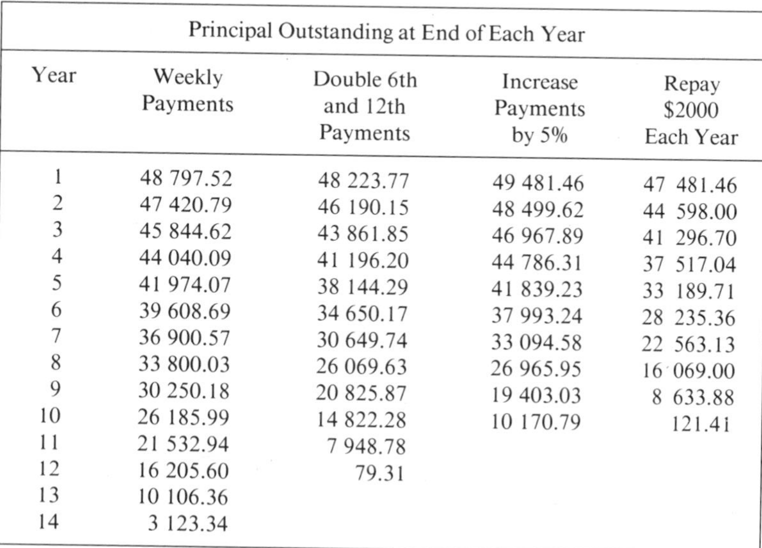
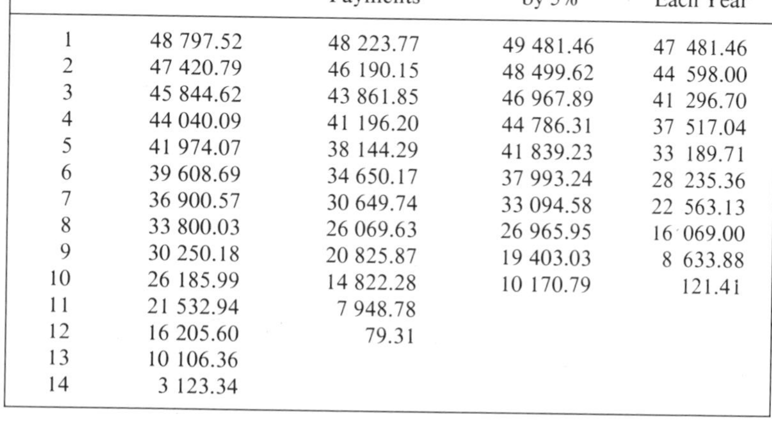

Principal Outstanding at End of Each Year				
Year	Weekly Payments	Double 6th and 12th Payments	Increase Payments by 5%	Repay $2000 Each Year
1	48 797.52	48 223.77	49 481.46	47 481.46
2	47 420.79	46 190.15	48 499.62	44 598.00
3	45 844.62	43 861.85	46 967.89	41 296.70
4	44 040.09	41 196.20	44 786.31	37 517.04
5	41 974.07	38 144.29	41 839.23	33 189.71
6	39 608.69	34 650.17	37 993.24	28 235.36
7	36 900.57	30 649.74	33 094.58	22 563.13
8	33 800.03	26 069.63	26 965.95	16 069.00
9	30 250.18	20 825.87	19 403.03	8 633.88
10	26 185.99	14 822.28	10 170.79	121.41
11	21 532.94	7 948.78		
12	16 205.60	79.31		
13	10 106.36			
14	3 123.34			

a) Which plan, if any, would a wage-earner probably be able to use? Why?

b) Estimate the total amount of interest saved under each plan compared with the regular mortgage in Table 2.

Mortgage Payments

Canadian law requires that mortgage interest rates be compounded semi-annually. Since the payments are usually made monthly, allowance must be made for the fact that the payment interval is different from the compounding period.

To use the methods of working with annuities, an equivalent monthly interest rate must be calculated. For a mortgage rate of i% per annum, compounded semi-annually, let j be the equivalent rate compounded monthly. Since both rates are equivalent, the amount after 6 months must be the same. That is,

$$(1 + j)^6 = 1 + \frac{i}{2}$$

$$1 + j = \sqrt[6]{1 + \frac{i}{2}}$$

$$j = \sqrt[6]{1 + \frac{i}{2}} - 1$$

This formula is used to calculate the monthly interest factors for mortgage interest rates of i% per annum compounded semi-annually. The following program can be used to calculate interest factors for any mortgage.

```
100 REM *** INTEREST FACTORS ***
110 INPUT "WHAT IS THE INTEREST RATE? ";I
120 PRINT:PRINT (1+I/2)^(1/6)-1
130 PRINT:INPUT "PRESS S TO STOP, RETURN TO CONTINUE ";Y$
140 PRINT:IF Y$<>"S" THEN 110:END
```

To determine a formula for the monthly payment, x, on a mortgage with an amortization period of n years, we use a time diagram.

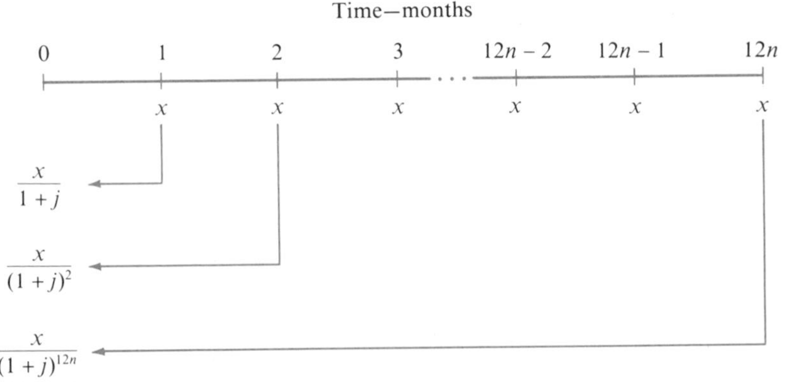

The total present value of the payments is the amount, A, of the mortgage.

$$A = \frac{x}{(1+j)^{12n}} + \frac{x}{(1+j)^{12n-1}} + \ldots + \frac{x}{(1+j)^2} + \frac{x}{1+j}$$

Using the formula for the sum of a geometric series:

$$A = \frac{x}{(1+j)^{12n}}\left[\frac{(1+j)^{12n}-1}{j}\right]$$

$$= \frac{x[1-(1+j)^{-12n}]}{j}$$

Solving for x: $x = \dfrac{Aj}{[1-(1+j)^{-12n}]}$, where $j = \sqrt[6]{1+\dfrac{i}{2}} - 1$

The following program uses these formulas to determine the monthly payment on any given mortgage. If desired, an amortization schedule will also be printed.

```
100 REM *** MORTGAGE PAYMENTS ***
110 INPUT "AMOUNT OF MORTGAGE? ";A
120 INPUT "AMORTIZATION PERIOD IN YEARS? ";N
130 INPUT "ANNUAL INTEREST RATE? ";I
140 J=(1+I/2)^(1/6)-1
150 PAY=A*J/(1-(1+J)^(-12*N))
160 PAY=INT(100*PAY+0.5)/100
170 PRINT:PRINT "MONTHLY PAYMENT: ";PAY
180 PRINT:INPUT "PRESS S TO STOP, RETURN FOR SCHEDULE ";Y$
190 PRINT:IF Y$="S" THEN 320
200 PRINT "PAYMENT INTEREST PRINCIPAL PRINCIPAL"
210 PRINT "NUMBER     PAID      PAID     OUTSTANDING"
220 FOR I=1 TO N*12
230 IN=INT(100*J*A)/100
240 PR=INT(100*(PAY-IN)+0.5)/100
250 BAL=INT(100*(A-PR)+0.5)/100
260 PRINT I;TAB(10);IN;TAB(20);PR;TAB(30);BAL
270 IF INT(I/12)<I/12 THEN 300
280 PRINT:INPUT "PRESS S TO STOP, RETURN TO CONTINUE ";Y$
290 PRINT:IF Y$="S" THEN 320
300 A=BAL
310 NEXT I
320 END
```

1. a) Prepare an amortization schedule for the mortgage of *Example 1* in Section 11-11.
   b) Prepare amortization schedules for the renewals of *Example 3* in Section 11-11
2. a) If the new house in the advertisement is purchased with a 10% down payment, determine the monthly payments at $15\frac{3}{4}\%$ for amortization periods of:
   i) 15 years; ii) 25 years; iii) 35 years.

   b) A 25-year mortgage is taken for a 1-year term. At renewal, interest rates have increased to $17\frac{3}{8}\%$. Determine the new monthly payment.

Review Exercises

1. Calculate the missing information:

	Principal P	Interest rate, r	Time t	Simple interest, I
a)	\$525.00	8%	21 d	
b)	\$720.00		153 d	\$28.67
c)	\$165.00	$11\frac{1}{4}\%$		\$ 3.05
d)		$8\frac{1}{2}\%$	230 d	\$13.12

2. On February 10, Nadine deposited $128.00 in a $6\frac{1}{2}\%$ daily interest savings account. She makes another deposit of $35.00 on March 18. Find the accumulated amount on:
   a) February 28; b) March 31; c) April 30.

3. Find the accumulated amount:
   a) $1450 for 7 years at 9% compounded annually
   b) $325 for 4 years at $8\frac{1}{2}\%$ compounded annually
   c) $618 for $5\frac{1}{2}$ years at $10\frac{1}{2}\%$ compounded semi-annually
   d) $460 for 30 months at 15% compounded monthly

4. Find the present value:
   a) $825 due in 3 years at 10% compounded annually
   b) $290 due in 7 years at $11\frac{1}{4}\%$ compounded annually
   c) $415 due in 5 years at $9\frac{1}{2}\%$ compounded semi-annually
   d) $1250 due in $4\frac{1}{2}$ years at 9% compounded monthly

5. Find the value of a $5000 Canada Savings Compound Interest Bond at $11\frac{1}{2}\%$ after: a) 4 years; b) 9 years.

6. How much should be invested at $12\frac{1}{2}\%$ compounded semi-annually to amount to $1150 in: a) $3\frac{1}{2}$ years? b) 8 years?

7. $450 accumulates to $905.21 in 7 years. What is the interest rate if it is compounded annually?

8. How much should parents invest on their daughter's first birthday so that $10 000 is available on her 18th birthday? The interest rate is $10\frac{1}{2}\%$ compounded semi-annually.

9. Find the accumulated amount of $625 invested for 4 years at 10% compounded:
   a) annually; b) semi-annually; c) monthly.

10. If $200 accumulates to $350 in 5 years with interest compounded semi-annually, what is the rate?

11. What annual rate, compounded monthly, is equivalent to an effective rate of 15% per annum?

12. Joshua opens a bank account, which pays 8% interest compounded annually, with a deposit of $1000. At the end of each year he deposits a further $1000, and he makes no withdrawals. How much will be in the account at the end of 6 years?

13. Find the amount of an annuity of $300 every 6 months for $7\frac{1}{2}$ years at 12% compounded semi-annually.

14. An account earns 9% compounded annually. What equal amounts must be deposited at the end of each year in order to have $15 000 at the end of 7 years?

15. How much must be deposited in a savings account earning 10% compounded annually in order to be able to withdraw $2500 at the end of each year for 5 years?

16. Find the present value of an annuity of $1600 every 6 months for 9 years at 10% compounded semi-annually.

17. An annuity earning 10% interest compounded semi-annually is purchased for $25 000. If the term is 10 years, what will be the semi-annual payments?

18. A $60 000 mortgage requires an annual payment of $5863 for 25 years. What is the annual interest rate?

19. A $10 000 9% Ontario Hydro bond, maturing June 1, 1998, is bought June 1, 1989. What is the purchase price if the yield is:
    a) 12%?
    b) $7\frac{1}{2}$%?

20. A $5000 bond, maturing March 15, 1995, pays $10\frac{1}{2}$% interest compounded annually. If it is purchased March 15, 1989 for $4700, what is the approximate yield rate?

21. A $70 000 mortgage is amortized at 11% over 30 years. Find:
    a) the monthly payment;
    b) the total amount paid;
    c) the total amount of interest paid.

22. In Exercise 21, how much is saved if the mortgage is amortized over 25 years?

23. A $45 000 mortgage is amortized at 13% over 20 years. Calculate:
    a) the monthly payment;
    b) the savings if the borrower pays $26 more per month.

24. In the amortization schedule of Table 2:
    a) what is the principal outstanding after: i) the 4th year? ii) the 10th year?
    b) how many years does it take to reduce the principal outstanding by $7500?
    c) how much interest is paid in the first 2 years?
    d) how much is saved if a $2500 payment is made at the end of the 3rd year?

25. The mortgage of Table 2 has an 8-year term. Determine the new monthly payment if the new interest rate is 16%.

Answers

Chapter 1

Exercises 1-1, page 3

1. b, c, e, f, h, i
2. a) 3^3 b) $2 \times 3 \times 7$ c) $2^2 \times 17$ d) 5×19
   e) $2 \times 3 \times 17$ f) 5×29 g) $5 \times 2^2 \times 3^2$
   h) $3^2 \times 5^2$ i) $2^2 \times 3 \times 19$ j) $3^2 \times 43$
3. a) $15 + 10 = 25$, $21 + 15 = 36$, $28 + 21 = 49$
   b) The sum is a square number.
4. a) 13, 16, 19 b) 162, 486, 1458
   c) 25,36, 49 d) 31, 43, 57 e) 91, 140, 204
   f) 56, 84, 120
5. a) $1 + 2 + 3 + 4 + 3 + 2 + 1 = 4^2$
   $1 + 2 + 3 + 4 + 5 + 4 + 3 + 2 + 1 = 5^2$
   $1 + 2 + 3 + 4 + 5 + 6 + 5 + 4 + 3 + 2 + 1 = 6^2$
6. 59
7. Three—169, 196, 961
8. Eight—13, 17, 31, 37, 71, 73, 79, 97
9. a) 65, 71, 77, 83, 89 b) 53, 65, 77, 89, 101
   c) 31, 41, 53, 67, 83 No.
10. a) 25, 36; 81, 100 b) 4, 16; 4, 36
    c) 9, 16; 16, 25
11. 33×3367, 39×2849, 231×481
13. a) 5, 13, 17, 29, 37, 41
    b) $4 + 1$, $4 + 9$, $16 + 1$, $25 + 4$, $36 + 1$, $16 + 25$
14. a) 3, 7, 11, 19, 23, 31, 43, 47
15. a) $1 + 10$ b) $1 + 3 + 15$ c) $1 + 28$
    d) $3 + 6 + 21$ e) $6 + 6 + 21$ f) $1 + 21 + 28$
16. Yes
19. a) i) 82 to 100 ii) $(n - 1)^2 + 1$ to n^2
20. b) 36

MM

1. b, d
2. a) $2^2 \times 17 \times 53$ b) $41 \times 71 \times 139$
   c) $3^2 \times 29 \times 47 \times 83$ d) $503 \times 13\,049$
3. $333\,333\,331 = 17 \times 19\,607\,843$

MAU

a) 491×499 b) 367×431 c) 197×389
d) 229×449

Exercises 1-2, page 9

1. a) 2.25 b) 0.4375 c) $0.41\overline{6}$ d) $0.\overline{407}$
   e) $0.\overline{2}$ f) $1.\overline{571\,428}$ g) $1.\overline{81}$ h) $0.\overline{25}$
2. a) $\frac{28}{11}$ b) $\frac{415}{999}$ c) $\frac{1619}{990}$ d) $\frac{322}{75}$ e) $\frac{3122}{999}$
   f) $\frac{283}{45}$ g) $\frac{157}{330}$ h) $\frac{5077}{999}$
6. a) $\frac{488}{333}$ b) $\frac{333}{110}$ c) $\frac{536}{99}$ d) $\frac{221}{300}$
   e) $\frac{14\,141}{9999}$ f) $\frac{3626}{4995}$
7. a) $\frac{9}{9}$
8. a) $0.\overline{4}$ b) $0.\overline{57}$ c) $0.\overline{31}$ d) $0.\overline{3}$
   e) $0.\overline{074}$ f) $0.\overline{15}$

9. b) i) $\frac{1}{9} = \frac{1}{10} + \frac{1}{10 \times 9}$ ii) $\frac{1}{12} = \frac{1}{13} + \frac{1}{13 \times 12}$
   iii) $\frac{1}{20} = \frac{1}{21} + \frac{1}{21 \times 20}$
10. b) i) $\frac{8}{9} = \frac{1}{2 \times 1} + \frac{1}{3 \times 2} + \frac{1}{4 \times 3} + \frac{1}{5 \times 4} + \frac{1}{6 \times 5} + \frac{1}{7 \times 6} + \frac{1}{8 \times 7} + \frac{1}{9 \times 8}$
    ii) $\frac{8}{17} = \frac{1}{3 \times 1} + \frac{1}{5 \times 3} + \frac{1}{7 \times 5} + \frac{1}{9 \times 7} + \frac{1}{11 \times 9} + \frac{1}{13 \times 11} + \frac{1}{15 \times 13} + \frac{1}{17 \times 15}$
11. Answers may vary.
    a) $0.45 = \frac{1}{3} + \frac{1}{15} + \frac{1}{20}$ or $\frac{1}{4} + \frac{1}{5}$ or $\frac{1}{4} + \frac{1}{6} + \frac{1}{30}$
    b) $\frac{1}{2} + \frac{1}{20}$ c) $\frac{1}{2} + \frac{1}{10} + \frac{1}{20}$
12. Same.

CP

5. Yes.

Exercises 1-3, page 15

1. a) −29 b) −3 c) 120 d) −50
2. a) −18 b) 53 c) −20.4 d) 60
   e) −3 f) −42
3. a) −36 b) −25 c) −15 d) −59
   e) $\frac{13}{3}$
4. a) $-\frac{39}{2}$ b) $\frac{77}{8}$ c) $\frac{9}{40}$ d) $\frac{1}{20}$ e) $-\frac{2}{3}$
   f) $\frac{11}{5}$
5. a) $\frac{3}{8}$ b) $-\frac{7}{72}$ c) $\frac{17}{6}$ d) $-\frac{13}{12}$ e) $-\frac{91}{12}$
   f) $-\frac{61}{30}$
6. a) $\frac{21}{5}$ b) 0 c) $-\frac{4}{5}$ d) 1 e) $\frac{5}{12}$
   f) $-\frac{137}{100}$
7. a) $-\frac{7}{6}$ b) $\frac{23}{72}$ c) $-\frac{11}{3}$
8. a) 3 b) −7 c) 12 d) −5 e) 4
   f) $\frac{5}{14}$
9. a) $-\frac{15}{112}$ b) −1 c) $-\frac{28}{27}$
10. $3846.67; $3190
11. a) −1 b) −3 c) $-\frac{9}{2}$ d) 2 e) 8
    f) −2
12. 50
13. a) 12 b) 14 c) 4 d) −1
14. a) 14 b) – c) 20 d) –

Exercises 1-4, page 19

1. a, c, d, e, g, h

2. a) 10 b) 1.6 c) 0.3 d) $\frac{7}{9}$ e) $\frac{11}{6}$
f) 3.9

3. a) $\sqrt{30}$ b) $\sqrt{21}$ c) $56\sqrt{6}$ d) $15\sqrt{42}$
e) $-96\sqrt{77}$ f) $75\sqrt{70}$

4. a) $3\sqrt{2}$ b) $2\sqrt{3}$ c) $5\sqrt{2}$ d) $4\sqrt{5}$
e) $5\sqrt{3}$ f) $4\sqrt{3}$ g) $4\sqrt{7}$ h) $2\sqrt{33}$

5. a) $30\sqrt{2}$ b) $140\sqrt{2}$ c) $48\sqrt{15}$
d) $-108\sqrt{10}$ e) $-180\sqrt{2}$ f) $140\sqrt{5}$

6. a) 180 b) $720\sqrt{3}$ c) $108\sqrt{5}$
d) $-360\sqrt{5}$ e) $-3780\sqrt{2}$ f) $-1680\sqrt{6}$

7. a) 5.5 b) 14.1 c) 11.2 d) 0.95
e) 12.2 f) 1.6

8. a) $2\sqrt{10}, 4\sqrt{3}, 5\sqrt{2}, 3\sqrt{6}, 2\sqrt{14},$
b) $-4\sqrt{6}, -4\sqrt{5}, -5\sqrt{3}, -6\sqrt{2}, -2\sqrt{17}$
c) $6\sqrt{3}, 4\sqrt{7}, 5\sqrt{5}, 3\sqrt{14}, 8\sqrt{2}$

10. 16 cm^2

11. a) $5\sqrt{3}$ b) $7\sqrt{2}$ c) $4\sqrt{3}$ d) $-8\sqrt{3}$
e) $2\sqrt[3]{7}$ f) $\frac{3}{4}\sqrt{12}$

MM

3. Yes.

Exercises 1-5, page 24

1. a) $3\sqrt{5}$ b) $3\sqrt{3}$ c) $5\sqrt{2}$ d) $13\sqrt{7}$
e) $8\sqrt{10}$ f) $9\sqrt{3}$

2. a) $2\sqrt{2}$ b) $7\sqrt{3}$ c) $5\sqrt{6}$ d) $-2\sqrt{2}$
e) $8\sqrt{7}$ f) $\sqrt{5}$

3. a) $2\sqrt{3}$ b) $26\sqrt{6}$ c) $9\sqrt{7}$ d) 0
e) $63\sqrt{6}$ f) $-4\sqrt{5}$

4. a) $\sqrt{15}+\sqrt{21}$ b) $28\sqrt{6}-12\sqrt{15}$
c) $30\sqrt{2}+20\sqrt{30}$ d) $90\sqrt{3}-63\sqrt{15}$
e) $16\sqrt{3}-36$ f) 154

5. a) $1+\sqrt{15}$ b) $-32+\sqrt{35}$ c) $-6-2\sqrt{3}$
d) $30-14\sqrt{6}$ e) $192+90\sqrt{2}$
f) $185-46\sqrt{35}$

6. a) $3\sqrt{7}$ b) $-\frac{1}{3}\sqrt{5}$ c) $-3\sqrt{13}$ d) $6\sqrt{14}$
e) $\frac{2}{5}\sqrt{11}$ f) $-15\sqrt{17}$ g) $8\sqrt{5}$ h) $\frac{2}{3}\sqrt{5}$

7. a) $2\sqrt{5}$ b) $27\sqrt{2}$ c) $-11\sqrt{6}$ d) $19\sqrt{2}$
e) $-17\sqrt{10}$ f) $10\sqrt{5}$

8. a) $12\sqrt{14}-30$ b) -72 c) $30(\sqrt{3}-\sqrt{2})$
d) $36\sqrt{2}+8\sqrt{21}-60$ e) 0
f) $64\sqrt{3}-48\sqrt{2}-144$

9. a) 3 b) 33 c) -32 d) $104-60\sqrt{3}$
e) $227+56\sqrt{15}$ f) $404\sqrt{2}+60\sqrt{42}$

10. a) 8 b) $-6\sqrt{3}$ c) $-\frac{1}{2}$ d) $4\sqrt{5}$
e) $\frac{15}{4}\sqrt{2}$ f) $-\frac{20}{3}\sqrt{2}$ g) $\sqrt{2}$ h) $\sqrt{3}$

11. a) i) $\sqrt{2}$ ii) $\sqrt{3}$ b) 4

12. a) i) 2 ii) $\sqrt{5}$ b) i) 9 ii) 8

13. $\frac{2\sqrt{3}}{3}$

Exercises 1-6, page 27

1. a) $\frac{2\sqrt{5}}{5}$ b) $\frac{7\sqrt{11}}{11}$ c) $-\frac{4\sqrt{3}}{3}$ d) $\frac{5\sqrt{14}}{7}$
e) $-2\sqrt{30}$ f) $\frac{12\sqrt{35}}{35}$ g) $3\sqrt{10}$ h) $-\frac{5\sqrt{21}}{3}$

2. a) $\frac{3\sqrt{30}}{10}$ b) $\sqrt{10}$ c) $-3\sqrt{6}$ d) $\frac{5\sqrt{6}}{4}$
e) $\frac{4\sqrt{21}}{3}$ f) $\frac{\sqrt{21}}{2}$ g) $\frac{4\sqrt{30}}{3}$ h) $\frac{27}{4}$

3. a) $\frac{6+4\sqrt{3}}{3}$ b) $\frac{35-3\sqrt{7}}{7}$ c) $\frac{20-2\sqrt{5}}{5}$
d) $2\sqrt{6}-1$ e) $\frac{8\sqrt{30}+5}{5}$ f) $3\sqrt{5}-1$
g) $\frac{10\sqrt{3}+3\sqrt{2}}{3}$ h) $\frac{\sqrt{6}}{2}$

4. a) $\frac{\sqrt{15}+\sqrt{6}}{3}$ b) $\frac{\sqrt{35}-\sqrt{15}}{4}$ c) $\frac{8\sqrt{11}+\sqrt{55}}{59}$
d) $\frac{2\sqrt{30}-2\sqrt{15}}{3}$ e) $\frac{-30\sqrt{2}-25\sqrt{6}}{13}$
f) $\frac{4\sqrt{105}+4\sqrt{70}}{5}$ g) $\frac{30\sqrt{3}-6\sqrt{6}}{23}$ h) $\frac{3\sqrt{55}+15}{2}$

5. a) $\frac{\sqrt{6}}{2}$ b) $\frac{\sqrt{32}+7\sqrt{6}}{10}$ c) $\sqrt{15}$ d) $\frac{42+17\sqrt{5}}{29}$
e) $\frac{27-7\sqrt{21}}{30}$ f) $\frac{13\sqrt{2}-3\sqrt{7}}{25}$

6. a, b, c, f

7. a) $\frac{\sqrt{2}}{2}$ b) $\frac{\sqrt{3}}{6}$ c) $\frac{\sqrt{2}}{10}$ d) $\sqrt{2}+1$
e) $\sqrt{3}-\sqrt{2}$ f) $\frac{2\sqrt{5}+3\sqrt{2}}{2}$

8. a) 4 b) $\frac{2\sqrt{5}+4\sqrt{2}}{3}$ c) $5\sqrt{2}-2$
d) $\frac{7\sqrt{5}}{5}-6$ e) $-2-\frac{7\sqrt{3}}{3}$ f) $\sqrt{2}+\frac{\sqrt{3}-3}{2}$

Exercises 1-7, page 30

1. a, b, d, h **2.** a, c, d, g, h

3. b, c—rational; a, d, e, f—irrational

4. a) Q', R c) N, I, Q, R
d) Q', R e) Q, R f) Q', R g) Q', R
h) Q', R i) I, Q, R

6. Answers will vary. Examples are:
a) 2.579 18 and 2.579 181 181 118...
b) −6.327 329 and −6.327 329 010 010 001...
c) 4.190 15 and 4.190 151 151 115...

7. a) $\frac{4}{9}, \frac{6}{9}$ b) $\sqrt{0.999\,999\,9}$

8. a) N, I, Q, R b) I, Q, R c) Q, R d) N, I, Q, R and I, Q, R e) Q', R f) –

Review Exercises, page 31

1. a) $2 \times 3 \times 5 \times 7^2$ b) $3 \times 5 \times 7 \times 13$ c) $2^2 \times 7 \times 11 \times 17$

2. a) $\frac{191}{110}$ b) $\frac{157}{99}$ c) $\frac{707}{333}$ d) $\frac{311}{99}$ e) $\frac{277}{333}$ f) $\frac{2257}{450}$

3. a) $0.\overline{3}$ b) $0.\overline{90}$ c) $0.1\overline{4}$ d) $0.\overline{518}$ e) $0.\overline{296}$ f) $0.946\,352\,4$

4. a) $\frac{88}{9}$ b) $-\frac{1}{3}$ c) $-\frac{51}{32}$

5. a) -55 b) $-\frac{1}{4}$ c) $-\frac{191}{43}$ d) $-\frac{1}{5}$

6. q:32, d:48 **7.** a) 60 b) 120 c) 1200 d) $-60\sqrt{42}$ e) 3780 f) $770\sqrt{21}$

8. a) $10\sqrt{2},\ 9\sqrt{3},\ 6\sqrt{7},\ 7\sqrt{6},\ 8\sqrt{5}$ b) $-5\sqrt{2},\ -4\sqrt{3},\ -3\sqrt{5},\ -2\sqrt{7},\ -\sqrt{19}$ c) $3\sqrt{6},\ 6\sqrt{2},\ 2\sqrt{26},\ \sqrt{111},\ 5\sqrt{5}$

9. a) $3\sqrt{30} + 16 - 10\sqrt{3}$ b) $8\sqrt{10} + 16\sqrt{6} - 12\sqrt{3}$ c) $14\sqrt{30} - 6\sqrt{13} - 4\sqrt{7}$ d) $7\sqrt{6}$ e) $8\sqrt{15} - 3\sqrt{70} - 8\sqrt{5}$ f) $21\sqrt{5} + 56 - 30\sqrt{7}$

10. a) $4\sqrt{6}$ b) $168\sqrt{2} - 105\sqrt{6}$ c) 113 d) $132 - 72\sqrt{2}$ e) $93 + 24\sqrt{15}$ f) $6\sqrt{6} + 45\sqrt{2}$

11. a) $3\sqrt{6}$ b) $\frac{-16\sqrt{5}}{5}$ c) $\sqrt{10}$ d) $3 + \sqrt{5}$ e) $\frac{42 - 4\sqrt{7} + 6\sqrt{14} - 4\sqrt{2}}{5}$ f) $\frac{9}{2}(\sqrt{10} - \sqrt{6})$

12. a, c, d, f, h

Chapter 2

Exercises 2-1, page 35

1. a) 2^7 b) a^8 c) $\left(-\frac{3}{4}\right)^5$ d) $(3x)^4$

2. a) 100 b) 196 c) -52 d) -9 e) 47 f) 6

3. a) 2187 b) 15 625 c) 2.0736 d) 31.006 277 e) 1.3841×10^{10} f) 1.0737×10^9

4. a) i) 800 ii) 6400
b) i) 2700 ii) 72 900
c) i) 12.5 ii) 1.5625
d) i) 2560 ii) 1310.72
e) i) 10.546 875 ii) 4.449 45
f) i) 2.737 566 ii) 4.163 508

5. a) 100×2^5 b) i) 800 ii) 12 800

6. a) \$20 800 b) \$65 000$(0.85)^n$

7. \$7320.50

8. a) 3^3 b) 5^3 c) $(-2)^5$ d) 9^3 e) $(-3)^4$ f) $(1.2)^4$

9. a) 2^7 b) 3^4 c) $3^6 = 9^3$ d) 2^{10}

10. a) $7^2, 3^3, 4^2, 3^2, 2^3$ b) $(-2)^8, 2^7, (-3)^4, (-5)^3, (-2)^9$ c) $(1.2)^3, (1.3)^2, (1.1)^5, 1.4$

11. a) \$42 100 b) \$67 500 c) \$30 000 $(1.07)^n$

12. a) \$1.12 b) \$1.31 c) \$1.92

13.

	M.C.	Lagos	N.Y.	Tokyo	Delhi	Calcutta
a)	28.8	9.1	16.2	17.3	11.2	17.1
b)	76.8	24.9	18.3	17.7	24.7	35.9

14. a) i) 25% ii) 6.25% b) $(0.5)^{\frac{n}{1600}} \times 100\%$

15. a) i) 90% ii) 81% iii) 59% iv) 12% b) i) 6.6 min ii) 22 min c) $100(0.9)^n$

16. a) i) 1.28 m ii) 0.27 m b) 7th

17. a) \$1700 b) \$10 000$(0.7)^n$

18. c) i) 9 ii) 4 iii) 3

MAU

1. Until about A.D. 2000

2. a) b) About 1.6×10^{12} barrels

3. An additional 30 years.

Exercises 2-2, page 41

1. a) x^{32} b) m^{10} c) y^{15} d) a^9 e) c^{27} f) x^{20}

2. a) $63x^{17}$ b) $5m^{12}$ c) $4n^6$ d) $-4a^{10}$ e) $96y^{21}$ f) $-243c^{20}$

3. a) $a^{16}b^7$ b) m^6n^4 c) $-42c^{20}d^{11}$ d) x^3y^6 e) $4a^{10}b^8$ f) $x^{12}y^{10}$

4. a) $9x^8$ b) $2000a^{18}$ c) $-1728m^{15}n^{33}$ d) $6x^5y^2$ e) a^5b^6 f) $-\frac{5}{2}c^8d^8$

5. a) 32 b) 16 c) -960 d) 48 e) -16 f) -1536

6. a) x^{5a+2} b) 3^{3m+4} c) c^{10a+8} d) $\frac{9}{2}a^{9x-4}$ e) r^{6xy} f) $x^{3m-1}y^{2n+3}$

7. a) 2^{3n} b) 2^{3n} c) 2^{6n+8} d) 2^{5n} e) 1 f) 2^{3n+3}

8. a) i) 1024 ii) 9 765 620 iii) 10 077 700 b) i) 8000 ii) 10^{15} iii) 10^{14} iv) 2.5×10^8 v) 10^{21} vi) 3.6×10^8

9. a) $18m^7$ b) $729m^{24}$ c) $\frac{5}{3}m^8$ d) $\frac{2025}{4}m^{14}$

10. a) $12a^6b^6$ b) $256a^8b^{18}$ c) $10a^4b^6$ d) $4a^{12}b^{12}$

11. a) x^{2a} b) x^{a^2} c) x^{5a-1}

12. a) i) 64 ii) 4096 iii) 16.8×10^6
iv) 2.8×10^{14} b) 2^{2n}, or 4^n

13. a) i) a^{11} ii) a^{14} b) i) bc^2 ii) b^2c^2
c) Since $8 = 5 + 3$, $a^8 = bc$.
Since $9 = 3 + 3 + 3$, $a^9 = b^3$.
Since $10 = 5 + 5$, $a^{10} = c^2$
All following powers of a can be found by multiplying one of the above by b or a power of b.

14. a) 304 b) $\frac{9}{5}$

16. a) 1 073 741 824 b) 244 140 625
c) 3 486 784 401

Exercises 2-3, page 44

1. a) 1 b) $\frac{1}{9}$ c) $\frac{1}{8}$ d) 1 e) $\frac{1}{5}$ f) $\frac{1}{64}$
g) $-\frac{1}{8}$ h) $\frac{1}{9}$

2. a) 1 b) 25 c) $\frac{9}{4}$ d) $\frac{49}{16}$ e) $\frac{9}{4}$
f) $\frac{81}{25}$ g) −8 h) $-\frac{2}{3}$

3. a) 0.1250 b) 0.0001 c) 0.0003
d) 0.1197 e) 0.0822 f) 0.8874
g) 97.6563 h) 0.2097

4. a) 147.746 b) 82.0348 c) 1197.009
d) 487.448 54 e) 1519.893 f) 327.619 05

5. a) i) 0.111 ii) 0.004 b) i) 0.010 ii) 0
c) i) 0.444 ii) 0.132
d) i) 0.890 ii) 0.747 e) i) 0.718 ii) 0.437
f) i) 1.181 ii) 1.517

6. a) iii b) i) 2500 ii) 312

7. a) $\frac{80}{9}$ b) $\frac{1}{4}$ c) $-\frac{1}{72}$ d) 4 e) 6
f) $-\frac{1}{16}$

8. a) $\frac{1}{8}$ b) $\frac{1}{9}$ c) $\frac{1}{36}$ d) 25 e) 8
f) $\frac{1}{49}$ g) $-\frac{1}{27}$ h) $\frac{9}{8}$

9. a) $\frac{9}{20}$ b) 4 c) −7 d) 0 e) $\frac{100}{289}$
f) $24\frac{31}{32}$

10. a) 7^{-1} b) 2^{-3} c) $\left(\frac{3}{5}\right)^{-2}$ d) $\left(-\frac{1}{5}\right)^{-3}$
e) 10^{-1} f) $(-9)^{-3}$

12. a) x^{-5} b) m^{-2} c) $40a^{-12}$ d) $-6c^{-3}d^6$
e) $24x^4y^4$ f) $4m^{-9}n^8$

13. a) $\frac{1}{9}$ b) 8 c) 25 d) 144 e) 7^{-9} f) $\frac{2}{3}$

14. a) 4 b) $\frac{16}{9}$ c) −10.5 d) 720 e) $\frac{1}{16}$
f) $\frac{7}{4}$

15. a) i) 125 g ii) 7.8 g b) i) 16 kg ii) 512 kg

16. $1588.80

17. a) i) a^2 ii) a
b) i) b^6c^{-1} ii) b^7c^{-3} iii) b^2c^{-1}

18. a) 0.003 906 25 b) 0.000 976 562 5
c) 0.000 002 56

Exercises 2-4, page 49

1. a) 8 b) 6 c) 2 d) 2 e) 20
f) −5 g) 0.3 h) 3

2. a) $7^{\frac{1}{2}}$ b) $135^{\frac{1}{2}}$ c) $12^{\frac{1}{3}}$ d) $21^{\frac{1}{4}}$ e) $29^{\frac{1}{2}}$
f) $19^{\frac{1}{5}}$ g) $(-91)^{\frac{1}{3}}$ h) $(0.7)^{\frac{1}{4}}$

3. a) 4 b) 64 c) 216 d) 9 e) 10
f) 8 g) 0.343 h) 0.064

4. a) 32 b) −32 c) 729 d) 8
e) 0.064 f) 81 g) 1.331 h) 128

5. a) $\frac{1}{3}$ b) $\frac{1}{2}$ c) $\frac{1}{5}$ d) $\frac{1}{2}$ e) $\frac{1}{9}$ f) $\frac{1}{3}$
g) $\frac{1}{2}$ h) 1

6. a) $\frac{1}{9}$ b) $\frac{1}{64}$ c) 27 d) $\frac{1}{4}$ e) 16
f) $\frac{1}{8}$ g) 125 h) $\frac{1}{32}$

7. a) $\frac{3}{4}$ b) 27 c) $\frac{1}{16}$ d) $\frac{9}{4}$ e) $\frac{8}{27}$
f) $\frac{343}{125}$ g) $\frac{625}{81}$ h) 1

8. a) 1.7783 b) 10.8140 c) 3.6593
d) 44.3127 e) 1.1017 f) 3.4471

9. a) i) 2074 ii) 2646 b) i) 1701 ii) 1311

10. a) $10^{\frac{2}{3}}$ b) $12^{\frac{5}{4}}$ c) $36^{\frac{3}{7}}$ or $6^{\frac{6}{7}}$ d) $94^{\frac{17}{5}}$
e) $25^{-\frac{4}{3}}$ or $5^{-\frac{8}{3}}$ f) $52^{-\frac{7}{2}}$

11. a) $2^{\frac{7}{3}}$ b) $6^{\frac{3}{4}}$ c) $2^{\frac{9}{2}}$ d) $5^{\frac{8}{5}}$ e) $7^{\frac{10}{3}}$ f) $3^{\frac{16}{7}}$

12. a) $V^{\frac{1}{3}}$ b) $V^{\frac{2}{3}}$

13. a) 6 b) 500 c) 27 d) 36 e) 80
f) 864

14. a) 3 b) −11 c) $\frac{1}{4}$ d) −1 e) 3 f) 9

15. a) 19.95 b) 199.5 c) 0.1995 d) 0.01995

16. a) 32 b) 2 c) 32 d) $\frac{1}{512}$ e) 16 f) 64

17. a) iii b) i) 279 ii) 348 iii) 433
c) i) 224 ii) 180 iii) 144

18. a) i) 610 ii) 820 iii) 1346
b) i) 410 ii) 336

19. a) 1.93 m^2

20. a) i) 88.4 min ii) 96.6 min
b) i) 1440 min ii) 35 850 km

21. a) i) 81% ii) 72.9% iii) $100(0.9)^n$
c) i) 92.9% ii) 87.2%
d) i) About 2.73 cm ii) About 6.58 cm

22. a) Renée b) i) 32.17 ii) 2.65

MAU

1. a) i) 19 ii) 62 b) i) 58 ii) 57
c) i) 72 ii) 85

2. 155

Exercises 2-5, page 55

1. a) $\frac{1}{2}$ b) 81 c) $\frac{1}{16}$ d) $\frac{1}{25}$ e) 64 f) $\frac{1}{49}$

2. a) 36 b) 2 c) 49 d) 4096 e) $\frac{1}{25}$ f) $\frac{1}{10}$

3. a) $\frac{9}{125}$ b) $3^{-\frac{2}{5}}$ c) $5^{-\frac{3}{2}}$ d) $\frac{16}{3}$ e) $\frac{1}{3}$ f) $\frac{1}{2}$

4. a) x^{-3} b) 1 c) m^2 d) t^{-1} e) n^{-3}
f) $x^{-\frac{5}{4}}$

5. a) m^5n^{-2} b) a^2b^{-2} c) x^2y^2 d) $6a^3b^{-4}$
e) $3x^{-\frac{3}{2}}$ f) $\frac{1}{2}m^3n^{-3}$

6. a) $\frac{1}{2}$ b) 3 c) 64 d) 5 e) 1 f) $\frac{1}{9}$

7. a) 125 b) $6^{\frac{17}{12}}$ c) $2^{-\frac{2}{5}}$ d) $5^{-\frac{1}{2}}$ e) 1
f) $2^{\frac{21}{10}}$

8. a) $\frac{2}{9}a^{\frac{17}{6}}$ b) $6x^{\frac{1}{6}}$ c) $x^{-1}y^{-1}\sqrt{10y^{-1}}$
d) $2m^7n^{-9}$ e) $5^{\frac{1}{2}}x^{\frac{1}{2}}$ f) $x^{\frac{-11}{2}}y^{-2}$

9. a) $a^{-6}b^9c^{-12}$ b) $3x^{-3}y^5z^{-2}$ c) $12x^{-2}y^3$
d) $12c^{\frac{-7}{3}}d^7$ e) $\frac{1}{2}x^2$

10. a) x^{6a} b) m^{n-3} c) m^5 d) c^{2a-2}
e) x^{2b} f) x^{9a-2b}

11. a) 3^{5x} b) 16 c) 5^{4a-1} d) 2^{10x+1}
e) 6^{-3a+6b} f) $2^{5m-n} \times 3^{-m+3n}$

12. a) a^8 b) $a^{\frac{-14}{3}}$ c) $a^{\frac{-10}{9}}$ d) 1 e) $a^{\frac{-13}{15}}$
f) $a^{\frac{-7}{2}}$

13. a) $2a + a^{-1}$ b) $5x^2 - 3x$ c) $6m - 3m^2$
d) $5\frac{1}{5}$ e) $28x^{\frac{20}{3}} + 12x^2$ f) $2\frac{2}{3}$

14. a) 3 b) $x^3 - x^7$ c) $m^{\frac{1}{2}} - m^{\frac{2}{3}}$ d) 11
e) $6a^4 - 2a^3 - 21a^2 + 7a$ f) $12x^3 - 19x^2 - 18x$

15. a) $(7y^{\frac{1}{m}})^{\frac{-1}{n}}$ b) $2\sqrt{2}x^{\frac{a}{2}}y^{\frac{3}{2a}}$ c) $\frac{a}{b}$ d) $m^{\frac{1}{3}}n^{\frac{1}{3}}$
e) a^{n-1} f) 1

Exercises 2-6, page 58

1. a) 5 b) 5 c) 4 d) 4 e) 7 f) 3
g) 3 h) 3 i) 4

2. a) 1 b) 4 c) 7 d) −1 e) 2 f) 0

3. a) 0 b) −2 c) 1 d) −2 e) $\frac{1}{4}$ f) $\frac{1}{3}$

4. 8 years **5.** 9.7 years

6. a) 1 b) 0 c) $\frac{4}{3}$ d) −1 e) $\frac{5}{2}$ f) $\frac{3}{2}$
g) $-\frac{2}{3}$ h) $-\frac{1}{2}$ i) $\frac{5}{2}$

7. a) 2 b) 3 c) 3 d) 6 e) 3 f) 3
g) 2 h) 0 i) $-\frac{1}{2}$

8. 4 months **9.** a) $25 \times 2^{\frac{n}{5}}$ b) About 43 years

10. a) $\frac{3}{2}$ b) −2 c) 6

11. a) 1.56 b) 2.84 c) 2.51

Review Exercises, page 59

1. a) 3^4 b) 6^4 c) $(-7)^5$ d) $(0.2)^5$
e) $(-1.5)^3$ f) $(2.5)^4$

2. a) \$29 775 b) \$37 590 c) $\$25\,000(1.06)^n$

3. a) i) 1.97 m ii) 1.43 m b) 11th

4. a) x^{10a+3} b) 2^{6b+4} c) c^{12a+3} d) $\frac{4}{3}t^{4u+8}$
e) w^{9xz} f) $w^{4m-1}x^{b+4}$

5. a) $108a^6b^6$ b) $243^3a^{27}b^{24}$ c) $4a^6b^2$
d) $\frac{729}{8}a^9b^{12}$

6. a) x^{-5} b) w^{-2} c) $36b^{-10}$ d) $-3c^{-1}d^{10}$
e) $36u^2y^4$ f) $2m^{-8}n^6$

7. a) \$3402.91

8. a) ii b) i) 150 ii) 75 iii) 38

9. a) $19^{\frac{2}{3}}$ b) $28^{\frac{5}{2}}$ c) $13^{\frac{2}{5}}$ d) $33^{\frac{3}{2}}$
e) $(-7)^{\frac{11}{3}}$ f) $43^{\frac{3}{10}}$

10. a) $A^{\frac{1}{2}}$ cm b) $A^{\frac{3}{2}}$ cm^3

11. a) 114.08 b) 588.032 c) 904.753 75
d) 43.2816 e) 2837.947 f) 483.500 45

12. a) 1414 b) 707

13. a) 81 b) $5^{\frac{1}{12}}$ c) $2^{\frac{-3}{5}}$ d) $7^{\frac{-7}{2}}$ e) 1
f) $(-6)^{\frac{21}{20}}$

14. a) 2^{6x} b) 3^8 c) 4^{2a+5} d) 5^{-3x-1}
e) 6^{2b-3a} f) $5^{4x-5w} \times 7^{-x-5w}$

15. a) $a^{\frac{15}{2}}$ b) $a^{\frac{33}{4}}$ c) a^{-2} d) $a^{\frac{-69}{16}}$ e) $a^{\frac{-13}{8}}$
f) $a^{-3.9}$

16. a) 4 b) 3 c) −1 d) 0 e) $\frac{1}{2}$ f) $-\frac{1}{2}$

17. a) 2 b) 5 c) 0 d) 5 e) $\frac{4}{3}$ f) $\frac{1}{2}$

18. a) 2 b) 4 c) 4 **19.** About $5\frac{1}{4}$ years

Cumulative Review (Chapters 1 and 2), page 61

1. a) $2 \times 3^2 \times 13$ b) 11×17 c) $2^2 \times 3 \times 5 \times 7$

2. a) $3.\overline{84}$ b) $0.\overline{740}$ c) $0.\overline{452}$

3. a) $-\frac{26}{5}$ b) $\frac{14}{9}$ c) $\frac{79}{5}$

4. a) 16 b) $-\frac{11}{32}$ c) $-\frac{35}{2}$

5. Rational: b, c Irrational: a, d, e, f

6. a) $2\sqrt{14}$ b) $24\sqrt{2}$ c) $36\sqrt{30}$ d) 224
e) $-90\sqrt{10}$

7. a) $13\sqrt{3}$ b) $-8\sqrt{2} - 4\sqrt{6}$ c) 53
d) $10\sqrt{2} - 6\sqrt{10} + 8\sqrt{30}$

8. a) $6\sqrt{35} + 32\sqrt{15}$ b) 28
c) $12\sqrt{3} + 8\sqrt{30} - 12\sqrt{6} - 16\sqrt{15}$
d) $95 + 30\sqrt{10}$

9. a) $\frac{11}{2}$ b) $\frac{12\sqrt{7}}{35}$ c) $8-3\sqrt{2}$ d) $\frac{30+2\sqrt{10}}{5}$
10. a) -12 b) 17 c) -409
11. a) 3^5 b) $(-4)^6$ c) $(-2)^{11}$ d) $(0.5)^5$
12. a) \$17.69 b) \$24.06 c) \$60.59
13. a) $8a^7b^6$ b) $24c^4b^{-8}$ c) $2y^3h^2$
d) $3x^{-5}y^{11}$ e) $64m^{24}n^{-6}$ f) x^{2a-7}
14. a) 3^{14n} b) 2^{19+2n} c) 5^{19n+8}
15. a) 20 b) 108 c) 64 d) $-\frac{19}{8}$ e) $-\frac{63}{8}$
f) $\frac{4}{9}$
16. \$4958.98 **17.** a) $17^{\frac{4}{3}}$ b) $19^{\frac{7}{2}}$ c) $73^{-\frac{1}{5}}$
18. a) 32 b) $\frac{2}{5}$ c) $\frac{1}{27}$ d) -25 e) $\frac{16}{9}$
19. a) 5 b) 3 c) -3 d) 4 e) $\frac{7}{5}$ f) $\frac{1}{2}$
20. 6 months

Chapter 3

Exercises 3-1, page 65

1. a) $8x+5$ b) $-7m-7$ c) $-4a+4b$
d) $-9x+13y$ e) $30a-7b$ f) $-5x-11y$
2. a) $4a^2+4a-7$ b) $5m^2+5m+3$
c) $8x^2-5x-13$ d) $5s^2+14s-12$
e) $-7x^2-19x-6$ f) $-6a^2-11a-15$
3. a) $x^2+5xy+3y^2$ b) $-6a^2-3ab-7b^2$
c) $17x^2-23xy+9y^2$ d) $9x^2+8xy-18y^2$
e) $-37s^2t-14st^2+28$ f) $-22x^2y+4xy^2-7$
4. a) $28a^4b^4$ b) $20x^5y^9$ c) $-24m^7n^8$
d) $54x^5y^{10}$ e) $-36m^6n^6$ f) $42a^4b^7$
5. a) $45a^6b^5$ b) $-56x^{13}y^7$ c) $225m^8n^6$
d) $-72x^{12}y^{13}$ e) $576a^{23}b^{13}$ f) $-288x^{22}y^{21}$
6. Sphere: $V=\frac{\pi}{6}d^3$, cone: $V=\frac{\pi}{12}d^2h$,
cylinder: $A=\frac{\pi}{2}d^2+\pi dh$
7. a) $-4xy^6$ b) $16m^4n^6$ c) $-17a^3b^{-5}$
d) $-4x^6y$ e) $17a^4$ f) $-29y^2$
8. a) i) $2xy$ cm ii) $\frac{y^2}{3x}$ cm b) $3x^2y$ cm
9. a) $\frac{4}{15}x^4y^{-4}$ b) $\frac{4}{9}x^3y^{-2}$ c) $\frac{-3}{28}mn$
d) $\frac{32}{9}x^4y^{-4}$ e) $\frac{-4}{15}a^2b^3c^{-1}$ f) $-x^{-2}yz^{-4}$
10. a) $\pi:2$ b) $\sqrt{2}\pi:4$ **11.** $5\pi:8$ **12.** $4:3$
13. a) $3:2$ b) $3:2$
14. a) $4\pi^2r^3$ b) $48\pi^2x^4y^5$ **15.** $4\sqrt{2}:3$

Exercises 3-2, page 68

1. a) $-4a-17b$ b) x^2-6y^2
c) $-2m^2-14m+11$ d) $12a^2-7ab+11b^2$
e) $-8ab-25bc-12ac$ f) $7m^2+3$
2. a) $-7x+34y$ b) $51a^2-36a$
c) $12m^2n-48mn^2$ d) $-6x^2-38xy+14x$
e) $31a^2+13ab+20a$ f) $26x^2y-41xy^2+7xy$
3. a) $25a-3b-41$ b) $-20x+11y-75$
c) $-8x^2-38x-2xy$ d) $31a^2-261a$
e) $-6m^3+49m^2-8m^2n$
f) $-4x^2+46x^2y-363xy$
4. a) $15x^2+29x-14$ b) $8m^2+46m+45$
c) $49x^2-42xy+9y^2$ d) $56a^2-123ab+55b^2$
e) $16x^2-9y^2$ f) $80x^2-174xy+54y^2$
5. $2xh+h^2$
6. a) $26x^2+38xy+17y^2$ b) $2a^2-47ab+32b^2$
c) $-13m^2-87mn+67n^2$
d) $33x^2+4xy+11y^2$ e) $-40xy$
f) $-42a^4+49a^2b-52b^2$
7. a) $10x^2-15y^2$ b) $-11x^2-12x+24$
c) $2a^2-12a+19$ d) $6m^2+154m+329$
e) $12x^2-60x+61$
f) $66a^4-60a^3b+75a^2b^2+72a^2b+24b^2$
8. a) $10m^3+9m^2+7m+24$
b) $6x^2-26xy-15x+28y^2+35y$
c) $6a^3-11a^2b-12ab^2+5b^3$
d) $15x^3+24x^2y-3xy^2+18y^3$
e) $2x^4-x^3-5x^2-17x-3$
f) $24a^5-28a^4b-16a^3b^2+28a^2b^3-8ab^4$
9. a) $x^3+3x^2-13x-15$ b) $4a^3+20a^2-a-5$
c) $2x^3-14x^2+30x-18$
d) $8m^3-14m^2n-109mn^2-105n^3$
e) $54a^3-24ab^2-135a^2b+60b^3$
f) $160x^3-320x^2y-750xy^2-315y^3$
10. a) $12xh+6h^2$ b) $3x^2h+3xh^2+h^3$
11. a) $-11x^2-103x+57$
b) $-49a^2+147ab-93b^2$
c) $4m^3+18m^2+16m-31$
d) $-13x^2-4xy+14x-5y^2$
e) $-20a^3+108a^2b+193ab^2-53b^3$
f) $6x^3+51x^2+22x-24$
12. a) Volume: $(12x^3+26x^2-26x-60)$ m^3
Surface area: $(32x^2+50x-14)$ m^2
b) $V=225$ m^3, $A_s=311$ m^2
13. Volume: $\pi(18x^3+21x^2-52x+20)$ cm^3
Surface area: $2\pi(15x^2-x-6)$ cm^2
14. $(0.20x+0.30vx+0.15x^2)$ m **15.** $mvx+\frac{1}{2}mx^2$
16. $(38-4t)$ m
17. $15x^3+54x^2y+17xy^2-4y^3$
18. n^2+2n+1, or $(n+1)^2$

Exercises 3-3, page 73

1. a) $3xy(2x + 5y - 9)$
b) $7m^2n(5mn^2 - 3n + 8)$
c) $4ab^2(3a^2 + 7ab - 11b^2)$
d) $9st^2(4s^3 - 5st - 2t^2)$
e) $5xy^3(4x^2 + 9xy - 7y^2)$
f) $6ab(7ab^2 - 3a^2 + 8b)$

2. a) $6x^2y^2(2x - 3y + 4)$
b) $4ab^2(7a^2 - 3ab - 12b^2)$
c) $15m^2(3m + 5n)(m - n)$
d) $13x^3y^3(3y^2 - 5y - 2x^2)$
e) $9a^2bc(6ab^2c - 4ac^2 + 7ab - 9c^2)$
f) $8x^2yz^2(3xy^2 + 10xy + 11y - 1)$

3. a) $(2a - 7)(3x + 5y)$
b) $(4x + 3y)(9x^2 - 8y)$
c) $(2a - 5b)(4a^2 + 7b^2)$
d) $(3m - 7n + 2)(5m^2 + 9n^2)$
e) $(4x^2 - 7x + 9)(12x^2 - 5xy - 1)$
f) $(7x - 2y)(4x^2 - 5xy + 1 - 11y^2)$

4. a) $(3x^2 - 11y^2)(5x^2y + 4)$
b) $(5m^2 + 3)(2m^2 - 7n^2)$
c) $2(4x - 7y)(3x^2 + y^2)$
d) $(4x^2 + 5xy - 3y^2)(6x^2 - 11y^2)$
e) $(2a - b)(a + 5b)(3a^2 + 4ab - 2b^2)$
f) $(5m^2 - 2mn + 3n^2)(2m^2 + 7mn - 13n^2)$

5. a) $(x + y)(m - n)$ b) $(2a - 3)(5x + 2y)$
c) $(3m + 2n)(3a + b)$ d) $(7x - 5y)(2a - 9)$
e) $(4x + 3)(7x - 4y)$ f) $(8x - 5y)(6x - 7)$

6. a) $(x - z)(x - y)$ b) $(x + 1)(x^2 + 1)$
c) $(7x - 2y)(3x^2 - 1)$ d) $(1 + a)(1 + b)$
e) $(2x - 3)(x + 1)(x - 1)$ f) $(x + y)(x + y - 1)$

7. a) $(x + 1)(x + 2)$ b) $(a - b)(2c + 3d)$
c) $(a^2 - 3)(a - 1)$ d) $(x + y)(x + y + 4)$
e) $a(1 + b)(1 - c)$ f) $(a - b)[a(a - b) - 1]$

8. $W = \frac{P - 2x}{2}$, $A = \frac{x(P - 2x)}{2}$ **9.** $\frac{\pi}{4}(a^2 - b^2)$

10. a) $\pi(x + y)$ b) $\frac{\pi x}{4}(x + 2y)$

11. a) i) $2\pi x(h + x + 2r)$ ii) $\pi hx(x + 2r)$
b) i) $2\pi ry$ ii) πr^2y

12. a) $a^2(a - 2)(a - b)$ b) $xy(x - 3)(x + y)$
c) $3m(m + 4)(m + n)$ d) $2ab^2(3a + 2)(a - b)$
e) $5m^2(2m - 3)(m - n)$
f) $4x^2y(2x - 3)(3x - y)$

13. Let $100x + 10y + z$ represent any three-digit number.
Then $100z + 10y + x$ represents the number formed by reversing the digits.
$100x + 10y + z - (100z + 10y + x) = 99x - 99z$
This is divisible by 99.
Therefore the difference between a three-digit number and the number formed by reversing the digits is divisible by 99.

14. Let $100x + 10y + z$ represent any three-digit number and $x + y + z = b$. Then $x = b - y - z$. Substitute this for x in the expression for the number:
$100(b - y - z) + 10y + z = 100b - 9(10y + 11z)$
This is divisible by 9 if, and only if, b is divisible by 9.
Therefore, a three-digit number is divisible by 9 if, and only if, the sum of its digits is divisible by 9.

15. Area of rectangle: lw
Area of four semicircles:
$\pi(\frac{l}{2})^2 + \pi(\frac{w}{2})^2 = \frac{\pi}{4}(l^2 + w^2)$
Total area of figure: $lw + \frac{\pi}{4}(l^2 + w^2)$
Diameter of circle: $\sqrt{l^2 + w^2}$
Area of circle: $\frac{\pi}{4}(\sqrt{l^2 + w^2})^2 = \frac{\pi}{4}(l^2 + w^2)$
Area of shaded portion:
$lw + \frac{\pi}{4}(l^2 + w^2) - \frac{\pi}{4}(l^2 + w^2) = lw$
The shaded area is equal to the area of the rectangle.

Exercises 3-4, page 75

1. a) $(x + 2)(x + 3)$ b) $(m - 5)(m - 4)$
c) $(a + 7)(a - 2)$ d) $(m + 3)(m - 8)$
e) $(x - 6)(x - 9)$ f) $(x - 7)(x + 12)$

2. a) $(2m + 1)(m + 3)$ b) $(5x - 2)(x - 1)$
c) $(3a - 1)(a - 3)$ d) $(4x - 3)(x + 1)$
e) $(3s + 2)(s - 1)$ f) $(2m + 7)(m - 1)$

3. a) $(3x + y)(x + 2y)$ b) $(2m - 3n)(m - n)$
c) $(3a - b)(a + 2b)$ d) $(5m + 2n)(m - n)$
e) $(7x - y)(3x - y)$ f) $(3x - y)(x - 5y)$

4. a) $(3s - 2)(2s + 5)$ b) $(2m + 5)(3m - 8)$
c) $(5a + 3)(2a + 9)$ d) $(4x + 9)(2x + 5)$
e) $(6m - 5)(4m - 3)$ f) $(7x + 8)(3x - 2)$

5. a) $(5p - 9q)(p + 2q)$ b) $(4m - 7n)(2m + 3n)$
c) $(5x - 3y)(3x - 5y)$ d) $(4s - 9t)(8s - 5t)$
e) $(6p + 5q)(4p - 3q)$ f) $(-3x + 2y)(2x + 7y)$

6. a) $4(3x + 1)(3x - 5)$ b) $7(2x - 3)(x + 7)$
c) $8(3x - 5)(2x - 5)$ d) $4m(2m + 3)(3m + 4)$
e) $5ab(2a - 3)(a - 7)$
f) $3mn(4m - 5)(-2m + 3)$

7. a) $(m^2 + 8)(m^2 - 2)$ b) $(3x^2 - y^2)(x^2 - 5y^2)$
c) $(a^2 - 3)(2a^2 + 5)$ d) $(3x^2 - 2y^2)(4x^2 + y^2)$
e) $(4m^2 - 3n^2)(5m^2 - 8n^2)$
f) $(2x^2 - 7y^2)(4x^2 + 3y^2)$

8. a) $3(2a^2 + 3)(a^2 - 5)$ b) $2x(x^2 + 2)(x^2 + 5)$
c) $5m(3m^2 - 2)(m^2 - 7)$
d) $4s(2s^2 - 3t^2)(2s^2 - 5t^2)$
e) $2p(5p^2 + 2q^2)(3p^2 + 4q^2)$
f) $8xy(3x^2 - 5y^2)(2x^2 + y^2)$

9. a) $(5x+3)(5x+4)$ b) $(6x-1)(3x-4)$
c) $(35m+2)(21m-4)$
d) $(3a+3b+1)(2a+2b+5)$
e) $(8p+4q-3)(4p+2q-1)$
f) $(15x^2+10y+3)(6x^2+4y-7)$

10. a) $(x+4)(x-1)(x+1)(x+2)$
b) $(x+1)(x+3)(x+2)(x+2)$
c) $(a+3)(a-1)(a+1)(a+1)$
d) $(y-4)(y+2)(y-3)(y+1)$
e) $(2a+1)(a+2)(2a-3)(a+4)$
f) $(3x+4)(x-2)(3x-5)(x+1)$

11. a) $(x-y)(5x-3y)$ b) $(2m-n)(13m-5n)$
c) $3(a-1)(a+3)$ d) $(2x+y)(11x-5y)$
e) $2(3s+2t)(s+4t)$ f) $3(2x-5y)(3x-y)$

12. a) 3 b) 5 c) 7 d) 9 e) 9 f) 13

CP

1. a) $(2x+1)(5x+8)$ b) $(2a-9)(4a-3)$
c) $(3x+5y)(4x-15y)$ d) $(2+3t)(12-5t)$

2. a) $6(x+5)(2x+3)$ b) $5(2x-7y)(5x+2y)$
c) $9(3a-8b)(6a-5b)$ d) $8(4-7m)^2$

3. a) $17(4x-1)(13x+18)$ b) $23(8x+5)(11x+13)$

Exercises 3-5, page 80

1. a) $(2x+5)(2x-5)$ b) $(4m+9n)(4m-9n)$
c) $(6a+11)(6a-11)$ d) $(3s+7t)(3s-7t)$
e) $(8x+13y)(8x-13y)$
f) $(20a+9b)(20a-9b)$

2. a) $3(4a+7b)(4a-7b)$
b) $2m(5m+3)(5m-3)$
c) $5x(2x+9y)(2x-9y)$
d) $7a(3a+4b)(3a-4b)$
e) $4xy^2(5x+9y)(5x-9y)$
f) $6y(3+8x)(3-8x)$

3. a) $(x^2+9)(x+3)(x-3)$
b) $3(2m^2+5n^2)(2m^2-5n^2)$
c) $2(2a+5b)(2a-5b)(4a^2+25b^2)$
d) $t\left(3s^2+\frac{1}{2}t\right)\left(3s^2-\frac{1}{2}t\right)$
e) $4y^2\left(\frac{2}{5}x+\frac{3}{7}y\right)\left(\frac{2}{5}x-\frac{3}{7}y\right)$
f) $(2x+y)(2x-y)(4x^2+y^2)(16x^4+y^4)$

4. a) $5(5x-9)(x+1)$ b) $(-4m+7)(8m-7)$
c) $(12x-13y)(12x+5y)$
d) $5(x-y)(-x-9y)$
e) $4(4m-3)(m+5)$
f) $(-8a+21b)(20a+9b)$

5. a) $(a+4)(a-2)(a^2+2a+8)$
b) $4(x-6)(x+3)(x^2-3x+18)$
c) $(2x-y)(x+2y)(2x^2+3xy+2y^2)$
d) $(3n+m)(2n-3m)(6n^2+7mn+3m^2)$
e) $(a-10)(a-3)(a+2)(a-15)$
f) $2(x-12y)(x+2y)(x-6y)(x-4y)$

6. a) $(x+5)^2$ b) $(m-7)^2$ c) $(2a+3)^2$
d) $(x-9y)^2$ e) $(6x+11y)^2$

7. a) $(7m+5)^2$ b) $3(2a-9)^2$ c) $(4s+11)^2$
d) $-2(4x-3y)^2$ e) $(3m-10n)^2$
f) $5(3x-7y)^2$

8. a) $(m+3-n)(m+3+n)$
b) $(2x-5-4y)(2x-5+4y)$
c) $(3a-2-7b)(3a-2+7b)$
d) $(x+4y-9)(x+4y+9)$
e) $(2s-5t+3)(2s-5t-3)$
f) $(5x-8+8y)(5x-8-8y)$

9. a) $(a-b+4c)(a+b-4c)$
b) $(x-y-7z)(x+y+7z)$
c) $(5-m-6n)(5+m+6n)$
d) $(2s+3t+2)(2s-3t-2)$
e) $(x-a-y)(x+a+y)$
f) $(a+b-c-1)(a-b+c-1)$

10. a) $(x-3y-5z)(x-3y+5z)$
b) $(3m-2n-7p)(3m+2n+7p)$
c) $(x+1)^2(x-1)$ d) $(a-b+4)(a+b-2)$
e) $(a^n+b^n)(a^n-b^n)$
f) $2(x+1)(x+3)(x-1)(x-3)$

11. $2\pi(R+r)(R-r+h)$

12. a) $A=\pi^2(a-b)(a+b)$
b) About 1.48×10^6 m^2

13. $kx(2T+x)(2T^2+2Tx+x^2)$

14. a) i) 6 ii) Not possible
b) Those values for which $2m-1$ is prime.

Exercises 3-6, page 82

1. a) $(z-3)(z^2+3z+9)$ b) $(y+1)(y^2-y+1)$
c) $8(x-2)(x^2+2x+4)$
d) $(a-2b)(a^2+2ab+4b^2)$
e) $(2x+3y)(4x^2-6xy+9y^2)$
f) $(4x+1)(16x^2-4x+1)$

2. a) $x(x^2+3x+3)$ b) $(2x+1)(4x^2-2x+1)$
c) $2(3x^2+6x+4)$
d) $(2x+2y+1)(4x^2+4y^2-4xy+4x-2y+1)$
e) $4b(3a^2+4b^2)$ f) $2x(x^2+3y^2)$
g) $2x(x^2+27)$

3. a) $(x+y)(x-y)(x^4+x^2y^2+y^4)$
b) $(x^2+y^2)(x^4-x^2y^2+y^4)$
c) $(2a-1)(2a+1)(16a^4+4a^2+1)$
c) $(1+4y^2)(1-4y^2+16y^4)$
e) $4xy(x^2+3y^2)(y^2+3x^2)$
f) $2(x^2+y^2)(x^4+14x^2y^2+y^4)$

4. a) $V=\frac{1}{3}\pi h(a^2+ab+b^2)$
b) When $b=a$, $V=\frac{1}{3}\pi h(a^2+a^2+a^2)$, or πa^2h

Exercises 3-7, page 86

1. a) $\frac{8m}{5n}$ b) $\frac{-5b^2}{8ac}$ c) $\frac{t^2}{3s}$ d) $\frac{-5x}{8y}$ e) $\frac{5m^5}{2n^3}$
f) $\frac{3x^2}{5}$

2. a) $\frac{2x-5y}{3x+4}$ b) $\frac{n(5m-6)}{2m+3}$ c) $\frac{a-2b}{2a-b}$
d) $\frac{3x-2y}{y-x}$ e) $\frac{4m^2-3n^2}{5m+2n}$ f) $\frac{2x^2-3x+7}{8-3x}$

3. a) $\frac{m+2n}{3m}$ b) $\frac{x-3y}{2xy}$ c) $\frac{2a+5b}{-4a}$ d) $\frac{5s^2t}{2s+3t}$
e) $\frac{3x-4y}{7xy}$ f) $\frac{-3mn}{2m-5n}$

4. a) $\frac{x+3y}{x-2y}$ b) $\frac{2m-5n}{m-3n}$ c) $\frac{3a-b}{2a+5b}$
d) $-\frac{4x-y}{2x+3y}$ e) $\frac{5m+3n}{2m+3n}$ f) $\frac{3x-8y}{5x+2y}$

5. a) 0 b) 0, 2 c) 4 d) -8, 1

6. a) 0 b) -5 c) 7, -1 d) 4

7. a) $\frac{14}{5}x$, all R except 0 b) $\frac{x+3}{3}$, all R except $\frac{1}{2}$
c) $\frac{m+2}{m+5}$, all R except -5
d) $\frac{8ab}{a+3}$, all R except ± 3
e) $\frac{x-1}{x+1}$, all R except 0, -1 f) $\frac{3x^3+2x^2}{x^2+7}$, all R

8. a) $\frac{5(2x-y)}{2(x+3y)}$ b) $\frac{4m(3m-2n)}{7n(2m-3n)}$ c) $\frac{y(3x-1)}{2x+3}$
d) $\frac{x(x-7)}{2(x+4)}$ e) $\frac{5y^2(x+2)}{3}$ f) $\frac{2b(3a+4b)}{5(3a-4b)}$

Exercises 3-8, page 89

1. a) $4mn$ b) $-\frac{9b^2}{8a^2}$ c) $\frac{2y^2}{5x^2}$ d) $\frac{35}{32s^3t}$
e) $-\frac{2y^2}{x^3}$ f) $\frac{-7ab}{8c}$

2. a) $36k^3$ b) $\frac{4k}{5}$ c) $128k^4$ d) $38\,880\,k^9$

3. a) $\frac{5a}{b^2}$ b) $\frac{375a^3}{2b^2}$ c) $24a^2b$ d) $\frac{a}{2b^3}$

4. a) $\frac{10x}{-y}$ b) $\frac{2(m-2n)}{7m(2m-n)}$ c) $\frac{2a^2(a-3b)}{3b}$
d) $\frac{y}{5x}$ e) $\frac{-12(2s+t)}{25s(2s-t)}$ f) $\frac{-4y}{5x}$

5. a) $\frac{4(x-3y)}{3}$ b) $\frac{2(3a+4b)}{3a^2}$ c) $\frac{-n}{9m}$ d) $\frac{y}{4}$
e) $\frac{6m(m-2n)}{n(m+2n)}$ f) $\frac{8a(a+b)}{-5b^2}$

6. a) $\frac{a+1}{a-1}$ b) $\frac{x-2y}{x+2y}$ c) $\frac{x-4y}{x(x-2y)}$
d) $\frac{3(m+3n)}{2(m+8n)}$ e) $\frac{s(3s+4t)}{2(2s+5t)}$ f) $\frac{x^2(3x-7y)}{3y(2x+5y)}$

7. 3 : 2 **8.** a) 28 : 25 b) 39 : 35

9. a) 2.25 b) 4

10. a) $R^2r^2 = \frac{a^2b^2c^2}{4(a+b+c)^2}$, $R = \frac{abc}{2(a+b+c)} \cdot \frac{1}{r}$
b) $R = \frac{1}{2}b$, $r = \frac{ac}{a+b+c}$

Exercises 3-9, page 93

1. a) $\frac{2y+3x}{xy}$ b) $\frac{8x-5}{x^2}$ c) $\frac{4y+11x}{x^2y}$
d) $\frac{7x-15y}{x^2y^2}$ e) $\frac{12z-9x}{xyz}$ f) $\frac{6y^2+19x^2}{x^2y^2}$

2. a) $\frac{5m^2-3n^2}{mn}$ b) $\frac{17a^2+5b^2}{abc}$ c) $\frac{8y^3+13x^2}{xy^2}$
d) $\frac{2s-11st}{t^2}$ e) $\frac{n(15mn+11)}{m^2}$ f) $\frac{23x^2-16y^3}{xy^2}$

3. a) $\frac{3x^2+2xy-5y^2}{xy^2}$ b) $\frac{2a^2-6ab-11b}{ab^2}$
c) $\frac{7x^2-14xy+5y^2}{x^2y^2}$ d) $\frac{16a^2+6ab-27b^2}{12ab}$
e) $\frac{45s^2-25st+12t^2}{20st}$ f) $\frac{-14x^2-3xy-12y^2}{28xy}$

4. a) $\frac{6x^2+40xy-35y}{20xy}$ b) $\frac{-20m^2+15mn+27n}{24mn}$
c) $\frac{-14a^2-4a+6ab-15b}{12ab}$ d) $\frac{9x^2-36xy-22y^2}{18xy}$
e) $\frac{-12m^2+33mn-25n^2}{30mn}$

5. a) $\frac{36x^2y+10x-12y^2}{15x^2y}$ b) $\frac{15a^2-28b-35ab^2}{20ab^2}$
c) $\frac{57m^2-56n+140mn}{28mn^2}$ d) $\frac{6x^2-92x^2y+9xy^2+8y^2}{24x^2y}$

6. a) $\frac{12m+41}{(m+3)(m+4)}$ b) $\frac{a(31a-32)}{(3a-4)(5a-2)}$
c) $\frac{13m(3m-1)}{(3m-7)(5m-3)}$ d) $\frac{2x^2+10x+2}{(x+5)(x+4)}$
e) $\frac{x^2+56x-4}{(3x-2)(2x+5)}$ f) $\frac{-11m^2+19m-23}{(5m-4)(2m-3)}$

7. a) $\frac{29a}{6(a-5)}$ b) $\frac{6(x+1)}{(x-2)(x+2)}$ c) $\frac{-2x+21}{14(2x-5)}$
d) $\frac{5(10m+7)}{3(2m-5)(2m+5)}$ e) $\frac{a(9a-8)}{(a-4)(a-2)(a+3)}$
f) $\frac{3x}{(x-4)(x-1)}$

8. a) $\frac{3x^2-17x+14}{(x-5)(x-4)(x-3)}$ b) $\frac{2(x^2-3x+10)}{(x-6)(x+6)(x-2)}$
c) $\frac{1}{(a+4)(a+6)}$ d) $\frac{6m^2-26m-5}{(m-5)(m-1)(m-4)}$
e) $\frac{2}{(x-4)(x-1)}$ f) $\frac{2(4a^2+9a-19)}{(a+7)(a+3)(a-5)}$

9. $\frac{dx}{v(v+x)}$ **10.** $\frac{280x}{p(p+x)}$ L **11.** $-\frac{kx(2r+x)}{r^2(r+x)^2}$

12. $\frac{2x}{80+x}$ h

13. a) $15-28m^2$ b) 8 c) 21 d) $a-3$

Exercises 3-10, page 96

1. Change in $P = \frac{2(w^2+w-6000)}{w(w+1)}$

2. a) $l = \frac{6000}{w}$ b) i) $\frac{6000x}{w(w+x)}$ ii) $\frac{2x(w^2+wx-6000)}{w(w+x)}$

3. a) 40 min
b) $\frac{2x}{3(20+x)}$ c)

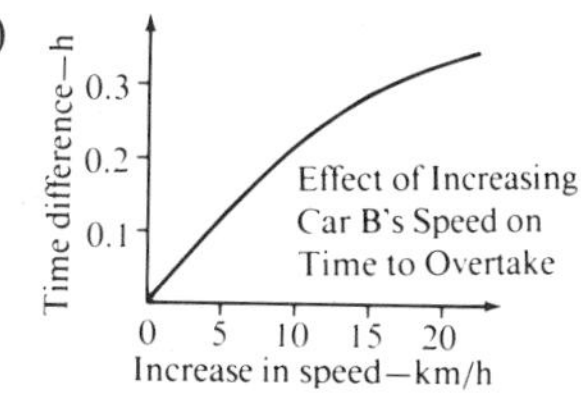

d) If $x < 0$, time to overtake > 40 min
If $x \leq -20$ km/h, B does not overtake A.

4. a) $t = \frac{5}{2(v-30)}$

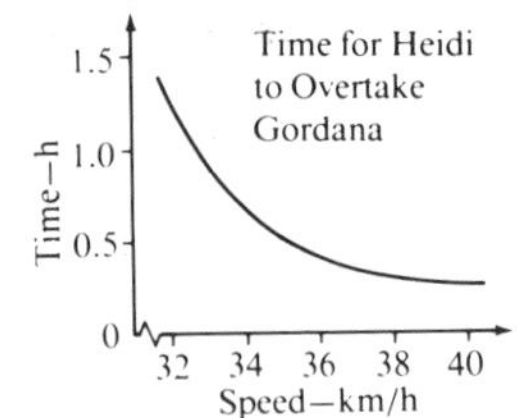

b) 37.5 km/h

5. $\frac{800x}{(v-80)(v+x-80)}$

6. a) $L = \frac{2x^2+2000}{x}$

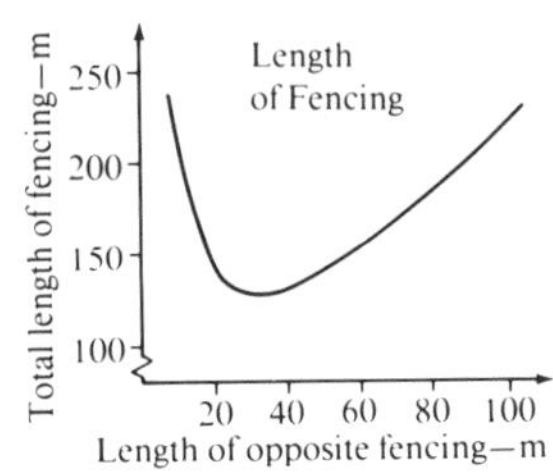

b) About 31 m by 65 m

7. a) i) $h = \frac{100}{x^2}$

ii) $A = \frac{x^3+400}{x}$

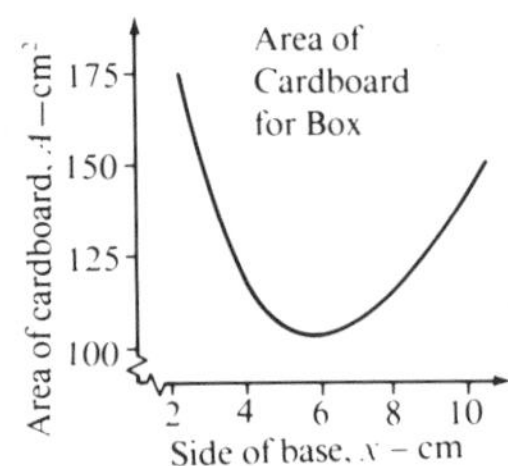

b) For minimum A, dimensions are: about 5.9 cm by 5.9 cm by 2.9 cm

8. a) $h = \frac{20(w+10)}{w-10}$,

b) $A = \frac{20w(w+10)}{w-10}$

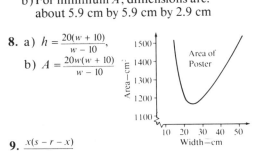

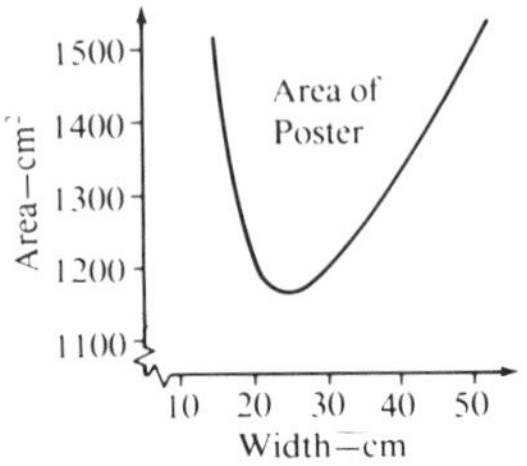

Area of Poster (Area—cm², Width—cm)

9. $\frac{x(s-r-x)}{r+s}$

10. a) 8 min

b) $T = \frac{3v+20}{v-10}$

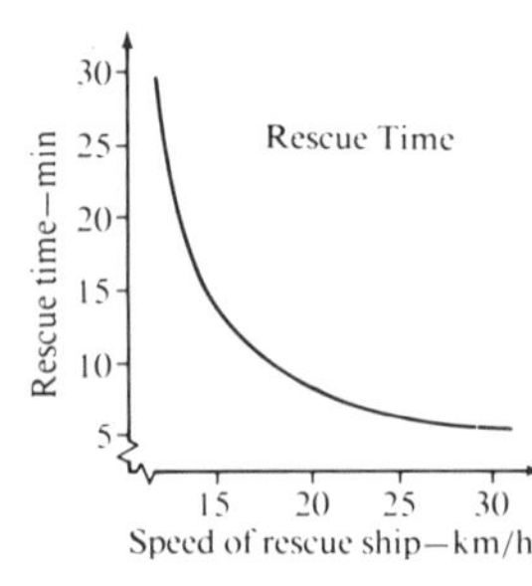

c) i) 28 min ii) 13 min

d) About 26 km/h

Review Exercises, page 99

1. a) $4m^2 - 11mn - 15n^2$
b) $-8s^2 + 6st + 8t^2$
c) $-3a^2 - 5ab - 12b^2$
d) $2mn^2(7mn + 3m - 12n)$

2. a) $56a^3b^4$ b) $-63a^4b^4$ c) $156x^{10}y^5$
d) $-182m^5n^4$ e) $24x^5y^2$ f) $-102s^{11}t^7$
g) $27x^7y^{12}z^5$

3. a) $\frac{39}{5}x^3$ b) $-10ab^{-2}$ c) $\frac{21}{64}x^{-1}$ d) ac

4. a) $7x^2 + 10xy + 7y^2$ b) $-5a^2 + 2ab - 5b^2$
c) $m^2 + 20mn + 2n^2$ d) $125(x-y)(x+y)$

5. a) $(a+2b)(2x-y)$ b) $(3m-2n)(2s+3t)$
c) $(6x-y)(3a+4)$ d) $(7x-4y)(5x-6)$

6. a) $(4x-3)(x-7)$ b) $(3w-5)(4w-3)$
c) $(3x+2)^2$ d) $(8m+3)(3m-5)$

7. a) $(3m-2n)(2m-n)$ b) $(a-b)(4a+3b)$
c) $(3a+7b)(5a-2b)$ d) $(-2x+3)(x-5)$

8. a) $(5x+1)(x+7)$ b) $-9(6m+1)$
c) $(2x+5)^2$ d) $(3x-4)^2$
e) $(a-b)(a-b+1)$
f) $(3x-5y+1)(3x+5y-1)$

9. a) ± 11 b) -6 c) $t=0$, or $s = -\frac{3}{2}$
d) $a = \pm\frac{5b}{3}$ e) $c = \frac{3d}{2}$, or $-\frac{4d}{3}$
f) $r = 0$, or $\frac{4s}{3}$, or $-\frac{3s}{4}$

10. a) $\frac{x-5}{2x}$ b) $\frac{3}{4}$ c) $\frac{a-2b}{2a+b}$ d) $\frac{3x^3y^2}{x-y}$

11. a) $\frac{8mn-5n+7m}{m^2n}$ b) $\frac{9x^2+4x-3y}{xy^2}$
c) $\frac{5s^4-2st+9t}{s^2t^2}$ d) $\frac{12mn-4n-15m^2}{10mn}$
e) $\frac{35x^2-24xy-6y^2}{21xy}$ f) $\frac{33n^2+51mn-30m^2}{15mn}$

12. a) $\frac{x+3y}{(x-y)(x+y)}$ b) $\frac{-x^2+5x+2}{(x-1)(x+1)}$
c) $\frac{4x^2-19x-4}{(x+2)(x-3)}$ d) $\frac{-7(x+3)}{(x+4)(x-3)}$
e) $\frac{(x+3)^2}{(x-1)(x+1)}$ f) $\frac{3a}{a-2}$

13. $-\frac{50x}{200-x}$ mm

Chapter 4

Exercises 4-1, page 103

1. a) ± 4 b) $\pm\frac{3}{2}$ c) ± 5 d) – e) ± 4
f) $\pm\frac{7}{3}$

2. a) 3.46 cm b) 5.66 m c) 1.22 km

3. a) 132.5 m b) 10.1 s

4. a) $\pm\sqrt{2}$ b) $\pm\sqrt{10}$ c) – d) $\pm 2\sqrt{2}$ e) $\pm\sqrt{3}$ f) $\pm\sqrt{7}$

5. a) ± 2 b) ± 4 c) $\pm\sqrt{\frac{7}{2}}$ d) $\pm 3\sqrt{3}$ e) ± 7 f) –

6. a) i) 25.5 km ii) 36.1 km b) i) 69.2 m ii) 276.9 m

7. a) $a = \sqrt{c^2 - b^2}$, $b = \sqrt{c^2 - a^2}$, $c = \sqrt{a^2 + b^2}$ b) $v = \sqrt{u^2 + 2as}$, $u = \sqrt{v^2 - 2as}$ c) $r = \sqrt{\frac{A}{\pi}}$ d) $r = \sqrt{\frac{V}{\pi h}}$

8. a) 5.6 cm b) 0.7 m c) 3 km

9. a) i) 201 cm^2 ii) 1963.5 cm^2 b) i) 4.9 cm ii) 10.4 cm

10. a) 2827 m^3 b) $r = \sqrt{\frac{3V}{\pi h}}$ c) i) 95 m ii) 82 m

11. a) $d = \sqrt{275C - 337.5}$ b) i) 25 cm ii) 30 cm c) $7.05

12. a) i) 1.93×10^2 kJ ii) 7.72×10^2 kJ b) i) 36 km/h ii) 113.8 km/h

13. 2.2 m/s

14. a) 15 b) 40.6 m^2 c) 3.92 m

Exercises 4-2, page 107

1. a) −3, 2 b) −1.5, 4 c) No roots d) −3.6, 1.5

2. a) 2.5, 4 b) 0.5, −4.5 c) −0.5, −1.5 d) 1.5, −1.7 e) 2.5 f) No roots

3. a) 1.5, −0.7 b) −2.3, 1.5 c) 2.5, −4.5 d) 0.6, −4.6 e) −0.5, −2.25 f) 5.7, 2.3

4. a) 0.5, 3 b) −2.5, 1.5 c) No roots d) −3.5, −4 e) −3.5 f) −0.5, 1.5

5. a) No roots b) Two roots **6.** c

7. a) $k < 13$ b) $13 < k < 16$

Exercises 4-3, page 112

1. a) 3, 1 b) −5, −3 c) 8, −7 d) $\frac{5}{2}$, −3 e) ±8 f) $\frac{2}{3}$

2. a) −5, 2 b) 7, 5 c) 6, −1 d) 0, 11 e) $\pm\frac{7}{2}$ f) $-\frac{3}{2}$, 5

3. a) 6 b) 3, −8 c) 4 d) 4, 7 e) $-\frac{3}{2}$, 5 f) $-\frac{5}{2}$

4. a) $x^2 - 3x - 10 = 0$ b) $x^2 - 6x + 9 = 0$ c) $x^2 - x - 12 = 0$ d) $12x^2 + 19x - 21 = 0$ e) $x^2 - 49 = 0$ f) $48x^2 - 38x + 5 = 0$

5. a) $-\frac{9}{5}$, 2 b) $-\frac{1}{2}, \frac{4}{3}$ c) −6, 1 d) $-\frac{7}{2}, \frac{2}{3}$ e) 6 f) $\pm\frac{6}{5}$

6. a) $\frac{5}{2}$, −3 b) −2, −4 c) −5, −4 d) $\frac{2}{3}$, 4 e) 5, 1 f) 7, −4

7. a) $\frac{3}{2}$ b) $-\frac{1}{2}$, 2 c) $-\frac{2}{3}$, 3 d) $\frac{4}{3}$, −1 e) 4, 6 f) $-\frac{2}{3}$, 5

8. a) 7, 8; −7, −8 b) 12, 13; −12, −13

9. a) 5; −4 b) 6; −5 **10.** 8, 9; −8, −9

11. −8, −7, −6, or 6, 7, 8 **12.** 20, 21 **13.** $k = 1$

14. a) $-\frac{1}{2}$, 4 b) $\frac{4}{5}, \frac{1}{3}$ c) $\frac{8}{5}$, −4 d) $\frac{2}{3}$, −3 e) $\frac{2}{3}, -\frac{7}{2}$ f) $\frac{3}{2}, \frac{9}{4}$

15. a) 2 : 1 or 3 : 1 b) −3 : 1 or −4 : 1 c) 1 : 2 or −5 : 1 d) 2 : 3 or −5 : 2 e) 5 : 3 or −3 : 2 f) 5 : 4 or 7 : 2

16. a) $k = -10$, $x = -2$ b) $k = -13$, $x = 8$ c) $k = -10$, – d) $k = 15$, $x = \frac{3}{2}$

17. a) $\pm\sqrt{-a}$ b) 0, a c) $\pm\sqrt{\frac{b}{a}}$ d) $\pm\sqrt{-\frac{a}{b}}$ e) a, b

18. a) ±2 b) ±1, ±3 c) 0, ±2 d) 0, $-\frac{5}{2}$, 3 e) ±2, ±1 f) ±3, $\pm\frac{1}{2}$, 0

19. 11, 12 or −11, −12

20. a) $-a$, b b) $\frac{a}{2}$, $2b$ c) $p + q$, $-p - q$ d) $2a + b$, $a - b$

CP

1. a) −4.5, 3.4 b) 4.137, 0.363 c) 2.25, −0.375 d) 1.618, −0.618

2. 4.142, 5.858, or 34.142, −24.142

Exercises 4-4, page 117

1. a) Yes b) Yes c) No d) No e) Yes f) Yes

2. a) 9 b) 1 c) 100 d) $\frac{49}{4}$ e) $\frac{9}{4}$ f) $\frac{1}{4}$ g) $\frac{121}{4}$ h) a^2 i) $\frac{b^2}{4}$

3. a) −6, 2 b) 3, −11 c) $3 \pm \sqrt{2}$ d) $8 \pm \sqrt{14}$ e) $\frac{3 \pm \sqrt{5}}{2}$ f) $\frac{-5 \pm \sqrt{13}}{2}$

4. a) $-6 \pm 2\sqrt{11}$ b) $9 \pm \sqrt{61}$ c) $\frac{3 \pm \sqrt{29}}{2}$ d) $\frac{1 \pm \sqrt{5}}{2}$ e) $\frac{-9 \pm \sqrt{17}}{2}$ f) $\frac{-5 \pm \sqrt{37}}{2}$

5. a) $-2 \pm \frac{\sqrt{6}}{2}$ b) $2 \pm \frac{\sqrt{21}}{3}$ c) $3 \pm \frac{\sqrt{30}}{2}$ d) $-1 \pm \frac{\sqrt{3}}{3}$

6. a) $3 \pm 3\sqrt{2}$ b) $\frac{-1 \pm \sqrt{41}}{4}$ c) $\frac{7 \pm \sqrt{41}}{4}$
d) $\frac{5 \pm \sqrt{19}}{2}$ e) $\frac{-3 \pm \sqrt{33}}{4}$ f) $\frac{1 \pm \sqrt{31}}{5}$
7. a) 2.16, −4.16 b) 1.18, −10.18
c) 2.64, −1.14 d) 1.25, −2.92
e) −0.31, −3.19 f) 3.84, 0.16

MM

1. −13, or 7 **2.** a) $\frac{-p \pm \sqrt{4q + p^2}}{2}$ b) 9, −5

Exercises 4-5, page 122

1. a) $\frac{1}{2}$, 2 b) −3, $-\frac{1}{2}$ c) −1, $\frac{14}{3}$ d) 1, $\frac{5}{4}$
e) $-\frac{2}{5}$, −1 f) $\frac{4}{3}$, $-\frac{5}{2}$
2. a) $\frac{2}{3}$, $\frac{1}{2}$ b) 7, $\frac{11}{2}$ c) $\frac{1}{2}$, $-\frac{1}{3}$ d) $-\frac{9}{2}$, 5
e) $-\frac{3}{2}$, 4 f) $\frac{2}{3}$, $-\frac{1}{2}$
3. a) 5.61, 0.89 b) 2.78, 0.72 c) 1.47, −1.14
d) 4.61, −0.11 e) 0.84, −0.24
f) −0.22, −2.28
4. a) 0.15, −1.35 b) 3.16, −0.16
c) 1.23, −1.90 d) 0.65, −1.15
e) 1.82, 0.18 f) 2.82, 0.18
5. 2.78 s
6. a) $\frac{4}{3}$, 0 b) ±4 c) $-\frac{7}{5}$ d) $\frac{3 \pm \sqrt{19}}{10}$
e) $\frac{5 \pm \sqrt{89}}{2}$ f) $\frac{5 \pm \sqrt{41}}{2\sqrt{2}}$
7. a) 4, $\frac{1}{4}$ b) $\frac{1}{2}$, $\frac{4}{3}$ c) $-\frac{2}{3}$, $\frac{3}{4}$ d) $\frac{11}{3}$, −9
e) 3, $-\frac{2}{5}$ f) $\frac{1}{5}$, $-\frac{2}{3}$
8. a) $\frac{-4 \pm \sqrt{26}}{2}$ b) −4, $\frac{2}{3}$ c) $\frac{7 \pm \sqrt{33}}{2}$ d) 1, $-\frac{4}{3}$
e) $-\frac{3}{2}$, $\frac{1}{2}$ f) $-\frac{2}{3}$
9. a) $\frac{3 \pm \sqrt{321}}{4}$ b) $\frac{5 \pm \sqrt{145}}{4}$ c) 2, 8 d) $10\sqrt{5}$
e) 2, 16 f) 2, $\frac{1}{2}$
10. a) $\frac{3}{4}$, $\frac{7}{6}$ b) $\frac{79}{4}$, −1 c) $\frac{1}{23}$, $-\frac{1}{25}$ d) $-\frac{4}{9}$, $\frac{4}{3}$
e) $\frac{17}{16}$, $\frac{1}{2}$ f) $\frac{25}{6}$, $-\frac{18}{5}$
11. a) i) 53.4 m ii) 80 m
b) i) 63 km/h ii) 110 km/h
12. a) i) 512.28 cm² ii) 5117.5 cm²
b) i) 4 cm ii) 15 cm
13. 1.62 **14.** a) 1.62, −0.62 b) −1.62, 0.62
15. a) $\frac{-q \pm \sqrt{q^2 - 4pr}}{2q}$ b) $\frac{-n \pm \sqrt{n^2 + 60}}{6}$
c) $\frac{-3 \pm \sqrt{9 + 4k}}{2}$ d) $-2 \pm p\sqrt{5}$ e) $\frac{-1 \pm \sqrt{1 + 4a}}{6}$
f) $-3m$, $2n$
16. $BM = DN \doteq 2.29$ cm
17. a) i) $\frac{5 \pm \sqrt{-3}}{2}$ ii) $\frac{7 \pm \sqrt{-83}}{6}$ iii) $\frac{-5 \pm \sqrt{-23}}{4}$
iv) $\frac{7 \pm \sqrt{-71}}{6}$
b) If $b^2 - 4ac < 0$ c) (i) and (ii)
18. a) i) $\frac{1 \pm \sqrt{5}}{2}$ ii) 2, −1 iii) $\frac{1 \pm \sqrt{13}}{2}$
iv) $\frac{1 \pm \sqrt{17}}{2}$
b) When n is the product of two consecutive integers.
19. a) i) $-\frac{4}{5}$, −45 ii) −5, $\frac{21}{4}$ iii) $\frac{29}{6}$, $\frac{35}{6}$
iv) $\frac{6}{5}$, $-\frac{3}{5}$ b) Sum = $-\frac{b}{a}$, product = $\frac{c}{a}$
20. a) $6b^2 = 25ac$ b) $mnb^2 = (m + n)^2ac$

Exercises 4-6, page 127

1. a) 25 b) 8 c) 0 d) −39 e) 289
f) −24
2. a) a, b, e b) c c) d, f
3. a) 2 real b) 1 real c) 2 real d) 2 real
e) 0 real f) 1 real
4. a) 3, −1 ii) 1 iii) −
5. a) i) $q^2 - 4pr > 0$ iii) $q^2 - 4pr < 0$
6. a) $|k| > 2$ b) $k > -\frac{4}{3}$ c) $|k| > 2\sqrt{6}$
7. a) $\pm 2\sqrt{7}$ b) $\frac{5}{6}$ c) 5, 3
8. a) No value of p b) $p > \frac{16}{9}$ c) $|p| > \frac{5}{2}$
9. a, c
10. a) 4, −8 b) $k \geqslant 4, k \leqslant -8$ c) $-8 < k < 4$
11. Yes, no
12. a) −24, −26; −25; −
15. i) c, e ii) b iii) a, d
16. a) When k is a perfect square.
b)

k	0	1	4	9	16
Roots	6, 6	8, 4	10, 2	12, 0	14, −2

c) When k is the square of a rational number.

Exercises 4-7, page 133

1. a) $\sqrt{5}\,i$ b) $7i$ c) $2 - 3i$ d) $-3 + 8i$
e) $13 - i$ f) $33 - 56i$
5. a) $\pm 2i$ b) $\pm 3i$ c) $\pm 5i$ d) $\pm 2\sqrt{3}\,i$
e) $\pm 3\sqrt{2}\,i$ f) $1 \pm i$
6. a) $10 + 6i$ b) 34 c) $7 - 4i$ d) 43 − 18
e) $8 - 16i$ f) $-60 - 63i$

7. a) $\frac{-3 \pm \sqrt{11}\,i}{2}$ b) $2 \pm i$ c) $\frac{-1 \pm \sqrt{7}\,i}{2}$
d) $1 \pm \sqrt{2}\,i$ e) $\frac{5 \pm \sqrt{3}\,i}{2}$ f) $\frac{-3 \pm \sqrt{7}\,i}{4}$

8. a) $\frac{2 \pm \sqrt{2}\,i}{3}$ b) $\frac{1 \pm \sqrt{5}\,i}{3}$ c) $\frac{-\sqrt{2}}{2}$ d) $1 \pm 2i$
e) $\frac{2 \pm \sqrt{10}\,i}{7}$ f) $-2 \pm \sqrt{11}$

9. $1 + i, 1 - i$

Exercises 4-8, page 136

1. a) $-5, -8$ b) $\frac{9}{2}, -\frac{17}{2}$ c) $\frac{8}{3}, -4$ d) $\frac{23}{5}, \frac{12}{5}$
e) $-5, \frac{15}{2}$ f) $-\frac{20}{7}, -2$

2. a) $\frac{3}{2}$ b) -2 c) $-\frac{3}{2}$ d) $-\frac{11}{2}$ e) $-\frac{1}{5}$ f) $-\frac{5}{3}$

3. a) Yes b) Yes c) No d) Yes
e) No f) No

4. a) i) 1, 5 ii) 3 iii) 4
b) i) 1 ii) 3 iii) 4, 5

5. a) $-\frac{q}{p}, -q$ b) $\frac{-3c}{c+d}, \frac{-2c-d}{c+d}$ c) $\frac{1-3f}{f}, f+2$
d) $a + b, a$

6. a) -1 b) 3 c) -4

7. a) $-\frac{3}{2}$ b) $-\frac{8}{11}$ c) 2

8. i) b ii) a iii) c

10. a) $x^2 - 5x + 6 = 0$ b) $4x^2 + 4x - 3 = 0$
c) $x^2 - 2x - 4 = 0$ d) $x^2 - 2x + 3 = 0$

11. a) The roots are reciprocals of each other.
b) $cx^2 - bx + a = 0$

12. a) 4 b) 7 c) $-\frac{4}{3}$ d) $\frac{-14}{3}$ e) 10
f) $2\sqrt{10}$

13. a) $\frac{181}{36}$ b) $\frac{1}{15}$

14. a) $\frac{\pm\sqrt{b^2 - 4ac}}{a}$ b) $\frac{-b + \sqrt{b^2 - 4ac}}{-b - \sqrt{b^2 - 4ac}}$ c) $\frac{b^2 - 2ac}{a^2}$
d) $-\frac{b}{c}$

15. $x^2 - 31x + 9 = 0$

Exercises 4-9, page 139

1. a) $x, x + 1$ b) $2x + 1, 2x - 1$ c) $x, x + 3$
d) $x^2 + (x + 3)^2$ e) $2x(2x + 2)$ f) $x^2 + \frac{1}{x^2}$

2. a) $\frac{80}{x - 12}$ b) $(2x + 40) \times (2x + 60)$ c) $\frac{x + 5}{x}$
d) $3x - 8x$ e) $\frac{16\,000}{x - 2} - \frac{15\,000}{x}$ f) $0.3x + 5$

3. 5 m **4.** 16 **5.** 5 cm **6.** 90 km/h
7. \$4.00 **8.** 3 cm, 5 cm, 7 cm
9. 90 km/h **10.** 35 km/h **11.** 120 km/h
12. 60 km/h **13.** 16 **14.** 75 **15.** 2 s
16. 24 min, 40 min **17.** About 311 km

Review Exercises, page 141

1. a) 4, -7 b) 3, -5 c) $\frac{\pm\sqrt{10}}{2}$ d) $\pm 3\sqrt{3}$

2. a) 7.33 cm b) 23.75 mm c) 4 km

3. a) $\frac{1}{2}, -6$ b) $-\frac{3}{2}, 4$ c) $\pm\frac{5}{2}$ d) $-\frac{13}{4}, \frac{11}{4}$

4. a) $x^2 - 6x - 7 = 0$ b) $2x^2 - 11x = 0$
c) $12x^2 - 7x - 12 = 0$
d) $64x^2 + 304x - 423 = 0$

5. a) 7, -2 b) 4, -8 c) $1, -\frac{1}{3}$ d) $\frac{5}{2}, -\frac{2}{3}$

6. a) 9, -2 b) $\frac{3}{2}, 2$ c) $2, -\frac{9}{2}$ d) $-1, 2$

7. 8 cm, 15 cm, 17 cm **8.** 6 s

9. a) 10 cm × 15 cm b) 15 cm × 20 cm

10. a) 10.8, -2.8 b) 6.95, -12.95
c) 4.6, -0.45 d) -1.9, -13.1

11. a) $\frac{-9 \pm \sqrt{57}}{4}$ b) $\frac{-1 \pm \sqrt{31}}{6}$ c) $\frac{8 \pm \sqrt{29}}{7}$ d) $\frac{-7 \pm \sqrt{449}}{20}$

12. a) 0.8, -3 b) 2, -5.3 c) $\frac{15 \pm \sqrt{5}}{10}$
d) 4.33, -3.67 e) 1.75, 0.67
f) 0.75, -0.8

13. a) 8 cm b) 11 cm **14.** 29.2 cm, 34.2 cm

15. a) $m = 4$, or -3 b) $m > 4$, or $m < -3$
c) $-3 < m < 4$

16. a **17.** Yes

18. a) $-9 + 6i$ b) 13 c) $7 - 2i$ d) $28 - 21i$

19. a) $\frac{1 \pm \sqrt{11}i}{2}$ b) $\frac{7 \pm \sqrt{35}\,i}{6}$ c) $\frac{-3 \pm \sqrt{23}\,i}{4}$
d) $\frac{1 \pm 3i}{10}$

20. a) $\frac{15}{8}$ b) $\frac{7}{3}$ c) $-\frac{11}{6}$ d) 5

21. a) 3 b) -1 c) $-\frac{9}{2}$

22. \$50 **23.** 90 m, 160 m **24.** 23 mm
25. 55 m, 30 m **26.** 50 min, 75 min

Cumulative Review (Chapters 3 and 4), page 143

1. a) $5m^2n - 8mn^2$ b) $-8a^3b^4$ c) $x^{23}y^{21}$
d) c^7d e) $-\frac{3}{5}r^{-3}$

2. 1 : 2

3. a) $5x + 26y - 27z$ b) $11x^2 - 9y^2 + 5xy$
c) $3a(a - 4b)$

4. $s = \sqrt{2r^2 + 8r + 16}$

5. a) $4x^2y^2(3x - y - 5xy)$ b) $(x + y)(a^2 + b^2)$
c) $x^2y^2(3x - 2)(5y - 4)$ d) $(4a + 1)(2a + 5)$
e) $(6b - 5c)(4b - c)$ f) $(2a - 7)^2$
g) $9(z - 4r)(z + 4r)$
h) $(y - m + 5c)(y + m - 5c)$
i) $(y - 5)(y^2 + 5y + 25)$
j) $(3a + 2d)(9a^2 - 6ad + 4d^2)$

6. a) 0 b) $-\frac{5}{2}$ c) 8 and −5
7. a) $\frac{a}{a+6}$ b) $\frac{(x^2+y^2)(x+8y)}{x+y}$ c) $\frac{(2y+3)(y-5)}{2y(y-3)}$
 d) $\frac{2(x-35)}{(x+1)(x-3)(x-7)}$ e) $\frac{2x(x-4)(x-1)+4}{x^2(2x+1)}$
8. a) $h = \frac{80}{w^2}$ b) $\frac{80(2w-1)}{w^2(w-1)^2}$
9. a) $\pm\sqrt{2}$ b) $\pm\sqrt{\frac{7}{2}}$ c) $\pm\sqrt{\frac{13}{2}}$
10. a) $-\frac{5}{2}$, 8 b) $-\frac{3}{2}$
11. a) $x^2 + 4x - 21 = 0$ b) $x^2 + 2x = 0$
 c) $40x^2 - 29x + 3 = 0$
12. a) −3, 5 b) 1, −6 c) $\frac{2}{5}$, 8 d) $\frac{3}{4}$, −7
 e) $\pm\frac{5}{4}$ f) $-\frac{2}{3}$
13. a) 1.396, −0.896 b) −2.38, 0.63 c) −2, $-\frac{1}{3}$
 d) 1.61, −2.28 e) 1.518, −1.318
 f) 2.593, 1.157
14. Different, real: a, b; Same, real: c;
 No real roots: d
15. a) All values b) $k > -\frac{3}{4}$
16. a) $|p| < 6$ b) $p > \frac{3}{4}$
17. a) $-22 - 3i$ b) $48 + 36i$
18. a) $-3 \pm 2i$ b) $\frac{1 \pm \sqrt{83}i}{6}$
19.

	Sum	Product
a)	11	−7
b)	$-\frac{2}{3}$	$-\frac{1}{3}$
c)	$\frac{2}{3}$	$\frac{4}{9}$

20. a) 1 b) −5
 c) −2
21. 2.93 cm
22. 28 cm, 12 cm

Chapter 5

Exercises 5-1, page 147

1. a) 2:3 b) 5:3 c) 3:4 d) $4x:5y$
 e) $3m:7$ f) $3a^2:2b$ g) 2:5 g) 4:3
2. Bronze—9:1, Brass—3:2, Pewter—3:1
3. a) Gina: Terry—3:2
 b) India or China: elsewhere—2:3
 c) teachers: students—2:35
 d) retired: not retired—3:22
 e) more than 5 years: less than 5 years—11:39
 f) muscles: brain—20:1
4. a) 92.5% b) 75 g 5. 6 and 8
6. a) 56, 21 b) 24, 9, or −24, −9
 c) 40, 15, or −40, −15
7. a) 90, 162 b) 55, 99
 c) 20, 36, or −20, −36 d) 10, 18 or −10, −18
8. a) 50:3 b) gasoline 9.4 L, oil 0.57 L
9. 2000:1 10. a) 3.2 b) 3200 km/h
11. a) $AC \doteq 4.3$ cm, $CB \doteq 5.7$ cm
 b) $AC = \frac{ax}{a+b}$ cm, $CB = \frac{bx}{a+b}$ cm
12. a) $2:\sqrt{5}$ b) $1:\sqrt{5}$
13. a) 3:10 b) $3:\sqrt{13}$ c) $10:\sqrt{13}$
14. a) 52 cm, 39 cm b) 12 m, 9 m
 c) 24 mm, 18 mm
15. 48°, 48°, 84°, or 40°, 70°, 70°
16. a) 1 b) $\frac{7}{8}$ c) $-\frac{5}{13}$
17. a) 4:3 b) 5:2 c) −2:7
 d) 2:1, or −2:1
18. $\pi:4$ 19. a) $x^2:2x+1$ b) $1 \pm \sqrt{2}$
20. 2:1, 1:2 21. About 16 000 000:1
22. a) 6:5 b) Yes. 5:4

Exercises 5-2, page 152

1. a) 48 b) 25 c) 22.5 d) 8 e) 8.25
 f) 28.125
2. 8.96 m 3. 120 km 4. 0.000 16 mm
5. About 85 m^3
6. Amazon: 18.9 cm, Yangtze: 16.6 cm,
 Mackenzie: 12.8 cm, Volga: 11.1 cm
7. 2 8. 7 9. grade 11: 72, grade 12: 54
10. a) 2 : 5 b) −4 : 3 c) 2:1 d) 1:1
 e) 5:9 f) $(d-b):(a-c)$
11. About 0.002 mm 12. About 54 m
13. About 250 000 km 14. 8:15 15. 15:4

Exercises 5-3, page 157

1. a) 14 b) 22.5 2. a) 6.4 b) 11.25
3. a) x: 2; y: −6, −14, −26 b) x: 20, 55; y: 0.8,
4. a) 36 b) ±2
5. a) x: 6; y: 6, 24, 73.5 b) x: 5, 8; y 2, 72
6. 3 km 7. a) 8 carats b) 6.3 mm
8. 4.5 L 9. 1548 cm^2 10. 7579 cm^3 11. 5.4
12. a) 55 km b) 12.35 km 13. 7.5 m^3
14. a) 2.14 L, 1.93 L b) 293°C, −131.5°C
15. a) Doubled b) Tripled c) Halved
16. a) i) 89.4 kg ii) 30.6 kg b) 0.85 g/cm^3
17. Mercury 88, Venus 224, Earth 365, Mars 689,
 Jupiter 4340, Saturn 10 702, Uranus 30 911,
 Neptune 60 777, Pluto 91 330

Exercises 5-4, page 161

1. a) 10 b) 2 **2.** a) 2 b) 5
3. a) x: 3; y: 30, 10, 4 b) x: −0.5, 0.2; y: 4, −3
c) x: 10, 2.5; y: 36, 2.25 d) x: 16, 0.25; y: 4, 6
4. a) 7 h b) 906 km/h
5. a) i) 16 units ii) 5.76 units
b) i) 69.3 m ii) 40 m **6.** 50 L
7. a) Halved b) Divided by 3 c) Doubled
8. a) 9, 4 b) 14.4% **9.** 2680 L
10. 500 kg **11.** 302.4 Ω
12. a) i) 52, 14 ii) 39, 28 b) About 51 km/h
13. a) 27 400 km/h b) 3629 km/h

MM

1. a) 37 680 km b) 5997 km **2.** 6%

Exercises 5-5, page 167

1. a) 3:4:7 b) 5:3:8 c) 3:5:4
d) $3m:8mn:5n$ e) $6z:4y:7$
f) $4a^2:6ab:9b^2$ g) $3a:b:2ab$
2. a) 5:4 b) 3:2 c) 15:8
3. a) 8:15 b) 5:2 c) 4:3
4. a) 15, 33 b) 25, 12 c) 65, 6
d) 22.5, 45 e) 16, 18.75 f) 67.5, 97.5
5. a) 15, $\frac{40}{3}$ b) 28.5, 37.5 c) 48, 62.5
d) 1, 60 e) 2.5, 10 f) 1, $\frac{17}{3}$
6. S: $50 000, M: $32 000, E: $18 000
7. $64,320, $40 200, $16 080
8. a) 1:2 b) 4:3 c) 2:3 d) 2:4:3
9. a) 3:2 b) 4:3 c) 2:1 d) 6:4:3
10. Lemonade: 2.25 L, orange juice: 3.75 L, ginger ale: 9 L
11. 24 cm, 48 cm, 56 cm **12.** 45°, 60°, 75°
13. 60°, 80°, 100°, 120° **14.** 15 cm, 20 cm, 25 cm
15. a) $\frac{18}{25}$ b) $\frac{11}{25}$ c) $\frac{11}{18}$
16. a) 2:1 b) 6:4:3
17. a) 4:5 b) 10:12:15 **18.** $116.63
19. About 1.29 times
21. a) 225 kg, 450 kg, b) 8000 kg c) 147 kg
22. Jean 12, Katherine 42, Lorna 18

Exercises 5-6, page 171

1. a) $\frac{AB}{PQ} = \frac{BC}{QR} = \frac{CA}{RP}$ b) $\frac{JP}{PK} = \frac{PX}{KY} = \frac{XJ}{YP}$
c) $\frac{MR}{GT} = \frac{RX}{TL} = \frac{XM}{LG}$ d) $\frac{YS}{KE} = \frac{SB}{EN} = \frac{BY}{NK}$
2. a) 6, 8 b) 15, 20 c) 11, 21 d) 8, 14
3. b) 2:3. c) 39°, 49°, 92° Yes
4. 9 m **5.** 1416 m **6.** 60 m
Yes

7. a) 11, 16.8 b) 5, 27 c) 10, 6.4 d) 15.6, 6
8. a) 3.75 b) $\frac{100}{7}$
9. a) i) 9 ii) 3:1 b) i) 6 ii) 2:1
10. 2 cm **11.** a) $\sqrt{2}$ cm b) 4:9
12. a) 9 cm, 20 cm, 15 cm
13. b) 9.6 cm, 12.8 cm, 7.2 cm **14.** 60 m
15. 192 m **16.** Yes

MAU

1. a) 8760 b) 525 600 c) 31 536 000
2. a) 330 million b) 77 million c) 460 000
d) 7600 e) 126
3. a) April 1 b) December 25
c) 5:30 p.m. December 31
d), e), f) 80 s, 40 s, 1 s before midnight December 31.

Review Exercises, page 175

1. a) 6:13 b) $3:7b$ c) 3:2
2. a) 21, 49 b) 42, 98 c) 39, 91
3. About 2:45 **4.** a) 18 b) 24
5. 297.5 m/s **6.** 15 **7.** Gr. 11: 68, Gr. 12: 51
8. a) x: 1.5, −1; y: −12 b) x: 32; y: −2.5, 1
9. a) $6750 b) 1.15 carats
10. a) t: 12; x: 9,16 b) x: 12; y: $\frac{8}{3}$, 8
11. a) i) 3.96 kg ii) 11.58 kg b) 9.49 g/cm^3
12. a) x: −72, 12; y: −16 b) x: 4, 12; y: 192
13. a) 5.3 h b) 96 km/h
14. a) w: 2.5; x: 4, 36 b) l: 20; m: ± 1; n:10
15. a) 4, 27 b) 26, 78
16. 48°, 54°, 78° **17.** 56°, 80°, 104°, 120°
18. a) 20 cm, 24 cm, 38 cm
19. 70.4 m **20.** 48

Chapter 6

Exercises 6-1, page 180

1. a) 10 b) $\sqrt{106}$ c) 17 d) $2\sqrt{17}$
e) $\sqrt{157}$ f) $2\sqrt{41}$
2. a) $\sqrt{145}$ b) $\sqrt{274}$ c) $5\sqrt{2}$ d) $\sqrt{346}$
e) $\sqrt{149}$ f) 25
3. a) (−2, −2) b) (9 , 1) c) (−1, −1)
d) $\left(8, -\frac{5}{2}\right)$ e) $\left(\frac{3}{2}, \frac{9}{2}\right)$ f) (3, 3)
4. a) (0, 1), (4, −2), (2, 5) b) The length of each side of $\triangle DEF$ is half the length of the corresponding side of $\triangle ABC$.

5. a) $PQ = \sqrt{2^2 + 2^2}$, or $\sqrt{8}$,
$QR = \sqrt{6^2 + 6^2}$, or $\sqrt{72}$,
$PR = \sqrt{8^2 + 4^2}$, or $\sqrt{80}$
$PQ^2 + QR^2 = PR^2$.
Therefore, $\triangle PQR$ is a right triangle.
b) Midpoint, M, of PR: (−3, 1).
$MP = \sqrt{2^2 + 4^2}$, or $2\sqrt{5}$
$MP = MQ = MR = 2\sqrt{5}$

6. a) i) (9, 0) ii) (0, 1)
b) i) (1, 0) ii) $\left(0, -\frac{7}{5}\right)$
c) i) $\left(\frac{1}{8}, 0\right)$ ii) $\left(0, -\frac{1}{6}\right)$
d) i) $\left(\frac{97}{26}, 0\right)$ ii) $\left(0, -\frac{97}{16}\right)$

7. a) Isosceles b) Scalene, right c) Scalene
d) Isosceles, right e) Scalene f) Isosceles

8. a) i) $\sqrt{17}, 2\sqrt{17}$ ii) $\sqrt{85}$ iii) $6\sqrt{17}$ iv) 34
b) i) $6\sqrt{5}, 2\sqrt{5}$ ii) $10\sqrt{2}$ iii) $16\sqrt{5}$ iv) 60
c) i) $2\sqrt{13}, 2\sqrt{13}$ ii) $2\sqrt{26}$ iii) $8\sqrt{13}$ iv) 52
d) i) $\sqrt{10}, 3\sqrt{10}$ ii) 10 iii) $8\sqrt{10}$ iv) 30

9. a) (−2, 2), (2, 0), (6, −2)
b) (−2, 6), (−6, 3), (−10, 0)
c) $\left(-\frac{5}{2}, 6\right)$, (2, 7), $\left(\frac{13}{2}, 8\right)$
d) $\left(-\frac{3}{4}, -7\right)$, $\left(\frac{5}{2}, -5\right)$, $\left(\frac{23}{4}, -3\right)$

10. a) (8, −2) b) (17, 8) c) (−7, −3)
d) (−9, 8)

11. $Q(0, -3)$, $M\left(\frac{9}{2}, 0\right)$

12. $\left(\frac{7}{2}, -2\right)$ is the midpoint of both diagonals.
Therefore, they bisect each other.

13. $\sqrt{73}, \sqrt{82}, \sqrt{85}$

14. a) Isosceles b) 90° c) 40 units^2

15. 532 km **16.** Freighter

17. (−40, 80), (160, 320), (360, 560)

18. (8, 4), (9, 2), (0, 0), (1, −2)

19. a) Midpoints of opposite sides: (3, 8) and (3, 0), (−3, 7) and (9, 1)
Midpoints of segments joining them: (3, 4) and (3, 4)
Therefore, segments joining midpoints of opposite sides bisect each other.

Exercises 6-2, page 184

1. a) 3 : 5 b) 3 : 2 c) 1 : 1 d) 1 : 2

2. a) 1 : 1 b) 4 : 7 c) 1 : 2 d) 4 : 5
e) 1 : 2 f) 7 : 1

3. a) 2 : 3 b) 2 : 1 c) 2 : 5 d) 1 : 4

4. 9, 12 **5.** 2 : 1 **6.** (−2, 5)

7. a) 1 : 4 b) 3 : 2

8. a) (9, 7.5) b) (4.8, 4)

9. Closer to A in (a) and (d).

10. Closest to A in (a); closest to B in (b)

11. $A(9, 0)$, $B(0, -6)$ **12.** (7, 1.9)

13. a) $\frac{1}{2}$ b) 2 **14.** b) i) 1 : 2 ii) 2 : 1

15. a) 12 b) 4 : 3, 2 : 1, 4 : 1; 1 : 1, 3 : 2, 3 : 1
2 : 3, 1 : 1, 2 : 1; 1 : 3, 1 : 2, 1 : 1

16. (−3, −8), (−12, −2)

17. a) (−1, 4), (3, 3) b) $\left(4, \frac{13}{3}\right)$, $\left(7, \frac{17}{3}\right)$

18. a) (9, 3), (15, 0) b) (2, 1), (−7, −5)

19. a) (14, 0) b) (3, −10)
c) $\left(4, -\frac{2}{3}\right)$ d) (−4, 0)

20. a) 4 : 5 b) 5 : 3 **21.** $\left(\frac{bx_1 + ax_2}{a + b}, \frac{by_1 + ay_2}{a + b}\right)$

Exercises 6-3, page 189

1. a) $\frac{9}{7}$ b) −1 c) 0 d) 4
e) Undefined f) $-\frac{4}{5}$

2. a) No b) Yes **3.** a, e, f

4. a) i) $\frac{2}{5}$ ii) $-\frac{5}{2}$ b) i) $-\frac{4}{3}$ ii) $\frac{3}{4}$
c) i) −2 ii) $\frac{1}{2}$ d) i) $\frac{3}{7}$ ii) $-\frac{7}{3}$
e) i) −1 ii) 1 f) i) 0.6 ii) $-\frac{5}{3}$

5. a) $\frac{3}{2}, -\frac{7}{4}, -\frac{2}{3}$ b) $-\frac{2}{7}, \frac{2}{5}, -2$ **6.** a

8. a) No b) Yes c) Yes

9. a) About 0.11 b) 3.62 m c) 45 cm

10. a) 48 m b) 1.05

11. a) (8, 2), (4, −6), (−2, 4)
b) (3, 0), (5, −6, (−9, −2)
c) (2, 7), (−2, −1), (−4, 3)
d) (8, 2), (0, −6), (4, 14)

12. a) (7, 3), (4, 7), or (−1, −3), (−4, 1)
b) (0, 5), (3, 7), or (4, −1), (7, 1)
c) (1, 8), (8, 5), or (1, −14), (7, −15)

14. a) (8, 2), (4, −2), or (0, 10), (−4, 6), or (0, 6), (4, 2)
b) (4, 6), (6, 2), or (−4, 2), (−2, −2), or (3, 3), (−1, 1)

15. (7, 0), or (3, 0)

16. (4, 0), or (5, 0), or (9, 0), or (14, 0)

Exercises 6-4, page 192

1. a) $2x - y - 9 = 0$ b) $4x - y - 14 = 0$
c) $x + y - 1 = 0$ d) $3x + y - 6 = 0$
e) $x - 2y + 2 = 0$ f) $y - 2 = 0$

2. a) $3x + 4y - 26 = 0$ b) $x - 4y + 7 = 0$ c) $3x + 2y - 15 = 0$ d) $3x - y = 0$ e) $y - 2 = 0$ f) $x - 4 = 0$
3. a, b, d **4.** a, d
5. a) 5 b) −4 c) −6 d) 0
6. a) $x - 3y - 14 = 0$ b) $5x + 2y + 7 = 0$ c) $2x - 9y - 82 = 0$ d) $7x + 3y - 18 = 0$ e) $2x - 7y + 21 = 0$ f) $x + 2y + 2 = 0$
7. $3x - 4y + 12 = 0, x - 8y - 16 = 0, 7x + 4y - 52 = 0$
8. a) i) $2x + 3y - 37 = 0$ ii) $2x + 3y - 28 = 0$ iii) $2x + 3y - 19 = 0$ iv) $2x + 3y - 10 = 0$ v) $2x + 3y - 1 = 0$ vi) $2x + 3y + 8 = 0$
c) The line moves parallel to itself.
9. a) i) $4x - y - 22 = 0$ ii) $3x - y - 17 = 0$ iii) $2x - y - 12 = 0$ iv) $x - y - 7 = 0$ v) $y + 2 = 0$ vi) $x + y - 3 = 0$ vii) $2x + y - 8 = 0$ viii) $3x + y - 13 = 0$
c) The line rotates about (5, −2).
10. a) $3x - 2y - 4 = 0$ c) $PA = PB = \sqrt{65}$
11. a) Yes b) No c) Yes
12. a) −1 b) 3 c) 0 d) $-\frac{5}{3}$
13. a) $x + y - 8 = 0$ b) $4x - y - 16 = 0$ c) $x - 4y - 38 = 0$
14. $x + 10y - 15 = 0, 7x - 11y + 3 = 0, 8x - y - 12 = 0$
15. $5\sqrt{5}$ **16.** 8

MAU

1. 4.5% **2.** 6.9 km
3. a) About 90 b) About 20 m c) About 3 min
4. About 150 m. Answers to Questions 3 and 4 depend on the assumptions made.

Exercises 6-5, page 198

1. a) $5x - y + 8 = 0$ b) $4x + y - 3 = 0$ c) $2x - 5y - 5 = 0$ d) $x + y + 6 = 0$ e) $4x + 3y - 1 = 0$ f) $5x - 8y + 4 = 0$
2. a) $2x + y - 3 = 0$ b) $x - y - 4 = 0$ c) $5x - 3y + 6 = 0$ d) $3x + 2y - 8 = 0$ e) $x + 4y + 4 = 0$ f) $5x - 4y + 20 = 0$
3. a) $y + 2 = 0$ b) $y - 3 = 0$ c) $y - 5 = 0$ d) $y = 0$
4. a) $x - 4 = 0$ b) $x + 3 = 0$ c) $x - 2 = 0$ d) $x = 0$
5. a) −6, 3 b) 8, 6 c) $\frac{7}{5}, -7$ d) $-\frac{15}{2}, -\frac{15}{9}$
6. a) 1, −4 b) $-\frac{2}{3}, 6$ c) $-\frac{5}{4}, -5$ d) $\frac{1}{7}, 2$
7. No. Lines parallel to one of the axes have only one intercept.
8. 10
9. c) i) The graph moves parallel to itself.
ii) The graph rotates about $(0, b)$.

10. a, d **11.** $3x + y - 25 = 0$ **12.** b, d, e
13. $3x + 2y - 19 = 0$ **14.** b, d
15. $5x - y - 3 = 0$
16. a) 0 b) 2 c) −2 d) −14 e) 25 f) 3
17. $x + y - 5 = 0$ **18.** $2x + 3y - 18 = 0$ or $x + 6y - 18 = 0$

Exercises 6-6, page 202

1. a) $x^2 + y^2 = 25$ b) $x^2 + y^2 = 144$ c) $x^2 + y^2 = 256$ d) $x^2 + y^2 = \frac{625}{16}$ e) $x^2 + y^2 = 0.09$ f) $x^2 + y^2 = 529$
2. a) i) (0, 0) ii) 5 iii) 10 iv) ±5 v) ±5
3. a) i) 9 ii) 11 iii) 8 iv) $\frac{7}{2}$ v) 6 vi) 1.5
4. a) 5 b) (−3, 4)
5. a) $x^2 + y^2 = 9$ b) $x^2 + y^2 = 16$ c) $x^2 + y^2 = 29$ d) $x^2 + y^2 = 10$
6. $\sqrt{58}$ **7.** a) ±4 b) $\pm\sqrt{7}$ c) ±2 d) $\pm 2\sqrt{3}$
8. c) (6, 8): on; (−10, 1): outside; (−7, −7): inside
9. a) Inside b) Outside c) Outside
10. (1, −2), (−3, 3), (0, 4) **11.** b) $y = -\frac{1}{2}x$
12. b) $y = 7x$ **13.** b) $y = \frac{3}{7}x$
15. $x^2 + y^2 = 25(3 - 2\sqrt{2})$

Exercises 6-7, page 205

1. a) (4, 1), 6 b) (2, −5), 3 c) (−7, −3), 4 d) (−2, 2), $\sqrt{5}$ e) (0, 8), 5 f) (−3, 0), $\sqrt{13}$
3. a) $(x - 6)^2 + (y - 2)^2 = 9$ b) $(x + 4)^2 + (y - 5)^2 = 49$ c) $(x + 1)^2 + (y + 3)^2 = 25$ d) $(x + 8)^2 + (y + 2)^2 = 4$ e) $(x - 3)^2 + y^2 = 1$ f) $x^2 + (y + 4)^2 = 36$
4. a) $(x - 1)^2 + (y - 2)^2 = 16$ b) $(x + 2)^2 + (y - 1)^2 = 9$ c) $(x - 1)^2 + (y + 2)^2 = 4$
5. b) Only C is on the circle.
6. a) $(x - 3)^2 + y^2 = 25$ b) (−2, 0), (8, 0)
7. a) i, ii, iii, iv b) iv, vi c) i, v, vi
8. a) (6, −2) b) $\sqrt{85}$ c) $2\sqrt{85}$ d) −3, 15 e) −9, 5
9. a) $(x - 2)^2 + (y + 3)^2 = 25$ b) $(x + 4)^2 + (y - 2)^2 = 89$ c) $(x - 5)^2 + (y - 4)^2 = 16$
10. a) $(x - 2)^2 + (y - 2)^2 = 8$
11. $(x - 3)^2 + y^2 = 25$, $(x + 3)^2 + y^2 = 97$

12. a) $(x-5)^2+y^2=45$, or $(x+7)^2+y^2=45$
13. b) No
14. c) 2 points: ii, v; 1 point: iii; 0 points: i, iv, vi
15. x-axis—4 : 3, y-axis—1 : 3
16. a) $(x-12)^2+(y-4)^2=16$
b) $(x+12)^2+(y-4)^2=16$, $x^2+(y+4)^2=16$, $x^2+(y-4)^2=16$
17. $(x-3)^2+(y-6)^2=10$ **18.** $\sqrt{5}$ or $2\sqrt{5}$
19. a) 1 b) $x^2+(y+3)^2=4$, $x^2+(y-3)^2=4$, $(x+4)^2+y^2=9$, $(x-4)^2+y^2=9$
20. $x^2+(y-2)^2=4$

Exercises 6-8, page 209

1. a) 24 b) $6\sqrt{3}$ c) $\sqrt{421}$
2. b) i) 10 ii) $5\sqrt{3}$ iii) $4\sqrt{3}$
3. a) 8 b) $\sqrt{37}$ c) $2\sqrt{2}$
4. a) $4x+3y-25=0$ b) $3x-4y-40=0$
c) $x+2y-5=0$ d) $3x+2y+13=0$
5. a) $2\sqrt{5}$ b) $\sqrt{65}$ c) $2\sqrt{10}$
6. a) $\sqrt{33}$ b) $2\sqrt{17}$ c) $\sqrt{73}$ d) $2\sqrt{14}$
7. 7 **8.** $(4, \pm 2\sqrt{6})$
9. a) $x-3y+10=0$ b) $y+4=0$
c) $x+y-2\sqrt{2}=0$ d) $3x-\sqrt{2}y-11=0$
10. $2x-3y-13=0$
11. $5x+2y+29=0$, $5x+2y-29=0$
12. b) $\sqrt{40}$
c) $PA=\sqrt{160}$, $PB=\sqrt{10}$. $PA \times PB=\sqrt{1600}$, or 40. $PT^2=40$
13. a) $\sqrt{(x_1-h)^2+(y_1-k)^2-r^2}$
b) i) 7 ii) $2\sqrt{6}$ iii) 0 iv) No real length
c) (0, 6) is on the circle. (0, 0) is inside the circle.
14. $x_1x+y_1y=r^2$ **15.** 4 **16.** 1.5 km

MAU
1. a) 4.4 km b) 54.6 km c) 391 km
d) 1597 km
2. a) 102m b) 407 m c) 4.9 km
3. 865 m **6.** a) 37 km b) 259 km
7. a) $1.86\sqrt{h}$ b) $2.60\sqrt{h}$ c) $11.7\sqrt{h}$

Exercises 6-10, page 216

1. a) 8 b) 21 c) 24 d) 41
2. 15.2 cm **3.** 6.3 cm
4. a) 13.60 b) 21.82 c) 18.97
5. a) 9.8 cm b) 9.2 cm c) 8 cm d) 6 cm
8. 17.2 m **9.** 3.4 m **10.** 35.65 m^2
12. 184 m

Review Exercises, page 219

1. a) 5 b) 13 c) 26 d) $\sqrt{137}$
2. a) $(-\frac{3}{2}, 2)$ b) $(3, -\frac{9}{2})$
c) $(\frac{9}{2}, -\frac{1}{2})$ d) $(-4, \frac{3}{2})$
3. a) Yes b) No c) No d) Yes
4. a) 13 b) 6 c) −9 d) $-\frac{9}{2}$
5. a) 1 : 4 b) 3 : 2
6. $A(8, 0)$, $B(0, 4)$ **7.** a) 4 b) $\frac{3}{8}$
8. a) No b) Yes c) Yes
10. $4x+y-14=0$, $3x+5y-19=0$, $6x-7y-4=0$
11. a) $x-y+1=0$ b) $2x+3y-6=0$
c) $y-3=0$
12. a) $x+3y=0$ b) $10x-11y-14=0$
c) $x-y+3=0$ d) $x+2y+5=0$
13. b, c **14.** b, d
15. a) $5x+4y-15=0$ b) $9x-8y-12=0$
c) $x-y+2=0$ d) $4x+3y-19=0$
16. a) $x^2+y^2=6.25$ b) $x^2+y^2=58$
c) $x^2+y^2=50$ d) $x^2+y^2=50$
17. (0, 7), (6, 3.5) **18.** b) $4y+x=0$
19. a) $(x+3)^2+(y+5)^2=80$
b) $(x-2)^2+(y+4)^2=29$
c) $(x-7)^2+(y+5)^2=90$
20. $(x-5)^2+(y-4)^2=20$ or 80
21. $x^2+(y-1)^2=40$, or $x^2+(y+11)^2=40$
22. 4 **23.** (25, 25) or (−25, −25) **26.** 4.58 m

Chapter 7

Exercises 7-1, page 223

1. a) (2, 3) b) (2, 0) c) (0, −4)
d) (4, −1) e) (3, 0) f) (2, 6)
2. a) (3, 2) b) (2, −3) c) (4, −6)
d) (3, 0) e) (3, −1) f) (3, 1)
3. a) $(\frac{5}{2}, \frac{3}{2})$ b) (3, 2)
c) Infinitely many solutions d) No solution
e) No solution f) $(\frac{1}{2}, \frac{1}{3})$
4. When their graphs are: a) intersecting, b) parallel, c) coincident, lines.
5. i) d ii) a, c
6. a) Infinitely many b) 1 c) 1
d) No solution
7. a) 1 b) Many c) 0 d) 0
8. a) b) Answers will vary. c) $3x+2y-16=0$
9. a) No b) Yes c) No d) Yes

Exercises 7-2, page 227

1. a and c; b and d.
2. a) ③ and ④, ④ and ①, ③ and ①;
b) ② and ④, ② and ①, ② and ③.
3. a) (2, 2) **5.** a and d; b and c
7. a) i) $x - y + 4 = 0$ ii) $3x - y + 10 = 0$
iii) $3x - 5y + 14 = 0$ iv) $x + 5y - 2 = 0$
v) $x - 7y + 10 = 0$ vi) $5x - 7y + 22 = 0$
8. b) When multiples of two inconsistent equations are added or subtracted, other inconsistent equations are obtained.
9. Answers may vary.
a) i) $w = 1, t = -1$ ii) $w = 3, t = 1$
b) i) $w = 1, t = -1$ ii) $w = 5, t = 1$
c) i) $w = 1, t = -3$ ii) $w = -4, t = 1$
10. (3, 2)

MAU
a) 3:38.0 b) 2018

Exercises 7-3, page 232

1. a) (2, 1) b) (6, −7) c) (−2, −3)
d) (2, −1) e) (−4, 2) f) (3, 4)
2. a) (4, −6) b) (3, 5) c) (3, 2)
d) (2, 3) e) (3, −4) f) (−2, 1)
3. a) (4, −5) b) (2, 1) c) (1, 2)
d) (19, −30) e) (3, 1) f) (−10, −2)
4. a) (5, −6) b) (3, 1) c) (−2, −3)
d) (3, 0) e) $\left(-\frac{5}{8}, -\frac{1}{4}\right)$ f) $\left(2, -\frac{7}{3}\right)$
5. a) (1.25, −0.50) b) (0.67, − 0.50)
c) (2.50, −3.00) d) (3.33, 3.50)
e) (2.23, 0.15) f) (2.09, 0.73)
6. a) (3, −3) b) (10, −1) c) (1, 3)
d) (8, 2) e) (3, 4) f) (−6, −3)
7. a) $m = 0, n = 3$ b) $m = 3, n = 2$
c) $m = 4, n = -3$ d) $m = -2, n -4$
8. $8x - 9y + 29 = 0$ **9.** a) $3x - 5y + 2 = 0$
10. $94x + 5y + 158 = 0$
11. a) $4x + 5y + 2 = 0$ b) $5x - 4y + 23 = 0$
12. a) (4, 1), (0, 4), (6, 5) b) (4, 7), (7, −2), (−2, 4)
13. a) Right, isosceles b) Not right, not isosceles
14. a) J$\left(\frac{6}{5}, \frac{26}{5}\right)$, K(6, 2) b) 5.77 units
15. a) A: $8x - 3y - 10 = 0$, B: $x - 9y + 39 = 0$
b) G$\left(3, \frac{14}{3}\right)$
16. a) 2 : 1 b) 1 : 2 c) 3 : 1
17. $am : b$ **18.** $x \doteq 3.86$ units^2, $y \doteq 5.14$ units^2
19. a) (2, −6) b) $\left(\frac{13}{27}, \frac{13}{7}\right)$
c) (3, 1), (3, −1), (−3, 1), (−3, −1)
d) (2, 5), (2, −5), (−2, 5), (−2, −5)

Exercises 7-4, page 236

1. Shirts: \$16, sweaters: \$28
2. Records: \$4.50, tapes: \$5.50
3. 164, 36 **4.** 150 World Oil, 300 Zinco Mines
5. 380 adult, 520 student
6. Technician: \$100, apprentice: \$40
7. Between goal lines: \$15, end zones: \$10
8. 54°, 54°, 72° **9.** 50°, 50°, 80°, or 70°, 70°, 40°
10. City: 310 km, highway: 140 km
11. 1188 km **12.** 48.5 km/h, 727.5 km/h
13. 12.5 km/h, 17.5 km/h **14.** 600
15. Tea: \$6.90/kg, coffee: \$3.85/kg
16. 400, 450 **17.** 10, 12, 15

MAU
1. a) i) 10 000 ii) 14 000 iii) 18 000
b) i) 3.5 ii) 4.75 iii) 6.2 c) 0.500 25
2. a) i) 4500 ii) 3000 iii) 1500
b) i) 0.8 ii) 1.25 iii) 2.2
c) 2.4996 d) 7500
3. a) 0.8 b) 4400

Exercises 7-5, page 241

1. a) (−3, 5, −1) b) (5, −1, 2)
c) (1, 3, −2) d) (4, 1, −3)
2. a) (−2, 1, 4) b) (1, 5, 2)
c) (3, 2, 1) d) (3, −1, 5)
3. a) (5, −1, 2) b) (−2, 4, 1)
c) (−2, 5, 7) d) (3, 5, −2)
4. a) $\left(\frac{1}{2}, \frac{1}{2}, 0\right)$ b) $\left(-\frac{9}{5}, \frac{31}{5}, \frac{9}{5}\right)$
c) $\left(\frac{1}{3}, \frac{1}{2}, \frac{1}{4}\right)$ d) $\left(\frac{2}{13}, \frac{3}{13}, \frac{1}{13}\right)$
5. a) (−1, 4, −3) b) (6, −9, 2) c) (2, 0, −2)
d) (3, 0, 7)
6. 31 **7.** 1, 3, 5 **8.** 15, 18, 24
9. 60, 40, 20 **10.** 426 **11.** 8, 10, 18
12. $I_1 \doteq 1.24$ A, $I_2 \doteq -1.32$ A, $I_3 \doteq 0.07$ A
13. Cu : Sn : Ni = 3 : 4 : 3
14. a) $\left(1, \frac{1}{2}, \frac{1}{3}\right)$ b) $\left(\frac{1}{2}, -\frac{1}{3}, \frac{1}{5}\right)$
c) (±4, ±3, ±2) d) (±2, ±5, ±3)
15. 2, 5, 1, 12

Exercises 7-6, page 245

1. 2 points: a, c 1 point: d 0 points: b
2. a) (8, 6), (−6, −8) b) No solution
c) (1.4, 4.8), (−3, −4) d) (0, −6)
3. a) (−1, 1), (3, 9) b) (4, −3), (−2, 6)
c) (−1, 3), (2, 0) d) No solution
4. 2 points: a 1 point: d 0 points: b,c

5. a) (1, 3), (−1, −3) b) (−3, 1)
c) (4, 4), (−5.6, −0.8) d) (8, 1), (-4, 7)
6. a) (3, −3) b) (2, 3), (5, 12)
c) (−3, 2), (1.7, −1.1) d) (3, 2), $(-4, -\frac{3}{2})$
7. a) (3, 4), (−3, −4) b) (−4, 3)
c) No solution
8. a) (4.9, −2.9), (1.1, 0.9) b) No solution
c) (4.9, 2.9), (1.1, −0.9)
9. a) Yes b) Yes c) No
d) No e) Yes f) Yes
11. a) (−7, −1), (1, 3) b) (2, −6), (−3.2, 1.8)
c) (−1, 3) d) (1, −1), (2.3, 4.2)
12. a) (0, 3), (3, 0)
b) (2, −3), (−3, 2), (3, 2), (−2, −3)

Exercises 7-7, page 250

1. a) (1, 2), (−1, −2) b) (2, −1)
c) (1, −3), (3, 1) d) No intersection
2. a) (0, −5), (3, 4) b) (−1, 1), (2, 4)
c) (4, −2) d) (−2, −6), (3, 4)
3. 3, 7 4. 4 cm, 2.5 cm
5. a) 7.1 s b) 112.6 m
6. a) (−2, 3), $\left(\frac{46}{13}, -\frac{9}{13}\right)$ b) (2, 3)
c) (−3, −4), $\left(-\frac{10}{3}, -\frac{35}{9}\right)$
d) (2.3, −1.15), (−2.3, 1.15)
e) No solution f) (−2, 2), $\left(-\frac{4}{3}, 3\right)$
7. (6, 8), (9.6, −2.8) 8. (−40, 0) and (−24, 32)
10. 8, 12 11. 6, 10 12. 90 m, 160 m
13. 9.7 cm, 2.3 cm
14. $x + 6y - 18 = 0$ or $2x + 3y - 18 = 0$
15. (3, 7), $(-\frac{5}{2}, \frac{3}{2})$
16. b) i) (4, 3), (3.8, 3.2) ii) No solution
17. b) $D(0, -5)$, $E(3, -4)$
18. a) $D(4, -3)$, $E(3, -4)$, $F(0, -5)$
19. $x \doteq 1.53$, $y \doteq 3.06$
20. a) $l = \frac{1}{4}(P + \sqrt{P^2 - 16A})$, $w = \frac{1}{4}(P - \sqrt{P^2 - 16A})$
21. a) (4.8, 2.4) b) i) Equal ii) Equal
22. a) $\left(\frac{-b}{1+m}, \frac{b}{1+m}\right) m \neq -1$,
or $\left(\frac{b}{1-m}, \frac{b}{1-m}\right) m \neq 1$
23. 90 km/h, 105 km/h 24. 36 km, 60 km/h

MAU

1. $A = 2.5s - 83.5$
2. a) 35.25 cm b) 49.4 cm

Exercises 7-8, page 255

1. a) No b) Yes c) Yes
2. $y = \pm 2x + 5$
3. a) $y = 2x - 1$ b) $y = -2x - 1$
4. $y = \pm 4x - 4$ 5. $12x + 4y + 25 = 0$
6. a) $y = 3x + 10$ b) $y = 3x - 10$
7. $y = 2x \pm 5\sqrt{5}$ 8. $y = -3$, or $y = 8x - 3$
9. $x + 2y = 10$, $2x + y = 5$ 10. $x + y + 4 = 0$
12. $x - 2y + 5 = 0$, $2x + y - 5 = 0$
13. $2x + y + 1 = 0$, $6x - y - 9 = 0$
14. 1.90 15. $x - 2y + 16 = 0$, $x - 2y - 4 = 0$

Review Exercises, page 257

1. a) (0, −3) b) (1, 5)
c) (2, 10) d) (−3, 0)
2. a) No solution b) (2, 3)
c) Coincident lines d) (6, 8)
4. a) $(-\frac{1}{2}, 4)$ b) (3, 2)
c) (5, 7) d) $(\frac{27}{11}, -\frac{15}{11})$
5. a) (2,23, 0.71) b) (1.38, 4.25)
c) (0.40, −0.03) d) (−0.53, −0.05)
6. $x - 3y + 9 = 0$
7. a) (3, −1), (5, 5) b) $2\sqrt{10}$
8. A: 4000 cards/min, B: 2500 cards/min
9. 4.25 h
10. a) (1, 4), (−1, −4) b) $(\frac{3}{5}, \frac{21}{5})$, (−3, −3)
c) (−2, 4), (3, 9) d) (−1, 9), (3, 5)
11. a) (2, −1), (6, 3) b) (2, 7), (6, 3) c) (6, 3)
12. a) (1, 1), (−2, 4) b) (4, 2), $(\frac{4}{5}, \frac{22}{5})$
c) (2, 5), $(\frac{10}{3}, 3)$ d) (4, 1), (7, 10)
13. 32, 8 14. 85.3 mm, 144.7 mm
15. 12m, 40m; 16m, 30m
16. a) $5 + \sqrt{5}$, $5 - \sqrt{5}$ c) 25
17. $y + 2x \pm 6\sqrt{5} = 0$
18. $y = -4.46x - 4$, $y = 2.46x - 4$
19. $4x - y - 4 = 0$ 20. $y = -3x \pm 12$

Cumulative Review (Chapters 5-7), page 258

1. a) 15 b) 63 c) −0.8 2. 16.3 kg
3. a) m: 18, 38.7; c: 10, 12.25
b) t: 36, 51.8; y: 24, 3.6
4. 16.6 cm 5. a) 8, 4.5 b) 24%
6. a) $a = \frac{40}{7}, b = \frac{30}{7}$ b) $a = \frac{60}{7}, b = \frac{21}{4}$
7. 1.25 L, 2.08 L

8. a) $x = 8.4, y = 16.7$ b) $x = 3.2, y = 5.1$
9. 12 m
10. a) i) $2\sqrt{2}$ ii) (5, 2)
b) i) $\sqrt{61}$ ii) (2, −0.5)
c) i) $2\sqrt{10}$ ii) (−6, −5)
12. 2 : 1 **13.** (−1.67, −1.33) or (−2.33, −0.67)
14. a) Yes b) Yes c) No
15.

	Slope	x-intercept	y-intercept
a)	$-\frac{3}{4}$	−4	−3
b)	$-\frac{1}{3}$	−5	$-\frac{5}{3}$
c)	0	—	3
d)	Undefined	−2	—

16. a) $3x - y - 3 = 0$ b) $2x + 3y - 26 = 0$
c) $2x + 5y - 20 = 0$ d) $4x - y - 24 = 0$
17. a) (4, 2), 5 b) (−3, 5), 4
18. a) $x^2 + y^2 = 100$ b) $(x - 3)^2 + (y - 7)^2 = 49$
c) $(x + 2)^2 + (y - 5)^2 = 121$
19. a) $(x + 4)^2 + (y + 4)^2 = 32$ b) Outside
20. 12 **21.** $2x - y + 10 = 0$
23. a) $\sqrt{51}$ b) $2\sqrt{153}$ c) 9.7
24. a) (−1, 2) b) − **25.** Answers will vary.
26. a) (−7, 0) b) (5, 2) c) (−2, −3)
d) $(\frac{1}{2}, 4, -3)$
27. 32 cars, 17 trucks **28.** 6
29. a) (2, 4) and (−2, −4) b) (−3, 5) and (2, 0)
30. a) (−5, −2) and (2, 5) b) (4, 6) and $(-\frac{9}{4}, \frac{21}{16})$
31. a) 12 and 2, 2 and −12
32. a) $y = -10x - 2$ and $y = -2x - 2$
b) $y = -\sqrt{3}x - 2$ and $y = \sqrt{3}x - 2$
33. a) $4y - 12x - 31 = 0$
b) $y = 3x + 10$ and $y = 3x - 10$

Chapter 8

Exercises 8-1, page 266

1. a) {(15, 2), (20, 10), (18, 15), (23, 30), (20, 25), (28, 40)}
b) D: {15, 18, 20, 23, 28}; R: {2, 10, 15, 25, 30, 40}
2. a) {(40, 45), (50, 55), (60, 50), (60, 65), (70, 80), (80, 70), (90, 80), (90, 85)}
b) D: {40, 50, 60, 70, 80, 90};
R: {45, 50, 55, 65, 70, 80, 85}
3. a) {(Craig, Colin), (Craig, Gayle), (Colin, Craig), (Colin, Gayle)}
b) D: {Craig, Colin}, R: {Craig, Colin, Gayle}
4. b) D(men, women): {100, 200, 400, 800, 1500}
R(men): {10, 20, 44, 102, 212},
R(women): {11, 22, 49, 115, 236}
5. b) D: {145, 150, 155, 160, 165, 170, 175, 180, 185}
R: {46, 48, 50, 53, 56, 60, 63, 67, 71}
6. a) D: {−2, −1, 1, 2, 3, 4}; R: {1, −1, 2, −2, 3, 0}
b) D: {−2, −1, 0, 1, 2, 3}; R: {3, 2, 1, 0, −1, −2}
c) $-4 \leqslant x \leqslant 1$; $-1 \leqslant y \leqslant 3$
d) $-3 \leqslant x \leqslant 3$; $-3 \leqslant y \leqslant 2$
e) $-2 \leqslant x \leqslant 2$; $-2 \leqslant y \leqslant 2$
f) $-4 \leqslant x \leqslant 2$; $-2.5 \leqslant y \leqslant 2.5$
7. b) D: {6.1, 8.1, 9.7, 10.3, 12.2, 14.0, 18.1}
R: {4.2, 5.3, 5.5, 7.5, 7.6, 9.1, 12.7}
8. a) {(1,1), (1,2), (1,3), (1,4), (1,5), (1,6), (1,7), (1,8), (1,9), (2,2), (2,4), (2,6), (2,8), (3,3), (3,6), (3,9), (4,4), (4,8), (5,5), (6,6), (7,7), (8,8), (9,9)}
b) D: {1, 2, 3, 4, 5, 6, 7, 8, 9}
R: {1, 2, 3, 4, 5, 6, 7, 8, 9}
9. a) {(Tobie, Lise), (Tobie, Suzette), (Tobie, Urbain), (Tobie, Claire), (Lise, Suzette), (Lise, Urbain), (Lise, Claire), (Suzette, Urbain). (Suzette, Claire), (Urbain, Claire)}
b) D: {Tobie, Lise, Suzette, Urbain}
R: {Lise, Suzette, Urbain, Claire}
10. a) $x \geqslant 0$; $y \geqslant 0$ b) $x \geqslant -1$; $y \geqslant 0$
c) D, R: all real numbers d) $x \neq 0$; $y \neq 0$
e) $x \neq 2$; $y \neq 0$ f) D: all real numbers; $y > 0$
11. a) D:{−1, 0, 1, 2, 3, 5, 6}; R:{−2, −1, 1, 2, 3, 4}
b) D, R: all real numbers
c) $-1 \leqslant x \leqslant 6$; $-1 \leqslant y \leqslant 4$
d) $-3 \leqslant x \leqslant 3$; $-3 \leqslant y \leqslant 3$
e) $x \geqslant -2$; R: all real numbers
f) $-2 \leqslant x \leqslant 6$; R:{−6, −4, −2, 0}
12. a), b), c) D, R: all real numbers
d) D: all real numbers; $y \geq 0$
e) $-5 \leqslant x \leqslant 5$; $-5 \leqslant y \leqslant 5$
f) $-1 \leqslant x \leqslant 1$; $-1 \leqslant y \leqslant 1$
13. b) D: {5, 10, 20, 25, 30}
R: {13:08, 27:23, 57:24, 74:17, 91:30}
14. b) $h \geqslant 0$; $v \geqslant 0$ c) About 11.2 m/s
15. b) Answers will vary. Example:
0 min $\leqslant t \leqslant$ 7 min; 15°C $\leqslant T \leqslant$ 100°C

Exercises 8-2, page 273

1. a) Yes b) No c) Yes
2. a) $x \geqslant 0$; $2 \leqslant y \leqslant 9$ c) $x \neq 0$; $y \neq 0$
3. a) Yes b) No c) Yes
4. a) Yes b) Yes c) Yes d) No
e) No f) Yes g) No h) No i) Yes

5. a) Yes; D, R: all real numbers
b) Yes; D: all real numbers; $y \geqslant -1$
c) No; $x \geqslant 1$; R: all real numbers
6. a) Yes b) $x \geqslant 0; h \geqslant 0$ c) 4.8 m
7. a) $w = 12 - x$ b) $A = 12x - x^2$
c) $l = \sqrt{2x^2 - 24x + 144}$
8. a) $w = \frac{24}{x}$ b) $P = \frac{2x^2 + 48}{x}$ c) $l = \frac{\sqrt{x^4 + 576}}{x}$
9. a) D: all real numbers; $y > 0$
b) $x \geqslant 0; y \geqslant 0$
c) D: all real numbers; $y \geqslant 0$
10. b) $t > 0$
R: {3, 3.50, 4, 4.50, 5, 5.50, 6, 6.50, . . .}
c) Yes. Every ordered pair has a different first coordinate.
11. a) Yes
b) $d > 0$; R: {2.50, 3.50, 4.50, 5.50, . . .}
12. a) $x \geqslant 3; y \geqslant 0$
b), c) D, R: all real numbers
d) $x \neq -2; y \neq 0$
e) D: all real numbers; $y \geqslant 1$
f) D: all real numbers; $y > 0$
13. a) i) $y = \frac{5(100 - x)}{x}$ ii) $y = \frac{5x}{100 - x}$
b) i) $0 < x \leqslant 100; y \geqslant 0$
ii) $0 \leqslant x < 100; y \geqslant 0$
14. a) No b) Yes

Exercises 8-3, page 277

1. a) -3 b) -8 c) 0.75
2. a) 2 b) 14 c) $\frac{1}{2}$
3. a) 6, 9. 0.75 b) -4, 38, -1
4. b) i) D, R: all real numbers ii) $x \geqslant 1; y \geqslant 0$
5. a) 2, 4, 2 b) -1.5, 3, 1 c) 2, -1, 2
6. a) $3m - 5$ b) $12x - 5$ c) $6x - 10$
d) $\frac{6}{x} - 5$ e) $6x - 2$
7. a) $5k + 1$ b) $5x - 4$
c) $10x + 6$ d) $21 - 15x$
8. a) 1, -27, -5 b) 25, 186, -6.5
c) $\sqrt{11}, \sqrt{-31}, \sqrt{2}$ d) $\frac{9}{2}, 24\frac{4}{5}, 2\frac{1}{4}$
e) 4, -150, -0.125 f) $\frac{8}{5}, \frac{20}{9}, 1$
9. a) D, R: all real numbers
b) D: all real numbers; $y \geqslant 1$
c) D: all real numbers; $y \geqslant -2.25$
11. a) $x \geqslant -5; y \geqslant 0$ b) $x \neq -2; y \neq 0$
c) D, R: all real numbers
d) D: all real numbers; $y \geqslant 3$
e) D, R: all real numbers
f) $x \geqslant 0, y \geq 1$

12. a) $2x^2 + 7x$ b) $2x^2 + 11x + 9$
c) $2x^2 + 15x + 22$ d) $8x^2 + 6x - 5$
e) $18x^2 + 9x - 5$ f) $2x^2 - 3x - 5$
13. a) $-2x - 9$ b) $11x + 3$ c) $15x^2 + 11x - 14$
d) $2x - 22$ e) $-4x - 9$ f) $48x + 8$
14. a) $x \geqslant 0; A \geqslant 0$
b) It is quadrupled.
c) $\frac{\sqrt{3}}{4}(6x + 9)$ d) $\frac{\sqrt{3}}{4}(h^2 - 2hx)$
15. a) $\frac{4}{7}$ b) $\frac{2}{7}$ c) -6 d) $-\frac{1}{2}$ or -1
16. a) 1 b) -6 c) $-\frac{3}{2}$
17. a) $-5, 2$ b) $-6, 3$ c) $-4, 1$
19. a) 1 b) 1 c) $n \in R, n \neq 0, -1$
20. b) $[g(x)]^n$ **21.** b) $f(x) = 3x$
22. b) i) Primes ii) Squares of primes
iii) Products of primes, or cubes of primes
iv) 4th powers of primes

Exercises 8-4, page 282

1. a,b,d **3.** b) $h = -300t + 10\,000$
4. b) 58°C **5.** a) C b) A c) B
6. b) $t = -6.5h + 15$ c) i) -30.5°C ii) 2.3
7. a) $y \doteq 0.67x$ b) 2.0 m c) 4.5 m
d) Possibly $1.0 \leqslant x \leqslant 5.0$
8. a) $l = 12 - w$ b) $0 < w < 12$
9. a) $y = x + 90; 0 < x < 90$
b) $y = 230 - x; 0 < x < 180$
c) $y = 180 - 2x; 0 < x < 90$
10. **11.**

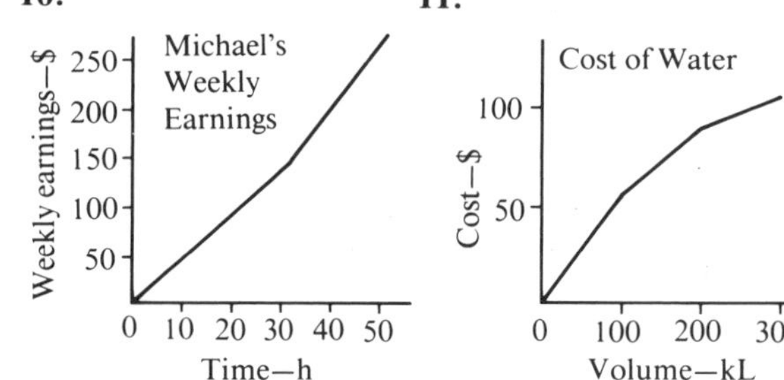

12. b) Yes c) 10 L/100 km
13. b) i) 58 L ii) 762 L
c) i) 8.2 L/100 km ii) 884 km
d) $0 \leqslant d \leqslant 884; 0 \leqslant n \leqslant 72.5$
14.

	a)	b)	c)	d)	e)	f)
m	$\frac{2}{5}$	$-\frac{4}{3}$	-2	3	-4	$-\frac{4}{7}$
b	7	10	4	-6	0	$\frac{37}{7}$

15. a) $h = 3l + 70$ b) 185 cm

16. a)

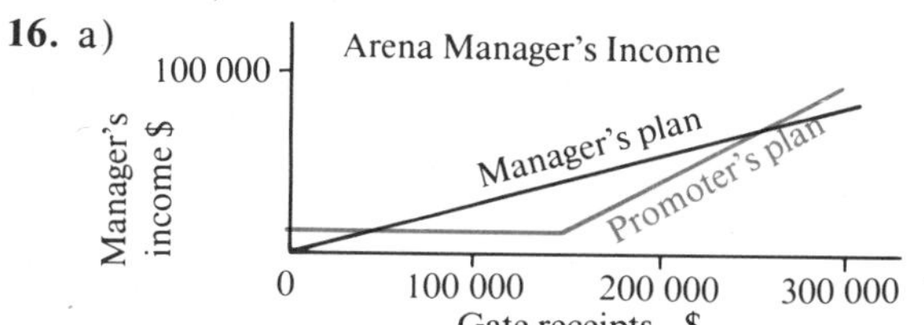

b) For gate receipts between \$40 000 and \$260 000.

17. a) $x + y = 8$ b) $2 < x < 8$

18. a) $\frac{8\pi}{3}R$ b) $3\pi R$

MAU

1. $D = 22S - 190$ **2.** a) About 77 million years b) About 2.2 cm/year

Exercises 8-5, page 289

1. a) Yes b) No c) Yes d) Yes e) Yes f) No

2. b) D: all real numbers; $y \geqslant 5$

3. b) D: all real numbers; $y \geqslant -7$

4. b) $t \geqslant 0$; $0 \leqslant h \leqslant 82$ c) 51.4 m

5. b) 42.5 cm

6. a) D: all real numbers; $f(x) \geqslant 0.5$
b) D: all real numbers; $g(t) \leqslant 5$

7. b) 289.2 m/s, 13 068 m

8. a) 593.5 m b) 11.5 s

9. a) Height is quadrupled.
b) Height is multiplied by 9.

10. a) $A = \pi x^2 - 20x\pi + 100\pi$
c) $0 < x < 10$

11. a) $A = (16 - 4\pi)r^2$ b) $A = (2\sqrt{2} - 1)\pi r^2$

12. 2 min, 8.5 h, 9 days, 15 years

13. a) $k \doteq 1.56$ b) 66 m

Exercises 8-6, page 292

1. b) The vertex is on the y-axis. When q is positive, the vertex is q units above the x-axis. When q is negative, it is q units below the x-axis.

2. a) iii b) iv c) ii d) i

3. a) $y = x^2 + 5$ b) $y = x^2$ c) $y = x^2 - 2$ d) $y = x^2 - 6$

4. a) i) up ii) (0, 1) iii) 1 iv) —
b) i) up ii) (0, −4) iii) −4 iv) ±2
c) i) up ii) (0, 2) iii) 2 iv) —
d) i) up ii) (0, −6) iii) −6 iv) ±2.5

5. a) i) up ii) (0, 5) iii) 5 iv) —
b) i) up ii) (0, −3) iii) −3 iv) ±1.7
c) i) up ii) (0, 2) iii) 2 iv) —
d) i) up ii) (0, 4) iii) 4 iv) —

7. a) $y = x^2 + 2$ b) $y = x^2 - 9$ c) $y = x^2 + 5$

Exercises 8-7, page 296

2. a) When $p < 0$, the graph of $y = (x - p)^2$ is to the left of that of $y = x^2$.
b) When $p > 0$, the graph of $y = (x - p)^2$ is to the right of that of $y = x^2$.

3. a) iii b) i c) iv d) ii

4. a) $y = (x + 2)^2$ b) $y = (x - 3)^2$ c) $y = (x + 4)^2$ d) $y = (x - 5)^2$

5. a) i) (−2. 0) ii) $x + 2 = 0$ iii) up, iv) 4
b) i) (−1, 0) ii) $x + 1 = 0$ iii) up iv) 1
c) i) (3, 0) ii) $x - 3 = 0$ iii) up, iv) 9
d) i) (4, 0) ii) $x - 4 = 0$ iii) up iv) 16

6. a) $y = (x + 2)^2$ b) $y = (x + 1)^2$ c) $y = (x - 3)^2$ d) $y = (x - 4)^2$

7. a) i) (−3, 0) ii) $x + 3 = 0$ iii) up iv) 9
b) i) (8, 0) ii) $x - 8 = 0$ iii) up iv) 64
c) i) (2, 0) ii) $x - 2 = 0$ iii) up iv) 4
d) i) (−4, 0) ii) $x + 4 = 0$ iii) up iv) 16

10. a) $y = (x - 4)^2$ b) $y = (x + 3)^2$ c) $y = (x - 7)^2$

11. a) c)

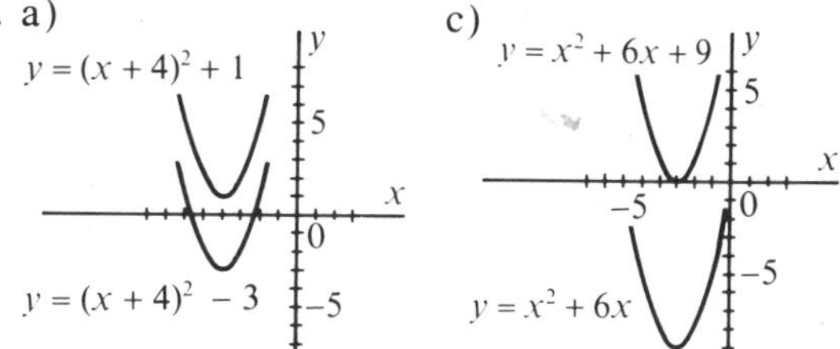

CP

2. a)	PARABOLA	2	0	0
b)	PARABOLA	−1	0	0
c)	PARABOLA	1	0	−16
d)	PARABOLA	3	2	−20
e)	PARABOLA	1	−2	0
f)	PARABOLA	−4	2	20
3. b)	PARABOLA	1	0	20
	PARABOLA	1	0	10
	PARABOLA	1	0	0
	PARABOLA	1	0	−10
	PARABOLA	1	0	−20

Exercises 8-8, page 301

1. b) The parabola is stretched more:
i) as a increases when $a > 0$;
ii) as a decreases when $a < 0$.

2. a) iii b) ii c) i d) iv

4. a) $y = 2x^2$ b) $y = -x^2$ c) $y = -\frac{1}{4}x^2$ d) $y = 6x^2$

5. a) $y = -2.5x^2$ b) $y = \frac{5}{9}x^2$ c) $y = \frac{4}{27}x^2$
d) $y = -3x^2$

6. $y = \frac{3}{4}x^2$

Exercises 8-9, page 304

1. a) i b) iii c) iv d) ii

3. a) i) (2, –1) ii) $x - 2 = 0$ iii) 3 iv) 1, 3
b) i) (–5, 9) ii) $x + 5 = 0$ iii) –16 iv) –2, –8
c) i) (1, –4) ii) $x - 1 = 0$ iii) –3 iv) –1, 3
d) i) (6, 16) ii) $x - 6 = 0$ iii) –20 iv) 2, 10

4. a) $y = (x - 2)^2 - 1$ b) $y = -(x + 5)^2 + 9$
c) $y = (x - 1)^2 - 4$ d) $y = -(x - 6)^2 + 16$

5. a) i) (5, 2) ii) $x - 5 = 0$ iii) 27 iv) —
b) i) (–3, –8) ii) $x + 3 = 0$ iii) 10
iv) –1, –5
c) i) (–1, 4) ii) $x + 1 = 0$ iii) 0 iv) 0, –2
d) i) (2, –8) ii) $x - 2 = 0$ iii) –6 iv) 6, –2

7. a) i) (–2, –5) ii) $x + 2 = 0$ iii) (0, –1), (–4, –1)
b) i) (3, 2) ii) $x - 3 = 0$ iii) (0, –7), (6, –7)
c) i) (4, –1) ii) $x - 4 = 0$ iii) (0, –9), (8, –9)
d) i) (–1, 4) ii) $x + 1 = 0$ iii) (0, 6), (–2, 6)
e) i) (1, 3) ii) $x - 1 = 0$ iii) (0, 1), (2, 1)
f) i) (5, –10) ii) $x - 5 = 0$ iii) (0, 90), (10, 90)

9. a) $y = 2(x - 4)^2 - 1$ b) $y = -\frac{1}{3}(x + 2)^2 + 3$
c) $y = -\frac{1}{2}(x + 3)^2 + 2$ d) $y = (x - 3)^2 - 4$

10. a) $y = (x - 3)^2 - 1$ b) $y = -2(x + 1)^2 + 4$
c) $y = 3(x - 2)^2 - 27$

12. a) $y = x^2 + 5$ b) $y = -\frac{1}{2}x^2 + 3$

Exercises 8-10, page 308

1. a) $y = (x - 3)^2 - 1$ b) $y = (x + 5)^2 - 11$
c) $y = 2(x + 1)^2 + 5$ d) $y = -2(x - 1)^2 + 7$
e) $y = 3(x - 4)^2 - 8$ f) $y = -5(x + 2)^2 - 10$

3. a) i) (3, 1) ii) $x - 3 = 0$ iii) (0, 10), (6, 10)
b) i) (–2, –1) ii) $x + 2 = 0$ iii) (0, 7), (–4, 7)
c) i) (5, 12) ii) $x - 5 = 0$
iii) (0, –13), (10, –13)
d) i) (1, 5) ii) $t - 1 = 0$ iii) (0, 8), (2, 8)
e) i) (–3, 16) ii) $n + 3 = 0$
iii) (0, –20), (–6, –20)
f) i) (–4, –3) ii) $v + 4 = 0$
iii) (0, –35), (–8, –35)

4. a) i) (2, 5) ii) $x - 2 = 0$ iii) (0, 7), (4, 7)
b) i) $\left(-\frac{3}{2}, -14\right)$ ii) $t + \frac{3}{2} = 0$
iii) (0, –14), (–3, –14)
c) i) $\left(\frac{7}{2}, \frac{25}{2}\right)$ ii) $j - \frac{7}{2} = 0$
iii) (0, –12), (7, –12)
d) i) $\left(\frac{2}{3}, -\frac{22}{3}\right)$ ii) $x - \frac{2}{3} = 0$ iii) (0, –6), $\left(\frac{4}{3}, -6\right)$
e) i) $\left(\frac{5}{4}, -\frac{3}{4}\right)$ ii) $v - \frac{5}{4} = 0$ iii) (0, –7), $\left(\frac{5}{2}, -7\right)$

5. a) i) –3 ii) $\left(\frac{5}{4}, -\frac{49}{8}\right)$ iii) $\left(\frac{5}{2}, -3\right)$, (1, –6)
b) i) –18 ii) $\left(\frac{9}{4}, -\frac{225}{8}\right)$ iii) $\left(\frac{9}{2}, -18\right)$, (1, –25)
c) i) 2.5 ii) $\left(-\frac{5}{2}, 0\right)$ iii) (–5, 2.5), (1, 4.9)
d) i) 0 ii) $\left(\frac{5}{4}, \frac{25}{8}\right)$ iii) $\left(\frac{5}{2}, 0\right)$, (1, 3)
e) i) 8 ii) $\left(\frac{7}{3}, -\frac{25}{3}\right)$ iii) $\left(\frac{14}{3}, 8\right)$, (1, –3)

6. a) $y = a\left(x + \frac{b}{2a}\right)^2 + \left(\frac{4ac - b^2}{4a}\right)$
b) $\left(-\frac{b}{2a}, \frac{4ac - b^2}{4a}\right)$, $x + \frac{b}{2a} = 0$, c

Exercises 8-11, page 312

1. a) Max., –4, 3 b) Min., –1, –2
c) Min., –1, –2 d) Max., 2, –3
e) Min., –12, 9 f) Max., 3, 2

2. a) 5, min., 3 b) –3, min., –1
c) 4, max., 1 d) –6, max., –2
e) –9, min., 0 f) 7, max., 0

3. a) 5 b) – c) 3 d) 0 e) – f) –4

4. a) $y = 2(x - 2)^2 + 7$
$y = 3(x + 2)^2 - 19$
$y = (x - 3)^2 - 2$
$y = -2(x - 1.5)^2 + 15.5$
$y = -\left(x + \frac{3}{2}\right)^2 - \frac{3}{4}$
$y = 1.5(x - 3)^2 - 3.5$

b) i) 7, min. ii) 2
i) –19, min. ii) –2
i) –2, min. ii) 3
i) 15.5, max. ii) 1.5
i) $-\frac{3}{4}$, max. ii) $-\frac{3}{2}$
i) –3.5, min. ii) 3

5. a) 4.8 m b) 0.6 s c) 1.58 s d) 3 m

6. a) 9 A b) 40.5 W **7.** 16.2 m, 1.8 s

8. a) 40 m b) 1 s c) 3.8 s d) 35 m
e) $h = -5t^2 + 10t$

9. 250 km/h

10. b) 50 km/h
c) $20 \leqslant v \leqslant 120$; $38 \leqslant C \leqslant 136$

11. a) 50 b) $99 000 000

12. a) 1655 m b) 18.4 s c) 36.7 s

13. $b = \pm 2\sqrt{ac}$, $a > 0$

Exercises 8-12, page 317

1. 4, –4 **2.** 6, 6 **3.** 30, 30 **4.** 10, – 10
5. 8, 8 **6.** 14, 14 **7.** 9, 3
8. 7, –9 **9.** 150 m by 300 m **10.** 5000 m^2
11. a) 400 m^2 b) 20 m by 20 m
12. 100 m by 150 m **13.** $15
14. 70¢ **15.** 12.5 cm **16.** 28.125 cm^2
17. 300 m by 200 m **18.** 14.1 cm, 15.9 cm
19. $\frac{1}{2}$ **20.** $\frac{p^2}{16}$ units^2 **22.** 3.33

Review Exercises, page 319

1. a) D, R: all real numbers b) $x \geqslant 0.5$; $y \geqslant 0$
c) D: all real numbers; $y \geq 0$
2. a) D: $\{-3, -2, -1, 0, 2, 3, 4, 6\}$
R: $\{-1, 1, 2, 3, 4, 5\}$
b) $x \geqslant -1$; $y \geqslant 1$ c) $-5 \leqslant x \leqslant 5$; $-3 \leqslant y \leqslant 3$
3. a) Yes b) D: $\{d|d > 0\}$, R: $\{A|A > 0\}$
c) 20 cm
4. a) $x \geqslant -2$; $y \geqslant 0$ b), c) D, R: all real numbers
d) $x \neq 1$; $y \neq 0$ e) D: all real numbers; $y \leqslant 1$
f) D: all real numbers; $y > 0$
5. a) $3x^2 + 2x + 8$ b) $12x^2 - 20x + 12$
c) $27x^2 - 30x + 12$
6. a) $\frac{1}{2}$ b) $-\frac{1}{4}$ c) $-\frac{10}{17}$ d) 1, or −2
7. a) 2, or −7 b) −2, or −3 c) 3, or −8
9. a) $\frac{3}{5}$, 11 b) −1, 3 c) $\frac{2}{3}, \frac{10}{3}$ d) −6, 5
10. a) D: all real numbers; $y \geqslant -\frac{64}{3}$
b) D: all real numbers; $y \leqslant \frac{81}{40}$
11. a) 2.78 m b) 3.26 m
12. a) $y = (x + 2)^2$ b) $y = (x - 5)^2$
c) $y = (x + 6)^2$
13. a) $y = 4x^2$ b) $y = -2x^2$ c) $y = \frac{3}{2}x^2$
d) $y = \frac{5}{3}x^2$ e) $y = -\frac{3}{2}x^2$ f) $y = \frac{3}{4}x^2$
g) $y = \frac{4}{5}x^2$ h) $y = -2x^2$
14. a) $y = -(x + 3)^2 + 4$ b) $y = 2(x - 2)^2 - 2$
c) $y = \frac{1}{2}(x - 4)^2 - 4$
15. a) i) (3, −4) ii) $x - 3 = 0$ iii) (0, 5), (6, 5)
b) i) (2, −13) ii) $z - 2 = 0$ iii) (0, −5), (4, −5)
c) i) (−10, −29) ii) $t + 10 = 0$
iii) (0, 21), (−20, 21)
d) i) (3, 7) ii) $q - 3 = 0$
iii) (0, −20), (6, −20)
16. 10, \$40 **17.** 11, −13 **18.** 90¢

Chapter 9

Exercises 9-1, page 324

1. a) Absolute value b) Exponential
c) Square root d) Cubic e) Reciprocal
2. a) Exponential b) Quadratic c) Linear
d) Cubic e) Exponential f) Reciprocal
g) Reciprocal h) Exponential
i) Square root j) Exponential

3. b) i), ii), iii) D: all real numbers; $y > 0$
4. b) $0 \leqslant x \leqslant 2$ i) $0 \leqslant y \leqslant \sqrt{2}$
ii) $0 \leqslant y \leqslant 2^{0.75}$ iii) $0 \leqslant y \leqslant 2$
iv) $0 \leqslant y \leqslant 2^{1.5}$ v) $0 \leqslant y \leqslant 4$
vi) $0 \leqslant x \leqslant 2^{2.5}$
5. None is a function.

Exercises 9-2, page 327

1. a) iv b) ii c) iii **3.** a) i b) iv

Exercises 9-3, page 329

1. a) i b) v c) vi **3.** a) ii b) iii

Exercises 9-4, page 332

1. a) iv b) ii c) vi **3.** a) ii b) iii
8. b) i) Vertical stretch by factor 2, or translation 1 unit left.
ii) Vertical stretch by factor 4, or translation 2 units left.

Exercises 9-5, page 336

1. a) iv b) ii c) vi **3.** a) ii b) iv
6. c **7.** a

Exercises 9-6, page 341

1. a, c
2. a) $y = x - 3$ b) $y = \frac{x + 1}{4}$ c) $y = \frac{1}{2}x$
d) $y = \frac{x + 4}{3}$ e) $y = 2x - 12$ f) $y = \frac{3}{2}(x + 1)$
4. a) Yes b) No c) No d) Yes
5. a) $f(x) = x - 6$ b) $f(x) = \frac{1}{2}x$
c) $f(x) = 3 - x$ d) $f(x) = 2(x + 3)$
e) $f(x) = \frac{x - 1}{5}$ f) $f(x) = \frac{x - 2}{2}$
6. a) No b) No c) Yes d) Yes
7. a) iii b) v c) iv **9.** $f(x) = 2x + 5$

Exercises 9-7, page 344

1. a) $y = \pm\sqrt{x}$ b) $y = \pm\sqrt{x + 1}$
c) $y = \pm\sqrt{x - 3}$ d) $y = \pm\sqrt{\frac{x - 5}{2}}$
e) $y = \pm\sqrt{4x + 8}$ f) $y = \pm\sqrt{4x + 2}$
2. a)

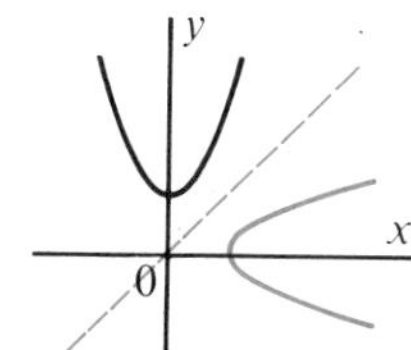

b)

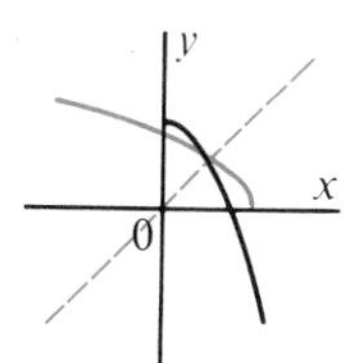

c) 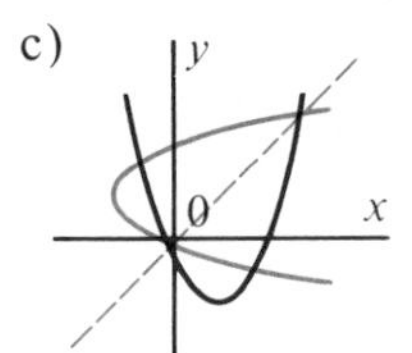

d) 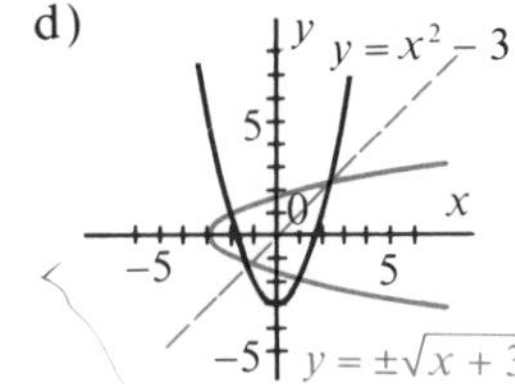

e) 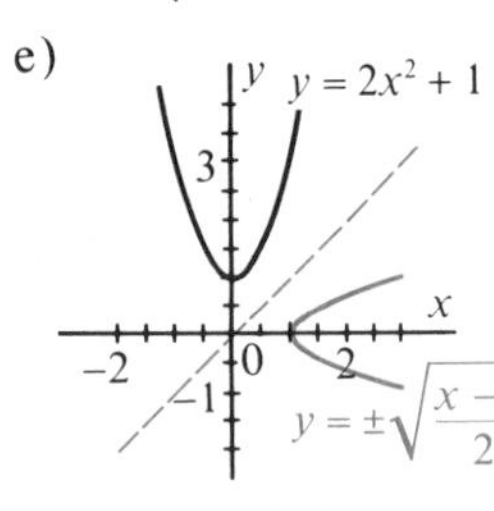

f) 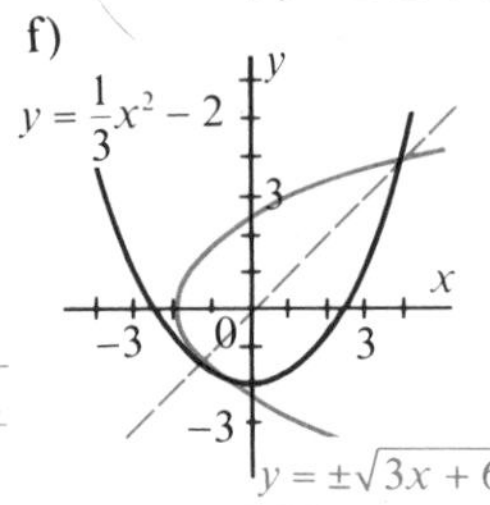

3. a) $f^{-1}(x) = \pm\frac{1}{2}\sqrt{x}$ b) $f^{-1}(x) = \pm\sqrt{1-x}$
c) $f^{-1}(x) = \pm\sqrt{\frac{2-x}{3}}$ d) $f^{-1}(x) = \pm\sqrt{x} - 3$
e) $f^{-1}(x) = \sqrt{\frac{x}{5}} + 2$ f) $f^{-1}(x) = \pm\sqrt{2x+6} - 1$

4. Answers may vary. a), b), e) $x \geqslant 0$
c) $x \geqslant -1$ d) $x \geqslant 2$ f) $x \geqslant 1$

5. a) No b) Yes c) Yes d) No

6. a) ii b) v c) iv

7. a) $y = (x-1)^2, x \geqslant 1$ b) $y = (\frac{3-x}{2})^2, x \leqslant 3$

Review Exercises, page 345

1. b) i), ii) $x \neq 0; y \neq 0$ iii) $x \neq 0, y \neq 1$

2. a) ii b) iii 5. a) iv b) ii

7. a) $f^{-1}(x) = x - 3$ b) $f^{-1}(y) = \frac{y}{3}$
c) $f^{-1}(x) = x - 2$ d) $f^{-1}(x) = 4x - 4$
e) $f^{-1}(y) = \frac{1}{4}(y-3)$ f) $f^{-1}(x) = 2 - \frac{x}{3}$

8. a) Yes b) Yes c) No d) Yes

9. a) $f^{-1}(x) = \pm\frac{1}{3}\sqrt{x}$ b) $f^{-1}(x) = \pm\sqrt{4-x}$
c) $f^{-1}(x) = \pm\frac{1}{2}\sqrt{1-x}$ d) $f^{-1}(x) = \pm\sqrt{x} + 2$
e) $f^{-1}(x) = \pm\sqrt{\frac{x}{3}} + 1$ f) $f^{-1}(x) = \pm\sqrt{3(x-5)} + 2$

10. a) iii b) ii c) v

Cumulative Review (Chapters 8 and 9), page 346

1. a) $-2 \leqslant x \leqslant 6; -2 \leqslant y \leqslant 2$
b) D: all real numbers; $y \geqslant 4$
c) $x \geqslant \frac{4}{3}; y \geqslant 0$
d) $x \neq -3; y \neq 0$

2. b, c

3. a) 42 b) $2x^2 + 3x - 1$ c) $24x^2 - 18x + 17$

4. a) −6, 4 b) −5, 3 c) −7, 5

5. b) $c = 0.7n$
c) i) 10.5 cups ii) 24.5 cups iii) 59 cups
d) 69

6. b) 45

7. b) i) About 3.5 m ii) About 1.8 s
c) Approximately: $0 \leqslant t \leqslant 1.8$; $0 \leqslant h \leqslant 10.4$

9. a) i) $(-7, 0)$ ii) $x + 7 = 0$ iii) Up iv) 147
b) i) $(3,0)$ ii) $x - 3 = 0$ iii) Down iv) −14
c) i) $\left(\frac{1}{2}, -\frac{3}{4}\right)$ ii) $x - \frac{1}{2} = 0$ iii) Down iv) −1
d) i) $(-6, -3)$ ii) $x + 6 = 0$ iii) Up iv) 15

10. a) $y = \frac{7}{4}x^2$ b) $y = 12(x+1)^2 + 4$
c) $y = -3(x+3)^2 - 2$ d) $y = \frac{5}{4}(x-3)^2 - \frac{5}{4}$

11. a) i) (2,3) ii) $x - 2 = 0$ iii) 7 iv) (4, 7)
b) i) (1, 3) ii) $x - 1 = 0$ iii) 5 iv) (2, 5)
c) i) (−8, −21) ii) $x + 8 = 0$ iii) 11
iv) (−16, 11)
d) i) (−2, −2) ii) $x + 2 = 0$ iii) −14
iv) (−4, −14)

12. 5000 m^2

13. a) Reciprocal b) Cubic c) Exponential
d) Absolute value e) Square root

16. a) $y = \frac{x+11}{3}$ b) $y = \frac{5}{3}(1-x)$ c) $f(x) = \frac{7-x}{4}$

18. a) $y = \pm\frac{1}{2}\sqrt{x+9}$ b) $y = 5 \pm \sqrt{x-9}$
c) $f(x) = 7 \pm \sqrt{x+2}$

Chapter 10

Exercises 10-1, page 352

2. a) *K M O* b) *K P V* c) *F B G* d) *D E F*

3. a) 10, 12, 14 b) 81, 243, 729 c) 25, 30, 35
d) 16, 22, 29 e) 1, $\frac{1}{2}$, $\frac{1}{4}$ f) 14, 17, 20
g) 16, −32, 64 h) $\frac{1}{64}$, $\frac{1}{256}$, $\frac{1}{1024}$

4. a) 2, 4, 6, 8, 10 b) 11, 12, 13, 14, 15
c) 3, 6, 9, 12, 15 d) 2, 4, 8, 16, 32
e) 9, 8, 7, 6, 5 f) 1, 2, 3, 4, 5

5. a) $t_n = 2n - 1$ b) $t_n = 5n$ c) $t_n = 5n - 1$
d) $t_n = 10^n$ e) $t_n = \frac{1}{2} \times 10^n$

6. a) 1, 4, 7, 10, 13 b) 1, 3, 7, 15, 31
c) 18, 15, 12, 9, 6 d) 7, 9, 11, 13, 15
e) $\frac{1}{4}, \frac{2}{7}, \frac{3}{10}, \frac{4}{13}, \frac{5}{16}$ f) $2, 2\frac{1}{2}, 2\frac{2}{3}, 2\frac{3}{4}, 2\frac{4}{5}$

7. a) 24, 34 b) 17, 53 c) 11, 76
d) 4, −32 e) $\frac{3}{7}, \frac{6}{13}$ f) $\frac{28}{27}, \frac{82}{81}$

8. a) v b) ii c) vi d) iii

9. a) $t_n = 2n$ b) $t_n = 3 + 2n$ c) $t_n = 2n - 5$
d) $t_n = 2^n$ e) $t_n = 2^n - 1$ f) $t_n = 19 - 3n$
g) $t_n = \frac{n}{2n-1}$ h) $t_n = \frac{n}{n+1}$ i) $t_n = \frac{2n-1}{2n+1}$
j) $t_n = n^2 + 1$

11. a) No b) Yes c) No d) Yes

12. a) $f(x) = x^5, f(x) = x^6$
b) $f(x) = ax^4 + bx^3 + cx^2 + dx + e$
$f(x) = ax^5 + bx^4 + cx^3 + dx^2 + ex + f$

13. a) 3, 4, 5 b) $t_n = n - 3$

14. a) 120°, 128.57°, 135° b) $t_n = \frac{180(n-2)}{n}$

15. a) 3, 7, 15, 31
b) $t_n = 2^{n+1} - 1$, where n is the number of squares.

Exercises 10-2, page 357

1. a) No b) Yes, 3 c) Yes, −1 d) No
e) Yes, 0 f) Yes, 8

2. a) 3; 13, 16, 19 b) 4; 11, 15, 19
c) −2; 8, 6, 4 d) −6; −26, −32, −38
e) 5; 22, 27, 32 f) −3; −6, −9, −12

3. a) 2, 5, 8, 11, 14 b) 7, 11, 15, 19, 23
c) −1, −4, −7, −10, −13 d) 12, 8, 4, 0, −4
e) −8, −3, 2, 7, 12 f) 25, 20, 15, 10, 5

4. a) 17 b) 51 c) $1 + 2n$

5. a) −4 b) −46 c) $14 - 3n$

6. a) 39 million and 13 million years ago.
b) 13 million years from now.

7. a) No; Yes.
b) 24th term in sequence: 1896, 1900, 1904,...

8. a) ii b) iv c) i d) v

9. a) 3, 10, 17, 24, 31 b) −3, 1, 5, 9, 13
c) 5, 7, 9, 11, 13 d) 16, 11, 6, 1, −4
e) −4, −1, 2, 5, 8 f) −10, −14, −18, −22, −26

10. a) 71, 104 b) t_{51} **11.** a) 72, 202 b) t_{67}

12. a) $t_n = 4n - 3$; 65 b) $t_n = 3n$; 63
c) $t_n = 5n - 9$; 56 d) $t_n = 47 - 6n$; −61
e) $t_n = 1 - 3n$; −29 f) $t_n = 17 - 8n$; −351

13. −3, 4, 11, 18,... **14.** 7, 11, 15 **15.** 87, 81, 75

16. 3, 8, 13,... **17.** 4, 11, 18,...

18. a) 24 b) 37 c) 20 d) 25 e) 32
f) 56

19. a) 2, 23, 30 b) 20, 14, −4 c) 17, 27, 32
d) 10, 17, 31 e) 8, 0, −4 f) 6, −3, −12

20. $\frac{10}{3}$ **21.** $5x - 8y = -1$ **22.** 29 **23.** Yes

24. 10 or −2

25. a) $t_n = (2n-1)(3n-2)$; No b) $t_n = 6n^2$; No
c) $t_n = \frac{n}{2n+1}$; No d) $t_n = \frac{(2n-1)(2n+1)}{2n(2n+2)}$; No

26. a) 4 b) 3 c) 1 d) 2

27. a) 3, 6, 11, 14, 19, 22, 27, 30, 35, 38
b) i) 3 ii) 4 iii) 3 iv) 3

CP

1. 5, 11, 17, 23, 29; 41, 47, 53, 59; 61, 67, 73, 79

3. 7, 157, 307, 457, 607, 757, 907

4. a) 5, 7 11, 13 17, 19; 17, 19 29, 31 41, 43
b) $a = 41, 43$ $d = 420$ 6 terms

5. 276 615 587 107

6. $2 \times 3^2 \times 5 \times 7 \times 11^2 \times 13 \times 17 \times 19 \times 31$

Exercises 10-3, page 364

1. a) Yes; 2 b) No c) Yes; $-\frac{1}{2}$
d) Yes; 0.1 e) No f) Yes; $-\frac{1}{3}$

2. a) 3; 81, 243, 729 b) −3; 405, −1215, 3645
c) 2; 48, 96, 192 d) $\frac{1}{3}$; $\frac{2}{27}, \frac{2}{81}, \frac{2}{243}$
e) $\frac{1}{4}$; $\frac{9}{64}, \frac{9}{256}, \frac{9}{1024}$ f) −4; 128, −512, 2048

3. a) 2, 6, 18, 54, 162 b) 5, 10, 20, 40, 80
c) 3, −15, 75, −375, 1875 d) 60, 30, 15, $\frac{15}{2}, \frac{15}{4}$
e) −4, 8, −16, 32, −64 f) 8, 24, 72, 216, 648

4. a) 96 b) 3072 c) $3(2)^{n-1}$

5. a) ii b) iv c) iii d) vi

6. a) No b) Yes c) No d) Yes

7. a) 2, −6, 18, −54, 162 b) 20, 10, 5, $\frac{5}{2}, \frac{5}{4}$
c) 3, 6, 12, 24, 48 d) 7, 21, 63, 189, 567
e) $\frac{1}{8}, \frac{1}{2}$, 2, 8, 32 f) −2, 10, −50, 250, −1250

8. a) $t_n = 2^n$; 1024 b) $t_n = 5(2)^{n-1}$; 20 480
c) $t_n = -3(-5)^{n-1}$; 234 375
d) $t_n = 12\left(\frac{1}{2}\right)^{n-1}$; 0.005 86
e) $t_n = 6\left(-\frac{1}{3}\right)^{n-1}$; 0.000 914 5
f) $t_n = 3(6)^{n-1}$; 139 968

9. a) 196 608 b) t_7 **10.** 2, ±6, 18, ±54, 162

11. 24 576, 12 288, 6144, 3072

12. a) ±8, ±32 b) 72, 432 c) ±6, ±24
d) ±1, ±25 e) 8, 4 f) 15, 75

13. $\frac{5}{4}$, 5, 20, 80,... **14.** ±3; ±6, 18, ±54

15. a) 6 b) 8 c) 11 d) 15 e) 9 f) 7

16. $\frac{1}{3}$ or 5 **17.** −1 or −6 **18.** 22.8 million

19. $\frac{9}{5}, \frac{6}{5}, \frac{4}{5}, \frac{8}{15}$; 9, −6, 4, $-\frac{8}{3}$ **20.** 1, 3, 9, 27, 81,...

21. 1, −2, 4, −8,...; $\frac{3}{7}, \frac{6}{7}, \frac{12}{7}, \frac{24}{7}$,...

22. 1, 3, 9, . . . ; 9, 3, 1, . . .

23. 1.41 **24.** b) t_{22}

Exercises 10-4, page 369

2. Sequence: a, e; Series: b, c, d, f

3. a) 4 b) 14 c) 16 d) −6

4. a) 4 b) 24 c) 40 d) −6
5. a) 3 + 3 + 3 + 3 + 3 b) 1 + 5 + 9 + 13 + 17
c) −2 + 0 + 2 + 4 + 6 d) 3 + 5 + 5 + 5 + 5
e) 3 + 5 + 7 + 9 + 11 f) 13 − 6 − 10 − 14 − 18
6. a) iii b) i c) v d) iv
7. a) i) $n^2 - n$ ii) $2n$
b) i) $3n^2 - 11n + 8$ ii) $6n - 8$
c) i) $2^{n-1} - 1$ ii) 2^{n-1}
d) i) $2n^2 - 7n + 5$ ii) $4n - 5$
e) i) $2(3^{n-1} - 1)$ ii) $4(3^{n-1})$
f) i) $n^2 - 6n + 5$ ii) $2n - 5$
8. $a + a + a + \ldots$
9. a) v b) iii c) vi d) i
10. a) $(n-1)^2 - 1$ b) $2^n - 1$ c) $2 - \frac{1}{2^{n-1}}$ d) n^3
11. a) i) $(n+1)^2 - 1$ ii) $(n+2)^2 - 4$
iii) $(n+3)^2 - 9$ b) $(n+4)^2 - 16$

MM

1\. a) 2. a) 3. a)

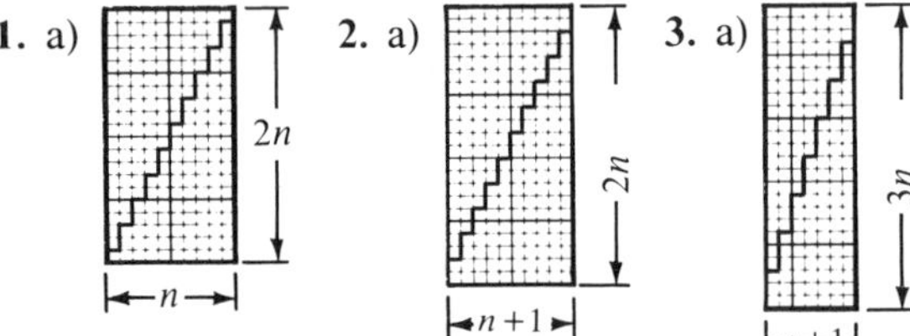

b) $S_n = n^2$ b) $S_n = n(n+1)$ b) $S_n = \frac{3n(n+1)}{2}$

Exercises 10-5, page 375

1. a) 210 b) 365 c) 290 d) 180
e) 600 f) −60
2. a) 276 b) 375 c) 552 d) 1020
3. a) ii b) vi c) v d) iii
4. a) 104 b) 2750
5. a) 345 b) 15 c) −2670
6. Job *A* **7.** 68 **8.** $975
9. a) 893 b) 598 c) 3604 d) −400
10. 3 + 10 + 17 + . . . **11.** 2 + 6 + 10 + . . .
12. 28 + 25 + 22 + . . . **13.** 1.5, 405
14. 3 + 7 + 11 + . . . **15.** 21
16. a) $n^2 + n$ b) n^2
17. a) i) 79; $4n - 1$ ii) 820; $2n^2 + n$
b) i) 125 ii) 15
18. a) $n^2 + 4n$ b) $3n^2 - 11n$ c) $2n^2 + 3n$
d) $\frac{5n^2 + n}{2}$ e) $\frac{21n - 3n^2}{2}$ f) $\frac{7n^2 + 15n}{2}$
19. b) $21 + 23 + 25 + 27 + 29 = 5^3$ c) $n^2 - n + 1$
20. b) $\frac{n^2 - n + 2}{2}$ c) $\frac{n(n^2 + 1)}{2}$ d) $t_n = \frac{n(n^2 + 1)}{2}$

MM

1. a) 55 b) 210 c) 465 d) 820
2. Yes **3.** Yes

Exercises 10-6, page 381

1. a) 63 b) 1092 c) 682 d) 77.5
2. a) 1562 b) 484 c) 93 d) 46.5
e) 605 f) 186
3. a) iv b) vi c) ii d) v
4. a) 0.093 75 b) 11.906 25
5. a) 1458 b) 2184
6. a) i) 8190 ii) 65 534 b) $2(2^n - 1)$
7. 397 mg **8.** 63 **9.** $10 737 418.23
10. a) 2186 b) 3906 c) 1533 d) $9841.\overline{3}$
e) 27 305 f) 63.875
11. 9
12. 2 + 10 + 50 + . . . or 72 − 60 + 50 − . . .
13. 2, 381; or −3, 1641
14. 3 + 15 + 75 + . . ., or 75 + 15 + 3 + . . .
15. a) $3^n - 1$ b) $5(2^n - 1)$ c) $4^n - 1$
d) $4(2^n - 1)$
17. 2047

MM

1. a) 65 536 : 17 b) 1 048 576 : 21
3. 1.21×10^{24} : 81

Exercises 10-7, page 387

1. a) 4 + 5 + 6 + 7 + 8 b) 5 + 9 + 13 + 17
c) 2 + 4 + 6 + 8 + 10 + 12
d) −5 + (−2) + 1 + 4 + 7
e) 7 + 5 + 3 + 1 + (−1) + (−3) + (−5)
f) −7 + (−2) + 3 + 8
2. a) $\sum_{k=1}^{7}(3k - 1)$ b) $\sum_{k=1}^{6}(2k + 1)$ c) $\sum_{k=1}^{6}(4k - 3)$
d) $\sum_{k=1}^{4}(30 - 6k)$ e) $\sum_{k=1}^{8}(6k - 4)$
f) $\sum_{k=1}^{7}(19 - 4k)$
3. a) iv b) ii c) iii d) vi
4. a) 192 b) 20 c) 210
5. a) 762 b) 252 c) 1092
6. a) −1 + 0 + 3 + 8 + 15
b) 4 + 7 + 12 + 19 + 28 + 39 + 52
c) 0 + 11 + 28 + 51
d) −3 + (−2) + 3 + 12 + 25 + 42
e) 2 + 2 + 0 + (−4) + (−10)
f) 4 + 12 + 22 + 34 + 48 + 64 + 82
7. a) $\sum_{k=1}^{n}(3k - 1)$ b) $\sum_{k=1}^{n}(23 - 5k)$ c) $\sum_{i=1}^{16}(6i - 3)$
d) $\sum_{k=1}^{12}(4k - 2)$ e) $\sum_{i=1}^{7}2(3)^{i-1}$ f) $\sum_{i=1}^{9}3(2)^{i-1}$
8. a) $a + a^2 + a^3 + a^4$ b) $a + 2a^2 + 3a^3 + 4a^4$
c) $a + 4a + 27a + 256a$
d) $-a + 4a^2 - 27a^3 + 256a^4$

9. a) $\sum_{i=1}^{5} 3i$ b) $\sum_{i=1}^{6} 2^i$ c) $\sum_{k=1}^{5} \frac{1}{k}$ d) $\sum_{k=1}^{5} -3(-2)^{k-1}$

10. a) 338 b) 180 c) 363

11. a) 62 b) 2728 c) $\frac{31}{16}$

12. a) $\sum_{k=1}^{n} k$ b) $\sum_{k=1}^{n} k^2$ c) $\sum_{k=1}^{n} k^k$ d) $\sum_{k=1}^{n} 3(2)^{k-1}$

13. a) −1 b) 0

14. $\sum_{k=1}^{n} [a + (k-1)d]$ b) $\sum_{k=1}^{n} ar^{k-1}$

Review Exercises, page 389

1. a) 4, 7, 10, 13, b) 0, 1, 4, 9 c) 3, 16, 39, 72
d) $-\frac{1}{2}, 0, \frac{1}{4}, \frac{2}{5}$

2. a) 23, 58 b) 29, 1021 c) $\frac{3}{8}, \frac{8}{23}$ (d) 2, −54

3. a) 2, 9, 16, 23 b) 1, 3, 9, 27 c) 21, 17, 13, 9
d) −2, −10, −50, −250

4. a) Arithmetic, −4 b) Geometric, 2
c) Geometric, $-\frac{1}{2}$ d) Arithmetic, 8

5. a) $4n - 2$ b) $2(3)^{n-1}$ c) n^3 d) $n + \frac{n}{n+1}$

6. a) $t_n = 7n - 5$ b) $t_n = 2(4)^{n-1}$ c) $t_n = 5^{n-1}$
d) $t_n = 24 - 5n$

7. 14, 20 b) 32, 128 **8.** a) −7 b) $\frac{16}{125}$

9. a) 29 b) 81 c) $1 + 4n$

10. 11.5, $26.5 - 1.5n$

11. a) 2916 b) $4(3)^{14}$ c) $4(3)^{n-1}$

12. 15 552, $2(6)^{n-1}$

13. a) 7 b) 29 c) 22 d) 9

14. 19 **15.** 153

16. 25, 22, 19,...

17. 2, 10, 50, 250,...

18. 61 **19.** 3, 6, 12, 24,...

20. Arithmetic: *a*, *e*; Geometric: *c*, *d*; Other: *b*, *f*

21. a) 8 b) 23 c) −7

22. a) 2 + 2 + 2 + 2 b) 3 + 5 + 7 + 9
c) 4 + 3 + 3 + 3 d) 1 + 5 + 9 + 13

23. a) 40, $\frac{1}{2}(3n^2 + n)$ b) −10, $\frac{1}{2}(31n - 7n^2)$
c) 70, $2n^2 + 4n$ d) 155, $5(2^n - 1)$
e) 23.25, $24\left(1 - \frac{1}{2^n}\right)$ f) 242, $3^n - 1$

24. a) 33 b) 432 **25.** a) 128 b) $2^{21} - 1$

26. 12 **27.** 8

28. a) 50 + 56 + 62 +... b) 4110

29. a) 2 + 6 + 18 +... b) $3^{17} - 1$

30. 1380 **31.** $44 089.92

Chapter 11

Exercises 11-1, page 395

3. a) $3.01 b) $389.15 c) 18.9%
d) 249 d e) $3061.88 f) $1.62

4. a) $4.19 b) $14.33 c) $4.26 d) $103.61

5. $138.22 **6.** a) $2191.15 b) $2537.04

8. 81 d **9.** $8\frac{3}{4}$%

10. a) $3.28 b) $4.35 c) $13.67 d) $10.08

11. a) $417.25 b) $419.91 c) $421.69

12. $1630.16, $232.88, $9.70

13. $611.76 **14.** $3301.89 **15.** $23.15

Exercises 11-2, page 399

3. a) $1500.73 b) $2802.21 c) $286.17
d) $1284.11

4. a) $1340.10 b) $1628.89 c) $2182.87

5. a) $201.16 b) $1005.79 c) $5028.93

6. $163 988 **7.** $161 919

8. a) $5412.50 b) $2572.28 c) $15742.39

9. a) i) $400 ii) $1550
b) i) 17 years ii) 9 years c) $3\frac{1}{2}$ years

10. 10 **11.** a) 10.5% b) 8.5%

12. a) $144.73 b) $2019.59 c) $3997.02
d) $1868.54

13. 16.3%. No **14.** 10.4% **15.** 6 years

16. Jan. $452.10, Feb. $1741.91, Mar. $1754.49,
Apr. $2510.65, May $1136.05, Jul. $1339.85

17. a) i) 7 years ii) 5 years b) i) 12% ii) 7%

18. a) $A = 1000(1 + i)^{10}$ c) i) $3900 ii) 11.6%

19. $130 million

Exercises 11-3, page 404

3. a) $256.58 b) $942.93 c) $282.27
d) $1483.17 e) $2209.11

4. a) $7023.31 b) $5549.30 c) $3897.45

5. $2029.64 **6.** $2747.47

7. a) i) $62 ii) $40
b) i) 9 years ii) 5 years c) $2000

8. $12\frac{3}{8}$% **9.** 4 years

10. $2056.48 **11.** $75 305.19

12. a) $1000 = P(1 + i)^n$ c) i) $320 ii) 7.2%

Exercises 11-4, page 408

1. a) $192.53 b) $320.71 c) $376.88
d) $3492.35

2. a) $214.62 b) $1252.54 c) $400.58
d) $4957.29

3. a) \$123.60 b) \$126.83
4. a) \$327.16 b) \$325.57
5. a) \$790.03 b) \$787.26
6. 7.72% **7.** \$1138.12 **8.** \$1432.49
9. a) \$827.78 b) \$801.40
10. a) \$526.60 b) \$442.25 c) \$376.40
11. $12\frac{1}{2}$ years **12.** 15 years 1 month
13. a) 7 years 1 month, 7 years 8 months
b) 6 years 1 month
14. \$473.06 **15.** \$1133.99

Exercises 11-5, page 411

2. a) i) \$109.20 ii) \$109.25
b) i) \$112.63 ii) \$112.50
c) i) \$111.02 ii) \$111.25
3. a) i b) i c) ii d) i
4. a) 8.681% b) 12.625% c) 11.296%
d) 9.925%
5. a) i b) i c) ii
6. a) 16.64%, 13.689% b) 9.381%, 12.962%
7. a) 8.16% b) 12.625% c) 16.075%
d) 9.925%
8. a) i) 13.541 56% ii) 13.175%
b) i) 8.806 13% ii) 8.649%
c) i) 10.237 96% ii) 10.026%
9. a) 6.152% b) 5.830%
10. a) No, 20.428% b) No, 0.047%
11. a) $r = i^2 + 2i$ c) i) 10.25% ii) 8.4%

Exercises 11-6, page 416

1. a) \$3600 b) $4\frac{1}{3}$ years c) \$1450
2. a) i) \$15 000 ii) \$23 000
b) i) \$49 000 ii) \$107 000
c) i) 21% ii) $8\frac{1}{2}$%
4. a) \$4506.13 b) \$3138.90 c) \$312.70
5. \$2257 **6.** \$4607.11 **7.** \$1076.92
8. a) \$1829.45 b) \$3460.35 c) \$4800.81
9. \$215.47 **10.** a) \$416.46 b) \$164.66
11. \$43.46 **12.** \$3799.47
13. \$4199.32 **14.** $10\frac{1}{2}$ **15.** \$1230.17
17. b) i) \$2775 ii) 14 years

Exercises 11-7, page 420

1. a) \$700 b) After $3\frac{1}{2}$ years c) \$280
2. a) i) \$3800 ii) \$2900
b) i) \$4500 ii) \$3200
c) i) 9% ii) 12%
3. a) \$300 b) \$200
5. a) \$3803.84 b) \$1136.59 c) \$1125.55
6. \$2311.44 **7.** \$46 388.64 **8.** \$678.64
9. \$8872.59 **10.** \$147.00 **11.** \$7175.66
12. \$1938.79 **13.** \$1141.14 **14.** 8
15. \$12 435.23

MAU

1. \$4000 + \$4100 + . . . + \$5000 = \$ 49 500
31 × \$5000 = \$155 000
Total: \$204.500
2. An interest rate.
3. At 8% compounded annually: \$63 138.11

Exercises 11-8, page 426

1. a) i) \$138 ii) \$144 iii) \$150
b) i) \$450 ii) \$240 iii) \$170
2. a) 9% b) 7% c) 10% d) 12%
3. 8% **4.** 6.5% **5.** 10.32% **6.** 13%
7. 12% **8.** a) 0.9% b) 11.35%
9. $14\frac{3}{4}$% **10.** 12.683%
11. a) 0.9% b) 11.35%

Exercises 11-9, page 429

1. a) i) \$10 000 ii) $12\frac{3}{4}$% iii) \$1275 iv) 10
b) i) \$6000 ii) 13% iii) \$780 iv) 14
c) i) \$2500 ii) 12% s.a. iii) \$1509 iv) 44
2. a) \$9000 b) 8%
c) At face value price, yield rate= bond rate = 12%
3. a) \$4729.64 b) \$5094.77
4. a) \$10 713.50 b) \$12 140.23
5. a) Bond rate < yield b) Bond rate > yield
c) Bond rate = yield
6. a) \$18 247.29 b) \$18 226.13 **7.** \$7124.76
8. \$813 300.68 **9.** \$701.88

Exercises 11-10, page 432

1. 9.9% **2.** 11% **3.** 9.2% **4.** 10.6%
5. a) 14.4% b) 11.6%
6. 16.5% **7.** 12.1% s.a.
8. a) i) \$995 000 ii) \$57 500
c) \$69 000 000

Exercises 11-11, page 437

1. a) \$522.20 b) \$469.56 c) \$457.64
2. a) \$309.57 b) \$373.83 c) \$439.92
3. a) \$540.50 b) \$79 720
4. a) \$747.66 b) \$164 298

5. a) i) $430.02 ii) $395.73 iii) $389.07
b) i) $47 403.60 ii) $88 719
iii) $133 409.40
6. a) $586.71 b) $166 215.60 c) $65 070.00
7. a) $773.93 b) $157 177.50 c) $44 322.60
8. a) $352.24 b) $61 683.84
9. a) 12 b) 14 c) 21
10. a) $312.92 b) $264.78
11. a) $880.43 b) i) $984.51 ii) $779.02
14. a) $440.96 b) $519.99 c) $506.89
d) $550.81 e) $52 921.20
15. a) $787.99 b) $318.93 c) $522.52

Exercises 11-12, page 443

1. a) i) $49 481.46 ii) $46 538.94
iii) $39 730.54 iv) $22 390.14
b) i) 9 years 10 months
ii) 15 years 4 months
2. a) $518.54 b) $6772.54
3. a) $6773.17 b) $517.91
4. a) $10 550 b) $9330 c) $8110 d) $2650
6. c) 15 years **7.** c
8. a) $542.12
b)

Interest Paid	Principal Repaid	Balance Outstanding
		$49 481.46
$482.88	$59.24	$49 422.22
$482.30	$59.82	$49 362.40
$481.72	$60.40	$49 302.00
$481.13	$60.99	$49 241.01

9. a) $697.43
b)

Interest Paid	Principal Repaid	Balance Outstanding
		$46 538.94
$637.09	$60.34	$46 478.61
$636.27	$61.16	$46 417.45
$635.43	$62.00	$46 355.45
$634.58	$62.85	$46 292.60

10. a) *A*: $1500 after 4 years; *B*: $1500 after 8 years;
C: $1500 after 12 years b) *A*
11. *A* **12.** About $18 000
14. Weekly: $32 000; Double 6th and 12th: $52 000;
Increase 5%: $69 000; Repay $2000: $62 000

CP

2. a) i) $1880.08 ii) $1725.62 iii) $1695.04
b) $1882.26

Review Exercises, page 448

1. a) $2.42 b) 9.5% c) 60 d d) $245.00
2. a) $128.43 b) $164.23 c) $165.11
3. a) $2650.66 b) $450.40 c) $1085.00
d) $667.74
4. a) $619.83 b) $137.50 c) $260.92
d) $834.98
5. a) $7728.05 b) $13 318.15
6. a) $752.31 b) $435.95 **7.** 10.5%
8. $1755.69
9. a) $915.06 b) $923.41 c) $930.84
10. 11.5% **11.** 14.06% **12.** $8922.75
13. $6982.80 **14.** $1630.36 **15.** $9476.97
16. $18 703.34 **17.** $2006.06 **18.** 8.5%
19. a) $8401.52 b) $10 956.83 **20.** 12%
21. a) $653.73 b) $235 342.80 c) $165 342.80
22. $33 217.80 **23.** a) $516.38 b) $16 539.96
24. a) i) $47 429.89 ii) $39 730.54
b) $8\frac{1}{3}$ years c) $13 469.94 d) $18 765.65
25. $659.23

Index